# Foundations in Statistics

## an introduction

third edition

# Foundations in Statistics

## an introduction

Victoria L. Mantzopoulos, Ph.D.

udmp
university of detroit mercy press
MMXV • Detroit, USA

Book Design by Alexandra T. Hichel

MMXV • Detroit, USA

Library of Congress Cataloging-in-Publication Data
Mantzopoulos, Victoria L.

Foundations in Statistics: An Introduction/Victoria L. Mantzopoulos—3rd edition
ISBN 13: 978-0-911550-99-3

*To my husband,*
*Konstantinos Ioannis Mantzopoulos*

*To my children,*
*Demitra and Alexia*

*Remembering all who have left us,*
*God Rest Their Souls*

# Contents

**CHAPTER 1: WHAT IS STATISTICS?**                                        **1**
    SECTION 1  Uses and Abuses                               2
    SECTION 2  Basic Terms and Concepts                     4
    SECTION 3  Data Collection and Sampling                12
    *Chapter 1 in Review*                                       17

**CHAPTER 2: DESCRIPTIVE GRAPHICS
FOR ONE OR TWO VARIABLES**                                                **21**
    SECTION 1  Frequency Distributions                     22
    SECTION 2  Bar Charts and Histograms                   29
    SECTION 3  Pie Charts and Line Graphs                  34
    *Chapter 2 in Review*                                       42

**CHAPTER 3: DESCRIPTIVE STATISTICS FOR ONE VARIABLE**                    **47**
    SECTION 1  Measures of Central Tendency                47
    SECTION 2  Measures of Dispersion                      64
    SECTION 3  Measures of Position                        76
    *Chapter 3 in Review*                                       84

**CHAPTER 4: DESCRIPTIVE MEASURES
OF TWO OR MORE VARIABLES**                                                **90**
    SECTION 1  Nominal Variables: Contingency Tables/Crosstabs    91
    SECTION 2  Scatterplots and Correlations               94
    SECTION 3  Ordinal Variables: Spearman's Correlation    99
    SECTION 4  Ratio or Interval Variables: Pearson's Correlation    103
    SECTION 5  Ratio or Interval Variables: Linear Regression    111
    *Chapter 4 in Review*                                       124

**CHAPTER 5: PROBABILITY SAMPLE SPACES**                                  **130**
    SECTION 1  List Method                                 130
    SECTION 2  Tree Diagrams                               134
    SECTION 3  Venn Diagrams                               138
    SECTION 4  Counting Rules                              144
    *Chapter 5 in Review*                                       150

**CHAPTER 6: CALCULATING PROBABILITIES**                                  **153**
    SECTION 1  Probability Theory                          154
    SECTION 2  Probability of the Union of Two Events      159
    SECTION 3  Complementary Probabilities                 167
    SECTION 4  Conditional Probabilities                   168
    SECTION 5  Joint Probabilities                         173
    SECTION 6  Joint and Conditional Probabilities Using Tree Diagrams    178
    SECTION 7  Combining the Addition and Multiplication Theorems    183
    *Chapter 6 in Review*                                       188

## CHAPTER 7: PROBABILITY DISTRIBUTIONS OF DISCRETE VARIABLES — **194**

| | | |
|---|---|---|
| SECTION 1 | Probability Distribution of a Discrete Random Variable | 194 |
| SECTION 2 | Discrete Probability Function | 200 |
| SECTION 3 | Mean and Standard Deviation of a Discrete Probability Distribution | 203 |
| SECTION 4 | Binomial Probability Distribution | 209 |
| SECTION 5 | Mean and Standard Deviation of a Binomial Distribution | 218 |
| *Chapter 7 in Review* | | 222 |

## CHAPTER 8: NORMAL PROBABILITY DISTRIBUTIONS — **227**

| | | |
|---|---|---|
| SECTION 1 | Continuous Random Variable | 228 |
| SECTION 2 | Normal Probability Distributions: Concept and Calculation | 230 |
| SECTION 3 | Normal Probability Table | 236 |
| SECTION 4 | Calculating Normal Probabilities | 243 |
| SECTION 5 | Normal Approximation of the Binomial Distribution | 251 |
| *Chapter 8 in Review* | | 260 |

## CHAPTER 9: SAMPLING DISTRIBUTIONS — **266**

| | | |
|---|---|---|
| SECTION 1 | Sampling Distributions | 266 |
| SECTION 2 | Central Limit Theorem | 275 |
| *Chapter 9 in Review* | | 283 |

## CHAPTER 10: INFERENTIAL STATISTICS — **288**

| | | |
|---|---|---|
| SECTION 1 | The Null and Alternative Hypotheses | 288 |
| SECTION 2 | Hypothesis Testing Using the Classical Approach for One Population Mean | 296 |
| SECTION 3 | Hypothesis Testing Using $P$-Values for One Population Mean | 308 |
| SECTION 4 | Confidence Intervals for One Population Mean | 317 |
| *Chapter 10 in Review* | | 326 |

## CHAPTER 11: $t$-TEST FOR ONE POPULATION MEAN — **331**

| | | |
|---|---|---|
| SECTION 1 | The $t$ Distribution | 331 |
| SECTION 2 | Hypothesis Test: Classical Approach for Mean Using $t$ | 332 |
| SECTION 3 | Hypothesis Test: $P$-Value for Mean Using $t$ | 344 |
| SECTION 4 | Confidence Interval for $t$ for One Mean | 350 |
| *Chapter 11 in Review* | | 356 |

## CHAPTER 12: OTHER ONE POPULATION TESTS — **361**

| | | |
|---|---|---|
| SECTION 1 | Hypothesis Test: Classical Approach for a Variance Using Chi-Square | 362 |

SECTION 2    Hypothesis Test: *P*-Value
             for a Variance Using Chi-Square                                      375
SECTION 3    Confidence Interval
             for a Population Variance Using Chi-Square                           382
SECTION 4    Hypothesis Test:
             Classical Approach for a Proportion Using *z*                        388
SECTION 5    Hypothesis Test: *P*-Value Approach
             for a Proportion Using *z*                                           393
SECTION 6    Hypothesis Test: Classical Approach
             for Correlation between Two Variables Using *t*                      398
SECTION 7    Hypothesis Test: *P*-Value Approach
             for Correlation between Two Variables Using *t*                      403
*Chapter 12 in Review*                                                            408

## CHAPTER 13:  TESTING AND ESTIMATING TWO POPULATIONS          414
SECTION 1    Two Independent Means: *z*                                           415
SECTION 2    Two Independent Means: *t*                                           428
SECTION 3    Two Proportions: *z*                                                 440
SECTION 4    Two Dependent Means: *t*                                             449
SECTION 5    Two Variances: *F* Distribution                                      460
*Chapter 13 in Review*                                                            470

## CHAPTER 14:  ADDITIONAL INFERENTIAL STATISTICS          476
SECTION 1    Multinomial Experiments (GOF)                                        476
SECTION 2    Testing Contingency Tables/Crosstabs (Matrices)                      483
SECTION 3    Testing Multiple Means:  Analysis of Variance (ANOVA)                493
*Chapter 14 in Review*                                                            509

## CHAPTER 15:  CASE STUDY          515

## APPENDIX A:  TABLES          522
Table A.1     Critical Values for Pearson's *r*                                   522
Table A.2a    Binomial Probabilities                                              523
Table A.2b    Factorials                                                          526
Table A.3     Normal Probability Distribution                                     527
Table A.4     *t* Distribution                                                    528
Table A.5     Chi-Square Distribution                                             529
Table A.6     *F* Distribution                                                    530
Hypothesis Testing                                                                536

## APPENDIX B:  GLOSSARY OF TERMS AND SYMBOLS          538

## APPENDIX C:  ANSWER KEY FOR SELECT QUESTIONS          547

## INDEX          559

# PREFACE

*Foundations in Statistics* is intended for a college or university beginning/introductory statistics class. Originally the objective was to provide a text that was math friendly for students in the social and behavioral sciences who may not particularly like math or be as confident with their math skills as others in more math-based studies.

Another goal of *Foundations in Statistics* is to have an introductory statistics textbook that can be completed in one semester. While this edition includes a few new procedures, the entire book can easily be competed in a typical semester.

The author understands the anxiety related to statistics. A major source of the anxiety is directly related to the mathematics. While math can not be ignored in doing statistics, it can be presented in a way that doesn't assume that all students are math majors.

Each chapter is divided into sections describing a specific procedure. All concepts and techniques are supported by at least one complete example. The examples are clearly stated and follow the same format throughout the book. Each example is described as an experiment and is followed by the answer and the solution. The solution is a step-by-step discussion, starting with a clear description of the experiment, what techniques are to be employed, why those techniques are employed, and how they are employed. Each section also includes a Learning Aid. The Learning Aid is used as a quick reference to the formula and application, including a fully illustrated application of the major techniques of that section. Each chapter ends with a Chapter In Review, presenting a full set of problems using the most important techniques of the chapter. The Chapter in Review allows the students to further sharpen their skills. All supporting statistical and mathematical tables are included in the appendices. Also included is a glossary of basic terms and concepts.

The author has taught statistics for more than 30 years. As a student of statistics, one of her professors said that all statistics is third-grade math made difficult with funny symbols and language. A second professor always said that statistics become intuitive. It does.

## New Features in This Edition

One major feature is that this edition integrates the TI-83/84 series calculator. Screenshots are incorporated in the examples wherever a calculator function is available. Because of the calculator, the classical hypothesis approach is presented but reduced while the *P*-value approach is expanded. A few new procedures and many new homework exercises have been added. Tables in the appendices have been updated.

# ACKNOWLEDGMENTS

I extend my deep appreciation to Megan Stoltze for her help with editing the manuscript and integrating calculator functions into this edition and to Alexandra Hichel for her time, support, and computer skills. In addition, Dr. Genevieve Meyers deserves special acknowledgment for her suggestions to enhance this edition. I remain thankful to those who have contributed to previous editions of this book including Lawrence Sledz, Samantha (Kas-Petrus) Reed and John David Feichtner. I am also profoundly grateful to Dr. Charles D. Elder, Wayne State University, for his encouragement and guidance that may date back many years but are still forefront in all of my academic endeavors. Finally, I want to thank my family for their support and patience. I've tried not to miss a moment of their lives.

# 1 WHAT IS STATISTICS?

**SECTION 1** *Uses and Abuses*
**SECTION 2** *Basic Terms and Concepts*
**SECTION 3** *Data Collection and Sampling*

People often ask why a social or behavioral scientist needs to learn mathematics. Why do nursing students or business students need it? What do numbers have to do with studying politics, sociology, or behavior? What do they have to do with medicine? People tend to associate statistics with mathematics and engineering. However, statistics is not simply mathematics; it is a science in and of itself that goes beyond the mathematics and numbers it employs. Today, almost all fields of study employ the techniques of statistics. For example, statistics help political scientists predict voting behavior. It helps psychologists formulate therapies. It helps engineers predict performance of machinery. It helps architects predict the strength of materials. Pharmaceutical companies use inferential statistics to evaluate the effectiveness of new drugs. Whether you become a researcher or a practitioner, you must learn to understand, evaluate, and apply statistical information.

**Statistics** Statistics is the science of collecting, classifying, presenting, analyzing and drawing conclusions based on data.

Statistics is the process of making generalizations on the basis of information. As a science, statistics is concerned with three areas: ***descriptives, probabilities, and inferentials.***

**Descriptive Statistics** The collection, presentation, and description of data.

Descriptive statistics is the collection and classification of data; describing and presenting data in a readable manner. The collection of data is briefly discussed in this text, but it is typically addressed more fully in a class on research design or research methods. The second area, describing and presenting data, is the focus of the first unit of this text. Included in the first unit are graphic displays and measurements such as means and standard deviations.

**Probabilities** A measure of the likelihood that certain given value of a random variable(s) or event will occur.

The second area, and thus the second unit of the text, is probabilities. A **probability** is a measurement that a value will occur. It is an educated, mathematical guess. Probability theories form the basis of *inferential statistics*, the third unit of the text.

> **Inferential Statistics** The predictions, conclusions, and generalizations made about a population based on sample information using the theories of probabilities.

The third area is the techniques applied in interpreting and drawing conclusions from the data (many authors put probability and inferential statistics as one area). For example, the two most common inferential techniques include hypothesis testing and population estimations.

It is important to remember that statistics is logic, with mathematics as the tool and application as the goal. The goal is to not only learn the mathematical procedures and formulas but also to understand what the numbers actually mean.

# Section 1

## Uses and Abuses

Statistics is used daily by virtually everyone. Even babies unknowingly apply the techniques of statistics. If an infant desires food, a diaper change, or satisfaction of another need, the infant can associate a cry with the resulting attention. Although the infant is not consciously testing a causal relationship, a recognizable pattern develops. Playing a game of chance employs the science of statistics, and usually the odds are against the player, as in gambling and lotteries. Making a decision whether or not to pursue a particular policy, buy an item, employ a method, or admit students to a college or university are applications of statistics.

People often say that numbers lie or that statisticians can manipulate numbers to prove any point. Some statisticians might attempt to make numbers lie, but these people are the exception, and even a novice can almost always identify them. Since many statisticians are paid for their work, if they manipulate data that is later proven false, they will not stay in business very long. For example, if I did a political poll and predicted that Candidate Smith will win the election with a landslide victory and then he loses miserably, what will be the chance that my polls will be taken seriously in the future?

More typically, the numbers do not lie, but the interpretation may be misleading or incorrect. This is often the case in the media. Information is usually presented with an oral explanation. One word alteration by the reporter or writer may make the oral statement wrong. Sometimes, the oral explanation is only slightly different than the visual information. Or the information and the explanation may coincide, but the listeners hear or think they see something else. That is, the consumer misunderstands and misapplies the information.

Most abuses center around the misapplication or incorrect presentation of correct data. Misrepresentation of data often occurs by distorting graphs and tables in such a way that the information is correct, but the visual interpretation is incorrect. Interrupting the axes in bar charts or line graphs distorts the visual by allowing the eye to compare the height of one bar to that of another when the full heights of the bars are not presented. Notice the bar charts in Figure 1.1.

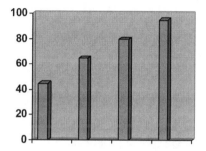 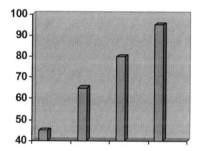

**FIGURE 1.1 Bar Charts Representing the Same Information**

Both charts present the same information. The first graph is correct. The drawing of the graph itself is important so that it does not distort the proportions of the bars. There is no distortion because the increments on the vertical axis are consistent and begin at 0. The heights of the bars in the first graph reflect smaller differences than those that appear to be shown by the second. The second chart interrupts the vertical axis by not beginning at 0 but instead at 40. The jump from 0 to 40 is not consistent with the increments that follow which are in tens. The inconsistent increments allow the visual understanding of the bars to be distorted. The second bar looks twice as high as the first bar, and the third bar looks three times as large as the first bar.

The third area of statistical abuse involves flaws in the research design. If the design is full of errors, so too will be the data and, therefore, the results. The major areas of concern are sample size, unbiased sampling, and unbiased questions. Most of these concerns are addressed in a research methods course.

# *Section 2*

## Basic Terms and Concepts

There are several terms and concepts that must be clearly understood before studying the techniques in statistics. The most important term is ***population***. The population is the ***universal set*** that is to be analyzed. Even if a ***sample*** is drawn from a population, it is the population about which generalizations are drawn.

> **Population**  A universal set of all individuals, objects, or measurements whose properties are being analyzed.

The population must be well defined by the researcher so that the inferences drawn are clearly understood. For example, if the researcher wants to describe student ages, the population must be clearly defined as all students in the class, in the school, in the state, in the country, or in the world. The researcher must be as specific as possible. Another example is if unemployment figures are to be studied, the population of employable must be defined clearly first.

It is often difficult to observe or test every element in a population. Sampling techniques allow a researcher to study a population by focusing on a smaller set of elements.

> **Sample**  A subset of the population.

---

**EXAMPLE 1.1**

**Experiment:** Seven hundred students were randomly selected from a list of all students at University of Detroit Mercy to determine the average age of all students. Identify the sample and the population.

**Answer:** The sample is the 700 students. The population is all students at University of Detroit Mercy.

**Solution:** The sample is the 700 students since it is the subset of the population. Samples are usually studied to infer to the population. The population is the larger set of which the sample is taken. Therefore, the population is all students at University of Detroit Mercy.

---

The objective of sampling is to collect a sample that is representative of the population. Typically, a sample should mirror the population. There are numerous reasons why it may not, however. One reason is that it is not intended to. However, when attempting to produce a sample that mirrors the population, two major problem areas are sampling error and systematic error. A *sampling error* is the error due to chance. It is the chance that the elements chosen for the sample are not representative of the population. Small samples tend to have a higher probability of containing sampling errors than do larger samples. For example, if one student is sampled to describe the average age of all students, the sample will probably not be representative of the population. However, if several students are sampled, the estimate will more likely be representative. Increasing sample size tends to decrease sampling error.

**Sampling Error** A sampling error due to chance.

**Systematic Error** A sampling error due to a bias in the sampling technique.

However, bigger is not always better. If the same kind of element is sampled every time and that element is only one type of many, a systematic error exists. A *systematic error* is a result of a bias in the selection process, such as only sampling women or only men when both are needed. This error will not be corrected by sampling more of the same elements. A systematic error is an error in the process of selecting elements in the sample, and it is not corrected by increasing sample size. An example of a systematic error is when people are selected for a public opinion poll by a researcher who stands on a street corner. Only people working or living in that area are likely to pass that particular corner. Another example is testing the average age of students at a college by observing only students enrolled in evening courses. These students tend to be older than students enrolled in day courses. A random selection of elements from the whole population tends to be the best method of preventing a systematic error. Randomization allows every element the same chance of being selected for a sample.

## EXAMPLE 1.2

**Experiment:** A local television station conducts an election poll of 2,000 people randomly selected from a telephone list of people who attended a morning talk show over the last two years. Identify the error.

**Answer:** Systematic error

**Solution:** There are two types of errors: sampling errors and systematic errors. A sampling error tends to occur when the sample size is too small to allow for a reliable inference to the population. A sample of 2,000 people is a good sample size and should not pose a substantial sampling error. A systematic error is an error associated with the selection process. Randomization usually controls systematic error. However, though randomization is noted, the list from which the names are drawn is suspect.

The list is generated by people who attend a local talk show. The people choosing to attend a talk show probably do not completely coincide with people who vote.

Samples and populations are tested and observed to collect information about certain characteristics of the elements. The characteristics or properties are referred to as *variables.* For example, if proper answers are designed, questions asked on a survey can be considered variables. Variables such as age, education, and marital status are characteristics about objects or individuals that can be described by different values. A *value* is a classification of a variable. Values are the answers to the questions on a survey. It either can be numerical or can be a nominal attribute that can be assigned numerical values. Age and years of education are variables whose values are numerical. Marital status is a variable, whose attributes such as single, married, or divorced, must be assigned numerical values for statistical calculations.

**Variable** A characteristic of objects, events, or individuals that has or can be assigned a numerical value.

As with the population, the variables that are tested must be clearly defined with the proper unit by the researcher in such a way that another researcher can fully comprehend and replicate the measurement if necessary. A variable must be operationally defined, with clear specifications for measuring the characteristics and the values that may be assigned to the responses. The operational definition must be concerned that the measurement does, in fact, measure the variable. That is, it must be determined if the measurement is a valid indicator of the variable.

**Value** One of the categories or responses of a variable.

Question: What is your marital status?          Variable: Marital Status
Answer: I am married.                                      Value: Married

The value of a variable associated with one element or individual of the population or sample is often referred to as datum. For example, if Ms. Duncan is a student in class and the variable *age* is observed, the value 25 years old is a single piece of data. Another variable, marital status can be defined. Ms. Duncan's marital status, single, is also a value that is a single piece of data.

**EXAMPLE 1.3**

**Experiment:** A sample of 500 college students is taken to determine if they engage in illegal activities such as drugs or alcohol use and whether that activity affects their school grades. Name three variables and possible values to those variables.

**Answer:** Variable 1 is usage of illegal drugs and its values would be yes or no. Variable 2 is usage of alcohol and its values would be yes or no. Variable 3 is school grades and its values would be A, B, C, D, or F, or a grade-point-average.

**Solution:** The variables are essentially the questions, which are whether or not they use drugs or alcohol and the grades. Values are essentially the possible answers to the questions, which would be yes or no and their grades.

**Discrete** Variables that can take only a finite number of possible values in any finite interval.

**Continuous** Variables that can take on an infinite number of possible values.

Most variables are classified as ***discrete or continuous***. Some are hybrid, meaning a variable can be partially discrete while being partially continuous. This kind of variable will not be discussed in this book. *Discrete variables* are those that can take on only a finite number of possible values in any finite interval. Discrete variables are often said to be counts, as opposed to measurements. Counts need not be full counts, or whole numbers, but instead are said to have a clear beginning and a clear end. *Continuous variables* measure and can take on any values within a finite interval. A measurement is limited by the measuring device. For example, a scale for weight is limited to the units the scale measures. One scale may report weight in full pounds, another in half pounds, and another in tenths of a pound. The measuring device, the scale, can take on infinite values, because a scale is developed to measure hundredths or thousandths of pounds. The distinction of discrete and continuous variables is important in statistics, because many techniques are better suited for one or the other.

**EXAMPLE 1.4**

**Experiment:** Identify the following variables as discrete or continuous.
a. Number of siblings
b. Distance from home to school
c. Temperature of the room

d. Number of red cars in the parking lot

e. Number of stars in the universe

**Answer:**

a. Discrete

b. Continuous

c. Continuous

d. Discrete

e. Discrete

**Solution:**

a. The number of siblings is discrete, because the number is a count. A finite number of siblings can be identified.

b. The distance from home to school is continuous, because distance is a measurement. Although a clear beginning and end of the measurement exist (home and school), any measurement reported is an estimate based on the limitations of the measuring device. One device may report miles, another may report kilometers, and yet another may report feet or yards. Each of these units will be an estimate where the distance is typically rounded to the nearest mile, kilometer, foot, or yard.

c. The temperature of the room is also continuous. Temperature is measured and not counted. There are an infinite number of ways a thermometer may estimate temperature such as in units of whole degrees or fractions of degrees. Only the measuring device limits measuring temperature.

d. The number of red cars in the parking lot is a count and, is, therefore, discrete. The experiment asks for a count of cars and not a measurement.

e. Even though the number of stars could be unlimited in the universe, we can only count them, so this is a discrete variable.

A set of values of a variable for each of the elements of a sample or population is also referred to by the noun *data*. For example, the set of ages for all students in the class is a set of data.

**Datum (singular)** The value of a variable associated with one element of the population or sample.

**Data (plural)** The set of values of a variable for each of the elements of the population or sample.

> **Parameter** A numerical characteristic of an entire population. Parameters are usually represented by Greek letters, such as $\mu$ or $\sigma$.

A *parameter* is a numerical characteristic of an entire population. A parameter is usually a fixed number and is often unknown. Parameters describe populations and are usually represented by Greek letters such as $\mu$ or $\sigma$. The letter $\mu$ (pronounced "mew"), for example, is the symbol that denotes the mean of a population; $\sigma$ (pronounced "sigma") denotes the standard deviation of a population. The general rule is that the calculation for a numerical characteristic such as a mean or standard deviation is the same or only slightly different for a population or a sample, but the symbol representing the measurement differs.

> **Statistic** A numerical characteristic of a sample. Statistics are usually represented by English letters, such as $\bar{x}$ or $s$.

A *statistic* is a numerical characteristic of a sample. As soon as sample data are taken, statistics can be calculated. Statistics describe samples and vary from sample to sample. Statistics are usually represented by English letters such as $\bar{x}$ (pronounced "x-bar") or $s$. The symbol $\bar{x}$ for example, denotes the mean of a sample, and $s$ denotes the standard deviation of a sample. Therefore, a mean may be represented by $\mu$ or $\bar{x}$, depending on whether it describes a population or a sample. Greek letters represent populations, and English letters represent samples.

| | |
|---|---|
| **Parameter = Population = Greek** | $\mu$  $\sigma$  $\sigma^2$  $\rho$ |
| **Statistic = Sample = English** | $\bar{x}$  $s$  $s^2$  $r$ |

An example of a parameter in the case study on fertility is the mean number of children ever born to all women in the world who have ever been married. The case study can only estimate this mean, since not all women in the world can be observed. A statistic is limited to the actual survey and is defined as the mean number of children ever born to all women in the survey.

Data were defined earlier as discrete or continuous. There is another useful way of classifying data according to their level of measurement. There are four levels of measurement: nominal, ordinal, interval, and ratio. A *nominal-level measurement* is data whose responses describe qualities or attributes that do not imply magnitude or value. Although values must be assigned for statistical purposes, the values do not specify magnitude. Examples of nominal-level data are religion, color of hair, marital status, or color of cars in a parking lot.

> **Nominal-level measurement** (also known as attribute or categorical measurement) Data whose values describe attributes that do not imply magnitude or order.

*Ordinal-level measurements* order data from lowest to highest or highest to lowest. Ordinal-level measurements rank data but do not otherwise note magnitudes. The difference between values is not clear beyond their placements in the ranked order. For example, if the students in a class are ranked from shortest to tallest, it is not clear whether the shortest person is 1 inch or 2 inches shorter than the second or whether the difference between the heights of the first and second shortest is the same difference as between the second and the third. Military rankings are ordinal-level measurements, as are most job rankings, both in public and private institutions.

> **Ordinal-level measurement** Data whose values are ranked or ordered from lowest to highest or highest to lowest.

*Interval-level measurements* are data that can be ordered and have measurable differences. For example, 41 degrees Fahrenheit is greater than 40 degrees Fahrenheit. Also, the distance between the temperature 40 degrees and 41 degrees is exactly the same distance as between 41 and 42 degrees. Temperature is a common interval-level measurement.

> **Interval-level measurement** Data whose values are ordered and have measurable differences.

The fourth level of measurement is ratio. *Ratio-level measurements* have all the features an interval-level measurement can have. In addition, ratio-level measurements also have an absolute-zero starting point. That is, a value of zero for a ratio-level measurement implies an absence of the variable. Zero means zero. Interval-level measurements may contain a zero, but the zero is sometimes arbitrarily set. Temperature is interval because it contains a zero that does not imply an absence of temperature. The fact that there are two popular measurements of temperature, Fahrenheit and Celsius, implies that a temperature of zero is not a natural starting place. Age, height, weight, and money are considered examples of ratio-level measurements. Age, for example, is ratio; zero years old reflects the absence of age. Information presented as a percentage is always considered ratio.

The strength of the ratio level measurement over interval is in the comparison of values of the same level. For example, temperature is interval and value comparison is not a true mathematical statement. That is, it is not true to say that temperature of 60 degrees is twice as warm as 30 degrees. Although it may be warmer, the comparison is flawed since temperature does not have an absolute zero starting point. On the other hand, ratio level measurements may be compared because zero is an absolute starting point. Therefore, a person 60 years old is mathematically twice as old as a person 30.

---

**Ratio-level measurement** Data whose values can be ordered, have measurable differences, and have a zero starting point.

---

### EXAMPLE 1.5

**Experiment:** Identify the following variables as nominal, ordinal, interval, or ratio.
a. Number of siblings
b. Distance from home to school
c. Temperature of the room
d. Color of the cars in the parking lot
e. Class standing

**Answer:**
a. Ratio
b. Ratio
c. Interval
d. Nominal
e. Ordinal

**Solution:**
a. The number of siblings is ratio since it is a count that begins at zero and is a count of measurable differences.

b. The distance from home to school is also ratio since it is a consistent measurement that begins at zero whether measured in miles, kilometers, feet, or yards.

c. The temperature of the room is interval if measured in Fahrenheit or Celsius. Although the measurement is consistent, zero is not a real starting point. That is, zero degrees only means it is cold; not the absence of heat in a true sense.

d. The color of the cars in the parking lot is nominal since it is simply an attribute and is not actually a measurement.

e. Class standing is ordinal as it is described in terms of freshmen, sophomore, junior, and senior. Students are put in these categories based on the number of credits earned. Once in the categories, students are simply in groups based on a low, medium, high concept.

**A LEARNING AID**
**VOCABULARY**

Research was conducted to describe childhood obesity in the U.S. A study of 5,000 randomly selected children from 6-16 years of age was conducted. The children were asked questions such as their age, height, and weight. The study found that 40 percent of these children were considered obese. Describe the population, sample, variables, type and level of the measurements, and a statistic.

**Step 1**

The population is the universal set of things that the study is describing which is children in the U.S. from the ages 6 to 16. The sample is the subset of the population that is actually sampled, therefore, 5,000 children.

**Step 2**

There are several variables identified. Variables are the questions, values are the possible answers. The questions that would be asked are age, height, and weight. All three variables are continuous because they are measurements and are all at the ratio level since they begin at an absolute zero and are therefore mathematically comparable. The statistic is 40 percent . A statistic is a value representing a sample.

## Section 3

### Data Collection and Sampling

Before any statistical procedures can be performed, a researcher needs data. There are two ways to obtain data, collect it or use someone else's. Either way, the statistical information is only as good as the data. Research design addresses issues such as the objectives, collection methods, the instrument such as the survey or *experiment*, sample size, and validity and reliability concerns. A methods or quantitative methods course focuses on all and more of these issues. However, some of these issues must be considered before statistical techniques can be applied to a set of data.

**Experiment** A planned activity that generates a set of data.

An *experiment* is a planned activity that generates a set of data. True experimental designs include the so-called hard or physical sciences such as chemistry and biology. True experimental designs allow the researcher to control and modify the environment surrounding the experiment. Social and behavioral sciences tend to focus on quasi-experimental designs, which are not usually conducted in a laboratory. A popular technique of quasi-experimental designs is to survey respondents. A survey is an instrument that allows researchers to observe respondents outside of a controlled, laboratory setting.

Since most quasi-experimental designs use survey data, data collection designs are important. The goal is to obtain a sample that is representative of the population and of the specific characteristics of interest. The most common sampling technique that results in a representative sample mirroring the population is known as a *random sample*. Mirroring suggests that every element in the population is represented in the same proportion in the sample. For example, if in your school there are more males (55 percent) than females (45 percent), ideally, a sample should comprise the same proportions.

Although the ideal situation may be to observe every element of a population, there are times when every element cannot or should not be used. When the whole population cannot or should not be studied, samples are usually taken. It is possible to describe a population after studying a sample drawn from that same population. For example, a light bulb manufacturer would not test every bulb in the factory to determine the average bulb's life. If he or she did, there would be no bulbs left to sell. Instead, the manufacturer would probably take a sample and use the sample to infer information about the whole population.

Sampling, thus, becomes very crucial in data analysis. To enable inferences or generalization from a sample to a population, a sample must be representative of the population. A representative sample must reflect the characteristics of the population the researcher deems relevant. Many situations call for a specific kind of sampling technique, such as intentionally overcounting or undercounting an element in a population.

> **Random Sample** A sample in which every element of the population has an equal probability of being included in the sample.

*Random sampling* is also referred to as simple random sampling or probability sampling. Random sampling occurs when every element or object of a population has an equal chance of being chosen for the sample. The result should be an unbiased sample that mirrors the population.

Random sampling cannot usually be accomplished by simply choosing elements appearing to be representative of a population. A haphazard selection of samples tends to be overrun with biases. For example, standing at a street corner to interview people walking past will be biased against those driving or those passing a different corner. Also, although family members and neighbors may seem to be "average", using family members and neighbors creates a definite bias. Several acceptable procedures reduce the risk of bias in using a sample to infer to a population.

One procedure for simple random sampling requires a list of all the elements of the population and a random number table. The procedure usually begins by listing and numbering each element of the population. A random number table is used to decide which elements from the population list should be selected. The numbers on the table of random numbers correspond to the numbers assigned to the elements of the population.

Another procedure for selecting sample elements is to use the random number generator available on many calculators and computers. Again, the elements of the population must first be listed and numbered. The numbers on the list of elements can then be drawn upon by matching the number on the randomly generated list.

A third method for simple random sampling is to enter the list of elements of the population in a computer and allow the computer to generate a sample list. Some computer software programs can produce a number of sample lists, each different from the other but all considered random samples.

Another form of sampling that can usually achieve the same goal as simple random sampling—but with less time and effort—is known as systematic sampling.

> **Systematic Sample** A sample determined by choosing every $k^{th}$ element after having begun by choosing the first element randomly. $k$ is approximated by dividing the population size by the sample size *(N/n)*.

In conducting a *systematic sample*, only one random number $k$ is needed to get started. All other elements are chosen by systematically selecting every $k^{th}$ element thereafter. For example, if 5,000 citizens vote at a particular precinct and a sample of 100 is needed, after randomly choosing the first voter, choosing every 50th (5,000/100 = 50) thereafter will result in a random sample of 100. So, if the first person is selected randomly, say the $25^{th}$ person, then the next selection is every $50^{th}$ person after, resulting in selecting the $75^{th}$, $125^{th}$, $175^{th}$, and so on. This is a much easier procedure than simple random sampling, which requires a full list and numbering of voters. Systematic sampling should not be used when a population is cyclical or repetitive with any distinct pattern. Systematic sampling would cause a serious error if used to select months of the year to determine unemployment. Unemployment tends to be cyclical-higher in certain times of the year and lower in others.

There are times when a characteristic of interest is not common among all elements of the population (for example, wanting only men, people with blonde hair, or students who are seniors). When this occurs, a ***stratified random sample*** is a practical way to partition the population, saving time and effort as well as reducing the sampling error.

> **Stratified Random Sample** A simple random sample taken from a subset or strata of the population.

A stratified sample can be used when testing whether hospital patients have had a cesarean delivery or a normal delivery. A random sample would require a list of all patients in a hospital, including men. It would be much easier, would require less time and effort, and would lead to fewer errors to stratify patients by sex and take a random sample of women, because only women deliver babies. Or better yet, only women in the maternity ward could be sampled. Another way to stratify is to identify patients in the various departments of the hospital and select a random sample of women in each department.

Another example of a stratified random sample is in the jury selection procedure. The judge needs to make sure jurors from both genders will be selected. The jurors could be separated into groups or stratas of men and women. Simple random samples from each strata could be generated and combined to a stratified random sample.

Another way of saving time and money is to use cluster sampling. Cluster sampling also partitions the data into ***subsets*** or clusters but then limits sampling to only a few of the subsets.

> **Cluster Sampling** A technique that limits sampling to a few subsets of the population considered to be representative of the population.

***Cluster sampling*** requires the subsets to mirror the population. Thus, information about the subset is necessary to determine if it is representative of the population. The subsets or clusters are first chosen randomly; then elements within the selected subsets are chosen randomly. One of the most common examples of cluster sampling occurs in public opinion polling. Because the country is too large to survey efficiently and the population of the country as a whole is similar to the population of certain states, sampling a few states may produce the sample results with a great savings of time and money. For example, 10 states may be randomly selected from the 50 states, followed by a random sample of perhaps 500 people in each of the 10 states. Each state represents a cluster and must have characteristics similar to the whole country.

Cluster sampling differs from stratified sampling in that cluster sampling requires the subset to be fully similar to the population, whereas stratified sampling is based on specific characteristics of interest to the researcher. Cluster sampling samples only a few of the subsets, whereas stratified sampling samples from every subset. Both require prior knowledge of the population and must be followed by simple random sampling once the subsets are identified.

Sampling is done to reduce the time and cost of observing every element of the population. The goal is to obtain a sample with minimum error attributed to the sampling procedure. Each sampling technique is not practical for every purpose. A researcher must choose a sampling technique carefully.

## A LEARNING AID
## RANDOM SAMPLES

Consider the population of a class of 99 students. Obtain a random sample of 20 students using a random number table.

### Step 1

List all the students by name and assign each a number beginning at 01 and ending at 99. Each student must be listed to allow each the same chance of being selected for the sample. A list of the whole population is obtained with each element assigned a number.

**For example:**

| | |
|----|----|
| 01 | Smith |
| 02 | Valdez |
| ... | ... |
| ... | ... |
| ... | ... |
| 50 | Williams |
| ... | ... |
| ... | ... |
| 99 | Jones |

### Step 2

Obtain a random numbers table. To use the table, begin anywhere on the table; then systematically read down, across, or diagonally. Numbers on the table correspond to numbers on the list of students. The table can always be adjusted for as many digits as needed by crossing over the columns.

### Step 3

Select the numbers from a table. For example, a segment may read:

|    |    |    |    |
|----|----|----|----|
| 92 | 63 | 07 | 82 |
| 40 | 19 | 26 | 79 |
| 54 | 57 | 53 | 49 |

Reading across the table, the following 10 numbers are chosen:

92, 63, 07, 82, 40, 19, 26, 79, 54, and 57

**Step 4**
Using the numbers just listed, select the corresponding numbers representing students. This list becomes the random sample and should represent the class, because no direct biases were created in the selection process.

| 92 Kahn | 63 Todd | 07 Jackson | 82 Lane | 40 Wright |
|---------|---------|------------|---------|-----------|
| 19 Lin | 26 Miller | 79 McFarland | 54 Carter | 57 Edwards |

# CHAPTER 1 IN REVIEW

1.1   Identify the following variables as discrete or continuous:
   a. The number of employees at the local retail store
   b. The number of patients admitted to a municipal hospital this week
   c. Temperature in the room
   d. Percent of university students in the College of Liberal Arts
   e. The amount of time it took a volunteer fire department to reach 10 fires

1.2   Identify the following variables as discrete or continuous:
   a. Distance from home to school
   b. Weight gain during pregnancy
   c. The number of students eating in the cafeteria during lunch hour
   d. The number of students attending class today
   e. The percent of university students receiving financial aid

1.3   Identify the following variables as nominal, ordinal, interval, or ratio:
   a. Number of fat grams in a brownie
   b. The temperature (in Fahrenheit) in the classroom
   c. The color of your pen or pencil
   d. Your letter grade on this quiz
   e. The amount of time for you to complete this homework

1.4    What type of error is not usually corrected by increasing sample size?

1.5    Identify the following variables as nominal, ordinal, interval, or ratio:
       a. Number of troops sent to foreign countries
       b. Number of penalties in a soccer match
       c. The place results of a 100-meter dash
       d. Letter grades received in a class

1.6    Identify the following variables as nominal, ordinal, interval, or ratio:
       a. Percentage of fans by sport
       b. The dollar amount lost by a local retailer for the year
       c. The type of sports watched by fans on television
       d. The ranking of students on the honor roll
       e. I.Q. test scores

1.7    The number of car-jackings is in decline in the U.S. Five major cities report an average decline of 15 percent per year over a 10-year period. The national data reports an average decline of 13 percent.
       a. Identify the population.
       b. Identify the sample.
       c. Identify a statistic.
       d. Identify a parameter.
       e. Identify the sample size.

1.8    A researcher wants to study the level of stress of students taking statistics. One hundred students are studied. The average stress indicator is 9.2 on a 0-to-10-point scale.
       a. Identify the population.
       b. Identify the sample.
       c. Identify a statistic.
       d. Identify a variable.
       e. Identify possible values of the variable.

1.9    A study was conducted identifying the top 10 causes of death of men. A survey of 5,000 men produced the following list: heart disease, cancer, stroke, pulmonary disease, accident, pneumonia and influenza, diabetes, suicide, kidney disease, and liver disease and cirrhosis.
       a. Identify the population.
       b. Identify the sample.
       c. Identify the sample size.
       d. Identify a variable.

1.10   The average cost for a wedding and a reception in the United States is $22,500. The average cost of weddings in the St. Louis area is $27,000.

    a. Identify the population.
    b. Identify the sample.
    c. Identify a statistic.
    d. Identify a variable.
    e. Identify parameter.

1.11   Note whether the following are nominal, ordinal, interval, or ratio data:
    a. Employee rankings based on productivity levels
    b. The number of patients admitted to a municipal hospital this week
    c. Temperature change in the room during the last hour
    d. Percent of university students in the College of Liberal Arts
    e. The amount of time it took a volunteer fire department to reach 10 fires

1.12   Describe the following measurements as nominal, ordinal, interval, or ratio:
    a. The number of ounces of milk in a glass
    b. A student's major in school
    c. A student's class standing (freshman, sophomore, etc.)
    d. A state's zip code system
    e. The temperature (in Celsius) outside an airplane flying at 30,000 feet

1.13.  A research study indicates that road congestion is sending people back to public transit systems. Ridership on public transit systems rose annually from 1995 to 2015 with an overall increase of more than 21 percent. In 2015 alone, more than 9.4 billion trips were registered on mass transportation systems.
    a. Identify the population.
    b. Identify a variable.
    c. Identify the variable noted above as discrete or continuous.
    d. Identify a second variable.
    e. Identify the second variable as discrete or continuous.

1.14   True or False?
    a. Greek letters always represent samples statistics.
    b. The sample should always be equal in size to the population.
    c. The variable, age, is discrete.
    d. A sample statistic always is represented by English letters.
    e. A continuous variable is a count.

1.15   True or False?
    a. Nominal level measurements are attributes.
    b. Ratio level measurements have an absolute starting point represented by zero.
    c. Interval level measurements are rankings.
    d. Nominal level measurements are always represented by numbers.
    e. Ordinal level measurements are rankings.

1.16  Forty-eight percent of Americans oppose allowing same-sex marriages to be legal.
Eighty-five percent of Evangelicals oppose ame-sex marriages as reported by a survey of 1,000 Evangelicals.

a. Name the population.
b. Name the sample.
c. What is the sample size?
d. Name the variable.
e. Is the variable discrete or continuous?
f. What level is the variable?
g. Name the parameter.
h. Name the statistic.

1.17  Identify the following data as nominal, ordinal, interval, or ratio level measurement. Also, identify each as discrete or continuous.

a. Occupation classification
b. Family income
c. Percent of employees with college degrees
d. Percent of employees who are female
e. Number of students who are political science majors

1.18  Identify the following data as nominal, ordinal, interval, or ratio level measurement. Also identify each as discrete or continuous.

a. A vehicle's gas mileage measured by miles per gallon
b. One's favorite color
c. Percent of students with cell phones
d. Number of songs saved on an mp3 player
e. The number of students attending class today

1.19  Identify the type of sample (random, systematic, stratified, or cluster) that is described.

a. Every seventh person at a local polling precinct is selected.
b. Students are divided into eight groups according to their gender and according to their class standing (first year, second, third, and fourth). One-hundred students are selected from each group.
c. A public opinion poll is taken from a computer-generated random list of all registered voters.
d. An accountant randomly selects client lists for auditing.

1.20  To determine if salaries have kept up with inflation, 100 people were surveyed. The mean salary increase for these 100 people was 2.2 percent per year. The inflation rate had increased 3.5 percent per year.

a. Identify the sample.
b. Identify the statistic.
c. Identify the statistic as discrete or continuous.

# 2 | Descriptive Graphics for One or Two Variables

**SECTION 1   Frequency Distributions**
**SECTION 2   Bar Charts and Histograms**
**SECTION 3   Pie Charts and Line Graphs**

The purpose of graphically presenting data is to reduce or summarize the data so that it is quickly comprehensible with the same or better understanding as if there were a full review of the data. For example, if every American is surveyed for marital status, more than 320 million answers would be obtained. A survey of the 320 million answers would probably not result in a full understanding of the distribution of marital status. However, a count of the number of responses in each category presented in an organized table would allow for rapid understanding of marital status in the United States.

The most common graphs and tables are frequency distributions, bar graphs, histograms, pie charts, and line graphs. Computer software programs provide a variety of graphs for which the user simply inserts the data and labels.

Whether composed by hand or computer, several precautions must be taken to ensure that a graph presents the data appropriately. Be certain that the visual does not distort the meaning of the data. Distortion is very common with bar charts and histograms in which the length of a bar is used to present a number of values. For example, the bar charts in Figure 2.1 represent the same information. Do the visuals provide the same understanding?

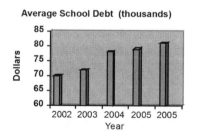 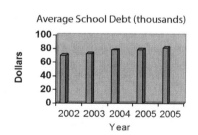

**Figure 2.1  Average Student Law School Debt**
**from Private Schools (thousands)**

The right chart is a more accurate presentation of the data. The visual shows that there are slight increases over the years 2002-2005. The left chart seems to reflect substantial increases over the same year. What is the difference in the charts? The left chart's vertical axis does not begin at 0 but instead at 60. The right chart begins correctly at 0. Since the left chart begins at 60, it exaggerates the heights of the bars (essentially cutting off the bottom half and then lengthening the bars). This exaggeration distorts the message and does not conform to the rules of diagrams. Increments should always be consistent. There are rare occasions when adjusting the increments would not lead to distortion.

Several general rules exist. Try to make the graphs and tables readable and easy to comprehend. Do not make them too complicated or too cluttered. Remember that simplicity is the objective. Round numbers, where appropriate, to reduce the number of digits. If numbers are in thousands, millions, or billions, consider dropping the zeros from the values and note the necessary multiplier in the variable label or title to the graph. Move unnecessary symbols out of the table and into value labels or titles. Symbols such as $ and % can be integrated in the column heads or title of the table so that they are not repeated with every value. Do not make the graphs too small or too large. Number and label all tables and graphs and all columns, axes, and legends. Note the source of data if applicable.

---

## *Section 1*

### Frequency Distributions

*Frequency distributions* provide a simple count of data in terms of the number or percentage of each value of a variable. Noting marital status of Americans as a count of the various responses is an example of a frequency distribution. Frequency distributions are characterized as ungrouped and grouped. An ungrouped frequency distribution is a simple count of each value for the data. Values grouped or categorized form *grouped frequency distributions*. For example, if the ages of students in class are presented in a tabulation as 20, 21, 22, and so on, the distribution is ungrouped. But if the ages are categorized in ranges of 20-24, 25-29, 30-34, and so on, the distribution is grouped.

The creation of an ungrouped frequency distribution begins by listing all the values of the variable. The number of occurrences for each value is counted and inserted in a column corresponding to the value. A total should be reported at the bottom of the table to verify that all the data are accounted for. For example, for the set of data 1, 1, 2, 2, 3, 3, 3, 3, 4, 4, 5, 5, 5, 5, and 5, a frequency distribution is begun by establishing a column for the values 1, 2, 3, 4, and 5. A column is also established for a count of each value. The value 1 occurs twice, the value 2 occurs twice, the value 3 occurs four times, the value 4 occurs twice, and the value 5 occurs five times.

| Value | Frequency |
|-------|-----------|
| 1 | 2 |
| 2 | 2 |
| 3 | 4 |
| 4 | 2 |
| 5 | 5 |
| **Total** | **15** |

## EXAMPLE 2.1

**Experiment:** The following data are ages of students in Dr. Mantz's philosophy course. Create a frequency distribution.

17  17  18  18  18  19  19  19  19  19  19  20  20  20  20

21  21  21  21  21  21  21  21  21  22  24  24  24  25  25

**Answer:** Ages of Students in Dr. Mantz's Class

| Age | Frequency |
|-----|-----------|
| 17 | 2 |
| 18 | 3 |
| 19 | 6 |
| 20 | 4 |
| 21 | 9 |
| 22 | 1 |
| 23 | 0 |
| 24 | 3 |
| 25 | 2 |
| **Total** | **30** |

**Solution:** Begin by labeling the table. The title should be precise but as succinct as possible. Clearly label the columns. The first is the variable age, and the second is the frequency, or number, of each age. Separate the column headings from the data. Write each age in the column for age. (Do not forget the value 23. Although it did not appear in the data, omitting it in the table would interrupt the increments reported.) Count the number of occurrences for each age and insert the count in the column labeled frequency. Total the frequencies to verify all data are accounted for. Some instructors may require closing the table with a line.

An ungrouped frequency distribution has the advantage of showing every piece of data. However, if there are dozens of values, an ungrouped frequency distribution can be cumbersome. A researcher strives to use as much data as possible but must also confront the manageability of the data. A grouped frequency distribution allows a large number of values to be presented in a condensed format. Table 2.1 shows a grouped frequency distribution that gives the ages of 7,720 women over the age of 30.

### TABLE 2.1
### Current Age Distribution of Women

| Age | Frequency |
|---|---|
| 30-34 | 1185 |
| 35-39 | 1007 |
| 40-44 | 980 |
| 45-49 | 841 |
| 50-54 | 897 |
| 55-59 | 691 |
| 60-64 | 643 |
| 65-69 | 662 |
| 70-74 | 489 |
| 75 and older | 325 |
| **Total** | **7720** |

The values in the distribution range from 30 to perhaps 100. To list 70 or more values would result in a very lengthy table. Collapsing the values into groups produces a manageable table without sacrificing too much of the data. It is, however, unclear where the frequencies occur in each group. For example, in the category 30-34, it is now unclear if the women are all 30, 31, or some combination of ages.

Each category in a grouped distribution is referred to as a class. Values in each class must be ***mutually exclusive***; that is, a value can occur in only one class. It is incorrect to make one category 30-35 and then make a second 35-40. A response of 35 could be listed in two classes. The smallest number in each class is called the lower class limit, while the largest number in each class is called upper class limit. Each class should have the same width (increment). The class width is calculated by subtracting the lower class limit of one class and from the next lower class limit. For the class 30-34, the class width is 5, which is determined by subtracting 30 (the lower limit of this class) from 35 (the lower limit of the next class). If one class width is 5 years, all class widths should be 5 years, with a possible exception of the first class and last class. Class widths should be small enough not to condense too much information. Four to twelve classes provide a good balance between not sacrificing information yet allowing for manageability. The first and last classes may be open-ended, such as in Table 2.1, where the last class is "75 and older." However, open-ended classes pose problems for further calculations and should be avoided if possible.

> **Grouped Frequency Distribution** A frequency distribution where:
> Values are collapsed into groups or **classes**.
> Values in each **class** must be mutually exclusive.
> A **lower class** limit is the lowest value in a specific class.
> An **upper class** limit is the highest value in a specific class.
> A **class mark** is the middle value in a specific class.
> A **class width** is the difference between the lower class limit and the next lower class limit (the number of values contained in a class).

## EXAMPLE 2.2

**Experiment:**

Identify the class width for the following grouped frequency distribution. Identify the lower class limit for the second class.

| Class | Frequency |
|-------|-----------|
| 0-9   | 11        |
| 10-19 | 10        |
| 20-29 | 9         |
| 30-39 | 10        |
| **Total** | **40** |

**Answer:** Class width = 10; lower class limit for second class = 10.

**Solution:** The class width for each class is the same and is determined by finding the difference between the lower class limit of one class and the lower class limit of the next class. Using the first class 0-9, the lower class limit is 0. The lower class limit of the second class is 10. The difference is 10 - 0 = 10.

There are several ways to present data in a frequency distribution. Thus far, the full count or tally has been presented. Another method of presenting the data is with a relative frequency. A **relative frequency** is the proportion of each value or class to the total. It can be stated as a percentage or a decimal number. When all values are accounted for, the total of the relative frequencies must equal 1.00, or 100%. To determine a relative frequency, divide the number of occurrences (frequency) for each value by the total number of responses. The symbol $f$ represents the frequency and the symbol $\Sigma f$ represents the summation of $f$. The calculation must be performed for each value or group.

**Relative Frequency** The proportion of the frequency of a value to the total number of occurrences.

$$\text{Relative Frequency} = f \Big/ \sum f$$

A *cumulative frequency* can also be used to present data in a frequency distribution. A cumulative frequency is a running count of the frequency for a value and all preceding values. The first value in a cumulative frequency is equal to the value in the frequency column, since no values precede it. The last value should equal the total number of occurrences. A cumulative relative frequency is a running count of the relative frequencies of a value and all preceding relative frequencies.

**Cumulative Frequency Distribution** A count of the frequencies or relative frequencies of a value to all preceding counts.

## EXAMPLE 2.3

**Experiment:** Calculate the relative frequency, cumulative frequency, and cumulative relative frequency for the following data.

| Class | Frequency |
|-------|-----------|
| 0-9 | 11 |
| 10-19 | 10 |
| 20-29 | 9 |
| 30-39 | 10 |
| **Total** | **40** |

**Answer:**

| Class | Frequency | Relative Frequency | Cumulative Relative Frequency |
|-------|-----------|--------------------|-------------------------------|
| 0-9 | 11 | .275 | .275 |
| 10-19 | 10 | .250 | .525 |
| 20-29 | 9 | .225 | .750 |
| 30-39 | 10 | .250 | 1.000 |
| **Total** | **40** | **1.000** | |

**Solution:** Begin by determining the relative frequency. Divide the frequency by the total number of occurrences. For the first class, 0-9, divide 11 by 40. For the second class divide 10 by 40. Repeat this procedure for the other two classes. The cumulative frequency is a running count of the occurrences. The first class has a cumulative frequency of 11. The second class has a frequency of 10 plus 11 from the first class (10 + 11 = 21). The third class is 11 + 10 + 9. The fourth class is the sum of all frequencies. The cumulative relative frequency repeats the cumulative method, but with the relative proportions added instead of the frequencies. The first cumulative relative frequency is the relative frequency, because no class precedes it. The second cumulative relative frequency is .275 from the first class plus .250 for the second class. The third class is then .275 +.250 + .225. The fourth class is the sum of all previous relative frequencies. The full calculations are illustrated in the following table.

| Class | Frequency | Relative Frequency | Cumulative Frequency | Cumulative Relative Frequency |
|-------|-----------|--------------------|----------------------|-------------------------------|
| 0-9 | 11 | $11/40 = .275$ | 11 | .275 |
| 10-19 | 10 | $10/40 = .250$ | $11 + 10 = 21$ | $.275+.250 = .525$ |
| 20-29 | 9 | $9/40 = .225$ | $11+10+9 = 30$ | $.275+.250+.225 = .750$ |
| 30-39 | 10 | $10/40 = .250$ | $11+10+9+10 = 40$ | $.275+.250+.225+.250 = 1.000$ |
| **Total** | **40** | **1.000** | | |

## A LEARNING AID
## Frequency Distributions

Calculate the relative frequency, cumulative frequency, and cumulative relative frequency for the following data for the ages of patients in a pediatrician's office on a particular day.

| Class | Frequency |
|-------|-----------|
| 0-3 | 10 |
| 4-7 | 6 |
| 8-11 | 3 |
| 12-15 | 1 |
| **Total** | **20** |

**Step 1**
Establish a column for the relative frequency. The relative frequency is determined by dividing the frequency of each value by the sum of all the frequencies (total number of observations). Since the total frequency is 20, each value can be divided by 20 to obtain the relative frequency. The relative frequencies must have a sum of 1.0.

| Class | Frequency | Relative Frequency |
|-------|-----------|--------------------|
| 0-3   | 10        | .50                |
| 4-7   | 6         | 30                 |
| 8-11  | 3         | .15                |
| 12-15 | 1         | .05                |
| **Total** | **20** | **1.00**         |

## Step 2

Establish a column for the cumulative frequency. The cumulative frequency is a running count of the frequency column. Add the frequency of a value to the frequencies of all preceding values. The first cumulative frequency is the same as the frequency. The last must equal the total, 20.

| Class | Frequency | Relative Frequency | Cumulative Frequency |
|-------|-----------|--------------------|----------------------|
| 0-3   | 10        | .50                | 10                   |
| 4-7   | 6         | 30                 | 16                   |
| 8-11  | 3         | .15                | 19                   |
| 12-15 | 1         | .05                | 20                   |
| **Total** | **20** | **1.00**         |                      |

## Step 3

Establish a column for the cumulative relative frequency. The cumulative relative frequency is a running count of the relative frequencies. The first value must equal the relative frequency of the first class and the last value must equal 1.00.

| Class | Frequency | Relative Frequency | Cumulative Frequency | Cumulative Relative Frequency |
|-------|-----------|--------------------|----------------------|-------------------------------|
| 0-3   | 10        | .50                | 10                   | .50                           |
| 4-7   | 6         | .30                | 16                   | .80                           |
| 8-11  | 3         | .15                | 19                   | .95                           |
| 12-15 | 1         | .05                | 20                   | 1.00                          |
| **Total** | **20** | **1.00**         |                      |                               |

# SECTION 2

## Bar Charts and Histograms

Frequency distributions are easier to visualize if they are presented graphically. A bar chart or a histogram graphically displays information contained in frequency distributions.

A bar chart, also known as a bar graph, displays discrete and continuous data of any level of measurement, although it is most commonly used for displaying nominal-level data. It is appropriate for grouped and ungrouped data. A bar chart may represent frequencies or relative proportions.

A *histogram* is a special type of bar chart. A histogram better represents continuous data at the interval and ordinal levels. A histogram may represent frequencies or relative proportions.

A bar chart can be distinguished from a histogram by noting whether the bars are separate or adjacent. Because bar charts represent nominal-level data or discrete data, the bars are not adjacent. Each bar is independent of the others. A histogram represents continuous data; hence the bars are adjacent so values are not interrupted. Bars also are adjacent when the bar chart is representing grouped data.

The creation of the two graphs is similar. A horizontal axis represents the numerical or alphabetic values of the variable. Alphabetic values refer usually to nominal-level data, such as marital status, with values including single, married, and divorced. A vertical axis represents the frequencies or proportions. Values are placed on the axes. Values representing the frequencies or proportions should be in equal intervals. The values on the vertical axis do not necessarily correspond to the reported frequencies. For example, if frequencies are 40, 41, and 42, the axis might contain the value 40, where bars for 41 and 42 would be drawn slightly above the mark of 40. The heights of the bars correspond to the frequencies or proportions. The widths of the bars in a histogram represent the class widths. Label the axes and avoid placing values at the top of the bars. Also avoid interrupting or omitting data either on the vertical or horizontal axes. Adjust the scales as necessary to avoid interrupting the axes. This adjustment is very important for bar charts and histograms because interrupting the axes results in a distorted visual.

The frequency distribution in Table 2.2 can be graphed as a bar chart. The variable in the distribution is marital status, a nominal-level measurement best represented by a bar chart and not a histogram.

## TABLE 2.2

## Marital Status of Students at the University

| Marital Status | Frequency | Relative Frequency |
|---|---|---|
| Single | 78 | .503 |
| Married | 51 | .329 |
| Divorced | 22 | .142 |
| Widowed | 4 | .026 |
| **Total** | **155** | **1.000** |

Begin by drawing the horizontal axis representing the values of the variable. The values of the variable marital status are single, married, divorced, and widowed. Draw the vertical axis representing the frequencies. The values on the vertical axis must represent the frequencies in such a way that the frequencies are neither too extended nor too clustered. Intervals must be consistent. A review of the values shows that the frequencies range from 4 for widowed to 78 for single. Intervals of ten would best represent all the frequencies. Begin the vertical axis at 0 and increase in increments of 10 to at least 80. Draw independent bars for each marital status. The height of the bar represents the frequency. Be sure to label all axes including the variable. The result is shown in Figure 2.2.

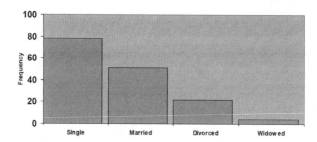

## Figure 2.2 Bar Chart Representing Marital Status of Students

The following grouped distribution can be transformed into a histogram. The variable is the age of patients visiting a doctor's office on a specific day. Age is a continuous ratio-level measurement that is best represented by a histogram.

| Ages of Patients | Frequency | Relative Frequency |
|---|---|---|
| 10-19 | 10 | .172 |
| 20-29 | 9 | .155 |
| 30-39 | 10 | .172 |
| 40-49 | 11 | .190 |

| | | |
|---|---|---|
| 50-59 | 8 | .138 |
| 60-69 | 10 | .172 |
| **Total** | **58** | **1.000** |

Begin by drawing the horizontal axis representing the values of the variable. Ages are grouped into 10-year classes. The lower limit of each class is the lower limit of the bar, and the upper class limit is the upper boundary of the bar. Draw the vertical axis representing the frequencies. The values on the vertical axis must represent the frequencies in such a way that the frequencies are neither too extended nor too clustered. Intervals must be consistent. A review of the values shows that the frequencies range from 8 for the age class 50-59 to 11 for the class 40-49. Intervals of length 2 would best represent all the frequencies. Begin the vertical axis at 0 and increase in increments of 2 to at least 12. Draw adjacent bars for each age class. The height of the bar represents the frequency. The result is shown in Figure 2.3.

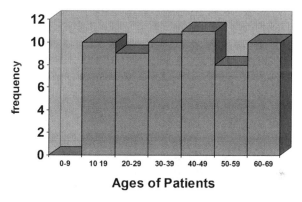

**Ages of Patients**

**Figure 2.3 Histogram for Ages of Patients**

## EXAMPLE 2.4
**Experiment:** Draw a histogram for the price of a loaf of rye bread of the same brand based on the following distribution from a survey of 50 local stores.

**Price of a Loaf of Rye Bread (in Dollars)**

| Price | Frequency |
|---|---|
| 1.25 | 5 |
| 1.26 | 7 |
| 1.27 | 9 |
| 1.28 | 8 |
| 1.29 | 10 |

|        |    |
|--------|----|
| 1.30   | 11 |
| **Total** | **50** |

**Answer:**

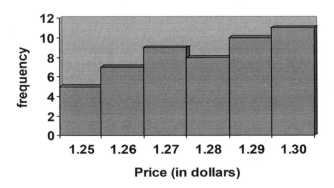

**Histogram for Prices of Rye Bread**

**Solution:** Begin by identifying price as a ratio-level measurement best represented by a histogram. Draw the horizontal axis representing the price of the bread. Note each price along the axis. Draw the vertical axis representing the frequencies. The values on the vertical axis need to represent the frequencies in such a way that the frequencies are neither too extended nor too clustered. Intervals must be consistent. A review of the values shows that the frequencies range from 5 for the price $1.25 to 11 for the price $1.30. Intervals of 2 best represent all the frequencies. Begin the vertical axis at 0 and increase in increments of 2 to at least 12. Draw adjacent bars for each price. The height of the bar represents the frequency.

The rules for drawing a bar chart or histogram bar chart for two variables is the same as for one variable. Simply split the bars for the second variable. The following bar chart represents two variables: Total U.S. Labor Force Participation and gender. Notice the gender bars are split.

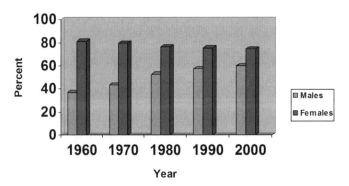

**Figure 2.4 Total U.S. Labor Force Participation Rates by Gender**

## A LEARNING AID
## BAR CHARTS AND HISTOGRAMS

Draw a histogram for the following distribution on infant mortality rates of 50 developed nations (rounded to whole numbers).

**Infant Mortality Rates of Developed Nations (per 1,000 Births)**

| Rate | Frequency |
|---|---|
| 8 | 3 |
| 9 | 6 |
| 10 | 10 |
| 11 | 8 |
| 12 | 10 |
| 13 | 7 |
| 14 | 6 |
| **Total** | **50** |

### Step 1

Identify the conditions for a histogram. A histogram is a type of a bar chart typically representing continuous-interval or ratio-level measurements. Infant mortality rate is a continuous ratio-level measurement (values are rounded).

### Step 2

Draw the horizontal axis. The horizontal axis represents the values of the variable infant mortality. The values for infant mortality range from 8 to 14. Label the axis.

### Step 3

Draw the vertical axis. The vertical axis represents the frequencies. The values on the vertical axis need to represent the frequencies in such a way that the frequencies are neither too extended nor too clustered. Intervals must be consistent. A review of the values shows that the frequencies range from 3 to 10. Intervals of 2 would best represent all the frequencies. Begin the vertical axis at 0 and increase in increments of 2 to at least 10.

### Step 4

Complete the histogram. Draw adjacent bars for each value of infant mortality. The height of the bar represents the frequency.

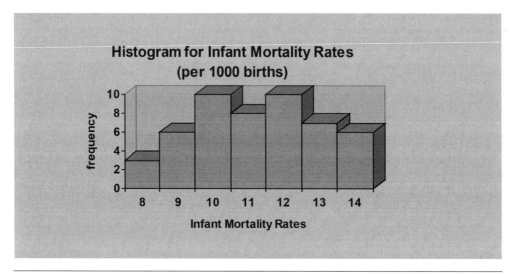

---

# SECTION 3

## Pie Charts and Line Graphs

Frequency distributions can easily be redone as pie charts and line graphs. Pie charts and line graphs are very popular displays of data because they are easily created and understood.

A *pie chart*, also known as a circle graph, is a circular diagram that is analogous to a pie, where each value of a variable is equivalent to a different-sized piece of the pie. Pie charts are typically used for nominal-level discrete variables and represent relative proportions. The values in the relative frequency column of a frequency distribution are easily represented in a pie chart.

Line graphs have become very popular in recent years. There are two types of line graphs: One represents frequencies and is known as a frequency polygon; the other represents cumulative frequencies or cumulative relative frequencies and is known as an ogive (pronounced "o-jive").

As with other displays, pie charts and line graphs should be kept as simple as possible. Keep unnecessary information out of the display. Move values and percentages to the titles or labels. Many computer software packages create pie charts and line graphs. Many of the packages put percentages or frequencies inside the graphs. Avoid the percentages and other information unless they are necessary for understanding the display. Remember that the purpose of a display is to present a visual aid to understanding. The actual values are not usually necessary.

A pie chart is created by dividing a circle into slices corresponding to the relative proportions of each value or category of the variable. For example, if 50% of a class is females and 50% are males, a pie chart is divided into two equal parts. The following distribution can be shown using a pie chart. Do not rearrange the order of the data as it is represented in a frequency table. For example if a frequency table of ages begins at 20 year olds, the first pie piece (slice) should start for the proportion of age 20. If the next age is 21, it must be placed next to 20; 22 is next to 23; and so on. It is optional as to whether the graph reads clockwise or counter-clockwise.

### TABLE 2.2 Marital Status of Students at the University

| Marital Status | Frequency | Relative Frequency |
| --- | --- | --- |
| Single | 78 | .503 |
| Married | 51 | .329 |
| Divorced | 22 | .142 |
| Widowed | 4 | .026 |
| **Total** | **155** | **1.000** |

Begin by drawing a circle. The circle will be divided into four categories, representing the four values single, married, divorced, and widowed. Focus on the relative frequency column of the distribution. Relative frequencies become percentages by moving the decimal to the right two places. The relative frequency of single students is .503, which is 50.3%. Draw a line across the circle representing slightly more than 50%. For married students, draw a line representing another 32.9%. For divorced students, draw a line representing another 14.2%. Finally, the remaining portion of the pie should be equivalent to 2.6% for widowed students. Remember not to rearrange the data as it is reported on the frequency distribution; the order of the pie must remain single, married, divorced and widowed. See Figure 2.5.

**Figure 2.5 Pie Chart Representing Marital Status of Students**

## Example 2.5

**Experiment:** Draw a pie chart for the price of a loaf of rye bread based on the following distribution from a survey of 50 local stores.

**Price of a Loaf of Rye Bread (in Dollars)**

| Price | Frequency |
|-------|-----------|
| 1.25 | 5 |
| 1.26 | 7 |
| 1.27 | 9 |
| 1.28 | 8 |
| 1.29 | 10 |
| 1.30 | 11 |
| **Total** | **50** |

**Answer:**

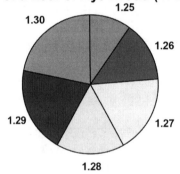

**Price of a Loaf of Rye Bread (in Dollars)**

**Solution:** Begin by understanding that a pie chart represents relative frequencies that are not presented in the frequency table. The relative frequencies must be calculated by dividing each frequency by the total frequency. Begin with the 1.25 value that has a frequency of 5. Divide the frequency 5 by the total 50. This results in a relative frequency of .10. Repeat this process for each frequency, dividing each by 50 and recording the answer. The table should be as follows:

**Price of a Loaf of Rye Bread (in Dollars)**

| Price | Frequency | Relative Frequency | |
|-------|-----------|--------------------|-----|
| 1.25 | 5 | (5/50) | .10 |
| 1.26 | 7 | (7/50) | .14 |
| 1.27 | 9 | (9/50) | .18 |

| 1.28 | 8 | (8/50) | .16 |
|------|-----|---------|-----|
| 1.29 | 10 | (10/50) | .20 |
| 1.30 | 11 | (11/50) | .22 |
| **Total** | **50** | | **1.00** |

Next, draw a circle for the pie. The first value 1.25 has a relative frequency of .10. Draw a straight line from the center point to the outer edge of the circle. The .10 is understood to be 10% (move the decimal to the right two places.) Divide the pie to represent a 10% piece. Label the section as 1.25. The percentage is not placed on the pie. The second piece of the pie is for the value 1.26 that is .14 or 14% of the pie.

Draw a line from the previous piece to represent the 14%. Label this piece as 1.26 (again, the percentage is not placed on the pie). (These two pieces together are 24%, almost a quarter of the pie). The next piece for the value 1.27 is .18 or 18% of the pie. Label this section as 1.27. Continue until all values, and therefore, pieces, of the pie are represented. Remember not to rearrange the order of the values.

A *frequency polygon* is a display that is similar to a histogram. A frequency polygon line typically begins and ends at zero. Dots placed at the tops of the bars of a histogram replace the bars and are connected, forming a line moving up and down across the values of the variable. As with a histogram, the horizontal axis represents the values of the variable. The vertical line represents frequencies. Do not rearrange the values of the variables from their reported order. If the data values are reported as A, B, C, and D, do not rearrange them as they are drawn (such as B, A, D, C).

The histogram in Figure 2.6 can be redone as a frequency polygon. Place the dots in the center of the bar representing the middle of each class. Extend the line at the beginning and end of zero. See Figure 2.7.

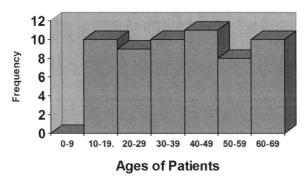

**Figure 2.6 Histogram for Ages of Patients**

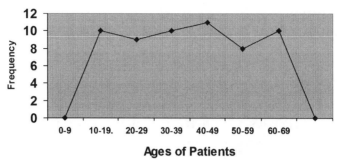

**Figure 2.7 Frequency Polygon for Ages of Patients**

If two variables are to be represented in a line graph, each variable is represented by a different line and typically with different data point symbols, such as a square and a diamond as in the diagram below representing Labor Force Participation and Gender. Avoid using only color since some readers maybe color-impaired.

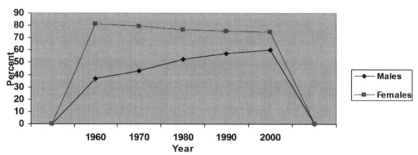

**Figure 2.8 Labor Force Participation Rates by Gender**

Figure 2.9 is another example of a two-variable line graph. The graph is representing the wage gap between men and women across ages. Again, the line for each gender must be distinguished by color or symbols on the lines. This graph is not representing the grid-lines, an option used to better emphasize the comparison of the values.

**Figure 2.9 Wage Gap Between Males and Females Across Age**

An *ogive* is a second type of line graph representing cumulative frequencies or cumulative relative frequencies. For an ogive describing cumulative frequencies, the line must begin at zero and end at the total number of observations for the table. An ogive displaying cumulative relative frequencies must begin at zero and end at 1.00 (or 100% if percentages are described). The lines on ogives increase as they travel across the graph. Lines may remain parallel for one or two values, but they must reach the total frequency of 1.00 for the last value. The following frequency distribution is for the price of a loaf of rye bread.

**Price of a Loaf of Rye Bread (in Dollars)**

| Price | Frequency | Cumulative Frequency |
|---|---|---|
| 1.25 | 5 | 5 |
| 1.26 | 7 | 12 |
| 1.27 | 9 | 21 |
| 1.28 | 8 | 29 |
| 1.29 | 10 | 39 |
| 1.30 | 11 | 50 |
| **Total** | **50** | |

The creation of an ogive begins with identifying the axes. The horizontal axis represents the values of the variable. For the price of bread, the values are 1.25, 1.26, and so forth. The vertical axis represents either the cumulative frequency or cumulative relative frequency. The values on the vertical axis must begin at 0 and increase in equal increments to the total frequency or 1.00. The ogive in Figure 2.10 represents the cumulative frequency, which begins at 0 and ends at 50.

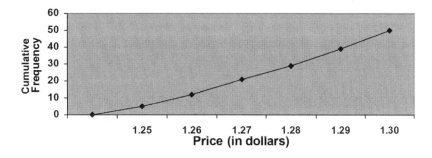

**Figure 2.10 Ogive for the Price of Rye Bread**

## EXAMPLE 2.6

**Experiment:** Draw a cumulative frequency ogive for the ages of children visiting a children's clinic on a single day.

| Age | Frequency | Cumulative Frequency |
|-----|-----------|----------------------|
| 0-4 | 10 | 10 |
| 5-9 | 15 | 25 |
| 10-14 | 7 | 32 |
| 15-19 | 3 | 35 |
| **Total** | **35** | |

**Answer:**

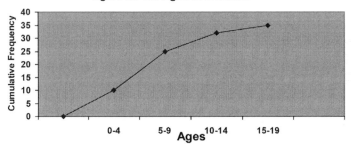

**Solution:** Begin by drawing the axes. The horizontal axis represents the ages of the children. The vertical axis represents the cumulative frequency. The vertical axis must begin at 0 and increase in increments representing cumulative frequencies until the total 35 is reached. Place a dot at each point of the interception of the value and its cumulative frequency. The last dot must be at 35. Connect the dots to form a line. The line in an ogive always increases or remains stable, but it must reach the total frequency of 35.

## A LEARNING AID
## FREQUENCY POLYGON—LINE GRAPH

Draw a frequency polygon for the following distribution of infant mortality rates of 50 developed nations (rounded to the nearest whole number).

### Infant Mortality Rates of Developed Nations (per 1,000 Births)

| Rate | Frequency |
|------|-----------|
| 8 | 3 |
| 9 | 6 |
| 10 | 10 |
| 11 | 8 |
| 12 | 10 |
| 13 | 7 |
| 14 | 6 |
| **Total** | **50** |

**Step 1**

Identify the conditions for a frequency polygon. A frequency polygon is a type of line graph representing frequencies and is similar to a histogram.

**Step 2**

Draw the horizontal axis. The horizontal axis represents the values of the variable infant mortality. The values for infant mortality range from 8 to 14. Label the axis.

---

8   9   10   11   12   13   14
**Infant Mortality Rate (per 1,000 Births)**

**Step 3**

Draw the vertical axis. The vertical axis represents the frequencies. The values on the vertical axis must represent the frequencies in such a way that the frequencies are neither too extended nor too clustered. Intervals must be consistent. A review of the values shows that the frequencies range from 3 to 10. Intervals of 2 would best represent all the frequencies. Begin the vertical axis at 0 and increase in increments of 2 to at least 10.

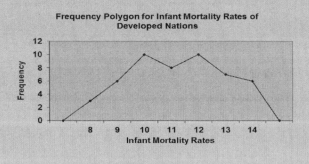

**Step 4**
Complete the frequency polygon. Place dots to represent the frequency of each value. The dots replace the bars of a histogram. Connect the dots by starting at zero and ending at zero.

## CHAPTER 2 IN REVIEW

2.1  A random sample of military enlistments during the last week denotes branchs of the armed services.

| Branch | Frequency |
|---|---|
| Army | 55 |
| Navy | 60 |
| Air Force | 40 |
| Marines | 45 |
| **Total** | **200** |

Construct a frequency distribution, including the relative frequency, cumulative frequency, and cumulative relative frequency.

2.2  Construct a pie chart representing the data from Problem 2.1.

2.3  A sample of the musical preferences of 70 people produces the following results:

| | |
|---|---|
| Pop | 18 |
| Classical | 12 |
| Country | 17 |
| Rock | 10 |
| Oldies | 13 |

Construct a frequency distribution, including the relative frequency, cumulative frequency, and cumulative relative frequency.

2.4  Construct a bar chart representing the data from Problem 2.3.

2.5  Construct a pie chart for the following data representing the percent of sales in a local restaurant.

Breakfast 35     |     Lunch 25     |     Dinner 40

2 .6 Construct a grouped frequency distribution for the ages of 30 students in Professor Constantine's class. Use class widths of 5.

| | | | | | | | | | | | | | | |
|---|---|---|---|---|---|---|---|---|---|---|---|---|---|---|
| 21 | 31 | 21 | 34 | 19 | 20 | 28 | 30 | 27 | 25 | 25 | 25 | 25 | 30 | 27 |
| 21 | 34 | 19 | 19 | 20 | 21 | 21 | 30 | 25 | 25 | 32 | 32 | 31 | 30 | 27 |

2.7 Construct a bar chart representing the data from Problem 2.6.

2.8 With class widths of 1 minute, draw a histogram for the number of minutes that it took a local ambulance company to reach 16 accidents.

| | | | | | | | |
|---|---|---|---|---|---|---|---|
| 1.6 | 5.4 | 2.8 | 7.7 | 3.5 | 4.5 | 3.1 | 2.4 |
| 3.0 | 7.7 | 2.5 | 3.9 | 7.0 | 5.3 | 1.9 | 4.2 |

2.9 A random survey of entry-level employees at the A & A Construction Company yields the following wages (dollars per hour):

| | | | | | | | | | |
|---|---|---|---|---|---|---|---|---|---|
| 8.85 | 8.25 | 8.35 | 10.15 | 8.25 | 8.50 | 9.75 | 10.10 | 10.50 | 7.25 |
| 9.40 | 8.00 | 9.75 | 11.95 | 7.50 | 8.50 | 11.10 | 9.20 | 9.35 | 8.25 |

a. Construct a grouped frequency distribution with class widths of $1.
b. Draw a frequency polygon.

2.10 Draw a pie chart for the following sample on the level of completed education in Cahokia, Illinois.

| Education | Frequency |
|---|---|
| Elementary | 325 |
| Secondary | 2,390 |
| Bachelor's | 950 |
| Master's | 300 |
| Doctorate | 35 |

2.11 In 2015, 54,275 doctoral degrees were conferred in the U.S. Among those, 74 percent were U.S. citizens and 26 percent were citizens of other countries. Construct a pie chart representing the citizenship of doctoral recipients.

2.12 Construct a line graph for the average amount of student law school debt (in thousands of U.S. dollars) from public law schools and private law schools (2 lines).

| Year | 2010 | 2011 | 2012 | 2013 | 2014 |
|---|---|---|---|---|---|
| Public | 143 | 148 | 150 | 158 | 164 |
| Private | 170 | 177 | 179 | 189 | 199 |

2.13 The following data represents exam scores on last semester's final exam. Complete the distribution with the relative frequency and the relative cumulative frequency.

| Exam Scores | Frequency (f) |
|:---:|:---:|
| 40-49 | 1 |
| 50-59 | 2 |
| 60-69 | 8 |
| 70-79 | 16 |
| 80-89 | 6 |
| 90-99 | 7 |
| **Total** | **40** |

2.14 Draw a frequency polygon for the following cholesterol levels of patients visiting Dr. Adam's office.

| Cholesterol Level | Frequency (f) |
|:---:|:---:|
| 190-194 | 8 |
| 195-199 | 10 |
| 200-204 | 16 |
| 205-209 | 7 |
| 210-214 | 4 |
| 215-219 | 6 |
| 220-224 | 2 |
| **Total** | **31** |

2.15 A sample of 12 starting salaries for graduates with a Bachelor of Science in Business Administration yielded the following results (data in thousands, rounded to nearest hundred):

50.0 │ 43.7 │ 59.1 │ 59.1 │ 38.8 │ 37.8 │ 42.3 │ 47.7 │ 42.8 │ 37.2 │ 45.5 │ 39.8

Create a frequency distribution representing the count, the relative frequency, and the cumulative relative frequency. Group the data in 10 thousands starting at 30.0 to 39.9.

2.16 The following data represent the number of suicides per 10,000 inhabitants in rural areas in Japan. Construct a grouped bar chart on the number of suicides. Use class widths of 10.

22  10  12  2  10  9  16  11  8  14  11  8  13  10
12  0  10  12  8  11  25  31  10  7  9  9  6  8

2.17 Create a bar chart of the following data on the life expectancy of a newborn in the United States in 2014 based on race and gender:

White female: 81.1, Black female: 77.8, Hispanic female: 83.7, White male: 76.4, Black male: 71.6, and Hispanic male: 78.9.

2.18 The following grouped frequency distribution represents the ages of women marrying in St. Clair County for the month of January.

| Age | Frequency (*f*) |
|-----|-----------------|
| 16-20 | 3 |
| 21-25 | 26 |
| 26-30 | 27 |
| 31-35 | 14 |
| 36-40 | 6 |
| 41-45 | 4 |
| **Total** | **80** |

a. Identify the class width.
b. Identify the upper limit of class 4.
c. Identify the class mark of the second class.

2.19 The following data are the ages of children visiting a doctor's office in a day.

| Age | Frequency (*f*) |
|-----|-----------------|
| 0-4 | 4 |
| 5-9 | 5 |
| 10-14 | 6 |
| 15-19 | 4 |
| 20-24 | 3 |
| **Total** | **22** |

a. Identify the class mark for the first class.
b. Identify the lower class limit for the last class.
c. Identify the upper class limit for the second class.
d. Identify the class width.

2.20 Create a pie chart for the following data on the marital status of women:

| | |
|---|---|
| Never married | 21% |
| Married | 55% |
| Divorced/Separated | 13% |
| Widowed | 11% |

2.21 Draw a bar chart representing the primary languages spoken in American households (in millions):

| | |
|---|---|
| English only | 215.4 |
| Spanish | 28.1 |
| Chinese | 2.0 |
| French | 1.6 |
| German | 1.4 |

2.22 Draw a pie chart for the primary language data presented in problem 2.21.

2.23 Draw a bar chart representing the change in gas prices from the last week (in cents).

| Monday | Tuesday | Wednesday | Thursday | Friday | Saturday | Sunday |
|---|---|---|---|---|---|---|
| +5 | 0 | -2 | +1 | +1 | +2 | +3 |

2.24 Draw a bar chart representing the average hospital stay in the U.S. by diagnostic category.

| | |
|---|---|
| Psychoses | 8.0 |
| Malignant Neoplasm | 6.7 |
| Pneumonia | 5.5 |
| Fractures | 5.4 |
| Heart Disease | 4.6 |
| Delivery | 2.6 |

2.25 Draw a line graph for the median price of a single-family home in the U.S. during the last several decades.

| | |
|---|---|
| 1975 | 66,300 |
| 1985 | 101,600 |
| 1995 | 157,500 |
| 2005 | 223,200 |
| 2015 | 210,500 |

2.26 Draw a line graph for the percent of births to unmarried women in the U.S. from 1980 to 2010.

| 1980 | 1990 | 2000 | 2010 |
|---|---|---|---|
| 18.4 | 28.0 | 33.2 | 41.2 |

# 3 DESCRIPTIVE STATISTICS FOR ONE VARIABLE

**SECTION 1   Measures of Central Tendency**
**SECTION 2   Measures of Dispersion**
**SECTION 3   Measures of Position**

Data can be presented in graphs and charts as a method of reducing what may be a long and cumbersome list of observations. Often, however, even graphs and charts are too cumbersome. Reducing the data to one or two numbers to represent the beginning, center, end, or dispersion of the data is another means of description. These numbers are referred to as measures of central tendency, measures of dispersion, and measures of position.

---

## SECTION 1

### Measures of Central Tendency

Measures of central tendency locate the center of a set of data. A *measure of central tendency* is a single number that describes the general order or magnitude of a set of data. Each measurement describes the center in a different way. A mean, for example, describes the average response. It is an arithmetic average. The *median* describes the midpoint of the data. It is the physical center where half of the values are lower and half are higher. Yet another measurement, the *mode*, describes the most common response. Each measurement, although correct, may result in a different description of the data. Since each measurement may describe the center of the data in a different fashion, some measurements are more suited for certain types of data.

The most common measure of central tendency is the *mean*, more commonly referred to as the average. The mean is an arithmetic average. It is a measurement that describes the center of a set of data when the data are summed and divided by the number of observations. Recall the usual approach described for calculating an average: add all the numbers and divide by how many there are.

**Mean** A measure of central tendency that describes the average response by summing the data and dividing by the total number of elements or observation.

If the mean represents a sample, the symbol is $\bar{x}$.
If the mean represents a population, the symbol is $\mu$.

Different symbols represent the mean of a sample and the mean of a population. Recall that *statistics* represent information about samples and are usually represented by English symbols. *Parameters* represent information about populations and are usually represented by Greek symbols.

---

**Formula for Calculating a Mean
(for raw data, non-frequency distribution only)**

$$\bar{x} = \frac{\sum x}{n}$$

where
$\bar{x}$ represents the sample mean.
$\Sigma$ (sigma) represents the summation of the values.
$x$ represents each value in the data.
$n$ represents the number of elements or observations in the sample.

---

The calculation of the sample mean requires adding the values of $x$ and dividing by the number of observations. For example, the mean for the values 3, 4, 5, 6, and 7 is the sum of the values ($3 + 4 + 5 + 6 + 7 = 25$) divided by the number of values (there are 5 values). The mean is $25 \div 5 = 5$.

---

**EXAMPLE 3.1**

**Experiment:** Calculate the mean score on an exam using the following data:

83, 93, 70, 65, 90, 100, 55, 52, 81, 73

**Answer:** $\bar{x} = 76.2$

**Solution:** The mean is calculated by summing all the values of $x$ and dividing by the total number of values.

$$\bar{x} = \frac{\sum x}{n} = 76.2$$

Calculator Press the STAT button and with "Edit…" highlighted, press ENTER and insert the data into List 1.

---

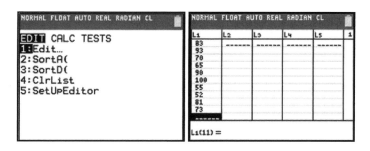

With the data in List 1, press STAT again and scroll right to "CALC." With "1: 1 – Var Stats" highlighted, press ENTER. The screen should appear as follows before pressing "Calculate." It is important that the frequency list is kept blank.

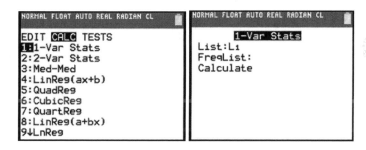

Highlight "Calculate" and press ENTER. The results screen should appear as follows:

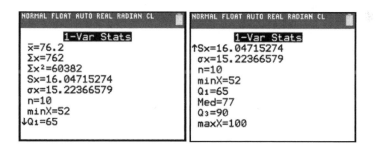

## EXAMPLE 3.2

**Experiment:** Calculate the sample mean number of children born to 20 women aged 35 to 55 years.

2   0   3   2   1   1   2   3   0   2   4   1   1   3   1   0   2   5   6   3

**Answer:** $\bar{x} = 2.1$

**Solution:** The mean is calculated by summing all the values of $x$ and dividing by the total number of values. The values have a sum of 42. Divide 42 by 20 (the number of women surveyed).

$$\bar{x} = \frac{\sum x}{n} = \frac{42}{20} = 2.1$$

**Calculator:** Plug the list of numbers into List 1 of a TI 83/84 calculator by pressing the STAT button. With "Edit…" highlighted, press the ENTER button. Once the data is entered, press STAT again, scroll right to CALC. With "1-Var Stats" highlighted, press ENTER. Keep the frequency list blank, highlight Calculate and press ENTER again.

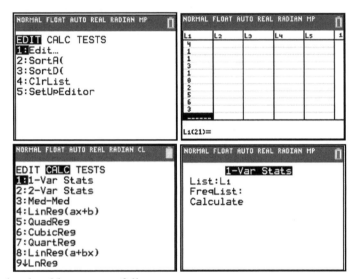

The results should appear as follows:

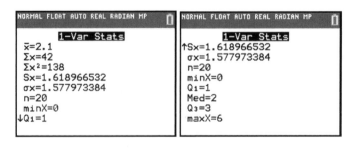

The mean can also be calculated when the data are arranged in a frequency distribution. A frequency distribution condenses the data so that a count of each value is reported. The values of *x* are either given separately or collapsed into groups or classes. Even if the data are not grouped, the values of *x* cannot simply be added to determine the mean. The number of occurrences of each value is given as a frequency. For example, if the value 2 occurs three times, merely adding the 2 to other values would fail to recognize that it actually occurred three times. Therefore, 2 must be added three times (2 + 2 + 2). When working with a frequency distribution, instead of adding each value the number of times it occurs, it is easier to multiply the value by its number of occurrences. That is, if 2 occurs 10 times, instead of adding 2 ten times, multiply 2 by 10, for a total of 20. The formula for the mean can be adjusted to note the multiplication of the values by their number of occurrences. The symbol *f* represents the frequency, or number of occurrences.

**Mean Formula for a Frequency Distribution
(For a Frequency Table Only)**

$$\bar{x} = \frac{\sum xf}{\sum f}$$

where
$\sum xf$ represents the sum of each value of *x* multiplied by *f*.
$\sum f$ represents the total number of occurrences, which is the sum of the frequencies.

The adjusted mean formula is applied to all frequency distributions. Do not attempt to apply the original mean formula to a frequency distribution, because it will not count all the occurrences and will result in a wrong answer. *Remember, a frequency distribution mean formula includes f; if the data contains an f, the formula must contain an f.* The denominator in the formula is also adjusted. Although most texts use *n* in the denominator, this text replaces *n* with $\sum f$ as a reminder to sum the occurrences and not the number of different values. Both symbols, *n* and $\sum f$, represent the total number of occurrences.

**EXAMPLE 3.3**
**Experiment:** Calculate the sample mean for the number of daily absences of students in a statistics class in the last 30 class meetings.

| Absences (*x*) | Frequency (*f*) |
|:---:|:---:|
| 0 | 8 |
| 1 | 7 |
| 2 | 5 |
| 3 | 5 |
| 4 | 5 |
| **Total** | **30** |

**Answer:** $\bar{X} = 1.73$ The average number of absence is 1.73 per day.

**Solution:** This is a frequency distribution that arranges the data around the number of occurrences for each value of *x*. For example, eight students missed 0 classes. Instead of listing 0, 0, 0, 0, 0, 0, 0, and 0, the frequency distribution reports the 0 and gives 8 occurrences. Calculating the mean can be performed by inserting Absences (*x*) into List 1 and the Frequency (*y*) into List 2 on your Calculator by pressing STAT and ENTER.

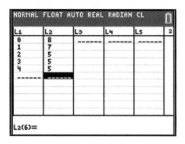

Press the STAT button, scroll over to CALC, and down to 1: 1-Var Stats and press ENTER. Set the List to List 1 and the Frequency List to List 2 and then press Calculate. NOTE: If you have an older version of a TI 83/84 calculator, the second screen below may not appear. Instead, it will read 1:1-Var Stats and the cursor will be blinking. Type $L_1$, $L_2$ and press ENTER.

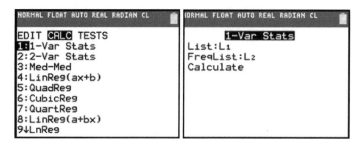

The results screen should appear as follows:

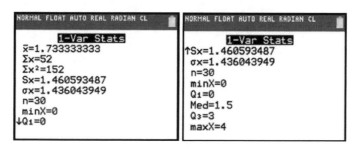

The mean for grouped frequency distributions is found using the same method as used for ungrouped frequency distributions. However, the calculation of a mean from a grouped frequency distribution is only an approximation since grouping of data involves the loss of precise information on individual observations. That is, if the absences of the students in the previous example were grouped as 0 and 1 with 15 combined observations, it would be impossible to know if all 15 students in the group missed no classes or 1 class. An assumption must be made as to a value of $x$ that will best represent each class. The most accepted value is referred to as the class mark, or the class *midpoint*. The class mark is the value in the middle of the class. For example, if a class is 10-12, the class mark, or midpoint, is 11. The value 11 is the best estimate of where the observations of that class fall. When the midpoint is not obvious, the class mark is determined by adding the lower and upper limit of the class and dividing by 2. In other words, the class mark is the mean of the values in each class. Every class has a unique class mark.

The class mark is necessary for the calculation of the mean of a grouped frequency distribution. The mean formula requires multiplying $x$ by the number of its occurrences. But a grouped frequency, by definition, does not have an $x$. Each class represents several values of $x$. The class mark is the estimate of $x$ and is used in the calculation of the mean.

**EXAMPLE 3.4**

**Experiment:** Calculate the mean birth rate (the number of births per 1,000 women) of 20 countries whose rates are given in the following grouped frequency distribution.

| $x$ | Frequency |
|-------|-----------|
| 10-19 | 4 |
| 20-29 | 8 |
| 30-39 | 3 |
| 40-49 | 3 |
| 50-59 | 2 |
| **Total** | **20** |

**Answer:** $\overline{x} = 30.0$

**Solution:** Identify the distribution as a grouped frequency distribution. The values have been collapsed into classes, with the observations reported. A grouped frequency distribution does not contain a value of $x$ for each class. An assumption must be made for each class as to where the frequency occurs. Do the four countries in the first class report a birth rate of 10, 19, or another value in the class? Since the information is not available, the assumption is that the countries report a value exactly in the middle of the class.

The value in the middle is referred to as the class mark and must be determined for each class. The value in the middle of 10 and 19 is calculated as 14.5 [(10 + 19)/2 = 14.5]. The class mark for the second class is (20 + 29)/2, or 24.5. The class mark for the third class is (30 + 39)/2, or 34.5. The class mark for the fourth class is (40 + 49)/2, or 44.5. Finally, the class mark for the fifth class is (50 + 59)/2, or 54.5. Place these values in a table. Note the class marks as the values of $x$.

The calculations of class mark can be done by hand or directly in the calculator as you plug the numbers into the list. Be sure your lists appear with class mark in List 1 and frequency in List 2.

Press the STAT button, scroll over to CALC, and down to 1: 1-Var Stats and press ENTER. Set the List to List 1 and the Frequency List to List 2 and then press Calculate. The results screen should appear as follows.

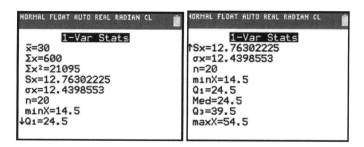

Calculate the mean by using the preceding equivalent formulas. Remember that the numerator is the sum of the *xf* column (600). Also remember that the denominator is the sum of the *f* column (20), representing the 20 birth rates reported.

$$\bar{x} = \frac{\sum xf}{\sum f} = \frac{\sum x}{n} = \frac{600.0}{20} = 30$$

There are advantages and disadvantages to working with the mean as a measure of central tendency. One advantage is that the mean is familiar to most people. Most people know how to calculate the mean, even if they do not know it as the mean. Another advantage is that the mean is calculated with all the available data. A researcher usually attempts to use as much of the data as possible, not discarding information. One more advantage is that the mean is suitable for ratio and interval data and therefore lends itself to further statistical manipulation; that is, the mean is often used for hypothesis testing, estimation, and other more advanced statistical procedures.

However, the mean has a few disadvantages. The mean may be a value that cannot or does not exist in the data. For example, the mean number of children may be determined as 2.5. But can a family have two and one-half children? Also, extreme values affect the calculation of the mean. The set of numbers 3, 4, 5, 6, and 7 has a mean of 5, but so, too, does the set of data 1, 2, 3, 4, and 15. The mean 5 is more appropriate for the first set of data than for the second. The second set includes the extreme value 15, which pulls the mean toward it. An extreme value is one that is not in sync with the others, such as the 15 in the set 1, 2, 3, 4, and 15. Another disadvantage is that the mean is not appropriately suited for nominal- and ordinal-level data. These data do not reflect true values of *x*, and the calculation of the mean can be misleading. For example, the mean does not make too much sense if we described the "average" sex of a student in class.

Another measure of central tendency is the **median**. The median identifies the middle value; exactly half of the data are above the median, and half are below. Visualize listing the data on a piece of paper, spaced equally with the lowest value at the upper edge and the highest value at the bottom edge. If the paper is folded in half, the value at the crease will be the median. Half of the values will be on the upper half of the paper, and half will be on the bottom half.

> **Median** $\tilde{x}$ The middle value of a set of data, where the data are arranged with half of the values above and half below the median.

The notation for the median is $\tilde{x}$. The symbol above the $x$ is a *tilde*. There are several steps in calculating the median. The first step is to arrange, or reorder, the data from the lowest value to the highest value. The second step is to calculate the position where the median value occurs. The position is determined by the expression $(n + 1)/2$; that is, add 1 to the number of values and then divide by 2. The symbol for the position is $i$. Position $i$ is not the median; it is the location of the median in the data.

$$i = \frac{n+1}{2}$$

The third step is to find the position determined in Step 2. If $i$ is calculated as 3, count down (or across, depending how the data are presented) to the third value in the ranked data. If $i$ is 4.5, count down to the position between the fourth and fifth values. The fourth step is to identify the median as the value in position $i$. When position $i$ is a whole number, such as 3, give the value found in the position as the median. If position $i$ is a fraction, such as 4.5, give the median as the value halfway between the existing values. The value between two positions is the mean of the values. For example, the numbers 1, 2, 4, and 5 are ranked from lowest to highest. Position $i$ is $(4 + 1)/2$, or 2.5. There is not a value in position 2.5. The median is determined by finding the value halfway between 2 and 4, which is $(2 + 4)/2$, or 3. The median is 3.

> **Steps in Calculating the Median by Hand**
> 1. Arrange the data from lowest to highest.
> 2. Calculate the position indicator $i = (n + 1)/2$.
> 3. Count across the data to the position $i$.
> 4. Identify the median as the value in that position.

The median is also found in the 1-VarStats function of the TI calculators. The example below illustrates the median, noted as "Med" on the calculator.

---

### EXAMPLE 3.5
**Experiment:** Find the median for the following set of data:

5,   2,   3,   6,   4,   3,   2,   5,   2,   7.

**Answer:** Med = $\tilde{x}$ = 3.5

**Solution:** Calculate the median for the given information by inserting the data into List 1, pressing STAT, scrolling to CALC and selecting 1: 1-Var Stats. The median is labeled "Med" in the results screen of the calculator.

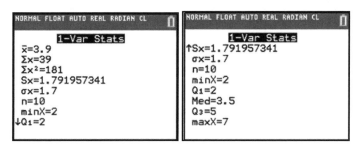

## EXAMPLE 3.6
**Experiment:** Find the median for the number of children born to 20 women ages 35-55.

$$2 \quad 0 \quad 3 \quad 2 \quad 1 \quad 1 \quad 2 \quad 3 \quad 0 \quad 2 \quad 4 \quad 1 \quad 1 \quad 3 \quad 1 \quad 0 \quad 2 \quad 5 \quad 6 \quad 3$$

**Answer:** Med = $\tilde{x}$ = 2

**Solution:** Determine the median by entering the data in $L_1$ by pressing the STAT button then ENTER with "Edit…" highlighted on your screen. The screen should appear as follows once data has been entered.

Press the STAT button and the right arrow button to highlight "1-Var Stats" under CALC. Set "List" to $L_1$ and keep "FreqList" blank. Highlight "Calculate" and press ENTER.

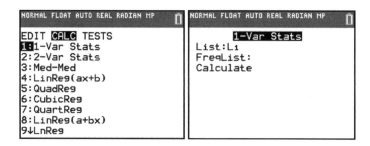

The results should appear as follows:

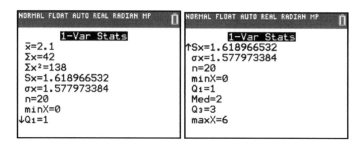

## Example 3.7

**Experiment:** Identify the median for the following data:

| x | f |
|---|---|
| 6 | 2 |
| 7 | 3 |
| 8 | 4 |
| 9 | 3 |
| 10 | 2 |
| **Total** | **14** |

**Answer:** Med $= \tilde{x} = 8$

**Solution:** Enter $x$ and $f$ in $L_1$ and $L_2$ of your calculator by pressing the STAT button and ENTER with "Edit…" highlighted. Once the data has been entered, press STAT again and scroll over to "CALC" and with "1-Var Stats" highlighted, press ENTER. Adhere to the following settings for "List" and "FreqList," highlight "Calculate" and press ENTER. The 83 and some of the 84 calculators will require that you type the $L_1$ and $L_2$ on the screen separated by a comma.

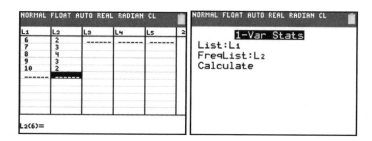

On the TI-83 and some of the TI-84 calculators, the settings screen will look like this:

1-Var Stats L
2

The results should appear as follows, indicating the median as 8.

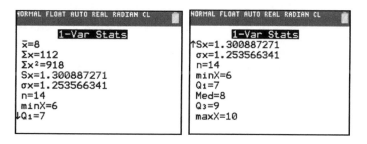

The median is a measure of central tendency that is most suited for ordinal-level data. An advantage of the median over the mean is that the median is not influenced by extreme values. Therefore, although used mostly for interval-level data, it is often used for interval- and ratio-level data where there are extreme values that would affect the arithmetic mean. Extreme values are values that are out of sync with other values. Such as the data set 1, 2, 3, 4, 15. The mean for this set is 5 (adding up the values and dividing by how many there are). The 15 is considered an extreme value, or one that lies outside the pattern of the others. Without the 15 in the data set, the mean would have been 2.5 (mean of 1, 2, 3, 4). However, with the 15 in the data, the mean doubled from 2.5 to 5. Therefore, the mean would probably not be the best measure of central tendency. The median would be more appropriate since breaking the data up right in the middle results in a median of 3. The median is commonly used to describe data such as income levels, housing costs, and other measurements of money that tend to contain extreme values.

Disadvantages with the median are many. It does not lend itself to further statistical techniques. It does not make use of the actual values in the data, but only of the number of values that exist. It does not necessarily involve an actual value in the data.

A third common measure of central tendency is the **mode**. The mode describes the center of the data as the most commonly occurring observed value. The mode is the value with the highest frequency, or the value that occurs more than any other.

> **Mode** The most commonly occurring observed value. The value that occurs more often than any other value.

There is no formula or calculation involved in determining the mode. It is determined by observing the data and noting the value with the greatest frequency. For example, the mode of the data 2, 3, 4, 4, 5, and 6 is 4, because it occurs twice, whereas other values occur only once. If the data are presented in a frequency distribution, the mode is the value with the greatest frequency. If the frequency distribution is reporting grouped data, then the mode is estimated as the class mark, or midpoint, of the class with the greatest frequency.

---

### EXAMPLE 3.8

**Experiment:** Determine the mode for the following set of data:

| $x$ | $f$ |
|-----|-----|
| 6 | 2 |
| 7 | 3 |
| 8 | 4 |
| 9 | 3 |
| 10 | 2 |
| **Total** | **14** |

**Answer:** Mode = 8

**Solution:** The mode is the value that occurs with the greatest frequency. The value 8 occurs more often than the other values, with a frequency of 4.

---

### EXAMPLE 3.9

**Experiment:** Determine the mode for the following data:

| Class | $f$ |
|-------|-----|
| 0-4 | 12 |
| 5-9 | 33 |
| 10-14 | 24 |
| 15-19 | 30 |
| 20-24 | 21 |
| **Total** | **120** |

**Answer:** Mode = Class 5-9 or class mark 7.

**Solution:** The data set is a grouped frequency distribution. The mode in a grouped frequency distribution is contained in the class with the greatest number of occurrences. The class 5-9 has the greatest frequency, 33.

The class mark is the estimate of the mode. The class mark for the class 5-9 is determined by finding the value in the middle of the class. The class mark and, therefore, the mode is (5 + 9)/2, which is 14/2 or 7.

The mode has a few advantages over the other measures of central tendency, including ease of identification. It does not require any calculation other than a class mark if it is determined for a grouped frequency distribution. Though the mode is applicable to all levels of data, it is best suited for nominal data.

The disadvantages of the mode are that it may not exist at all, or many may exist. That is, there are times when each value of $x$ occurs with the same frequency. Sometimes two or more values may occur with equal frequency. If there are two values that have the greatest frequency, the data are referred to as bimodal. A three-way tie is called tri-modal.

Yet another measure of central tendency is a *midrange*. The midrange is the value exactly in the middle of the lowest and highest value in the set. It is found by averaging the lowest and highest value; that is, adding the lowest and highest value and dividing their sum by 2. The midrange has no abbreviation or symbol.

**Midrange** The midrange is the numerical value exactly halfway between the lowest and highest values in a set of data.

$$Midrange = \frac{Max + Min}{2}$$

where *Max* and *Min* represent the highest and lowest values of the data, respectively.

## EXAMPLE 3.10

**Experiment:** Determine the midrange for the following data:

| Class | $f$ |
|-------|-----|
| 0-4 | 12 |
| 5-9 | 33 |
| 10-14 | 24 |
| 15-19 | 30 |
| 20-24 | 21 |
| **Total** | **120** |

**Answer:** Midrange = 12

**Solution:** The data set is a grouped frequency distribution. The midrange works the same whether the data is in a table or not and whether the table is grouped or ungrouped. The midrange is the value exactly halfway between the lowest and highest values. Add them and divide by two. The lowest value on the table is 0. The highest value is 24. The midrange is

$$Midrange = \frac{Max + Min}{2} = \frac{24 + 0}{2} = \frac{24}{2} = 12$$

## A LEARNING AID
## MEASURES OF CENTRAL TENDENCY

In a recent measles epidemic, one hospital in the city reported 20 cases, one hospital reported 18 cases, one hospital reported 6 cases, four hospitals reported 4 cases, and three hospitals reported 2 cases. Find the mean, median, mode, and midrange of the number of epidemic cases for the 10 hospitals.

**Solution:**
The mean, median, mode, and midrange can be found by entering the data into $L_1$ and $L_2$ and utilizing the "1-Var Stats" function. Treat $L_1$ as the list of number of cases reported from hospitals and $L_2$ as the frequencies. Once entered, the screen should appear as follows. Run the "1-Var-Stats" function and set "List" to $L_1$ and "FreqList" to $L_2$. The TI-83 and some of the TI-84 calculators will require that you type the $L_1$ and $L_2$ on the screen separated by a comma $(L_1, L_2)$.

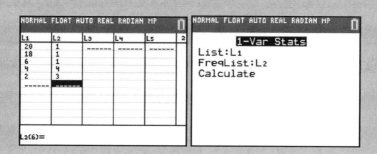

On the TI-83 and some of the TI-84 calculators, the settings screen will look like this:

```
1-Var Stats L₁,L
                ₂
```

Highlight Calculate and press ENTER to display the following results.

**Calculate the mean.** The mean is the sum of the values of *x* divided by the number of values.

$$\bar{x} = \frac{\sum x}{n} = \frac{66}{10} = 6.6$$

**Calculate the median.** The median is noted as Med = 4.

**Identify the mode.** The mode is the most common occurrence. There are four hospitals reporting 4 cases. Because 4 occurs more than any other value, the mode is 4.

**Identify the midrange**. The midrange is the value in the middle of the lowest and highest value. It is found by taking the average of the two values.

$$Midrange = \frac{Max + Min}{2} = \frac{20 + 2}{2} = \frac{22}{2} = 11$$

# SECTION 2

## Measures of Dispersion

In the ideal research environment, the choice of the measure of central tendency would not be difficult. If everyone were alike, the mean, median, and mode of any measurements would be the same. However, variety does exist. Most researchers focus on the average as the measure of central tendency. Calculating an average implies that all observations are not identical and that variation exists. The variation is the degree to which observations vary from the average. The amount of variation can be calculated with a ***measure of dispersion***.

Measures of dispersion often supplement the mean. For example, the set of data 5, 5, 5, 5, and 5 has a mean of 5, as does the set 1, 2, 3, 4, and 15. The nature of the sets is different, with the first having no variation and the second having variation. To understand the degree of the variability of the data, the mean can be supplemented with a measure of dispersion. The larger the measure of dispersion, the more variability that exists. If no variation exists, the measure of dispersion is 0.

Just as with averages, there are many measures of dispersion, each having its advantages and disadvantages. Variability can be measured by finding the difference between the highest and lowest values, known as the range. The most widely used measures of dispersion are the ***variance*** and the ***standard deviation***. The variance and standard deviation measure the squared deviations of the values from the mean.

The ***range*** is a simple way to calculate the dispersion of values. The range is calculated by subtracting the lowest value from the highest value. Be sure to scan the data carefully for the highest and lowest values, especially if the data are not ranked.

**Range** A measure of dispersion that identifies the difference between the lowest and highest value.

$$Range = Max - Min$$

where
  *Min* represents the lowest value.
  *Max* represents the highest value.

**EXAMPLE 3.11**

**Experiment:** Calculate the range for the following set of data:

$$3 \quad 4 \quad 6 \quad 7 \quad 7 \quad 8 \quad 10$$

**Answer:** Range = 7

**Solution:** The range measures the difference between the highest and lowest values. Be sure to scan the data carefully to identify the highest and lowest values. The highest value is 10 and the lowest value is 3. The range is the highest (10) minus the lowest (3).

$$\text{Range} = Max \text{ - } Min = \ 10 \text{ - } 3 = 7$$

The *variance* is a widely used measure of dispersion. It is also referred to as the average squared deviation and measures the average squared deviation of the values from the mean. After the mean is identified, the distance of each value from the mean is measured, squared, summed, and divided by the number of values minus 1. For example, if the mean is 5 and a value is 4, the distance from 5 to 4 is measured and squared. If another value is 7, the distance from 5 to 7 is measured and squared. This is repeated for each value and the squared distances are summed and divided to give an average of the squared deviations. Variances are never negative. The size of the variance reflects the amount of dispersion, with a larger variance implying more variability than a small variance. Note that the variance is obtained by squaring the deviations, therefore, the variance represents squared units. If weight is represented in pounds, for example, then the variance is squared pounds.

**Variance** The average squared deviation of values from their mean.

If the variance represents a sample, it is denoted by $s^2$.
If the variance represents a population, it is denoted by $\sigma^2$.

The symbol representing a variance differs if it describes a sample or population. The symbol for a sample variance is $s^2$, and the symbol for a population variance is $\sigma^2$ (pronounced "sigma squared"). It is important to become familiar with the notations, because both will be used in later formulas. There are also two different formulas for calculating the variance. Although both are applied to samples, each formula has an advantage, depending on the presentation of the data.

**Formulas for Calculating the Sample Variance $s^2$**
(not to be used for frequency distributions)

$$s^2 = \frac{\sum (x - \bar{x})^2}{n - 1}$$

**or**

$$s^2 = \frac{\sum x^2 - (\sum x)^2 / n}{n - 1}$$

where
   $x$ represents each value of the data.
   $\bar{x}$ represents the sample mean.
   $n$ represents the total number of observations.

The numerator of both formulas is referred to as the ***sum of the squares***. The concept of the sum of the squares is important in the next chapter. Essentially, to find the sum of the squares, the distances of the values of $x$ from the mean are determined, squared, and summed. The variance is then determined by dividing the sum of squares by $n$ - 1. The notation $n$ - 1 is also referred to as the ***degrees of freedom***. The first formula, with the numerator $\Sigma(x - \bar{x})$, is more suited to whole-number data. Subtracting and squaring fractions is cumbersome and can be more easily achieved with the second formula. Also, the first formula requires use of the mean. If the mean is not available or is too time consuming to calculate, the second formula can be used. Both formulas result in the same answer for all data. Most researchers tend to favor the second formula.

Calculate the population variance with the sum of the square numerator from either of the previous formulas, and divide by the total number of elements in the population. The calculations for the population mean, variance, and standard deviations contain $n$ in the denominator, noting the total population size, instead of $n$ -1. Remember to use the appropriate Greek letter in describing population parameters.

**EXAMPLE 3.12**
**Experiment:** Calculate the mean and variance for the number of children visiting a pediatrician's office over the last 8 days:

3, 4, 4, 5, 6, 7, 7, 8

**Answer:** $\overline{X} = 5.5$ and $Sx^2 = 3.14$

**Solution:** Begin by entering the data into $L_1$ of your calculator. Once the data has been entered, press the STAT button, right arrow to CALC and with "1-Var Stats" highlighted, press ENTER. Adhere to the following settings, highlight Calculate, and press ENTER.

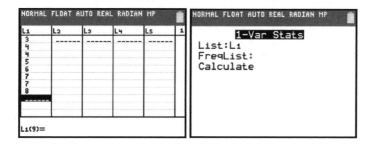

The screen should appear as follows. Scroll down to view all of the answers provided. The calculator only shows the standard deviation (to be discussed below). The variance requires the square of the standard deviation. The standard deviation is noted as $Sx = 1.772810521$. Therefore, the variance is $1.772810521^2 = 3.14$.

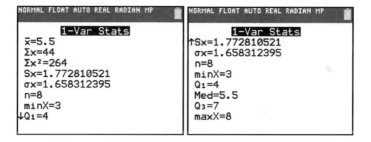

The variance is a measure of the squared deviations. It is difficult for most people to understand information reported in square units. For example, if a variance measures dispersion in years, its value is given in years squared. The variance can be extended one step further by returning the result to the same unit of measurement as the original data. Extending the variance calculation by taking the square root of it to produce a new statistic that is referred to as the ***standard deviation***. The standard deviation is the square root of the variance, which is given in the original unit of measurement. If years are involved, then the variance is in years squared, and the standard deviation is in years. If the original data has unit of years, then the unit of variance will be years squared, while the standard deviation is in years.

**Standard Deviation** The square root of the average squared deviation from the mean. The standard deviation is the square root of the variance.

If the standard deviation represents a sample, then the symbol is *s*.
If the standard deviation represents a population, the symbol is *σ*.

Notice that the symbols for the variance and standard deviation are similar. The variance involves squared values, and therefore it includes an exponent ($^2$). The standard deviation does not include the exponent. Remember to use the appropriate English or Greek symbol, depending on whether a sample or a population is described. As with variances, the larger the standard deviation, the more dispersion exists in the data. Standard deviations and variances are never negative. If all the data are exactly equal to the mean, the standard deviation is 0.

There are two ways of approaching the calculation of the standard deviation. Either the variance is calculated and then the square root is taken, or the variance formula is noted as the standard deviation with the square root symbol over the complete formula.

**Formula for Calculating the Standard Deviation**
**(not to be used for a frequency distribution)**

$$s = \sqrt{\frac{(x - \bar{x})^2}{n - 1}}$$

**or**

$$s = \sqrt{\frac{\sum x^2 - (\sum x)^2 / n}{n - 1}}$$

**or simply**

$$s = \sqrt{s^2}$$

Note that the TI calculators report sample standard deviation as $Sx$ and population standard deviation as $σx$.

**EXAMPLE 3.13**
**Experiment:** Calculate the standard deviation for the following ages of children visiting a pediatrician's office:

3, 4, 4, 5, 6, 7, 7, 8

**Answer:** $s = 1.77$

**Solution:** Enter the data into $L_1$ as follows. Once the data has been entered, press the STAT button, right arrow to CALC and with "1-Var Stats" highlighted, press ENTER. Adhere to the following settings, highlight Calculate, and press ENTER. The results will appear as follows. Remember that if using an older version of the 83/84 calculator, the $L_1$, $L_2$ must be typed.

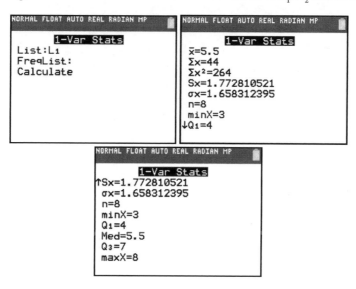

$$s = \sqrt{\frac{\sum x^2 - (\sum x)^2 / n}{n-1}} = \sqrt{\frac{264 - 44^2/8}{8-1}} = 1.77$$

If the sample variance has already been calculated, then the calculation does not need to be repeated to find the standard deviation. Simply take the square root of the variance.

An adjustment of the variance and standard deviation formulas is necessary for frequency distributions. Recall that the mean formula is adjusted by multiplying each value of $x$ by its frequency. The same adjustment must be made when calculating the variance and standard deviation of a frequency distribution. If the frequency distribution is grouped, a class mark must be identified first and applied in the formula as $x$. *All formulas for frequency distributions must include the product of $x$ and $f$.* Remember, $\Sigma f$ is equivalent to $n$, the number of observations.

**Variance and Standard Deviation for a Frequency Distribution**

$$s^2 = \frac{\sum f(x - \bar{x})^2}{\sum f - 1}$$

or

$$s^2 = \frac{\sum x^2 f - (\sum xf)^2 / \sum f}{\sum f - 1}$$

$$s = \sqrt{s^2}$$

**EXAMPLE 3.14**

**Experiment:** Calculate the sample variance and standard deviation of the following grouped frequency distribution.

| $x$ | Frequency |
|-----|-----------|
| 10-19 | 4 |
| 20-29 | 8 |
| 30-39 | 3 |
| 40-49 | 3 |
| 50-59 | 2 |
| **Total** | **20** |

**Answer:** $s^2 = 162.82$ and $s = 12.76$

**Solution:** Identify the distribution as a grouped frequency distribution. Find the class mark for each class, which will then be used as the estimation of the $x$ value. The class mark for each class is found by adding the lower and upper limits and dividing by 2. The class mark for the first class is $(10 + 19)/2$, or 14.5. For the second class, the class mark is $(20 + 29)/2$, or 24.5. Calculate each class mark. Place the class marks in a separate column to assist in the calculations.

| Class | Class Mark (x) | $f$ |
|-------|----------------|-----|
| 10-19 | 14.5 | 4 |
| 20-29 | 24.5 | 8 |
| 30-39 | 34.5 | 3 |
| 40-49 | 44.5 | 3 |
| 50-59 | 54.5 | 2 |
| **Total** | | $\Sigma f = 20$ |

Enter class marks into $L_1$ and frequencies into $L_2$ of your calculator by pressing the STAT button, then the ENTER button when "Edit..." is highlighted. The entered data in both lists should appear as follows. Once completed, press the STAT button, arrow to the right to highlight Calculate and "1-Var Stats" and press ENTER. Set "List" to $L_1$ and "FreqList" to $L_2$. The 83 and some of the 84 calculators will require that you type the $L_1$ and $L_2$ on the screen separated by a comma ($L_1, L_2$).

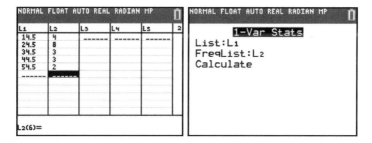

On the TI-83 and some of the TI-84 calculators, the settings screen will look like this:

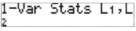

The results will appear as follows:

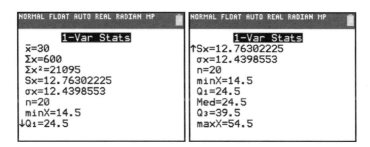

$$s^2 = \frac{\sum x^2 f - \left(\sum xf\right)^2 \Big/ \sum f}{\sum f - 1} = \frac{\sum x^2 - \left(\sum x\right)^2 / n}{n - 1} = \frac{21{,}095 - 600^2 / 20}{20 - 1}$$

Standard Deviation $Sx = 12.76$

Variance $= s^2 = 12.76^2 = 162.82$

## EXAMPLE 3.15

**Experiment:** Calculate the sample variance and standard deviation of the following ungrouped frequency distribution representing the number of absences per student per semester.

| Absences | Frequency |
|:--------:|:---------:|
| 1 | 5 |
| 2 | 12 |
| 3 | 22 |
| 4 | 21 |
| 5 | 10 |
| **Total** | **70** |

**Answer:** $s^2 = 1.27$ and $s = 1.128$

**Solution:** Identify the distribution as a frequency distribution. The calculations will require an $x$ column and $f$ column. The summations $\Sigma f$, $\Sigma x^2 f$, and $\Sigma xf$ columns are necessary for the final calculations and will be obtained on the calculator result screen.

| $x$ | $f$ |
|:---:|:---:|
| 1 | 5 |
| 2 | 12 |
| 3 | 22 |
| 4 | 21 |
| 5 | 10 |
| | $\Sigma f = 70$ |

$$s^2 = \frac{\sum x^2 f - \left(\sum xf\right)^2 / \sum f}{\sum f - 1} = \frac{\sum x^2 - \left(\sum x\right)^2 / n}{n-1} = \frac{837 - \left(229^2 / 70\right)}{70 - 1}$$

Standard Deviation $Sx = 1.128$
Variance $s^2 = 1.128^2 = 1.27$

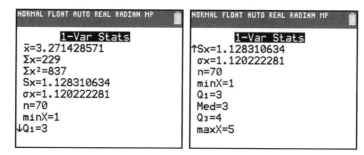

Standard deviations provide valuable information both as a supplement to means and as measure showing the fluctuation in the data. The actual definition of a standard deviation is the average deviations (distances) of values from their mean. But its usefulness goes well beyond simply noting the dispersion. To fully understand its usefulness, there are two theorems (rules) that can be applied: Chebyshev's Theorem and the empirical rule.

**Chebyshev's Theorem** Chebyshev's Theorem claims that the proportion of any distribution of values will fall within an interval below and above the mean.

Chebyshev's Theorem The proportion of any distribution of values will fall within $k$ standard deviation below and above the mean is at least $1 - \dfrac{1}{k^2}$, where $k > 1$.

This theory results in telling us that:

At least 75% of all scores will fall within 2 standard deviations below and above the mean.

At least 89% of the data fall within 3 standard deviations above and below the mean.

There is another rule known as the empirical rule that offers similar information if a variable is normally distributed (a concept introduced in Chapter 8).

**Empirical Rule** The empirical rule describes the proportion of data that will fall within an interval below and above the mean.

- At least 68% of the data will fall within one standard deviation below and above the man.
- At least 95% of the data will fall within two standard deviations below and above the mean.
- At least 99% of the data will fall within three standard deviations below and above the mean.

The mean, standard deviation, and either Chebyshev's Theorem or the empirical rule help us understand a set of data. For example, a statistics course test produces a mean of 76 with a standard deviation of 5. If we assume that the test scores distribute normally, the empirical rule can be applied to determine the test scores of at least 68% and at least 95% of the students. The first calculation for 68% is: 76 – 5 (1 standard deviation below the mean) and 76 + 5 (1 standard deviation above the mean). The result is that over 68% of students scored between 71 and 81. For 95% of the data the calculation is 76 – 5 – 5 (or 2 standard deviations below) and 76 + 5 + 5 (2 standard deviations above). Therefore, 95% of the scores fall within 66 and 86. More than 99% of the test scores would be plus and minus another standard deviation or 61 and 91. By the way, this is one of the methods professors use to determine grades when a strict grading curve is applied.

## SO WHAT DOES THIS ALL MEAN?
## MEANS AND STANDARD DEVIATIONS

Let's say that there are two pediatricians. In Dr. Cheng's office, the mean age of all her patients is 6 years, with a standard deviation of 3 years. Meanwhile, the patients in Dr. Abdul's office also have a mean of 6 years, but with a standard deviation of 5 years. How do the ages differ from both pediatricians' offices?

Assuming that all patients' ages distribute normally, the empirical rule states that typically, slightly more that 68% of data fall within one standard deviation below and above the mean. It could be concluded that about 68% of Dr. Cheng's patients are between 3 to 9 years old (the mean of 6 + and – the standard deviation of 3). Similarly, it could be concluded that about 68% of patients in Dr. Abdul's office are between ages of 1 and 11 (the mean of 6 + and – the standard deviation of 5).

How valuable is this information to the pediatrician's office? Since Dr. Cheng's patients are typically 3 to 9 years old, she will need to adjust everything from the waiting room toys and magazines to the medications that are age appropriate. She probably does not need to keep a huge supply of diapers but will need a lot of vaccines for preschool and kindergarten students. She'll be working with a lot of kids who are starting to lose their first teeth and those who are starting to grow out of ear infections.

Dr. Abdul's office will need to work a little differently. She will regularly have patients from the newborn babies to those starting puberty. She may need several sizes of diapers and acne medicines. She may need to always have in stock pain and fever medications for the newborn, the toddler, the preschooler, the elementary child, and the pre-adolescent child. She will be seeing children who will be getting their first tooth to those who will be losing their last baby tooth. Her waiting room needs to be child-proofed yet accommodating for the older child.

## A LEARNING AID
## MEASURES OF DISPERSION

In a 30-mile-per-hour speed zone, 10 randomly selected cars are checked for speed. Find the range, variance, and standard deviation of the motorists' speeds. The speeds re in miles per hour:

$$22, 32, 38, 27, 39, 23, 29, 30, 31, 29$$

**Step 1**

Calculate the range. The range is the difference between the highest and lowest values. Be sure to scan the data carefully when identifying the highest and lowest values. The highest value is 39 and the lowest value is 22. The range is: Range = *Max - Min* = 39 - 22 = 17

**Step 2**

Calculate the sample variance. The variance is the average squared deviation from the mean. There are two formulas for the variance. One formula requires the calculation of the mean, the other does not. Since the mean is not reported, it may be more convenient to calculate the variance with the formula that does not include the mean. Plug the following data into List 1 of an 83 or 84 series calculator by pressing STAT and with "Edit..." highlighted, press the ENTER button.

$$x = 22, 32, 38, 27, 39, 23, 30, 31, 29$$

$$s^2 = \frac{\sum x^2 - \left(\sum x\right)^2 / n}{n-1} = \frac{9274 - 300^2 / 10}{10 - 1} = 30.44$$

The standard deviation returns the data to the original unit of measurement. That is, the variance 30.44 is in miles per hour squared. The standard deviation is in miles per hour.

Although the variance is not directly reported on the TI-83/84 calculators, it can be found by squaring the standard deviation. The standard deviation is reported as *sx*. The variance will need to square the *sx* value.

With the data entered in List 1, select "1-Var Stats" on the calculator by pressing STAT, scrolling over to CALC, and pressing ENTER. Adhere to the following settings. In some calculators, the second screen shot may not appear, if not, it may require just pressing $2^{ND}$ and then the 1 button to insert $L_1$. The results will appear as follows.

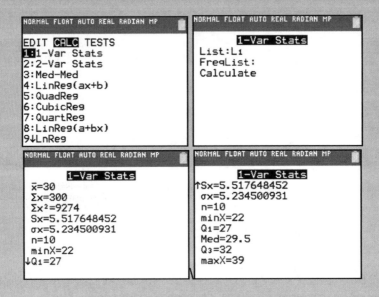

The standard deviation is noted as $Sx=5.52$
The variance $s^2 = 5.52^2 = 30.47$

## SECTION 3

### Measures of Position

Means and standard deviations are important values that describe data from one population. However, it is often necessary to describe or compare data across two populations. There are also times that it is not just the value that is of importance but its relative position to other values. Measures of position are useful for these situations. Measures of position allow for comparing data within one population or between different populations.

The ***standard score***, or ***z-score***, is a ***measure of position*** that allows data from the same or different populations to be compared. It's like comparing apples to oranges after they have all been standardized on a new scale. The principle of the standard score is to standardize data to one scale. Standardized data can be compared to other standardized data in regard to their relative positions. The standard score is a popular measure of position and lends itself to further statistical techniques. (A full discussion of the standard score is presented in Chapter 8.)

**Standard score, or z-score** A measure of position based on the number of standard deviations that a given value of x is from the mean.

The standard score is a standardized standard deviation. It measures the number of standard deviations a given value is from the mean. When values are compared from different populations, a z-score is calculated for each value based on its mean and standard deviation. All means on the standardized scale are adjusted to a z-score of 0.

**Calculation for the Standard Score, or z-Score**

$$z = \frac{x - \mu}{\sigma} \qquad z = \frac{\text{raw data value - mean of the data}}{\text{standard deviation}}$$

where
  x is a value.
  $\mu$ is the population mean.
  $\sigma$ is the standard deviation of the population.

A scale can be drawn to help visualize the values. For example, after the conversion of raw data to a z-score using the formula above, a z-score of -1.5 can be compared to a z-score of 2.5. The scale describes the 0, the z-score for the mean. The standard deviation of 1 above and below the mean equal to a z-score of 1 and -1, respectively. The -1.5 describes a value 1.5 standard deviations below its mean. The 2.5 describes a value 2.5 standard deviations above its mean.

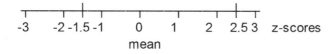

## EXAMPLE 3.16

**Experiment**: Yolanda received a score of 78 on her statistics exam with Professor Miller, where the mean score was 73 and the standard deviation was 3. Michelle received a score of 83 on her statistics exam with Professor Charles, where the mean score was 81 and the standard deviation was 5. Did Yolanda or Michelle do better relative to each of their classes?

Answer: Yolanda did better, relative to her class, than did Michelle.

**Solution**: Determining if a student did better relative to another student requires comparing the positions of the students on a standardized scale. Each student's score must be standardized with the $z$-score formula and then compared. Begin by calculating Yolanda's score using the information from her class. Second, calculate Michelle's score.

Yolanda:
$$z = \frac{x - \mu}{\sigma} = \frac{78 - 73}{3} = \frac{5}{3} = 1.67$$

Michelle:
$$z = \frac{x - \mu}{\sigma} = \frac{83 - 81}{5} = \frac{2}{5} = 0.40$$

Compare the standardized scores. Although Michelle's original score is higher than Yolanda's, Yolanda's standard score is higher. That is, Yolanda did better relative to her class than Michelle did to her class.

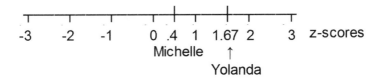

## EXAMPLE 3.17

**Experiment:** Crispy Potato Chips claim its bags of chips contain 16 ounces with a standard deviation of .5 ounces. A bag was weighed at random and contained 16.2 ounces. Saltine Potato Chips claim their bags also contain an average of 16 ounces with a standard deviation of .3 ounces. A random bag of its chips contained 16.3 ounces. Since manufactures want to be consistent with the weight claimed on the label, which is more consistent to the label?

**Answer:** Crispy Potato Chips

**Solution:** To compare data from two different populations, $z$-scores are performed on each set of information. The $z$-scores are then compared. Begin by calculating Crispy Potato Chip information. The $x$ value is 16.2, the mean is 16 and the standard deviation is .5.

Crispy Potato Chips: $z = \dfrac{x - \mu}{\sigma} = \dfrac{16.2 - 16}{.5} = \dfrac{.2}{.5} = 0.4$

Next, calculate the $z$-score for Saltine Potato Chips. The information for Saltine's is $x = 16.3$, mean = 16, and the standard deviation = .3.

Saltine Potato Chips: $z = \dfrac{x - \mu}{\sigma} = \dfrac{16.3 - 16}{.3} = \dfrac{.3}{.3} = 1.0$

The question is which chip company bags are most consistent. Consistency in weight claimed on the label is reflected by being close to the mean. The mean on a standard score is a value of 0. Therefore, consistency is the one closest to zero. Compare the standardized scores. Crispy Potato Chips has a $z$-score of .4. Saltine Potato Chip has a $z$-score of 1.0. Crispy bags are the most consistently closer to the mean. Notice the placement on the scale. (Note, in manufacturing, even a negative score below the mean may be mathematically closer to zero than a positive number.)

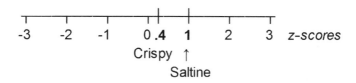

Other common measures of position include quartiles and percentiles. **Quartiles** and percentiles partition data into several equal parts. Quartiles divide data into four equal quarters. **Percentiles** divide data into100 equal parts. Although not addressed here, other divisions exist, such as deciles, which divide data into 10 equal parts. The principle in partitioning data is to determine what proportion of values is lower and/or higher than a particular score. For this reason, percentiles and quartiles are important tools in education. Entrance exams for universities are based on percentiles, whereas admission is often based on quartiles.

> **Quartile** A measure of position that divides data into four equal parts. The first quarter is denoted by $Q_1$, the second by $Q_2$, and the third by $Q_3$.

**Percentile** A measure of position that divides data into 100 equal parts. Each percentile is denoted by *P* with a subscript indicating the value of the percentile.

The steps involved in determining quartiles include arranging the data, calculating the position *i*, adjusting *i*, counting the data to the adjusted *i* position, and identifying the quartile or percentile. The data should be arranged from lowest to highest. In the formula, *k* equals the quartile number or percentile number.

**Calculating the Position of Quartiles and Percentiles**

$$i = \frac{n(k)}{100}$$

where
   *i* is the position of the quartile or percentile.
   *k* is the quartile or percentile in question.
   *n* is the number of cases or scores.
   *k* for percentiles is equal to the percentage in question.

   *k* for quartiles is $Q_1 = 25$, $Q_2 = 50$, or $Q_3 = 75$.

The position *i* must be adjusted. When *i* is not a whole number, the position will be the whole number rounded up from *i*. For example, if *i* = 3.1, *i* is rounded up to 4. If *i* = 3.9, *i* is rounded up to 4. If the calculation of *i* results in a whole number, *i* must be adjusted by adding 0.5. Adding the 0.5 allows the position to fall between two values. For example, if *i* is 6, adjust *i* by adding .5 so that *i* = 6.5. Only one of these adjustments occurs. Either *i* is rounded up or .5 is added but not both.

After *i* is adjusted, count the values of the data to the adjusted position *i*. If *i* falls between two values, the quartile or percentile is the value midway between the values. The midway value is determined by adding the values and dividing by two. *Remember that i is only the position where the quartile or percentile is located in the original set of ordered data.*

**Steps in Locating Quartiles and Percentiles**
1. Arrange the data from lowest to highest.
2. Calculate the locator known as position *i*.
3. Adjust *i*:
   a. Add 0.5 to the value if *i* is a whole number.
   b. Round up to the next whole number is *i* is a fraction.
4. Count across (or down) the data to find the value in position *i*.
5. Identify the quartile or percentile value.

**EXAMPLE 3.18**

**Experiment:** Find the third quartile and the 90th percentile in the examination scores for Professor Miller's class. The scores are:

86  74  75  81  99  89  65  55  93  76

**Answer:** $Q_3 = 89$, $P_{90} = 96$

**Solution:** There are five steps in identifying quartiles and percentiles. The first step is to arrange the data from lowest to highest. The arranged data are:

55  65  74  75  76  81  86  89  93  99

Calculate position $i$ for the quartile and percentile. The calculation of $i$ requires the total number of cases to be multiplied by the quartile value or percentile value, and divided by 100. The $k$ value for the third quartile is 75. The $k$ value for the 90th percentile is 90.

$$i_{Q3} = \frac{n(k)}{100} = \frac{10(75)}{100} = \frac{750}{100} = 7.5$$

$$i_{P90} = \frac{n(k)}{100} = \frac{10(90)}{100} = \frac{900}{100} = 9$$

Adjust $i$ as necessary. The $i$ for quartile 3 is 7.5. An $i$ value that is a fraction must be rounded up to the next whole number. Therefore, $i = 7.5$ becomes $i = 8.0$, The value for quartile 3 will be in the eighth position. The $i$ for the 90th percentile is a whole number, 9. An $i$ value that is a whole number is adjusted by adding .5. Therefore, the value for the 90th percentile will be in position 9.5. Count across the data to the eighth position. Quartile three is 89. Count across the data to position 9.5. The 90th percentile is the value midway between 93 and 99. The value midway is determined by adding the values and dividing by 2. The 90th percentile is (93 + 99)/2, or 96.

55  65  74  75  76  81  86  89  93  99

Position 8 ↑

Position 9.5 ↑

**A LEARNING AID**
**MEASURES OF POSITION**

Consider the sample of students taking an advanced placement test for college credit. Calculate the standard score of a student receiving a 76, where the mean is 69.83 and the standard deviation is 15.12. Identify the third quartile and the 80th percentile.

45  50  52  61  64  72  76  79  81  83  84  91

**Step 1**

Calculate the standard score. The experiment notes the population is tested; therefore, the *z*-score uses the values of $\mu$ and $\sigma$. The value of *x* in question is 76. The score 76 is .41 *z*-scores above the standardized mean of 0. It can be used to compare with students' scores from other years.

$$z = \frac{x - \mu}{\sigma} = \frac{76 - 69.83}{15.12} = \frac{6.17}{15.12} = .41$$

**Step 2**

Identify the third quartile. Six steps are required in identifying quartiles. The first step is to arrange the data. The data are arranged from lowest to highest. Calculate position *i*. The value of *k* for $Q_3$ is 75.

$$i = \frac{n(k)}{100} = \frac{12(75)}{100} = \frac{900}{100} = 9.0$$

Adjust *i*. Add .5 to *i* when it is a whole number. The adjusted value is 9 + .5 = 9.5. Count across the data to value in the position 9.5. The third quartile falls between the values 81 and 83. The value 82 is the value of the third quartile.

45  50  52  61  64  72  76  79  81  83  84  91
Position 9.5  ↑

**Step 3**

Identify the 80th percentile. Percentiles are determined the same way as quartiles. The data are arranged from lowest to highest. Calculate *i*.

$$i = \frac{n(k)}{100} = \frac{12(80)}{100} = \frac{960}{100} = 9.6$$

Adjust *i*. Round up to the next whole number when *i* is a fraction. The value 9.6 is rounded up to 10. The 80th percentile is the value 83, which is in the 10th position.

45  50  52  61  64  72  76  79  81  83  84  91
Position 10  ↑

## A LEARNING AID
## Measures of Central Tendency, Dispersion, and Position

The amount of time (in minutes) that it took a local ambulance company to reach 10 accidents are:

| 1.6 | 5.4 | 2.8 | 7.2 | 3.5 | 5.4 | 7.7 | 7.0 | 5.4 | 4.2 |

a. Find the mean.

b. Find the median.

c. Find the mode.

d. Find the range.

e. Find $s^2$.

f. Find $s$.

g. Find $Q_1$.

Run the 1-VarStats function to retrieve the following values from your calculator.

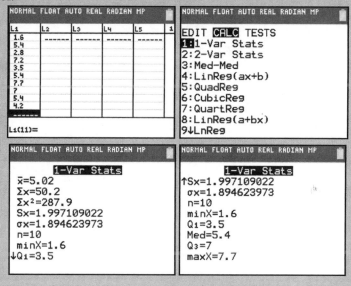

### Step 1
The mean formula for a non-frequency table, raw data is:

$$\bar{x} = \frac{\sum x}{n} = 5.02$$

### Step 2
The median is the middle value after the values are arranged in order from lowest to highest. If it is not identifiable by the eye, then a position indicator can be calculated.

$$\text{Med} = 5.4$$

**Step 3**
The mode does not have a formula. It is simply the value that occurs more than the others. The value 5.4 repeats 3 times. The mode is 5.4.

**Step 4**
The range is the distance from the maximum value to the minimum.

$$Range = Max\text{-}Min = 7.7 - 1.6 = 6.1$$

**Step 5**
Although the standard deviation is equivalent to the square root of the variance, the TI calculators do the reverse. Find the standard deviation by using 1-Var Stats and square it for the variance. The standard deviation is $Sx$ on the calculator.

$$s^2 = \frac{\sum x^2 - \left(\sum x\right)^2 / n}{n-1} = 1.997^2 = 3.988$$

**Step 6**
The standard deviation is the square root of the variance. It is indicated as $Sx$ on the test result screen.

$$s = 1.997$$

**Step 7**
Identify the quartile. In the calculator, it is noted as $Q_1$ under "1-Var Stats".

$$Q_1 \text{ is } 3.5$$

## CHAPTER 3 IN REVIEW

3.1   Calculate the mean and standard deviation cell phone bill for a sample of 15 students (rounded to the nearest dollar).

59   63   45   54   72   58   45   79   78   42   58   60   62   58   40

3.2   Arrange the data in Problem 3.1 as a grouped frequency distribution with class widths of 10. Calculate the mean and standard deviation using the formula appropriate for a frequency distribution.

3.3   The following data represents a sample of 38 exam scores on last semester's final exam.

| Score | Frequency (f) |
|-------|---------------|
| 40-49 | 1 |
| 50-59 | 2 |
| 60-69 | 8 |
| 70-79 | 16 |
| 80-89 | 6 |
| 90-99 | 5 |
| **Total** | **38** |

a. Calculate the sample mean.
b. Calculate the sample variance.
c. Calculate the sample standard deviation.
d. What is the class mark of the third class?
e. Which class contains the median?
f. Identify the mode.

3.4 Calculate the mean and standard deviation for the time it took a woman to win the Boston Marathon during the last 9 years (time converted to decimal form).

    2.48    2.38    2.42    2.40    2.42    2.33    2.38    2. 43    2.42

3.5 Find $Q_1$, $Q_3$, $P_{60}$, and $P_{20}$ for the closing prices of AIBT stock on each business day for the last several weeks.

    27.5    28.2    27.5  28.9    28.9    24.5    21.1    29.2    27.5    25.8  25.5
    28.2    28.9    29.3  29.5    29.0    28.4    27.5    28.9    26.5    26.0  26.8

3.6 A class of third-grade students, when given a standardized examination, was found to have a mean score of 70 with a standard deviation of 6. Each child's score was changed to a standard $z$-score for comparison with his or her classmates.
a. What is the $z$-score for a child who scored 81?
b. What is the $z$-score for a child who scored 68?

3.7 The following grouped frequency distribution represents the ages of women marrying in St. Clair County during the last month. Find the sample mean and standard deviation.

| Years | f |
|-------|---|
| 16-20 | 10 |
| 21-25 | 31 |
| 26-30 | 47 |
| 31-35 | 12 |
| **Total** | **100** |

3.8 Calculate the mean and standard deviation of high-speed Internet costs for the following 20 students:

| Cost (dollars) | $f$ |
|---|---|
| 10-14 | 3 |
| 15-19 | 8 |
| 20-24 | 5 |
| 25-29 | 4 |
| **Total** | **20** |

3.9 Find the mean and the standard deviation of the following distribution of the cholesterol levels (mg/dL) of patients visiting Dr. Adam's office.

| Cholesterol Level | $f$ |
|---|---|
| 190-194 | 1 |
| 195-199 | 4 |
| 200-204 | 3 |
| 205-209 | 6 |
| 210-214 | 9 |
| 215-219 | 6 |
| 220-224 | 2 |
| **Total** | **31** |

3.10 What is the standard score for a student who spends 8.5 hours a week studying when the average student studies 7.2 hours with a standard deviation of 4.5?

3.11 A sample of 18 starting salaries for liberal arts college graduates yielded the following results (data in thousands, rounded to nearest hundred):

$$40.0 \quad 48.3 \quad 42.7 \quad 39.1 \quad 39.1 \quad 36.8 \quad 27.7 \quad 30.8 \quad 37.2$$
$$31.3 \quad 28.0 \quad 30.8 \quad 32.3 \quad 30.8 \quad 34.4 \quad 30.8 \quad 43.1 \quad 40.8$$

a. Find the mean.
b. Find the median.
c. Find the mode.
d. Find the range.
e. Find the standard deviation.

f. Find the variance.
g. Find $Q_1$.
h. Find $Q_2$.
i. Find $P_{40}$.
j. Find $P_{79}$.

3.12 Apply the empirical rule to the data in 3.11 to determine the ranges around the mean of starting salaries for 68 percent, 95 percent, and 99 percent of liberal arts college graduates.

3.13   The following data represent the number of suicides per 10,000 inhabitants in rural areas in Japan. Calculate the mean and standard deviation.

22  10  12   2  10   9  16  11   8  14  11   8  13  10
12   0  10  12   8  11   5   7  10   7   9   9   6   8

3.14   Andrea and Joe bought the same cell-phone from different companies. Andrea paid $99 through Cells-To-Go which sells it on average for $110 with a standard deviation of $40. Joe paid $90 from Cells-R-Us which sells it on average for $100 with a standard deviation of $30. Who received a better deal relative to the store averages?

3.15   Three prospective cashiers take a mathematical test to determine their counting skills. Which of the following prospective cashiers scored the highest relative to their class? Show the calculation used to determine the answer.

| Prospective Cashier | Score | Mean | Standard Deviation |
|---|---|---|---|
| Samantha | 60 | 62 | 5 |
| Alauna | 63 | 60 | 2 |
| Ike | 63 | 58 | 5 |

3.16   Calculate the mean and standard deviation of the following data representing the number of music CDs produced last year by the 6 leading recording studios. (data rounded to nearest million)

102        90        120        250        155        180

3.17   Water in a local community is tested for various toxins. The average amount of lead in the water is 122 ppb, with a standard deviation of 22 ppb. The average amount of chlorine is 200 ppb, with a standard deviation of 30 ppb. The water in Ms O'Kelley's home is tested, and it produces 150 ppb of lead and 230 ppb of chlorine ppb. Which toxin level is relatively higher?

3.18   Find the average number of nuclear warheads stored in 10 countries.

2258    2090    1650    1365    1248    1085    910    650    595    582

3.19   Find the mean and standard deviation for the cost of monthly rent in a sample of 10 one-bed-room apartments in the university district.

665    525    515    525    450    600    610    575    525    695

3.20 What is the $z$-score for a value of $x$ that equals to the mean?

3.21 If a population has a mean of 26 with a standard deviation of 4.5, what is the $z$-score for 23?

3.22 The following sample represents the number of penalties per game for 10 games in the World Cup soccer matches:

$$19 \quad 15 \quad 18 \quad 21 \quad 17 \quad 14 \quad 19 \quad 22 \quad 23 \quad 22$$

a. Calculate the mean.      d. Calculate the standard deviation.
b. Calculate the median.      e. Calculate $Q_1$.
c. Find the mode.      f. Find $P_{93}$.

3.23 Calculate the mean and standard deviation of the number of troops sent to different foreign countries in the last 10 years (in thousands).

| Number of Troops (in thousands) | $f$ |
|---|---|
| 0 - 9 | 3 |
| 10-19 | 1 |
| 20-29 | 5 |
| 30-39 | 5 |
| 40-49 | 4 |
| **Total** | **18** |

3.24 The following data represents the number of days in the hospital for 30 pneumonia patients.

| | | | | | | | | | |
|---|---|---|---|---|---|---|---|---|---|
| 4 | 4 | 5 | 5 | 5 | 4 | 6 | 5 | 5 | 5 |
| 2 | 3 | 5 | 3 | 6 | 2 | 4 | 5 | 5 | 7 |
| 5 | 4 | 3 | 3 | 4 | 5 | 5 | 4 | 4 | 4 |

Calculate the mean, median, mode, range, variance, standard deviation, $Q_1$, $Q_3$, $P_{60}$, $P_{20}$.

3.25 Manufacturer A of an asthma inhaler claims that the medication becomes effective within 15 minutes with a standard deviation of 2.5. Manufacturer B claims that its inhaler becomes effective within 10 minutes with a standard deviation of 4.6. Calculate the $z$-score for each assuming the population mean for all inhalers is 12.5 minutes.

3.26 Apply the empirical rule to identify the values and percentages within one, two, and three standard deviations for cell phone bills with an average of $55.00 and a standard deviation of $11.00.

3.27 Apply the empirical rule to identify the values and percentages within one, two, and three standard deviations of the deployment time a Navy sailor spends on a Navy carrier. The actual average deployment is 6 months with a standard deviation of 1.5 months.

3.28 Apply the empirical rule to describe the values representing 68 percent, 95 percent, and 99 percent of the data around the mean for a new mid-size automobile with an average of $20,320 and a standard deviation of $1,250.

3.29 Describe the values representing 95 percent of American's weight gain over the Thanksgiving and Christmas holidays with an average of 4.5 pounds and a standard deviation of 1.5.

3.30 The average amount of time a preschool child spends in daycare each week is 7.2 hours with a standard deviation of 1.9 hours. Apply the empirical rule to describe the values for 95 percent of the preschool children's time spent in daycare each week.

# 4 DESCRIPTIVE MEASURES OF TWO OR MORE VARIABLES

**SECTION 1** *Nominal Variables: Contingency Tables/ Crosstabs*
**SECTION 2** *Scatterplots and Correlations*
**SECTION 3** *Ordinal Variables: Spearman's Correlation*
**SECTION 4** *Ratio or Interval Variables: Pearson's Correlation*
**SECTION 5** *Ratio or Interval Variables: Linear Regression*

Chapters 1 through 3 describe and condense data from one variable. Most of the questions scientists ask involve the relationships between two or more variables. The techniques for describing a single variable are referred to as ***univariate analysis***. Describing the relationship of two variables is referred to as ***bivariate analysis***, and describing three or more variables is referred to as ***multivariate analysis***. For example, describing the age of students is a form of univariate analysis. Describing the age and gender of students is bivariate, and describing the age, gender and religious affiliation of students is multivariate.

Multivariate analysis is one of the most important techniques in quasi-experimental designs. These designs often depend on statistical techniques to identify the relationships between variables. Social sciences, health sciences, business and behavioral sciences generally do not enjoy the luxury of laboratory experiments, where the complete environment is controlled. Understanding that most social problems are very complicated, statistical techniques are developed to isolate the relationships among some variables.

It is important to distinguish the difference between explaining relationships and explaining causality. Measures of description, such as correlations, describe the strength and sometimes the direction of the relationship of two variables. Regression analysis predicts and projects movement between two or more variables. Neither directly measures causation. For example, a correlation may exist between turning on the lights and it being night. However, turning on the lights does not cause it to be night.

When working with values for two variables, it is important to keep the values aligned. A value for one variable, $X$, must be considered with the value for a second variable, $Y$, for the same case. For example, a soldier's rank must be aligned with the same soldier's years in service. It would not be appropriate to test the relationship of rank and years in service using one soldier's rank with another soldier's years in service. When data are paired across two or more variables, the data are referred to as *ordered pairs*.

> **Ordered Pairs** A pair in which a value for variable *X* is associated with a corresponding value for variable *Y*.

Recall from Chapter 1, a variable is described with various levels of measurements. The levels of measurements include nominal, ordinal, interval, and ratio. A review of the levels of measurement is necessary before deciding which measure of comparison is appropriate. Nominal-level measurements are attributes and are usually, but not always, non-numeric. ***Contingency tables*** are the most appropriate comparison for nominal-level measurements. Ordinal-level measurements rank or put things in order. A correlation coefficient known as ***Spearman's correlation*** is most appropriate for ordinal level measurements. Interval variables are real measurements but where zero is arbitrarily set. Ratio level measurements are also real measurements where zero is an absolute starting point or the absence of the measurement. Interval- and ratio level measurements are usually compared by using ***Pearson's correlation*** or a ***linear regression.***

In this chapter, the relationship between variables will be studied. The relationship includes any trend or pattern in the data. Where data show a significant trend or pattern, the relationship is described as ***dependent***. If no significant trend or pattern exists, the relationship is said to be ***independent***. A pattern or trend does not require that the relationship will always exist. It does not address issues of causation.

---

# SECTION 1

## Nominal Variables: Contingency Tables/Crosstabs

A nominal variable is one that categorizes or describes the attributes of data. Nominal variables do not specify magnitude, value, or order. Examples of nominal variables include sex, race, religion, marital status, color of hair, and color of car. When one or two nominal level measurements are compared, a ***contingency table*** shows the relationship between the values of the two variables. A contingency table is also used if only one variable is nominal even if the other variable is of a higher level of measurement such as interval or ratio. They may also be used when both variables are different levels of measurements. A contingency table is a convenient way of reading and describing the relationship between two variables because it is a two-dimensional picture. The outcomes of one variable are overlapped with the outcomes of another variable. The construction of a contingency table begins with ordered pairs. Ordered pairs give values for two variables for the same case. Each combination of ordered pairs represents a cell. A count determines the value in each *cell*.

> **Contingency Table** A table that represents the relationships of two variables and their events. The outcomes of a variable are overlapped with the outcomes of another variable. The overlaps are referred to as cells.

In most computerized statistical programs, contingency tables are known as *crosstabulations*, or *crosstabs*. The cells of the table describe the overlapping information from the two variables. For example, in the table below, if the gender (a nominal-level measurement) and ages of students (a ratio-level measurement) in a certain school are represented in a contingency table, a cell could be constructed by filling with the number of students who report being less than 25 years old and female. Another cell could contain those students who report being less than 25 years old and male. The bottom row and the most right column represent the totals for each value of the variables. The value 2,900 in second row and second column indicates that 2,900 females report being less than 25 years old. The value 7,712 at the far right of the first row gives the total number of females in the school. The value 15,000 at the bottom right corner of the table is the total number of students in the school.

| Gender | Age | Less than 25 | 25-34 | 35-44 | More than 44 | Total |
|--------|-----|--------------|-------|-------|--------------|-------|
| Female | | 2,900 | 3,254 | 1,120 | 438 | **7,712** |
| Male | | 2,460 | 3,196 | 1,088 | 544 | **7,288** |
| **Total** | | **5,360** | **6,450** | **2,208** | **982** | **15,000** |

Contingency tables can be interpreted by describing if trends exist. A trend may simply be whether there appears to be more items or people in certain cells than others. For example, the table above indicates that most students are 25-34 years old, regardless of gender (6,450 students are in this age category while the number of females and males in this age group are about equal). Note, this is a preliminary discussion of contingency tables. A full discussion with a mathematical procedure to test the relationship of the variables will be described in Chapter 12.

### EXAMPLE 4.1
**Experiment:** Interpret the following contingency table describing the number of people favoring the nonsmoking rule on airplanes and their gender.

| Gender ↓ | Favor Rule→ | Yes | No | Total |
|---|---|---|---|---|
| Male | | 24 | 16 | 40 |
| Female | | 14 | 6 | 20 |
| **Total** | | **38** | **22** | **60** |

**Answer:** Although there are fewer women surveyed, proportionately there appear to be more women than men in favor of the nonsmoking policy. Disregarding gender, more people (38) are in favor of the nonsmoking policy than are opposed (22).

## A LEARNING AID
## TWO NOMINAL VARIABLES: CONTINGENCY TABLE

Construct a contingency table for the following data for a survey questioning whether voters would pay for a new education program through a sales tax increase and/or an income tax increase (Y = yes, N = no).

**Sales tax**

Y Y N N N Y N N N N Y N Y N N Y N N Y Y N Y
Y Y Y N N Y N N

**Income tax**

N Y N Y Y Y N N Y Y N N Y Y N N N Y Y Y Y N
N Y Y N N Y N N

### Step 1

A contingency table shows the ***intersection*** data classified according to two variables. The values in each column must be aligned. There are four combinations of responses. A voter could respond with a yes to the sales tax and a yes to the income tax. A voter could also respond with a yes to the sales tax and a no to the income tax. Another response might be no to the sales tax and no to the income tax, or no to the sales tax and yes to the income tax.

### Step 2

Draw a two-by-two table representing the four responses. There are two responses (yes or no) for the first variable and two responses (yes or no) for the second variable.

**Step 3**

Count the number of answers that fulfill the characteristics of each cell. Place the count in the appropriate cell. Place the row and columns totals at the outside.

| Income Tax ↓ | Sales Tax→ | Yes | No | Total |
|---|---|---|---|---|
| Yes | | 8 | 7 | 15 |
| No | | 5 | 10 | 15 |
| **Total** | | **13** | **17** | **30** |

**Step 4**

Interpret the table. Even though the sample is small, there appears to be a trend. Those who support a tax increase seem to support it for both types. Those oppose a tax increase oppose it for both types. Both the yes/yes and no/no cells are the largest. Voters are evenly split on the single issue of income tax, 15 supporting and 15 opposing. However, there are more voters who oppose a sales tax increase than support it, 17 to 13.

---

# SECTION 2

## Scatterplots and Correlations

Another visual illustration depicting the relationship of two variables is a ***scatterplot***. A diagram known as a ***scatter diagram*** or ***scattergram*** allows a visual analysis of the relationship of the variables. The scatter diagram plots the values of *x* and *y* as a pair of coordinates on coordinate axes. Each ordered pair is represented on the diagram. The values of the variable *X* are plotted along the horizontal axis, and the values of the variable *Y* are plotted along the vertical axis. The intervals plotted for the values should be consistent for each value. That is, if *x* is 0, 10, and 20, do not plot 40, 50, and 60 without an interval for 30. Do not interrupt the intervals unless there will be no distortion to the visual meaning of the diagram. Values on the axes do not necessarily correspond to the reported values. If the reported value of *x* is 39, the value on the axis may be 40. To plot a point, trace up from the *X* axis at the corresponding *x* value and across from the *Y* axis at the corresponding *y* value. Place a dot at the intersection. Continue this process for each ordered pair.

## EXAMPLE 4.2

**Experiment:** Draw a scatterplot for the following ordered pairs:

| x: | 3 | 4 | 3 | 6 | 7 | 2 | 3 | 7 | 5 | 5 | 4 | 5 |
|----|---|---|---|---|---|---|---|---|---|---|---|---|
| y: | 4 | 4 | 5 | 7 | 8 | 4 | 3 | 7 | 6 | 5 | 5 | 7 |

**Answer:**

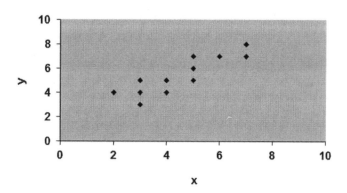

**Solution:** Draw and label the *X* and *Y* axes. Review the values of *x* and *y* to determine the intervals for plotting the values. The variable *x* values range from 2 to 7 and the variable *y* values range from 3 to 8. No distortion of the diagram would occur with single-digit intervals from 0 to 10. Begin with the first ordered pair of *x* = 3 and *y* = 4. Trace up from the *x* axis at the value 3 and across from the *y* axis at the value 4. Place a dot at the intersection of the 3 and 4. For the second ordered pair of *x* = 4 and *y* = 4, trace up from the *x* axis at 4 and across from the *y* axis at 4. Place a dot at the intersection. Continue this process for the remaining 10 sets of ordered pairs.

In the scatterplot for Example 4.2, there appears to be a pattern created by the dots. The dots tend to move upward from left to right. As the value of *x* increases, so, too, does the value of *y*. When the plotting of ordered pairs depicts a clear pattern upward, it is referred to as a *positive pattern*. If the plotted dots are clustered close together, the pattern depicts a strong positive linear relationship, and if all the dots are exactly in line, the pattern depicts a perfect positive relationship. If the pattern depicts a case where one variable consistently decreases as the other increases, the relationship is referred to as a *negative linear pattern*. The clustering of a negative pattern also determines if the relationship is strong or perfect. Where no pattern appears, no relationship exists. If a pattern is circular or semicircular, then no linear relationship exists. The most common patterns are shown in Figure 4.1.

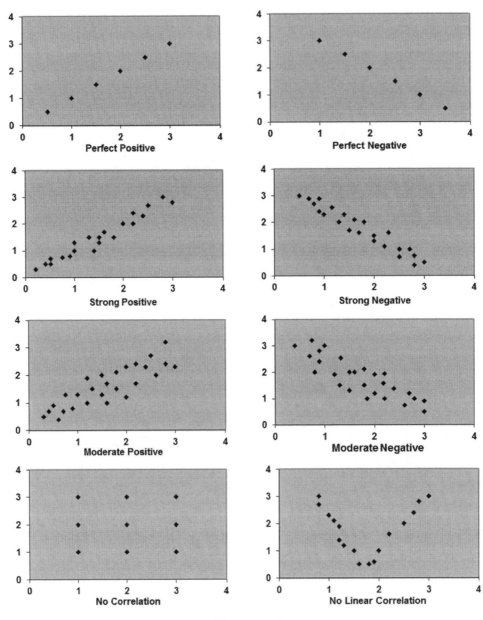

**Figure 4.1**

Scatterplots and scattergrams suggest whether there is a relationship between two variables. But this suggestion is based on a highly subjective, visual inspection of the diagram. A mathematical measure of association known as a correlation coefficient determines if a relationship exists between two interval or ratio variables. The two most popular techniques to describe the relationship of two variables are the ***Pearson's product moment correlation coefficient*, *r*,** and ***Spearman's r.*** While other coefficients exist, these two are the most popular and will be fully described in the next two sections of this chapter. The notation for a correlation is $r$ for sample data. The corresponding population parameter is denoted by the Greek letter $\rho$ (pronounced "rho," like the "ro" in road). Because $r$ measures the relationship of ordered pairs from sample data, $\rho$ measures the relationship of all ordered pairs from a population.

> **Correlation Coefficients** Measures the strength and direction of the relationship between two ordinal, interval or ratio variables.
>
> The notation of a correlation coefficient of a sample is $r$.
> The notation of a correlation coefficient of a population is $\rho$.

Several generalizations apply to most correlation coefficients. Correlations describe the strength, direction, and statistical significance of the relationship of two variables. That is, do the variables tend to move together in a predictable manner, and how do they move? All correlations have values ranging from -1 to 1. A value of -1 represents a perfect negative relationship, whereas a 0 represents no linear relationship (there may be other relationships that are not addressed here) and +1 represents a perfect positive relationship. Other values between –1, 0, and 1 are described as strong, moderate, or weak, or combinations thereof. A value approaching –1 or 1 is strong, a value close to -.5 or .5 is moderate, and values that approach 0 are weak. A value such as -.75 or .75 may be considered moderately strong.

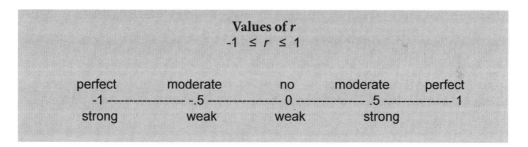

**Values of $r$**
$$-1 \le r \le 1$$

| perfect | moderate | no | moderate | perfect |
| --- | --- | --- | --- | --- |
| -1 ---------------- | -.5 ---------------- | 0 ---------------- | .5 ---------------- | 1 |
| strong | weak | weak | strong | |

The direction of the correlation is determined by the $r$ value as negative or positive. Any negative $r$ value implies that as the values of one variable increase, the values of the other variable decrease. Any positive $r$ value implies that the values of both variables increase or decrease simultaneously.

Positive relationship    as $x \uparrow y \uparrow$      Negative relationship    as $x \downarrow y \uparrow$
                     or as $x \downarrow y \downarrow$                                       or as $x \uparrow y \downarrow$

For example, a positive relationship exists between education level and income. In general, as a person's level of education increases ($x$ increases in years), his/her income tends to increases ($y$ increases in income level). An example of a negative relationship is between a woman's education level and the number of children born to a woman. As women are more educated ($x$ increases in years of education), the number of children she has tends to decrease ($y$). In general, a woman with more education tends to have fewer children than a woman with less education.

The statistical significance of a correlation coefficient is usually generated by a calculator or is determined by comparing a calculated value to a value on a table. This will be discussed more in later chapters.

## A LEARNING AID
## SCATTERPLOTS AND CORRELATIONS

Draw a scatterplot depicting the relationship between the cost of passenger airline travel and the travel distance. (Both values are given in hundreds; that is, $100 = 1$, 100 miles = 1.)

| Distance: | 2.5 | 7.0 | 8.0 | 2.3 | 6.0 | 10.0 | 8.3 | 7.3 | 5.0 | 4.5 |
|---|---|---|---|---|---|---|---|---|---|---|
| Travel costs: | 2.0 | 3.5 | 4.2 | 2.2 | 3.1 | 8.9 | 6.5 | 5.9 | 3.0 | 2.8 |

### Step 1

A scatterplot is a graph describing two variables. Let $x$ be the distance traveled and let $y$ be the cost of travel. The $x$ variable, distance, goes on the horizontal axis. The $y$ variable, travel costs, goes on the vertical axis. The values for the $x$ variable range from 2.5 to 10, therefore, values starting at zero should increase in single digits or in twos. The $y$ variable values range from 2.0 to 8.9 and therefore should also increase from zero in single digits or in twos. The first dot on the graph should represent the first ordered pair 2.5 and 2.0. Go across the $x$ axis to 2.5 and up the $y$ axis to 2.0. Place a dot at the intersection. The second ordered pair is 7.0 and 3.5. Go up the $x$ axis to 7.0 and across the $y$ axis to 3.5. Follow this pattern for the rest of the ordered pairs. The graph should have 10 dots representing the 10 ordered pairs.

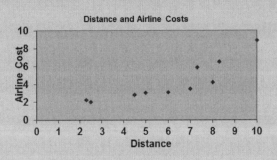

98

**Step 2**

Describe the relationship. The overall pattern of the dots seems to be ascending through the table. An imaginary line could be drawn right up through the middle of the dots from the left hand corner to the top right corner. Since the line seems to ascend, the relationship is positive. A positive relationship suggests that as distance increases, so too does the cost of the airline ticket. As to the strength of the relationship, the values seem to be clustered relatively close to the imaginary line, therefore, there seems to be a moderately strong to strong relationship.

# SECTION 3

## Ordinal Variables: Spearman's *Correlation*

An ordinal variable ranks or orders data from lowest to highest. Examples of ordinal-level variables include alphabetizing a seating chart, arranging people according to weight or height, or positioning military leaders according to rank. Variables that can be ranked can be compared with a variety of statistical techniques. The most popular technique for describing the relationship of two ordinal variables is the Spearman rank correlation coefficient.

The *Spearman rank correlation coefficient*, also known as Spearman's *r*, describes whether a relationship exists and the direction of the relationship between two ordinal-level measurements. Spearman's *r* reports whether the variables move in the same or different directions: That is, do both variables simultaneously increase and decrease, or does one increase while the other decreases?

**Spearman's rank correlation coefficient** Measures the strength, direction and statistical significance of the relationship between two ordinal-level variables. The notation is $r_s$.

The calculation of Spearman's *r* begins with identifying the difference between the paired data. Identify one variable as *X* and the second as *Y*. The difference of the ordered pair is $x - y = d$. The value *d* for each ordered pair must also be squared for the calculation. When working with ranked data, a common problem occurs with rankings that are tied. Ranked data that are tied are assigned the mean of the rankings if they had not been tied. For example, if students are ranked according to height and the second, third, and fourth shortest students are the same height, then all three students are ranked as 3, because the mean is $(2 + 3 + 4)/3 = 3$. If the first and second students are tied, their rankings are 1.5, with the mean of 1 and 2.

**Formula for Calculating Spearman's $r$**

$$r_s = 1 - \frac{6\sum d^2}{n(n^2 - 1)}$$

where
$d = x - y$ and $d^2$ is the squared difference of each ordered pair
$n$ is the number of ordered pairs.

It is mathematically proven that a correlation coefficient defined by the above formula will have a value ranging from -1 to 1. A value of -1 or 1 means there is a perfect relationship between the variables. -1 is a perfect negative relationship. As the values of one variable increase, there is a corresponding decrease in the values of the second variable. 1 is a perfect positive relationship. The values of the two variables increase and decrease simultaneously. A value of 0 means there is no relationship. Values close to 0, negative or positive, are referred to as weak. Values around -.5 and .5 are moderate and values approaching -1 and 1 are viewed as strong.

Values of $r_s$ $\quad -1 \leq r_s \leq 1$

### EXAMPLE 4.3

**Experiment:** Students at the Phoenix Institute ranked their professors. As part of the tenure process, faculty were also asked to rank other professors. The top five professors (in reverse order, where 5 is the highest and 1 is the lowest) are listed here where $X$ represents student's ranking and $Y$ represents faculty's ranking to that particular professor. Do the students and faculty tend to agree?

|  | Student $(X)$ | Faculty $(Y)$ |
|---|---|---|
| Prof. Dodd | 3 | 1 |
| Prof. Mimick | 2 | 2 |
| Prof. Lee | 4.5 | 4 |
| Prof. Elder | 4.5 | 5 |
| Prof. Pye | 1 | 3 |

**Answer:** $r_s =. 575$; yes, the students and the faculty tend to agree.
**Solution:** Spearman's $r$ is the measure of association for ranked data. The data are ranked with ties, such as the apparent tie for the fourth and fifth position

by the students, reported using the mean of the values of the tied positions. Arrange the table with columns for $d$, the difference between $x$ and $y$, and for $d^2$. Calculate the coefficient.

| | Student $x$ | Faculty $y$ | $d$ $(x-y)$ | $d^2$ |
|---|---|---|---|---|
| **Prof. Dodd** | 3 | 1 | 2.0 | 4.00 |
| **Prof. Mimick** | 2 | 2 | 0.0 | 0.00 |
| **Prof. Lee** | 4.5 | 4 | 0.5 | 0.25 |
| **Prof. Elder** | 4.5 | 5 | -0.5 | 0.25 |
| **Prof. Pye** | 1 | 3 | -2.0 | 4.00 |
| | | | | $\Sigma d^2 = 8.50$ |

$$r_s = 1 - \frac{6\sum d^2}{n(n^2 - 1)} = 1 - \frac{6(8.5)}{5(5^2 - 1)} = 1 - \frac{51}{5(24)} = 1 - .425 = .575$$

The coefficient .575 implies that there is a positive moderate relationship between the students' and the faculty's rankings. In other words, they tend to agree more than they tend to disagree.

## EXAMPLE 4.4

**Experiment:** Is there a relationship between the rankings of the top 10 states storing nuclear weapons in 1980 and 2000? (1 indicates the lowest number stored and 10 the highest number stored) Let $x$ be the rankings in 2000 and $y$ be the rankings in 1980.

| State | 2000 Ranking | 1980 Ranking |
|---|---|---|
| South Carolina | 1 | 1 |
| New Mexico | 2 | 11 |
| North Dakota | 3 | 3 |
| Texas | 4 | 6 |
| Washington | 5 | 5 |
| California | 6 | 4 |
| Louisiana | 7 | 9 |
| Michigan | 8 | 6 |
| Virginia | 9 | 8 |
| Wyoming | 10 | 10 |

**Answer:** No, $r_s = .406$.

**Solution:** Spearman's $r$ is the measure of association for ranked data. The data are ranked from lowest to highest or highest to lowest. Arrange the table with columns for $d$, the difference between $x$ and $y$, and for $d^2$. Calculate the coefficient.

| State | 2000 Ranking $x$ | 1980 Ranking $y$ | $d$ $(x - y)$ | $d^2$ |
|---|---|---|---|---|
| South Carolina | 1 | 1 | 0 | 0 |
| New Mexico | 2 | 11 | - 9 | 81 |
| North Dakota | 3 | 3 | 0 | 0 |
| Texas | 4 | 6 | - 2 | 4 |
| Washington | 5 | 5 | 0 | 0 |
| California | 6 | 4 | 2 | 4 |
| Louisiana | 7 | 9 | - 2 | 4 |
| Michigan | 8 | 6 | 2 | 4 |
| Virginia | 9 | 8 | 1 | 1 |
| Wyoming | 10 | 10 | 0 | 0 |
| | | | | $\Sigma d^2 = 98$ |

$$r_s = 1 - \frac{6 \sum d^2}{n(n^2 - 1)} = 1 - \frac{6(98)}{10(10^2 - 1)} = 1 - \frac{588}{10(99)} = 1 - .5939 = .406$$

The coefficient .406 implies that there is a moderate positive relationship between the states' rankings in terms of the number of nuclear weapons for 2000 and 1980. Because the coefficient is fairly small, there does not appear to be a relationship between a state's ranking in the years 2000 and 1980.

**A LEARNING AID**
**SPEARMAN'S *r***

Eight nations report the following data on their infant mortality rate and general mortality rate, where the rate is given as number of death per 1,000 during one particular year. Rank the data. Does there appear to be a relationship between the two mortality rates?

| | Canada | U.S. | Sweden | U.K. | France | Japan | China | Spain |
|---|---|---|---|---|---|---|---|---|
| **Infant Mortality** | 8.1 | 10.5 | 6.4 | 9.6 | 10.0 | 6.2 | 50 | 9.6 |
| **Mortality** | 7.0 | 9.0 | 11.0 | 11.0 | 10.7 | 6.0 | 8 | 8.1 |

**Step 1**

Rank the data from lowest to highest. The lowest score should be ranked 1 and the highest score, 8. Be sure to use the mean for values that tie. For example, Sweden and the U.K. tie for the worst general mortality rate. Since they tie for the seventh and eighth positions, both are assigned the position 7.5 ((7 + 8)/2 = 7.5). Rewrite the ranked data.

| | Canada | U.S. | Sweden | U.K. | France | Japan | China | Spain |
|---|---|---|---|---|---|---|---|---|
| **Infant Mortality** | 3 | 7 | 2 | 4.5 | 6 | 1 | 8 | 4.5 |
| **Mortality** | 2 | 5 | 7.5 | 7.5 | 6 | 1 | 3 | 4 |

**Step 2**

Let $x$ represent the ranks of countries in terms of infant mortality rate from low to high, and let $y$ represent the rank of countries in terms of general mortality rate from low to high. Rearranging the data in a column, calculate the Spearman rank correlation coefficient

$$r_s = 1 - \frac{6\sum d^2}{n(n^2 - 1)} = 1 - \frac{6(69.5)}{8(8^2 - 1)} = 1 - \frac{417}{8(63)} = 1 - .827 = .173$$

**Step 3**

Interpret the results. A correlation of .173 suggests there is some correlation between the rankings of these nations' infant mortality rates and general mortality rates. The small correlation that does exist is positive, which does suggest that as a nation's infant mortality ranking increases, so does its general mortality rate ranking.

# SECTION 4

## Ratio or Interval Variables: Pearson's Correlation

Interval and ratio variables are the highest levels of variables. Both determine the difference or distance between the values of the variable. For example, there is a measurable difference between 1 inch and 2 inches. It is the same measurable difference as between 3 inches and 4 inches. Ratio-level variables have all the characteristics of interval-level variables, along with a zero starting point. An interval-level variable may contain a zero, but the zero does not imply an absolute absence of the variable. Temperature is an interval variable, but $0°$ does not imply the absence of temperature. However, age is a ratio variable, because 0 years is the absence of age.

A measure of association known as a linear correlation coefficient determines if a relationship exists between two interval or ratio variables. The most popular technique to describe the relationship of two interval or ratio variables is the Pearson's product moment correlation coefficient, $r$. As does Spearman's $r$, Pearson's $r$ measures both the strength and direction of the relationship of two variables. It is proven mathematically that Pearson's $r$ also has values ranging from -1 to 1, as does Spearman's $r$. A value of -1 represents a perfect negative relationship, whereas a 0 represents no relationship and +1 represents a perfect positive relationship. Any negative $r$ value implies that as the values of one variable increase, the values of the other variable tend to decrease. Any positive $r$ value implies that the values of both variables increase or decrease simultaneously. Unlike Spearman's $r$, Pearson's $r$ assumes the relationship is linear-meaning that a consistent pattern upward or downward exists. Pearson's $r$ should not be applied to nonlinear relationships.

**Pearson's Product Moment Correlation Coefficient**  Measures the strength, direction, and statistical significance of the relationship between two interval or ratio variables. The notation of a correlation coefficient between two variables of a sample is $r$. The notation of a correlation coefficient between two variables of a population is $\rho$.

**Values of $r$**
$$-1 \leq r \leq 1$$

Pearson's $r$ represents a sample statistic. The corresponding population parameter is denoted by the Greek letter $\rho$ (pronounced "rho," like the "ro" in road). Because $r$ measures the relationship of ordered pairs from sample data, $\rho$ measures the relationship of all ordered pairs from a population. The calculation of Pearson's $r$ is based on the sum of the squares of $x$, $y$, and $xy$. Recall that the sum of the squares is the numerator of the variance formula. The distances of the $x$ values are measured against the mean of $x$, whereas the $y$ values are measured against the mean of $y$ and the ordered pairs $xy$ are measured against the mean of $xy$.

## Formula for Calculating Pearson's *r*

$$r = \frac{n\sum xy - \sum x \sum y}{\sqrt{n\sum x^2 - \left(\sum x\right)^2} \sqrt{n\sum y^2 - \left(\sum y\right)^2}}$$

where
- *n* is the number of ordered pairs.
- $\sum xy$ is each *x* value multiplied by its *y* value, summed.
- $\sum x$ is the sum of the *x* values.
- $\sum y$ is the sum of the *y* values.
- $\sum x^2$ is the squares of the *x* values, summed.
- $\left(\sum x\right)^2$ is the sum of the *x* values, squared.
- $\sum y^2$ is the squares of the *y* values, summed.
- $\left(\sum y\right)^2$ is the sum of the *y* values, squared.

## EXAMPLE 4.5

**Experiment:** Calculate Pearson's *r* for the following set of paired data.

| *x*: | 3 | 4 | 3 | 6 | 7 | 2 |
| *y*: | 4 | 4 | 5 | 7 | 8 | 4 |

**Answer:** *r* = .922

**Solution:** Pearson's *r* is a measure of association describing the strength and direction of the linear relationship of two interval or ratio variables.

First begin by clearing any old data stored in lists of the calculator. Press the STAT button, scroll down to highlight "4:ClrList" and press ENTER. The screen will display: "ClrList." Press: 2$^{ND}$ and then $L_1$ (this is above the number 1), and ENTER. Repeat this process for clearing other lists on the calculator.

To input the new data, Press: STAT and highlight "1: Edit" and press ENTER. Input values of *x* into $L_1$ and values of *y* into $L_2$. The screen should look like this:

Once the data are entered, press STAT. Then, click the right arrow twice to highlight "TESTS". Scroll down to "F:LinRegTTEST" and press ENTER. Adhere to the following settings then highlight "Calculate" and press ENTER. Scroll down to the bottom of the screen, which displays the results of the test to view Pearson's correlation coefficient.

Numbers (summations) cannot be found without utilizing the "2-Var Stats" function.

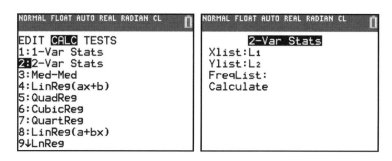

Some professors may like to see the summations in the formula. If so, they can be found using the calculator function, "2-Var Stats." This function can be found by pressing STAT, scrolling right to CALC, and by pressing the "2" button to select the function. When "2-Var Stats" is on the screen with a blinking cursor, type the names of the lists where the data is located, such as $L_1$ and $L_2$. Highlight "Calculate" and press ENTER to view the list of summations.

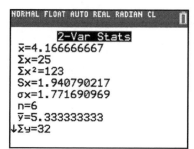
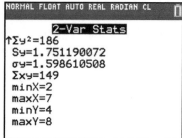

$$r = \frac{n\sum xy - \sum x \sum y}{\sqrt{n\sum x^2 - \left(\sum x\right)^2}\sqrt{n\sum y^2 - \left(\sum y\right)^2}} = \frac{6(149) - (25)(32)}{\sqrt{6(123) - 25^2}\sqrt{6(186) - 32^2}}$$

$$= .922$$

The interpretation of Pearson's $r$ requires three things: strength, direction, and statistical significance. The strength of the relationship is determined by the size of the value. A value of 1 or -1 implies a perfect relationship. A perfect relationship occurs when all the values of $x$ and $y$ are equal to the mean. A value approaching 1 or -1 implies a strong relationship, whereas a value near 0 implies a very weak relationship and a value of 0 implies no relationship. However, what is considered strong or weak may also depend on the sample size. As more ordered pairs are sampled, the size of significant $r$ representing a linear relationship decreases. There is an increased risk of committing an error with a small sample versus a large sample. The error in accepting an $r$ of .800 for 5 cases is greater than the error in accepting an $r$ of .800 for 500 cases. The direction refers to the relationship as positive or negative as determined by the sign of the calculated value. If the calculated value is negative, then the relationship of the values of the variables is negative. A positive $r$ describes a positive relationship.

## EXAMPLE 4.6

**Experiment:** Interpret the $r$ value .922 calculated in Example 4.5.

**Answer:** Strong and positive.

**Solution:** A .922 *r* value suggests that the relationship is positive. As *x* increases, so too does *y*. Since the value is near 1.0, the relationship is very strong.

## EXAMPLE 4.7

**Experiment:** Ten couples are surveyed to determine if there is a relationship between the educational levels of each couple. Given the following data, in years of education, describe the relationship.

Woman's education (*x*):  12  14  12  13  16  16  18  12  13  14
Man's education (*y*):  13  16  12  16  17  16  18  17  14  14

**Answer:** *r* = .667; there is a positive, moderately strong relationship between the educational levels of the man and woman in each couple. That is, as a woman's education increases, so too does the man's education.

**Solution:** Formal education is a ratio-level variable, because there is a measurable difference between 10 years of education and 11 years. Also, 0 years of education means the absence of a formal education. Pearson's *r* measures the association of ratio-level variables. Pearson's *r* will describe the direction and strength of the data and whether the relationship is statistically significant.

Plug *x* values into $L_1$ and *y* values into $L_2$, press STAT, scroll to "TESTS" and highlight "F:LinRegTTest" and press ENTER. Adhere to the following settings, highlight "Calculate" and press ENTER. Scroll to the bottom of the screen to view the value of *r*.

Also note the formula for *r*, shown below. For the summations used in the formula, utilize "2-Var Stats," which can be found by pressing STAT, scrolling right to CALC. Depending on the calculator, type $L_1$, $L_2$ and then press Enter. Otherwise, the List *x* and List *y* will appear in which the $L_1$ and $L_2$ can be entered.

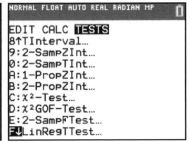

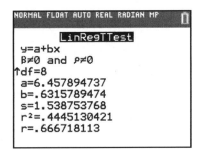

$$r = \frac{n\sum xy - \sum x \sum y}{\sqrt{n\sum x^2 - \left(\sum x\right)^2}\sqrt{n\sum y^2 - \left(\sum y\right)^2}} = \frac{10(2166) - (140)(153)}{\sqrt{(10(1998)) - 140^2}\sqrt{10(2375) - 153^2}}$$

$$= .667$$

Interpret the results: An *r* value of .667 implies that the relationship is positive and moderately strong. A positive relationship suggests that as the woman's educational level increases, the man's increases.

## A LEARNING AID
## PEARSON'S *r*

Determine if a relationship exists between the age at marriage of a woman and the number of children she bears.

| Age at marriage($x$): | 22 | 14 | 18 | 19 | 16 | 26 | 28 | 22 | 23 | 18 | 20 | 21 |
|---|---|---|---|---|---|---|---|---|---|---|---|---|
| Number of children($y$): | 3 | 6 | 5 | 5 | 6 | 3 | 2 | 2 | 4 | 4 | 4 | 4 |

### Step 1

Identify the variables as interval or ratio. Both variables are ratio, because there is measurable distance between age as well as between the number of children.

### Step 2

Draw a scatterplot. A scatterplot is one way to determine if a relationship exists between ratio variables. Draw and label the axes. The *x* axis is horizontal and the *y* axis is vertical. Scan the values of *x* and *y* to determine the intervals for the diagram. The *x* values range from 14 to 28; therefore, 5-year increments will allow for easy display. The *y* values range from 3 to 6, so increments of 1 are appropriate. Begin with the first ordered pair, where *x* = 22 and *y* = 3. From the *x* axis, trace up from the value of 22 (which is between the values of 20 and 25) to the *y* value 3. Place a dot at the point (22, 3). Continue this process for each of the ordered pairs.

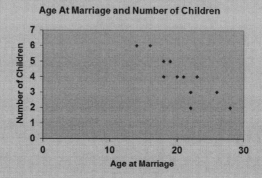

**Age At Marriage and Number of Children**

The scatterplot displays a negative relationship, where the values of *Y* decrease as the values of *X* increase. If a woman is older when she marries, she tends to have fewer children. The relationship also seems very strong because the dots are clustered close together in a linear pattern.

The scatterplot can also be viewed on a TI calculator by first plugging the *x* and *y* values into L₁ and L₂. Double check the values in both lists and press the 2ND button and then the Y = button. The calculator should display "STAT PLOTS" as shown below. With"1:Plot1" highlighted, press ENTER.

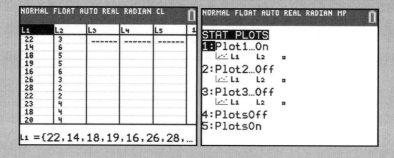

Adhere to the following settings. With "On" and the image of a scatterplot highlighted, be sure that the proper lists are designated for *x* and y. Once completed, press the GRAPH button, located on the top right of your calculator. Press the ZOOM button, and then 9 (9:ZoomStat) to view the scatterplot. It should appear as follows.

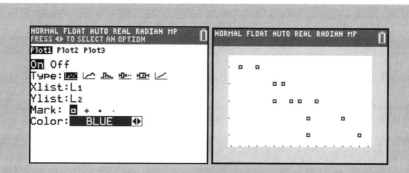

**Step 3**

Calculate Pearson's $r$. Pearson's $r$ shows the strength and direction of the relationship between two ratio intervals. With the $x$ and $y$ values in $L_1$ and $L_2$, press the STAT button and select "F:LinRegTTest" under TESTS. The $r$ value is displayed at the bottom of the screen and should appear as follows:

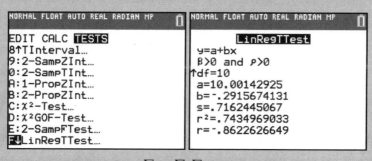

$$r = \frac{n\sum xy - \sum x \sum y}{\sqrt{n\sum x^2 - \left(\sum x\right)^2}\sqrt{n\sum y^2 - \left(\sum y\right)^2}} = -.862$$

**Step 4**

Interpret the results. An $r$ value of -.862 implies that the relationship is negative and strong. A negative relationship suggests that as the woman's age at marriage decreases, the number of children she bears increases.

# SECTION 5

## Ratio or Interval Variables: Linear Regression

Correlation analysis measures the relationship between two variables by describing how the variables vary together. The relationship between $X$ and $Y$ is the same as it is for $Y$ and $X$. Correlation analysis describes the direction and strength of the relationship, but it does not predict the effects of one variable on another.

The relationship between two or more variables is determined by a regression analysis. Regression analysis predicts or projects the effect of one variable on another. Regression analysis focuses on the linear relationship and is used to predict the effect of the movement of one variable on another variable.

The variable that is to be predicted is known as the ***dependent variable, Y***. The dependent variable is the output variable—that is, the one that is affected by the other variable or variables. The variable that is used to predict movement in dependent variable $Y$ is known as the ***independent variable, X***. The case in which one independent variable $X$ predicts $Y$, is known as a *bivariate regression analysis*. The case in which two or more independent variables predict $Y$ is known as a *multivariate regression analysis*.

The identification of the independent and dependent variable is important. The dependent variable is the variable to be predicted. The independent variable predicts movement in the dependent variable. The independent variables are the inputs, and the dependent variable is the result.

**Independent Variable, *X*** The variable that predicts a change in the dependent variable. The input variable.

**Dependent Variable, *Y*** The variable that is predicted or projected by the independent variable or variables. The output variable.

Regression analysis assumes linearity. In a bivariate regression, a line could be drawn through the middle of the data displayed on a scatterplot. The regression analysis will define the beginning of the line and the slope of the line as it either ascends or descends through the data. The line is referred to as the ***line of best fit, least-squares line***, or ***regression line***. From this line, a prediction for $y$ can be made given any value of $x$. The predictions are based on a calculation minimizing the error created by predicting $y$ with sample information, also known as observed values. The most common method of predicting $y$ for regression problems is known as the ***least-squares method***.

The regression line is given in the form of $\hat{y} = a+bx$, (also written $\hat{y} = mx+b$ *or even* $\hat{y} = b + mx$), where $a$ represents the ***y-intercept*** and $b$ is the ***slope*** of the line. The $y$-intercept is the place where the predicted $y$ value is when $x$ is zero. The slope determines the increase or decrease in $y$ for every unit increase of $x$. The predicted value of $y$ is denoted by $\hat{y}$ (y-hat); the $y$-intercept is $a$; and the slope is $b$.

For example, if $\hat{y} = a + bx$ *is* $\hat{y} = 10 + 5x$, the $y$-intercept value *(a)* equals 10. This means that the line on the graph would start at 10 for $y$ where $x$ is 0. In other words, the first ordered pair would be drawn at 0 for $x$ and 10 for $y$. If the slope is 5, then the line would go up (since it is positive) 5 more points every time $x$ increased by 1 point. Put this information together you have ordered pairs of (0, 10), (1, 15), (2, 20), (3, 25), and so forth. Notice $x$ is increasing by 1 only but $y$ is increasing by 5 after the starting point of 10.

> **Regression Line or Line of Best Fit** A straight line predicting values of $y$ from values of $x$ using the least-squares method.
>
> $$\hat{y} = a + bx$$
>
> (also known as $\hat{y} = b + mx$ or $\hat{y} = mx + b$)
>
> where
> > $\hat{y}$ is the predicted value of $y$.
> > $a$ is the $y$-intercept.
> > $b$ is the slope of the regression line.
> > $x$ is the given value of $x$.

The $y$-intercept value, $a$, and the slope, $b$, must be calculated before the predicted value, $\hat{y}$, can be determined. The slope could be calculated first since its formula is relatively simpler. The slope describes how the line ascends or descends through the data. It explains the unit increase or decrease in $y$ for every unit increase in $x$. For example, if $y$ is weight in pounds, $x$ is age in years, and the slope is .5, $y$ increases ½ pound for every increase in age.

> **Formula for Calculating the y-Intercept**
>
> $$y\text{-intercept } (a) = \frac{\sum y \sum x^2 - (\sum x) \sum xy}{n(\sum x^2) - (\sum x)^2}$$
>
> where
> > $n$ is the number of ordered pairs.
> > $\Sigma xy$ is each $x$ value multiplied by its $y$ value, summed.
> > $\Sigma x$ is the sum of the $x$ values.
> > $\Sigma y$ is the sum of the $y$ values.
> > $\Sigma x^2$ is the squares of the $x$ values, summed.
> > $(\Sigma x)^2$ is the sum of the $x$ values, squared.

> **Formula for Calculating Slope**
>
> $$\text{Slope } (b) = \frac{n(\sum xy) - \sum x \sum y}{n(\sum x^2) - (\sum x)^2}$$

Notice the slope formula is similar to the correlation formula. The correlation coefficient also included information about the $y$ value in the denominator. Both formulas attempt to minimize the squares of the deviations. Because it minimizes the squares of the deviations, the slope formula is also referred to as the regression coefficient and as the least-squares formula.

To determine the regression line, calculate the slope and the $y$-intercept; place the values in the formula for the line of best fit. The regression line is not solved for one value unless a specific value of $x$ is given; that is, the regression line is given as $\hat{y} = a + bx$, with values inserted for $a$ and $b$ but not for $\hat{y}$ and $x$. When a value is given for $x$, the predicted value $y$ is determined. The values of y-intercept and slope can be used to draw the regression line on a scatter diagram.

In other words, a second dot would be placed at a $y$ of .288 for $x$ of 1. (Found by taking the -.483 and adding .771 = .288). The method continues by adding .771 to the previous $y$ for every increase of 1 in $x$. The dots are connected to form a regression line.

## EXAMPLE 4.8

**Experiment:** Calculate the regression equation for explaining the cost of passenger airline travel based on travel distance. (Both values are given in hundreds; that is, $100 = 1,100$ miles $= 1$.)

| Travel costs: | 2.0 | 3.5 | 4.2 | 2.2 | 3.1 | 8.9 | 6.5 | 5.9 | 3.0 | 2.8 |
| Distance: | 2.5 | 7.0 | 8.0 | 2.3 | 6.0 | 10.0 | 8.3 | 7.3 | 5.0 | 4.5 |

**Answer:** $\hat{y} = a + bx = \hat{y} = -.483 + .771x$

**Solution:** Begin by noting the dependent variable and independent variable. In general, the cost of travel depends on distance traveled. It is reasonable to let $x$ represent the distance traveled. The dependent variable, $y$, the variable being explained, is the cost of passenger airline travel. Distance predicts the costs, and therefore distance is the independent variable $x$.

Clear out the old data and then plug $x$ values into $L_1$ and $y$ values into $L_2$. When the data is entered, press the STAT button again, scroll over to "CALC" and down to "8:LinReg($a+bx$)" and press ENTER. Adhere to the following settings under LinReg($a+bx$), highlight Calculate and press ENTER.

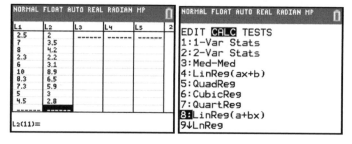

The results will be appear as the figure below.

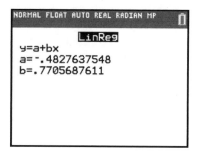

If the professor requests the summations to be inserted in the formula, they can be found by pressing STATS, scrolling right to CALC, and down to the "2-Var Stats" function. Indicate the lists where the original data are located, highlight "Calculate," and press ENTER.

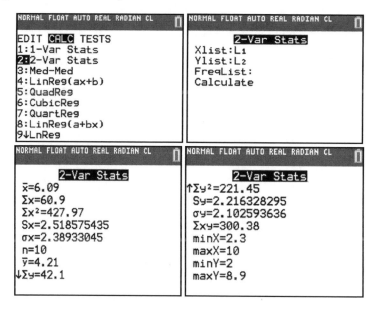

$$a = (y\text{-intercept}) = \frac{\sum y \sum x^2 - (\sum x)\sum xy}{n(\sum x^2) - (\sum x)^2} = \frac{(42.1)(427.97) - (60.9)(300.38)}{10(427.97) - (60.9)^2}$$

$$= -.483$$

$$b = \text{Slope} = \frac{n(\sum xy) - \sum x \sum y}{n(\sum x^2) - (\sum x)^2} = \frac{10(300.8) - (60.90)(42.10)}{10(427.97) - 60.90^2}$$

$$= .771$$

The intercept is -.483. This means that $y$ is -.483 when $x$ is 0. In other words, if a graph was drawn, the $y$ value starts at -.483 where $x$ is 0. However this does not mean the distance traveled implies a negative cost. Notice that the range of distance in the data is from 2.5 to 10; this equation is valid for $x$ in this range.

The slope implies that for every unit increase in $x$, there is a .771 unit increase in $y$. This means that for every 100-mile increase in distance, there is an increased cost of $77.10 (distance and costs are in hundreds).
State the equation with the slope and the intercept:

$$\hat{y} = -.483 + .771\, x$$

Draw the regression line on the scatterplot. The $y$-intercept is at -.483, which means the first dot would be below the $x$ axis where $y$ is -.483. For an increase of 1 in $x$, there is a .771 increase in $y$ from where it began (which was -.483).

| $x$ | $y$ | Calculation |
|---|---|---|
| 0 | -.483 | $y$ equals $a$ -.483 |
| 1 | .288 | add slope .771 to $a$ -.483 |
| 2 | 1.059 | add slope .771 to previous $y$ value .288 |
| 3 | 1.83 | add slope .771 to previous $y$ value 1.059 |
| 4 | 2.601 | add slope .771 to previous $y$ value 1.83 |
| … | … | …… |
| … | … | …… |

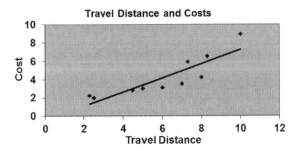

Travel Distance and Costs

While a value for *y* may be found by adding *b (slope)* to each of the previous *y* values, the process may be long and tedious. The real usage of the regression equation is to mathematically calculate an expected value of *y* for an appropriate given value of *x*.

## EXAMPLE 4.9

**Experiment:** A researcher wants to determine if the annual income of a guilty defendant has an impact on the number of years he/she is sentenced. The following data are the incomes of defendants convicted of the same crimes and their length of sentence. Calculate the regression line. If a defendant's annual income is \$50,000, ($x = 50$), what sentence would be expected if convicted?

| *x* | 39.6 | 102.2 | 345 | 20.5 | 15.5 | 80.9 | 450.5 | 10.6 |
|-----|------|-------|-----|------|------|------|-------|------|
| *y* | 20 | 5 | 4 | 20 | 24 | 10 | 2 | 20 |

**Answer:**
$\hat{y} = 18.8526 + - .043x$ (or $\hat{y} = 18.8526 - .043x$)
If $x = 50$, $\hat{y} = 16.703$.

**Solution:** The experiment asks to find the regression line. The regression line is the line of best fit solving for the *y*-intercept line and the slope and then stating the equation $\hat{y} = a + bx$.

Determining the regression line can be done by plugging *x* and *y* values into L$_1$ and L$_2$, pressing STAT and selecting "8: LinReg(*a*+*bx*)" under CALC. With the following settings, the calculator will display the results.

The calculation for the *y-intercept* line is:

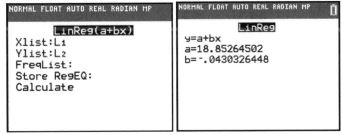

The calculation for the *y*-intercept line is:

$$a = \frac{\sum y \sum x^2 - (\sum x)\sum xy}{n(\sum x^2) - (\sum x)^2} = \frac{105(341305.92) - 1064.8(5387)}{8(341305.92) - 1064.8^2}$$

$$= 18.8526$$

The calculation for the slope is:

$$b = \frac{n\sum xy - \sum x \sum y}{n\left(\sum x^2\right) - \left(\sum x\right)^2} = \frac{8(5387) - 1064.8(105)}{8(341305.92) - 1064.8^2} = -.043$$

State the equation by placing the values calculated above in their appropriate positions. This is the answer to the regression line.

$$\hat{y} = 18.8526 + -.043x$$

Next solve for the second part of the question. If a defendant's income is $50,000, ($x = 50$), what sentence would be expected if convicted? Place the $x$ value 50 in the equation from above and solve.

$$\hat{y} = 18.8526 + -.043x$$
$$= 18.8526 + -.043(50)$$
$$= 18.8526 + -2.15$$
$$= 18.8526 - 2.15$$
$$= 16.703$$

Again, the regression equation not only allows for the identification of the line of best fit for the data displayed in a scatter diagram, it also predicts values of $\hat{y}$ given values of $x$. When a value of $x$ is given, an expected value of $\hat{y}$ can be determined. The expected value is predicted as the average value of $y$ for the specific $x$ value. Place the stated value of $x$ in the regression equation and solve for $\hat{y}$. Give the predicted $y$ value as the average value expected to occur for the $x$ value. The equation can be solved for any number of $x$ values, however, the calculated value of $y$ may not be meaningful if $x$ is out of the range of the given $x$. It is not unusual for an actual $x$ value in the data to have a different value than that predicted when completing the regression equation. This will happen since the calculated value is the predicted average value. That is, the calculated value $\hat{y}$ is the average for all $y$ values at a specific $x$ value.

## EXAMPLE 4.10

**Experiment:** Refer to the regression line obtained in Example 4.8. Given the regression equation $\hat{y} = -.483 + .771x$, where $x$ represents the distance traveled and $y$ represents the cost of traveling $x$ miles. Calculate the predicted cost of airline travel based on the travel distance of 200 mi. (Remember that the data are in hundreds, so 200 miles = 2.0)

**Answer:** $105.90

**Solution:** The predicted value of $y$ is determined by placing the $x$ value in the equation. Calculate $\hat{y}$ and multiply the $\hat{y}$ value by 100 to yield dollars.

$$\hat{y} = -.483 + .771x$$
$$= -.483 + .771(2)$$
$$= -.483 + 1.542$$
$$= 1.059$$
$$1.059(100) = \$105.90$$

$105.90 means that, on average, airline travel cost $105.90 for a 200-mile trip. Some may pay a little more or less.

### EXAMPLE 4.11

**Experiment:** Predict $\hat{y}$ with the equation $\hat{y} = 2 + 4x$, when

$$\text{a. } x = 3 \quad \text{b. } x = 10 \quad \text{c. } x = 5 \quad \text{d. } x = 20$$

**Answer:**

$$\text{a. } \hat{y} = 14 \quad \text{b. } \hat{y} = 42 \quad \text{c. } \hat{y} = 22 \quad \text{d. } \hat{y} = 82$$

**Solution:** Place each value of $x$ in the regression equation.
a. $\hat{y} = 2 + 4(3) = 2 + 12 = 14$
b. $\hat{y} = 2 + 4(10) = 2 + 40 = 42$
c. $\hat{y} = 2 + 4(5) = 2 + 20 = 22$
d. $\hat{y} = 2 + 4(20) = 2 + 80 = 82$

## REVERSE IT?

In some cases, the dependent variable and independent variable can be interchanged. The regression calculation can be reversed to predict an $x$ value when the $\hat{y}$ is given. This is simple algebra. To isolate the $x$ value from the equation, begin by subtracting the *y-intercept* from the $\hat{y}$ and from itself to remove it from the right side of the equation. Now the right side of the equation should be only the slope and the $x$. To remove the slope from the right side of the equation, divide both sides by the slope value. Now everything is removed from the right except the $x$ but the left side should have only one value. The result is the predicted $x$ value.

For example, suppose an employer making donuts is concerned with pay and productivity. Usually the productivity, the number of donuts in dozens produced by an employee per day, is the $y$ variable that could be predicted by hourly rate of the employee's pay, the $x$ variable. Assume a regression equation may be:

$$\hat{y} = 2 + 4x$$

Usually an *x* value for pay is inserted and productivity is calculated. If a person is paid $8.00 an hour, they would, on average, produce 34 dozen donuts.

Now try to reverse the process. What if the employer is expected to produce 50 dozen per employee per day, how much would the employer pay hourly to that employee, on average, to get the results needed? That is, the productivity is given ($\hat{y}$ = 50 dozen donuts) and the *x* value (pay) must be found.

Begin with the equation and insert the $\hat{y}$ value. Subtract the *y-intercept* from $\hat{y}$ to remove it from the left and right side of the equation. Divide both sides by the slope to isolate the *x* value.

| | |
|---|---|
| $\hat{y} = 2 + 4x$ | State the Line of Best Fit. |
| $50 = 2 + 4x$ | Insert the $\hat{y}$ value given, 50. |
| $50 - 2 = (2 - 2)\,4x$<br>$48 = 4x$ | Subtract the *y*-intercept from both sides…i.e., subtract the 2 from the right and left sides. |
| $\dfrac{48}{4} = \dfrac{4x}{4}$ | Divide both sides by the slope. (Divide both sides by 4.) |
| $12 = x$ | The answer is $12.00. |

## MULTIPLE REGRESSIONS

The basic rules for calculating the line of best fit that predicts one variable from another variable can be extended to allow the predictions to be derived from two or more variables. Predictions based on one variable are known as *bivariate* linear regressions. Predictions based on two or more variables are known as *multivariate,* or *multiple linear regressions.*

The multiple regression requires a least-squares slope equation for each of the independent variables. If the bivariate equation for one independent variable is $\hat{y} = a + bx$, the multivariate equation for two independent variables is $\hat{y} = a + b_1x_1 + b_2x_2$, and the equation for three independent variables is $\hat{y} = a + b_1x_1 + b_2x_2 + b_3x_3$. Since the calculations for multiple regressions are very complex and time consuming, they are usually performed with a computer software program such as SPSS, SAS, STATA, or Minitab.

One independent variable:     $\hat{y} = a + b_1x_1$
Two independent variables:     $\hat{y} = a + b_1x_1 + b_2x_2$
Three independent variables:     $\hat{y} = a + b_1x_1 + b_2x_2 + b_3x_3$

Although the calculation of the multiple regression is complex and not detailed in this text, the application of the multiple regression can be addressed. Like the bivariate regression, the predictive power of the multiple regression equation is important.

## EXAMPLE 4.12
**Experiment:** Predict the average number of children born to women who have never lost a child, married at age 35, and are currently 50 years old. Use the following multiple regression equation:

$$\hat{y} = .46 + .42x_1 + (-.292x_2) + .225x_3$$

Number of children ↑        ↑      ↑      ↑ Current age

Lost a child ⌐     ⌐Age at marriage

**Answer:** $\hat{y} = 1.49$

**Solution:** A multiple regression equation predicts a dependent variable based on two or more independent variables. The dependent variable is the number of children born to women, which may be partially predicted by the number of deaths of children the women have experienced, the age when they married, and their current age. The equation can be solved by inserting the information from the experiment statement. Since this woman never lost a child, the value of $x$, is 0. The value 0 is placed in position $x$, as the number of children's deaths the women have experienced. The value 35 is the second independent variable, the age at which they married. The value of the third independent variable, current age, is 50. Solve the equation.

$$\hat{y} = .46 + .42(0) + -.292(35) + .225(50)$$
$$= .46 + 0 + (-10.22) + 11.25$$
$$= 1.49$$

The equation suggests that, on average, a woman experiencing no death of a child, married at age 35, and currently 50 years old could have had 1.49 children.

## EXAMPLE 4.13
**Experiment:** Explain the meaning of each of the terms in the following equation, where $y$ is a job performance rating (where 1 is poor and 5 is an excellent rating), $x_1$ is the number of years of employee experience, $x_2$ is the number of years of education for the employee, and $x_3$ is employee's age.

$$\hat{y} = -1.8 + 2.10x_1 + 2.98x_2 + .35x_3$$

**Answer:** Job performance is predicted by 3 independent variables. The equation describes the job rating increasing by 2.10 units for every year increase in experience, 2.98 units for every year increase in education, and .35 units for every year increase in age.

**Solution:** The equation is multiple regression equation because it is predicting a *y* variable with three independent variables. The first value is the y-intercept, denoting job rating is -1.8 where *x* values are 0. A value describing the slope is reported for each independent variable. A slope value describes the amount of change in *y* for every unit increase in *x*. Therefore, the notation 2.10x1 describes a positive 2.10 increase in job performance for every year increase in employee experience.

## A LEARNING AID
## TWO RATIO/INTERVAL VARIABLES: LINEAR REGRESSION

A bagel factory owner wants to predict the number of dozens of bagels an employee produces in one day based on the employee's pay (per hour). Calculate the regression line for the following sample data. Draw line on a scatter plot.

| Pay: | 5.50 | 4.50 | 4.25 | 6.25 | 5.10 | 7.90 | 6.50 | 8.00 |
|------|------|------|------|------|------|------|------|------|
| Productivity: | 20 | 18 | 17 | 25 | 21 | 28 | 26 | 30 |

Begin by noting the dependent variable and independent variable. The dependent variable, *y*, the variable being explained, is productivity. Pay is predicting productivity, and therefore pay is the independent variable, *x*.

Begin by plugging *x* values into $L_1$ and *y* values into $L_2$. When the data is entered, press the STAT button again, scroll over to "CALC" and down to "8:LinReg(a+bx)" and press ENTER. Adhere to the following settings under LinReg(a+bx), highlight Calculate and press ENTER.

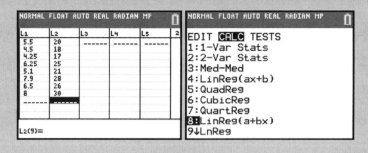

The answers appear on the screen as follows:

Calculate the $y$-intercept. If the instructor wants the summations noted, they can be found by going to STAT, scroll to CALC, down to 2:VARSTATS, and enter $L_1$, $L_2$.

$$a = \frac{\sum y \sum x^2 - \left(\sum x\right)\sum xy}{n\left(\sum x^2\right) - \left(\sum x\right)^2} = \frac{(185)(302.295) - (48)(1156.8)}{8(302.295) - (48)^2}$$

$$= 3.48$$

The intercept is 3.48. This means that $y$ is 3.48 when $x$ is zero. Calculate the slope:

$$b = \frac{n\left(\sum xy\right) - \sum x \sum y}{n\left(\sum x^2\right) - \left(\sum x\right)^2} = \frac{8(1156.80) - (48.00)(185)}{8(302.29) - 48.00^2}$$

$$= 3.27$$

The slope implies that for every unit increase in $x$, there is a 3.27 unit increase in $y$; that is, for every dollar more an employee is paid per hour, the employee produces 3.27 dozen bagels more each day.

**Step 4**

State the equation with the slope and the intercept. The equation does not solve for any value. It is the equation that is used if additional questions are asked.

$$\hat{y} = 3.48 + 3.27x$$

Draw the regression line on the scatter plot. The *y* intercept is at *x* at 3.48. For every increase of 1 in *x*, there is a 3.27-unit increase in *y*.

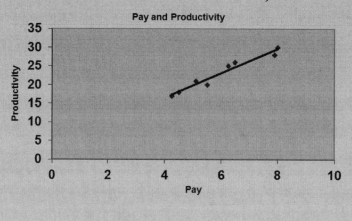

---

# CHAPTER 4 IN REVIEW

4.1   To determine if a relationship exists between the miles per gallon (MPG) estimated by the car manufacturers and the actual MPG recorded by consumers, the following data are collected:

| Automakers | 29 | 28 | 28 | 24 | 27 | 27 | 24 | 38 |
|---|---|---|---|---|---|---|---|---|
| Consumers | 27 | 27 | 25 | 20 | 22 | 25 | 23 | 36 |

a. Calculate the correlation coefficient.
b. Interpret the correlation.
c. Determine the line of best fit.
d. If the manufacturer claims 25 MPG, what should the consumer expect?
e. If the manufacturer claims 30 MPG, what should the consumer expect?

4.2   Identify the following as nominal, ordinal, interval, or ratio.
a. Miles per gallon for a vehicle
b. Vehicle class size (compact, mid-size, full...)
c. Number of cylinders in a vehicle
d. Vehicle cost
e. Vehicle color
f. Car manufacturer

4.3   To determine if insurance companies are playing politics with policyholders, a study across 9 years reports the following data on insurers' assets and the industries campaign contributions to Federal elections:

| Year | '05 | '06 | '07 | '08 | '09 | '10 | '11 | '12 | '13 |
|---|---|---|---|---|---|---|---|---|---|
| **Contributions (Millions $)** | 24 | 32 | 32 | 30 | 35 | 41 | 40 | 46 | 50 |
| **Assets (Billions $)** | 225 | 255 | 305 | 325 | 325 | 310 | 290 | 300 | 350 |

a. Calculate the correlation coefficient.
b. Determine the line of best fit on how the contribution depends on the assets sizes.
c. Interpret the slope of the regression line.
d. If the industry contributes $35 million, what will be the expected assets?
e. If the industry contributes $45 million, what will be the expected assets?

4.4   To determine if a relationship exists between a person's weight and his restaurant bill, the following data were collected.

| **Weight** | 190 | 220 | 180 | 124 | 127 | 127 | 151 |
|---|---|---|---|---|---|---|---|
| **Bill** | 10 | 17 | 15 | 10 | 10 | 12 | 15 |

a. Draw a scatterplot.
b. Calculate the correlation coefficient.
c. Determine the line of best fit on how the bill depends on weight.
d. Draw the regression line on the scatterplot.
e. If a person's weight is 150, what would be the expected bill?
f. If a person's weight is 110, what would be the expected bill?

4.5   Determine if the population (rounded to nearest million) of a city predicts the monthly cost of housing (rounded to nearest $1,000) for a family of four.

| | **Tokyo** | **Mexico City** | **Mumbai** | **San Paulo** | **New York City** |
|---|---|---|---|---|---|
| **Population** | 37 | 20 | 17 | 21 | 21 |
| **Housing** | 6 | 3 | 3 | 2 | 6 |

a. Calculate the correlation coefficient.
b. Calculate the regression line.
c. Draw a scatterplot including the line of best fit.
d. If a city has 15 million people, what is the expected cost of housing?
e. If a city has 20 million people, what is the expected cost of housing?

4.6   The following data represents the cell phone bills of 9 students based on their age. (Bills rounded to the nearest dollar)

| x Age | 30 | 25 | 22 | 28 | 20 | 20 | 18 | 19 | 20 |
|-------|----|----|----|----|----|----|----|----|----|
| y Bill | 88 | 98 | 85 | 90 | 90 | 75 | 80 | 95 | 80 |

a. Calculate the correlation coefficient.
b. Calculate the line of best fit.
c. If a student is 25 years old, what is his/her expected phone bill?
d. If a student is 35 years old, what is his/her expected phone bill?

4.7   Calculate the correlation coefficient between the following rankings for divorce rates in selected countries in 1995 and 2015. (Countries ranked lowest to highest where 1 is lowest).

|  | 1995 | 2015 |
|---|------|------|
| **Italy** | 1 | 1 |
| **Sweden** | 6 | 5 |
| **U.S.** | 5 | 6 |
| **Greece** | 2 | 3 |
| **Austria** | 3 | 2 |
| **United Kingdom** | 4 | 4 |

4.8   Given $\hat{y} = -1.96 + .986x$
a. Find $\hat{y}$, if $x = 5$.
b. Find $x$, if $\hat{y} = 4$.

4.9   If $x_1 = 3$, $x_2 = 20$, and $x_3 = 60$, Find the value of $\hat{y}$, where $\hat{y}$ is given by $\hat{y} = 1.2 + .823x_1 + (-.248x_2) + .326x_3$.

4.10  Draw a graph representing the line of best fit for the equation $\hat{y} = -1 + 1.5x$.

4.11  Explain the meaning of a slope $b = 30$, where $x$ is the production of 1 automobile and $y$ is pay in dollars.

4.12  Explain the meaning of a slope $b = -2.5$, where $x$ is outside temperature in Fahrenheit and $y$ is a heating bill in dollars.

4.13  True or False?
a. The dependent variable predicts the independent variable.
b. The line of best fit is also known as a correlation.
c. If the regression slope is calculated as 1.5, there is a 1.5-unit decrease in $y$ for every increase in $x$.
d. Regression analysis concerning three or more variables is known as bivariate regression analysis.
e. A negative $r$ implies that the two variables decrease together.

4.14 Describe at least two trends from the following contingency table representing party identification and support for the death penalty for those accused of first-degree murder.

**Death Penalty for Murder**

| Party I.D. ↓ Support → | Yes | Sometimes | No | Total |
|---|---|---|---|---|
| Republican | 59 | 14 | 10 | 83 |
| Independent | 28 | 4 | 10 | 42 |
| Democrat | 8 | 5 | 27 | 40 |
| Total | 95 | 23 | 47 | 165 |

4.15 Calculate the correlation between the percentage of births to unmarried women for selected countries between the years 1960 and 2010.

| Country | 1960 | 2010 |
|---|---|---|
| U.S. | 5.2 | 40.6 |
| Canada | 4.4 | 27.3 |
| France | 6.2 | 52.6 |
| Japan | 1.1 | 2.1 |
| Sweden | 11.4 | 54.7 |
| U.K. | 5.1 | 44.7 |

4.16 Calculate the Spearman's correlation coefficient for the rankings of the following regions for oil consumption and reserves. Interpret the results. (1 = lowest, 7 = highest)

| Region | Oil Consumption | Reserves |
|---|---|---|
| North America | 7 | 3 |
| Eastern Europe | 6 | 4 |
| Western Europe | 5 | 2 |
| Asia | 4 | 1 |
| Latin America | 3 | 5 |
| Middle East | 2 | 7 |
| Africa | 1 | 6 |

4.17 Explain the movement of two variables when a correlation coefficient is -1.0.

4.18 Describe at least 2 trends that may exist in the following contingency table representing gender and marital status of 500 students at the University of Detroit.

| Gender ↓     Status→ | Single | Married | Divorced | Total |
|---|---|---|---|---|
| Males | 150 | 50 | 20 | 220 |
| Females | 210 | 40 | 30 | 280 |
| Total | 360 | 90 | 50 | 500 |

4.19 Calculate the expected age at marriage ($y$) for a woman whose current age, $x_1$, is 50, whose education, $x_2$, is 12 years, and whose husband's education, $x_3$, is 12 years. Use the following regression equation.

$$\hat{y} = .982 + .210x_1 + .217x_2 + .376x_3$$

4.20 The following data represents the amount of money a family spends on food per week and the number of people in the household in a particular urban area.

| Number in household | $x$ | 2 | 3 | 3 | 4 | 2 | 4 | 5 |
|---|---|---|---|---|---|---|---|---|
| Food expenditure | $y$ | 70 | 90 | 80 | 100 | 80 | 110 | 135 |

a. Calculate the correlation coefficient.
b. Interpret the correlation coefficient (strength and direction).
c. Calculate the regression line.
d. What is the expected food expenditure for a family of 4?
e. What is the expected food expenditure for a family of 6?

4.21 The following data were collected to determine if there is a relationship between amount of time spent in a state for a presidential candidate and the number of people voting in the election.

| Time (hours) | 20 | 15 | 40 | 5 | 6 | 15 | 19 | 34 | 14 | 8 |
|---|---|---|---|---|---|---|---|---|---|---|
| Voters (millions) | 13 | 12 | 20 | 1.5 | 2.5 | 14 | 9 | 18 | 10 | 3.5 |

a. Draw a scatter plot.
b. Interpret the scatter plot, indicate the expected strength and direction.

4.22 The following data are used to determine if there is a relationship between midterm grades and final grades.

| Midterm Grades $x$ | 92 | 84 | 80 | 71 | 32 | 90 | 89 | 76 |
|---|---|---|---|---|---|---|---|---|
| Final Grades: $y$ | 87 | 82 | 80 | 71 | 24 | 87 | 88 | 77 |

a. Calculate the correlation coefficient.
b. Interpret the correlation coefficient.
c. Calculate the line of best fit.
d. Interpret the slope.
e. If a student scores a 90 on the midterm, what score can be expected on the final?

4.23 The following data represent the number of hours per week that high school seniors spend watching TV and their grade point average.

| TV | $x$ | 5 | 8 | 9 | 3 | 15 | 10 | 10 |
|----|-----|-----|-----|-----|-----|-----|-----|-----|
| GPA | $y$ | 3.5 | 3.0 | 2.5 | 3.8 | 2.0 | 3.0 | 2.5 |

a. Calculate the correlation coefficient.
b. Calculate the regression line.
c. What is an expected GPA for a child who watches 6 hours of TV?
d. If parents want their child to maintain a GPA of 3.0, on average how much time should they limit TV watching?

4.24 The following data represent the marriage and divorce rates of selected countries for the year 2008 (per 1,000 population aged 15-64).

| Country | Marriage | Divorce |
|---------|----------|---------|
| U.S. | 10.6 | 5.2 |
| Canada | 6.4 | 3.4 |
| France | 10.3 | 3.2 |
| Japan | 9.4 | 3.1 |
| Germany | 6.6 | 3.5 |
| Italy | 6.3 | 1.3 |
| Sweden | 8.3 | 3.5 |
| U.K. | 8.5 | 4.0 |

a. Calculate the correlation coefficient.
b. Interpret the correlation coefficient.
c. Calculate the line of best fit.
d. If a marriage rate is 10, what is the expected divorce rate?
e. If a marriage rate is 5, what is the expected divorce rate?
f. If a divorce rate is 5, what is the expected marriage rate?

# 5 PROBABILITY SAMPLE SPACES

*SECTION 1*  **List Method**
*SECTION 2*  **Tree Diagrams**
*SECTION 3*  **Venn Diagrams**
*SECTION 4*  **Counting Rules**

Students of statistics seem to have unnecessary trouble understanding elaborate and sometimes complicated definitions. Definitions of probabilities top the list on the frustration index. Although the definitions cannot be dispensed with, it is hoped that some of the confusion can. Remember: probabilities are simply educated guesses. They are the best guesses about what might happen. The person determining the probability usually has some information, background, or experience with what has happened in the past. Guesses are not made blindly.

Because it is the nature of statistics to present variations of themes and formulas, it is always important to keep in perspective the fact that the principles are the same. In other words, as the nature of the data differs, so too will the formulas, but the principles of probability will remain the same—probabilities are still educated guesses. It is now time to plunge into the definitions of probabilities and their formulas. Do not be led astray about their purpose in making an educated guess.

Most textbooks treat *sample space* and probability concepts as one and the same. At the other extreme, some textbooks treat them as two separate and distinct concepts. They are neither the same nor totally distinct. The sample space must be known before probabilities can be calculated. There are many different ways to describe a sample space. This chapter outlines three methods for describing sample space.

---

## SECTION 1

### List Method

When confronted with a situation in which a person is trying to predict an outcome of an *event*, one of the first questions the person might ask is, "What can happen?" This question usually means, "What are all the possible outcomes?" It is then followed by the probability part of the question: "What is the chance that…will happen?" This latter part involves the probability, and it cannot usually be answered without the answer from the first question: What can happen?

Label the first part of the question as the sample space. When citing all the outcomes, the sample space is defined. A student in class may ask, "Will the instructor show up today?" The student must ask, "What are the possible outcomes?" There are only two possible outcomes related to this question—the instructor will show up, or the instructor will not show up. The student would have to know these two possibilities before asking a second question: "What is the chance the instructor will not show up?" This is now a probability question that will be answered based on information about past behavior, weather, or any other pertinent information. Calculating the probability is discussed in Chapter 6. This section focuses only on the sample space.

**Sample Space** The set of all possible outcomes of an experiment. The sample space is symbolized by *S*.

**The List Method Format:** *S* = {( ), ( ), ( ),....}
where ( ) represents each outcome. All outcomes or combinations form the sample space and are enclosed in brackets.

A sample space can be represented by a variety of techniques. This section focuses on the listing method illustrated in the definition. Tree diagrams and Venn diagrams are discussed later.

The list method simply lists the possible outcomes within parentheses and brackets. If one variable or attribute is considered, there is only one item in each parenthesis. If there are two variables or attributes, each combination of two things is put in a parentheses. If there are three variables or attributes then each parentheses must contain three items. Each possible combination is treated differently and is reported in separate parentheses.

---

**EXAMPLE 5.1**

**Experiment:** Observe the sex of the next baby born at General Hospital. List the sample space.

**Answer:** *S* = {(M), (F)}

**Solution:** The sex of the baby has two possible outcomes, male or female. There are no other possible combinations.

---

If there are two parts to an experiment, then the sample space represents all the possible combinations of outcomes. Each combination must be ordered in the same way each time they are listed. These ordered combinations are called ordered pairs.

The listing format of the sample space given in the definition illustrates the use of ordered pairs: $S = \{(\ ), (\ ), (\ ), \ldots\}$. Each pair of parentheses includes an ordered pair. The sample space is the set of ordered pairs representing all possible combinations.

---

**EXAMPLE 5.2**

**Experiment:** Observe the sex of the next two babies born at General Hospital. List the sample space.

**Answer:** $S = \{(M, M), (M, F), (F, M), (F, F)\}$

**Solution** The first baby may be a male and the second baby may also be a male. Thus, the first possible outcome can be noted as (M, M). If the first baby is a male and the second is a female, a second combination is possible (M, F). However, the reverse is also possible. The first baby may be a female and the second a male, giving a third possible combination (F, M). Finally, the first and the second babies may both be females. This final combination is (F, F). There are no other possible combinations; therefore the set of combinations is enclosed in brackets.

Remember, in this example it is not important where one starts or which combination of the pairs is written first. It is important that the ordering within the pairs remains the same. The first baby's sex is always the first letter and the second baby's sex is always the second letter within each pair of parentheses.

---

**EXAMPLE 5.3**

**Experiment:** In a random sample of voters, list the possible outcomes for party identification (Democrat, Independent, and Republican) and gender.

**Answer:** $S = \{$(Democrat, Male), (Democrat, Female), (Independent, Male), (Independent, Female), (Republican, Male), (Republican, Female)$\}$.

**Solution:** The sample space lists each possible combination of outcomes. There are two variables, party identification and gender. List each of the possible answers for party identification with each of the possible answers on gender. There are a total of six combinations.

---

**Event** An event is usually a subset of the sample.

An event is a specified combination of elements that form a subset of the sample space. The event is usually the narrative, such as "two males are born." The elements are the ordered pairs of the sample space that fulfill the criteria of the event, such as (M, M).

## EXAMPLE 5.4

**Experiment:** In Example 5.2 the experiment was to observe the sex of the next two babies born at General Hospital. List some of the possible events and elements in those events.

| Event<br>(The Narrative) | Set of Elements in Each Event<br>(The Ordered Pairs) |
|---|---|
| 1. Two males are born | {(M, M)} |
| 2. Only one male is born | {(M, F), (F, M)} |
| 3. Only one female is born | {(M, F), (F, M)} |
| 4. Two females are born | {(F, F)} |
| 5. Both are the same sex | {(M, M), (F, F)} |
| 6. Both are opposite sex | {(M, F), (F, M)} |

**Solution** The list contains only some of the events that can be identified. Begin by identifying various sets of outcomes known as events: Two males are born; two females are born; etc. The second step is to list the elements that make up each event.

## A LEARNING AID
## SAMPLE SPACE

You are driving your car, and you approach an intersection with a traffic signal. What could happen to the color of the traffic light when you approach the light? Put this event into the perspective of what you have learned about sample spaces. List the sample space.

**Step 1**

Ask yourself, "What can happen?" This question asks, "What are all the possible outcomes?"

**Step 2**

Ask yourself, "What are the possible outcomes?" Assuming that the traffic signal is functioning properly, the signal could be red, green, or yellow.

**Step 3**
List the sample space: The possible outcomes define the sample space. The listing method can be used: $S = \{(R), (Y), (G)\}$, where R means the light is red, etc.

**Step 4**
Ask yourself, "What is the chance the light will be green?" You now have a probability question.

**Note:** Sample space and probabilities are not the same, but they are not totally separate. The sample space must be known before a probability can be calculated.

# SECTION 2

## Tree Diagrams

A *tree diagram* is another method of illustrating a sample space. It can be used to represent the same sample space as the listing method. Although sometimes cumbersome to draw, a tree diagram can often provide a clearer picture of sample space. A tree diagram begins with the trunk. The trunk **branches** to the possible outcomes for the first phase of an experiment. The tree diagram then branches out for the outcomes of the second phase, the third phase, and so forth. Drawing tree diagrams can be helpful when calculating probabilities.

**Tree Diagram** Another way of illustrating sample space in which a branch represents each possible outcome.

**EXAMPLE 5.5**
**Experiment:** Observe the sex of the next baby born at General Hospital. Illustrate the sample space using a tree diagram.

**Answer:**

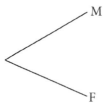

**Solution:** The diagram illustrates the two branches, which depict two possible outcomes.

**EXAMPLE 5.6**

**Experiment:** Observe the sex of the next two babies born at General Hospital. Illustrate the sample space using a tree diagram.

Answer:

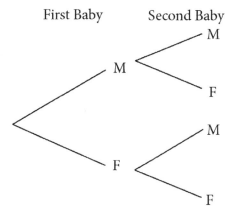

**Solution:** The trunk of the tree branches to the possible outcomes for the sex of the first baby. From each of these outcomes, extend the branches to show the possible outcomes of the second event. It might look as if there are four possibilities for the second baby; this is not the case. The branches for the second baby represent the combinations based on the sex of the first baby. Looking back at Example 5.2, the listed sample space had four possible outcomes: $S = \{(M, M), (M, F), (F, M), (F, F)\}$. The tree diagram illustrates the same four combinations. The diagram is interpreted as follows:

The first baby is a male or a female; if the first baby is a male then the second baby could be another male or it could be a female. If the first baby is a female (the lower half of the diagram), then the second baby could be a male or another female.

**Branch** Each combination or outcomes of a sample space illustrated in a tree diagram. Each branch can be numbered.

To assist in the discussion of a tree diagram, branches are often numbered. Then outcomes that qualify for an event can easily be identified.

**EXAMPLE 5.7**

**Experiment:** Observe the sex of the next three babies born at General Hospital. Illustrate the sample space with a tree diagram. Label each branch.

**Answer:**

| First Baby | Second Baby | Third Baby | Branch | Outcome |
|---|---|---|---|---|
| M | M | M | 1 | (M, M, M) |
| | | F | 2 | (M, M, F) |
| | F | M | 3 | (M, F, M) |
| | | F | 4 | (M, F, F) |
| F | M | M | 5 | (F, M, M) |
| | | F | 6 | (F, M, F) |
| | F | M | 7 | (F, F, M) |
| | | F | 8 | (F, F, F) |

**Solution:** When reading the solution, a finger may be used to follow along the branches. Branch 1, (M, M, M), is the event that all three babies born at General Hospital are males. Branch 2, (M, M, F), shows that the first baby is a male, the second is a male, and the third is a female. Branch 3, (M, F, M), shows that the first baby is a male, the second is a female, and the third is a male. Branch 4, (M, F) shows the first baby is a male, the second is a female, and the third is a female. Branch 5, (F, M, M) shows the first baby is a female, the second is a male, and the third is a male. Branch 6, (F, M, F) shows the first baby is a female, the second is a female, and the third is a female. Branch 7, (F, F, M) shows the first baby is a female, the second is a female, and the third is a male. Branch 8, (F, F, F), shows that all three babies are females.

In Example 5.7 a wide range of events may occur; they are identified in the following table. The branches and elements further describe the events.

| Event (The Narrative) | Branch (Number) | Elements (Specific Ordered Pairs) |
|---|---|---|
| No males | 8 | {(F, F, F)} |
| No females | 1 | {(M, M, M)} |
| Only one male | 4, 6, 7 | {(M, F, F) (F, M, F) (F, F, M)} |
| Only two males | 2, 3, 5 | {(M, M, F) (M, F, M) (F, M, M)} |
| Only one female | 2, 3, 5 | {(M, M, F) (M, F, M) (F, M, M)} |
| Only two females | 4, 6, 7 | {(M, F, F) (F, M, F) (F, F, M)} |
| Two or more females | 4, 6, 7, 8 | {(M, M, F) (F, M, F) (F, F, M) (F, F, F)} |
| Two or more males | 1, 2, 3, 5 | {(M, M, M) (M, M, F) (M, F, M) (F, M, M)} |
| Exactly 3 females | 8 | {(F, F, F)} |
| Exactly 3 males | 1 | {(M, M, M)} |

## A LEARNING AID
## TREE DIAGRAMS

You are driving to a friend's house. Along the way, you must proceed through two intersections. Both intersections have traffic signals. Using what you have learned about tree diagrams, illustrate the events of the changing traffic signals of both intersections.

### Step 1

First, draw a tree diagram illustrating the sample space for the color changes of the traffic signal at the first intersection. The sample space is Red, Green, and Yellow representing all the possible outcomes of the color of one traffic light.

### Step 2

Extend the tree diagram to include the sample space for all the possible outcomes of the traffic signal changes of both intersections. For example, if the first traffic light is red, the second light (which is independent of the first) may be red, yellow or green. There should be three lines coming out of the first red branch representing the three colors for the second light if the first was red. Three lines must also come out of the first yellow light since the second light may also be red, yellow, or green. The same for the first green light. Number the branches.

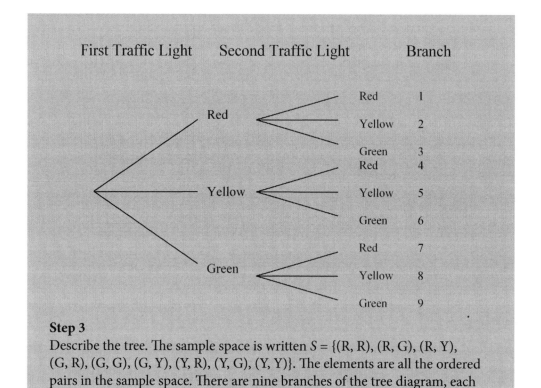

**Step 3**
Describe the tree. The sample space is written $S$ = {(R, R), (R, G), (R, Y), (G, R), (G, G), (G, Y), (Y, R), (Y, G), (Y, Y)}. The elements are all the ordered pairs in the sample space. There are nine branches of the tree diagram, each illustrating an ordered pair of the experiment.

---

# SECTION 3

## Venn Diagrams

*Venn diagrams* offer a third way of illustrating a sample space (in addition to the listing method and tree diagrams).

**Venn Diagram** A pictorial illustration of subsets of a sample space. A rectangle usually represents the sample space. Subsets are also known as events and are usually represented by capital letters.

The universal set is depicted in a Venn diagram as a large rectangle. All other sets are depicted as circles within the rectangle. The universal set is represented by the symbol $S$ (sample space). A subset (event) is a set of elements occurring within a universal set. It is depicted in a Venn diagram as a circle. The relationships of the subsets are illustrated by the relationships of the circles.

**Universal Set**  The set of all elements that occur in an overall frame of reference. All other sets occurring within its boundaries are subsets of the universal set.

The following definitions illustrate various relationships of subsets in the sample space. The symbols presented (such as $\cup$ or $\cap$) are used frequently in calculating probabilities. The manner in which the circles in a Venn diagram are presented in regard to the other circles is also important. The circles will be a guide to later calculations.

**Union of *A* or *B***  The set of all elements in *A* or *B*, which also includes those in both sets. The union of *A* or *B* is denoted by
$$A \cup B$$

The key word in the definition of **union** is the word "or". An element in a union of two sets must be in one set or the other or both. Set union is represented by the shaded areas in the Venn diagram of Figure 5.1.

Venn Diagram

$A \cup B$

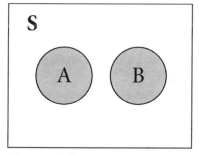

**Figure 5.1**

**Intersection of Sets *A* and *B***  The set of elements in both *A* and *B*. It is the area where the two sets overlap. The intersection of *A* and *B* is denoted by
$$A \cap B$$

The key word in this definition is the word "and". An element in an intersection must occur in both *A* and *B*; that is, it occurs in set *A* and it occurs in set *B*. Thus, it occurs twice; on a Venn diagram, it is in the area where the two sets overlap. It is the shaded area of the Venn diagram in Figure 5.2.

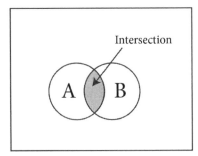

Venn Diagram

A ∩ B

**Figure 5.2**

**Subset** When every element of one set is also an element of a second set. "A is a subset of *B*" is denoted by

$$A \subseteq B$$

Figure 5.3 shows $A \subseteq B$. It is read, "*A* is a subset of *B*." Notice that all the elements in *A* are in *B*, but not all the elements in *B* are in *A*.

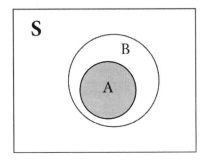

Venn Diagram

A ⊆ B

**Figure 5.3**

If all elements of *A* are in *B* and every element of *B* is in *A* then *A* = *B*. See Figure 5.4.

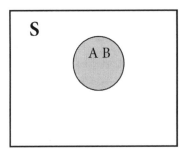

**Figure 5.4**

**Complement** The set of all elements in the universal set that are not in a given set. The complement of set *A* is denoted by *A′*.

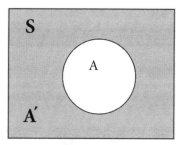

**Figure 5.5**

Be careful when defining ***complementary sets***. If there are two subsets in a universal set, then the complement of one set does not necessarily equal the other set. The complement of *A* is all elements that are not in *A*. See Figure 5.5. It follows that the union of a set and its complementary set is the universal set. Therefore, $A \cup A' = S$. This relationship is represented by the shaded area in the Venn diagram in Figure 5.6.

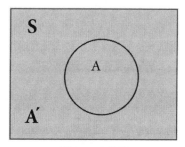

**Figure 5.6**

**Empty Set** A set with no elements. The empty set is represented by the Greek symbol $\Phi$.

**Mutually Exclusive Sets** When the intersection of two sets are empty, they are mutually exclusive.

If two sets are mutually exclusive, then their intersection is the ***empty set*** (there is no overlap of the two events). No element of set *A* can be an element of set *B*. Therefore, we can say that $A \cap B = \Phi$ Mutually exclusive sets *A* and *B* are shown in Figure 5.7.

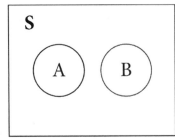

**Figure 5.7**

**Final note:** There may be many subsets in a universal set. The rules of unions and intersections hold for more than two sets. For example, $A \cup B \cup C$ is defined as those elements that are in $A$ or $B$ or $C$. $A \cup B \cup C$ is illustrated for mutually exclusive events by the shaded areas Figure 5.8.

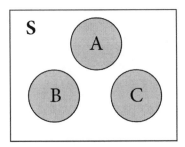

**Figure 5.8**

The intersection of $A \cap B \cap C$ for events is illustrated in the area noted as 6 of the Venn diagram of Figure 5.9.

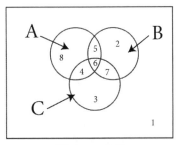

**Figure 5.9**

**EXAMPLE 5.8**

**Experiment:** Let $S$ be the students in a class. Let $A$ be the female students and let B be the students who are seniors. Define the following sets, describe them, and illustrate each with a Venn diagram.

      a. $A \cup B'$      b. $A \cup B$      c. $A \cap B$      d. $B'$

**Answer:**

a. $A \cup B'$ is the union of $A$ and the complement of $B$. Therefore, $A \cup B'$ is the set of all female students who are not seniors.

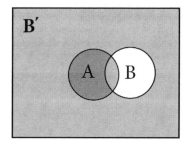

b. $A \cup B$ is the union of $A$ and $B$. It is the set of all female students and all seniors. In other words, it comprises all female students and all male seniors.

c. $A \cap B$ is the intersection of $A$ and $B$. It is the set of female students who are also seniors. It is the area where the two sets overlap.

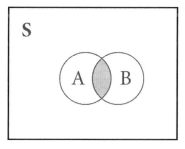

d. $B'$ is the complement set of $B$, or all elements that are not in $B$. That is, $B'$ is the set of all students who are not seniors.

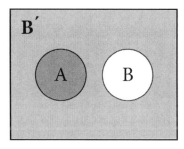

**A LEARNING AID**
**VENN DIAGRAMS**
The following Venn diagram illustrates three subsets within the universal set. The regions of subsets *A*, *B*, and *C* are numbered. Describe the following regions using (a) symbols and (b) words.

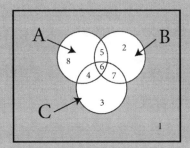

**Step 1**
Describe region 8 of subset *A*.
a. $A \cap B' \cap C'$
b. The set of all the elements in *A* that is not in *B* and not in *C*.

**Step 2**
Describe region 7.
a. $A' \cap B \cap C$
b. The set of all the elements in both *B* and *C*, but not in *A*.

**Step 3**
Describe region 6.
a. $A \cap B \cap C$.
b. The set of all the elements that are in *A*, *B*, and *C* simultaneously.

---

# SECTION 4

## Counting Rules

A tree diagram is an excellent tool for organizing and visualizing how many outcomes are possible in an experiment. However, sometimes we are interested in only how many outcomes or combinations are possible without a desire to create a complete tree diagram. The counting rule will easily help calculate the number of outcomes or combinations without diagramming the experiment. When two or more events occur, the counting rule requires that number of outcomes in each event is multiplied to the number of outcomes in each of the other events. That is, the first event can happen in *m* ways multiplied by the second event happening in *n* ways.

> **Counting Rule** For a sequence of two or more events, the total number of outcomes is found by multiplying $m$ and $n$. If three or more events exist, continue multiplying the number of ways they may happen to the others.
>
> $$m \cdot n$$
>
> where:
>  $m$ is the number of ways the first event may happen a.
>  $n$ is the number of ways the second event may happen.

The counting rule is also known as a **fundamental counting rule** or the **multiplication rule of counting**. An example of the counting rule applies to the baby examples discussed before. If the sex of the next 2 babies is observed, the number of combinations is $m$, the 2 different gender possibilities for the first baby multiplied by $n$, the 2 different gender possibilities of the second baby. That is, 4 combinations exist obtained by multiplying the 2 (male or female) to the 2 (male or female). If 5 babies are observed, the number of combinations is (2) (2) (2) (2) (2) = 32. Remember that this would be the same answer as the number of branches on a tree diagram; it is simply faster than attempting to draw 32 branches.

---

**Example 5.9**

A new cell phone was just put on the market. It comes in 3 different colors, 4 different entertainment packages, and 3 different data packages. The store owner wants to set up the store computer for each scenario to allow the employees to more quickly serve customers. How many different outcomes exist?

**Answer:** 36

**Solution:** The counting rule requires the multiplication of the number of ways each event may happen. Three colors multiplied by 4 entertainment packages, multiplied by 3 different data packages.

$$(3)(4)(3) = 36$$

---

Another counting method is to find the number of different ordered arrangements of an event. Ordering means all the different combinations are counted separately. Sequencing is important. This means that two items may look the same in that the same elements are in each, but if the order is different, they are counted separately. For example, in describing the sex of two babies, a male and a female (M, F), would be considered different that a female and a male (F, M). Therefore, when order is important, (M, F) and (F, M) are different and counted as two separate outcomes.

When counting for the number of ordered arrangements, the factorial rule applies. A factorial is the multiplication of a whole number by all whole numbers less than it to 1. In other words, the product of the number decreasing to one. (Many calculators have a factorial key typically identified by *!* or *x!*) For example, 5! is (5)(4)(3)(2)(1) or 120. 10! is (10)(9)(8)(7)(6)(5)(4)(3)(2)(1) equals 3,628,800.

**Factorial Rule**  The factorial rule represents the number of different ways *n* items can be arranged in order.

$$n!$$

where

$n!$ equals the factoring of the total number of available items, *n*.
**Note:** A factorial table is available in the Appendix, Table A.2b

Arranging items in order must take into account that the first item selected may occur *n* different ways. But the second item may occur only *n*-1 different ways since the first position is no longer available. The third item is then *n*-2 different ways because positions 1 and 2 are taken, and so forth.

**Example 5.10**
A road race of 6 cars is taking place. How many different combinations or arrangements are possible for the end result of the race?

**Answer:** 720

**Solution:** The factorial rule applies as the order of the cars finishing is important. The factorial rule is *n!*. *n* is 6, therefore, 720.

6! is essentially (6)(5)(4)(3)(2)(1) = 720, but should be solved by using a calculator. Begin by pressing the number six so that it appears on the calculator's blank screen. Once completed, press the MATH button, right arrow over to "PROB" and press the 4 button to select "4:!".

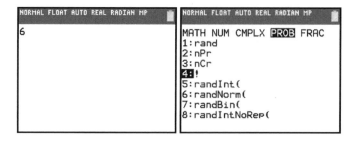

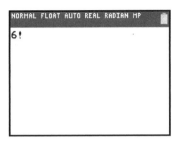

When "6!" has appeared on the screen, press the ENTER button, and the calculator will display its numerical value.

The factorial rule applies when all of the items are considered for the arrangement or sequencing. When not all of the items are to be included but order is still important, arrangements are known as permutations. Permutations represent the number of outcomes when order is important and the selection includes only some of the items from the total. For example, if 10 items exist, how many arrangements of 5 items can be made when order is important? The total number of items is represented by $n$, and the number for selection is represented by $r$.

**Permutations** Permutations are arrangements of items when order is important and selection is limited. The number of permutations (or arrangements) of a number of items, $r$, from $n$ available items is calculated:

$$_nP_r = \frac{n!}{(n-r)!}$$

where
   $n$ represents the total number of available items.
   $r$ is the number of items to select from $n$ and must be less than or equal to $n$.
   Appendix Table A.2b contains factorials to assist in the calculation.

**Example 5.11**

A road race of 6 cars is taking place. How many different combinations of first, second and third place finishes are there?

**Answer:** 120

**Solution:** The permutation pule applies since the order of the finishes is important and the selection of interest is the first, second, and third places.

It is necessary to first acknowledge that the road race of 6 cars is $n$ and to consider the possible arrangements for the top three spots, designates $r$ as 3.

With the TI-84 Plus, begin by pressing the MATH button and scrolling to "PROB". Press the 2 button to select "2:nPr". Once selected, plug in 6 for $n$ and 3 for $r$, the press ENTER, and the calculator will display its numerical value.

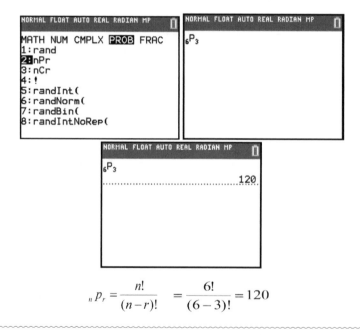

$$_{n}P_{r} = \frac{n!}{(n-r)!} = \frac{6!}{(6-3)!} = 120$$

Yet another counting rule applies when a selection of $r$ items is taken from $n$ available items, but the order is not important. This is known as the combination rule. The combination rule is similar to the permutation rule except that order is not taken into account. Remember the two babies? For permutations, the (B,G) and the (G,B) are counted separately because order is important. For the combination rule, they are the same and are counted as 1. Combinations do not count separately the different orderings of the same items.

***Combinations*** Combinations are arrangements of items when order is NOT important and selection is limited. The number of combinations of a number of items, *r*, from *n* available items is calculated:

$$_nC_r = \frac{n!}{r!(n-r)!}$$

where
  *n* represents the total number of available items.
  *r* is the number of items to select from *n* and must be less than or equal to *n*.
  Appendix Table A.2b contains factorials to assist in the calculation.

---

**Example 5.12**

A road race of 6 cars is taking place. How many different combinations of first, second, and third place finishes are there when the order of the places are not important?

**Answer:** 20

**Solution:** The combination rule applies since the order of the finishes is not important and the selection of interest is the first, second, and third places.

Begin by pressing the MATH button and scrolling right to highlight "PROB." Press the 3 button to select "3: nCr". Designate *n* as 6 and *r* as 3 and press ENTER. The calculator will display the numerical value.

```
NORMAL FLOAT AUTO REAL RADIAN MP
MATH NUM CMPLX PROB FRAC
1:rand
2:nPr
3:nCr
4:!
5:randInt(
6:randNorm(
7:randBin(
8:randIntNoRep(
```

```
NORMAL FLOAT AUTO REAL RADIAN MP
6C3
                              20
```

$$_nC_r = \frac{n!}{r!(n-r)!} = \frac{6!}{3!(6-3)!} = 20$$

# CHAPTER 5 IN REVIEW

5.1   A coin is flipped once. The coin may land on heads or tails. List the sample space.

5.2   A student is randomly selected. List the sample space for the student's sex.

5.3   A student is randomly selected. List the sample space for the student's class standing.

5.4   A student is randomly selected. List the sample space for the student's sex and class standing.

5.5   From a deck of cards, draw a Venn diagram for the events that a card may be randomly drawn and that it is a Jack or a red card.

5.6   Draw a Venn diagram for single digits 1 through 9 with the events a number is greater than 4 or an even number.

5.7   Draw a Venn diagram for single digits 1 through 9 with the events a number is greater than 5 or less than 6.

5.8   From a deck of cards, draw a Venn diagram for the events that a card may be randomly drawn and that it is a diamond or a red card.

5.9   Three coins are placed in a box: a quarter, a dime, and a nickel. One coin is drawn at random and then replaced. A second coin is drawn at random and then replaced.
      a. Draw a tree diagram illustrating the exercise.
      b. Describe any three events and their elements.
      c. List the sample space.

5.10  See Exercise 5.9 above. Repeat the exercise, but this time do not replace the coin drawn on the first draw.
      a. Draw a tree diagram illustrating the exercise.
      b. Describe any three events and their elements.
      c. List the sample space.

5.11  True or False?
      The complement of set $A$ is the set of all elements in the universal set not in $A$ and is denoted by $A'$.

5.12  Define and describe the shaded area of each Venn diagram:

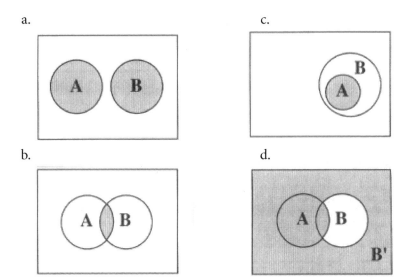

5.13   Identify each graph as mutually exclusive or non-mutually exclusive.

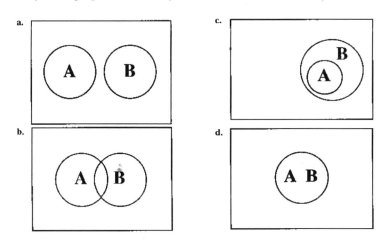

5.14   A box contains three marbles. One marble is red, one is black, and one is yellow. One marble is drawn from the box. Are the events red, black, and yellow mutually exclusive?

5.15   Three marbles are placed in a box. One is black, one is green, and one is yellow in color. One marble is drawn at random and then replaced. A second marble is drawn at random and then replaced. Does the sample space change?

5.16   Three marbles are placed in a box. One is black, one is green, and one is yellow in color. One marble is drawn at random and not replaced. A second marble is then drawn at random. Does the sample space change?

5.17 Draw a tree diagram describing the outcomes of flipping two coins (one flip then a second, with replacement).

5.18 A student is required to take college algebra before taking statistics. But not all students are required to take statistics. Draw a tree diagram depicting taking algebra and taking statistics.

5.19 Flip a coin. If it lands on the tail, flip it again. But if it lands on the head, roll a die. Draw a tree diagram representing the experiment.

5.20 Draw a tree diagram representing the outcomes of flipping one coin three times. List the sample space.

5.21 A young woman has been informed by her doctor that she is expecting identical triplets. List the sample space with regard to sex.

5.22 True or False?
a. If two events are mutually exclusive, they share an intersection.
b. If replacement between events occurs, the sample space changes.
c. The union of an event and its complement equals the sample space.
d. The sample space is the set of all possible outcomes.

5.23 In flipping a coin 5 times and observing the heads or tails, how many different outcomes are obtained?

5.24 Of the 10 students in the student organization, 3 are selected for the executive board. How many different combinations are possible? What if each student can be nominated for only one office?

5.25 How many different ways can 5 people fit in a car? How many different ways if Emily must be the driver?

5.26 Calculate the following:

a. $_5P_3$　　　　　　　　　　e. $_{12}P_3$

b. $_8P_5$　　　　　　　　　　f. $_5C_3$

c. $_6P_6$　　　　　　　　　　g. 8!

d. 2!3!　　　　　　　　　　h. 6!/2!

5.27 Students are grouped according to sex and class standing (freshmen, sophomore, junior, senior). How many categories are possible?

# 6

# *Calculating Probabilities*

**SECTION 1**   **Probability Theory**
**SECTION 2**   **Probability of the Union of Two Events**
**SECTION 3**   **Complementary Probabilities**
**SECTION 4**   **Conditional Probabilities**
**SECTION 5**   **Joint Probabilities**
**SECTION 6**   **Joint and Conditional Probabilities Using Tree Diagrams**
**SECTION 7**   **Combining the Addition and Multiplication Theorems**

In Chapter 5, sample space is shown to be a means of answering the question "What can happen?" And understanding sample space is necessary for calculating probabilities. Calculating probabilities gives an answer to the question "What is the chance that…might happen or has happened?"

Probabilities are educated guesses about what might happen or what has happened based on information that we have obtained or observed. It is our best guess about what can happen based on what has happened in the past or what should theoretically happen. For example, suppose a basketball player steps up to the free-throw line. We say he shoots 70% from the line. This means that, on the average, he makes the shot 7 out of 10 times. What is the probability he will make the next shot? The best guess is that he has a 70% chance, since that is what he has been doing in the past. A chance of 70% is a probability of .70.

**Probability** The relative frequency with which an event can be expected to occur. It is calculated as:

$$P(A) = \frac{n(A)}{n(S)}$$

where
   $P$ stands for probability.
   $n(A)$ stands for the number of outcomes in event A.
   $n(S)$ is the total number of outcomes in the sample space.

The following symbols are used frequently:

   $P$       the probability of

   $P(A)$    the probability of event $A$

   $n(A)$    the number of outcomes in event $A$

   $n(S)$    the number of outcomes in the sample space

| | |
|---|---|
| < | less than |
| > | greater than |
| ≤ | less than or equal to |
| ≥ | greater than or equal to |
| ≠ | not equal to |
| ∪ | the union of two or more events |
| ∩ | the intersection of two or more events |

# SECTION 1

## Probability Theory

Probability theory is divided into three different types: experimental, theoretical, and subjective. All probabilities are calculated using the same formula. There are two important properties associated with probabilities. Property 1 states that probabilities are values greater than or equal to 0 and less than or equal to 1. In other words, a probability is always between 0 and 1, inclusive, where 0 represents no chance of occurrence and 1 represents a certain occurrence. A probability of 0.5 represents a 50-50 chance that something will occur.

> Property 1: $0 \leq P(A) \leq 1$
> Property 2: $P(S) = 1$
> (The sum of the probabilities of all outcomes is 1.0.)

Property 2 states that the sum of the probabilities of all outcomes of the sample space S must equal 1.0. Thus, all outcomes must be known. Each probability must fulfill property 1. The sum of all probabilities must be 1.0.

> **Experimental Probabilities** Also known as empirical, or observational, probabilities. The observed proportion of times an event occurs in a series of similar experiments. Experimental probability is usually denoted by $P'$.

*Experimental probabilities* are determined by empirical observation; that is, an experiment is observed and each outcome is recorded. Then the probability is determined from these observations. For example, suppose a basketball player shoots a ball 5 times. Each shot is observed as is whether or not she scores. Suppose she makes 3 of 5 shots. The probability of her making a shot is then $P(A) = n(A) / n(S)$, or $3/5 = .6$. If one were to guess whether she would make her next shot, the best guess would be that she has a 60% chance (or a probability of .6) of making the next shot.

The probability of .6 is the best educated guess based on what is known or has been observed from her past record.

---

**EXAMPLE 6.1**

**Experiment:** The 2015 leading free throw shooter of the Detroit Pistons basketball team has made 143 of the 158 attempts up to this point in the season. What is the probability that he will make his next attempt?

**Answer:** $P'(A) = .905$; a 90.5% chance

**Solution:** The probability is 143/158 which is the number of times he made it divided by total attempts. This probability may change after additional observations. Each time he attempts a free throw, the probability will depend on all previous successes divided by the attempts.

$$P'(A) = \frac{n(A)}{n(S)} = \frac{143}{158} = .905$$

---

**Theoretical Probabilities** Probabilities in cases where all outcomes are equally likely to occur. Theoretical probability is denoted by $P$.

Theoretical probabilities differ from observational probabilities. With theoretical probability, all possible outcomes must be equally likely. An observed probability contradicting a theoretical probability does not necessarily mean that the theoretical probability is wrong. Consider a typical example. Assuming that a coin is symmetric and its weight is equally distributed, if tossed, there is an equal chance that it will land heads up or tails up. Therefore, since there are only two possible outcomes, following the rules of probability, each event (a head or a tail) has a probability of ½ , or .5, or a 50% chance. The theoretical probability of either event is .5. Consider again the examples of babies being born at General Hospital. Assume that there is an equal chance that the next baby born is a boy or girl. What is the probability that it is a boy? Since there are only two possibilities, both with an equal chance of occurring, probability is .5 that the baby will be a boy. What is the chance that, of the next two babies born, both are boys? Look at the sample space, or tree diagram, shown in Figure 6.1. There are four possible outcomes. One is the event two boys (see the shaded elements on the tree diagram). Therefore, the probability of two boys equals 1/4 (1 outcome of interest divided by the total of 4 possible outcomes). Probabilities are generally not left as fractions: 1/4 gives a probability of .25.

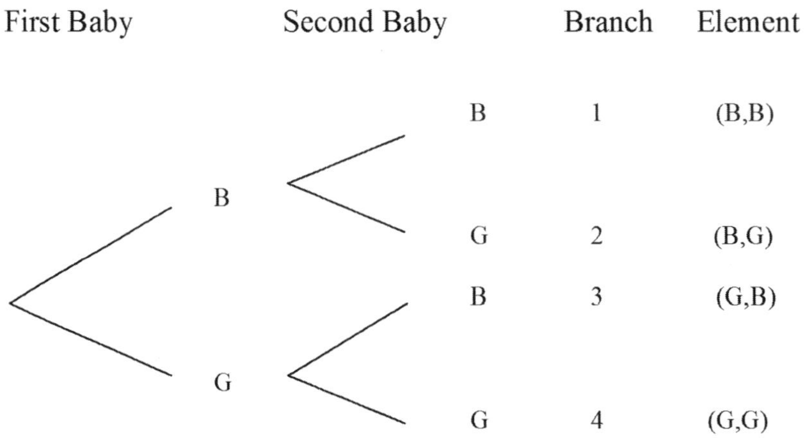
First Baby
Second Baby
Branch
Element
B
G
B
G
B
G
1
2
3
4
(B,B)
(B,G)
(G,B)
(G,G)

**Figure 6.1**

### EXAMPLE 6.2

**Experiment:** What is the probability that, of the next two babies born at General Hospital, at least one is a boy?

**Answer:** *P* (at least one boy) = .75

**Solution:** Of the four total outcomes, three make up the event. The sample space for all the outcomes is $S = \{(B, B), (B, G), (G, B), (G, G)\}$. The first three outcomes each have at least one boy (note that (B, B) also fulfills the event, even though it involves two boys). The probability is found by dividing the 3 outcomes that make up the event by the total number of outcomes, which is equal to 4; 3 divided by 4 equals the probability, .75. When performing calculations, show all steps.

$$P(A) = \frac{n(A)}{n(S)} = \frac{3}{4} = .75$$

### EXAMPLE 6.3

**Experiment:** In tossing a coin 10 times, what is the probability that on the first toss it will be heads? The second toss? The third toss?

**Answer:** *P* (heads) = .5 for the first, .5 for the second, and .5 for the third.

**Solution:** Use the formula *P*(heads) = *n*(heads) / *n*(total tosses); the first toss has two possible outcomes and the head is one of the two; therefore, *P*(heads) = ½, or .5. For the second toss, there is still only 1 chance from 2 possible outcomes; therefore, *P*(heads) = ½ or .5. The third toss is again the same: *P*(heads) = ½, or .5. Theoretically, the probability that the result will be heads on any given toss will remain .5. When performing calculations, show all steps.

$$P\ (A) = \frac{n(A)}{n(S)} = \frac{1}{2} = .5$$

Observational probabilities do not always match theoretical probabilities. As the number of observations increase, the observational probability will approach the theoretical probability. If a coin is tossed continuously, eventually it will be observed that there are 50% heads and 50% tails. The empirical probability for any one toss will stabilize at about .5 for each subsequent toss. Thus, the observational probability will be approximately the same as the theoretical probability, both at or near .5. This is explained by the *Law of Large Numbers*.

**Law of Large Numbers** As the number of times an experiment is done increases, the observed probability will approach the theoretical probability.

If the experiment of tossing a coin 10 times and observing the number of heads is repeated, it will eventually reach a point where the cumulative observational probability of heads will stabilize around the theoretical probability of 0.5. Although it may continue to vary slightly, the variation will continue to decrease as the experiment is repeated.

Although theoretically different, the law of large numbers is analogous to a more familiar idea that may help in understanding the concept. If one wants to find the average age of students in a school, start by asking one student. Is one student's age going to be very representative of the average age of all the students in the school? Probably not. How about asking two students? Three? Four? As more and more students are asked, the average age observed will get closer to the actual average age. Thus, the law of large numbers is similar to the sampling discussed earlier. The larger the number of observations, the closer one gets to the true probability.

**Subjective Probabilities** Educated guesses based on personal judgment.

*Subjective probabilities* are educated guesses based on personal judgment. They are neither observed nor theoretical. Subjective probabilities depend on correctly assessing a situation. Weather forecasting is a good example. A weather forecaster predicts what the temperature may be. He or she usually predicts the chance of rain or snow. A forecaster uses personal judgment in assessing weather patterns, radar, barometers, and other equipment. The meteorologist can then make an educated guess when stating, "There is a 30% chance of rain today."

## A LEARNING AID
## PROBABILITY THEORY

You live in a township that is about to hold an election for the township supervisor. June Smyth is the candidate running on the Republican ticket. Of the registered voters in your township eligible to vote in this election, 80% are Republicans. These same voters have, in the past, voted Republican in the U.S. presidential and congressional races as well as state elections. Based on this information alone, what is the probability that June Smyth will be elected as your next township supervisor?

### Step 1

**What is a probability?**

A probability is an educated guess about what can happen or what is expected to happen based on information that you have obtained or experienced.

### Step 2

**Is the question presented an experimental, theoretical, or subjective probability?**

At this point, it is a subjective probability, because your decision is based on personal judgment about the given information. However, it borders on the experimental by using as the foundation for personal conclusion a statistic verifiable by past performance, from which you are deriving judgment.

### Step 3

**What is the probability that June Smyth will win the election?**

June Smyth has an 80% chance of winning the election, or a probability of .8 of being elected.

### Step 4

**Is the probability of .8 a legitimate guess?**

Yes; .8 is a legitimate guess. A probability is always between 0 and 1, where 0 represents no chance of an occurrence and 1 represents a certain occurrence.

**Step 5**

Go one step further. What is the maximum collective vote June Smyth could get? The answer to this question is 100%, which is a probability of 1.0 of being elected. In Property 2 of probability theory, the sum of the probabilities of all outcomes of an event must equal 1. For example, if she has a probability of 0.8 of being elected, the probability she will not be elected is 0.2; 0.2 + 0.8 = 1.0.

## SECTION 2

### Probability of the Union of Two Events

The union of sets *A* and *B* was previously defined as the set of all elements that are in *A* or in *B*, which includes those elements in both. The union is represented by *A* ∪ *B*. To find the probability of the union of two sets, add the probability of event *A* to the probability of event B. If there are elements that are in both *A* and B, then the probability of the elements in both sets must be subtracted so they are counted only once. To make the calculations easier, first count each set fully, find how many elements have been counted twice, and then subtract the probability of the double-counted elements. This process is known as the ***Addition Theorem for Two Events***. The key to remembering that unions involve the Addition Theorem is the words "either" or "or".

**Addition Theorem for Two Events**

$$P(A \cup B) = P(A) + P(B) - P(A \cap B)$$

where
  *P* stands for probability.
  *A* stands for event *A*.
  ∪ denotes the union of two events.
  *B* denotes event *B*.
  ∩ stands for the intersection of two events.

**Example 6.4**

**Experiment:** What is the probability that, on a single roll of a die, the outcome will be either 4 or an even number?

**Answer:** $P(A \cup B) = .5$

159

**Solution:** This is a union because it asks for either one of two events or the other. These events are not mutually exclusive, because in this experiment 4 falls into both events. The following Venn diagram illustrates this situation:

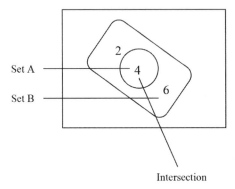

Intersection

The Venn diagram shows the two sets overlap. Set *A*, (4), is completely encased in set *B*, (2, 4, 6). Although the answer may be visually obvious, the formula must still be followed. In later experiments the answer will not be so obvious. The probability is calculated using the addition theorem for two events: *P(A ∪ B) = P(A) + P(B) - P(A ∩ B)*.

Before calculating, recall that *P(A)* is the probability that the roll of the die is a 4. *P(B)* is the probability that the roll of the die is an even number. *P(A)*, *P(B)*, and *P(A ∩ B)* are calculated using the formula *P(A) = n(A) / n(S)* =1/6; *P(B)* = 3/6; *P(A ∩ B)* = 1/6, representing the 4 that is in both sets. When performing calculations, show all steps.

$$P(A \cup B) = P(A) + P(B) - P(A \cap B)$$
$$P(4 \cup \text{even}) = P(4) + P(\text{even}) - P(4 \text{ and even})$$
$$= 1/6 + 3/6 - 1/6$$
$$= 3/6 = 1/2$$
$$= .5 (\text{don't leave fractions})$$

The addition formula holds true for any pair of events. But in special cases, the formula can be simplified. When sets or events are mutually exclusive, the addition theorem can be shortened as follows: $P(A \cup B) = P(A) + P(B)$. When events are mutually exclusive, they cannot happen together. This means that no elements are found in both sets; therefore, since the intersection is empty, the probability is zero.

**Special Addition Rule** Probability of the union of two mutually exclusive events.

$$P(A \cup B) = P(A) + P(B)$$

where
  *P* stands for probability.
  *A* stands for event *A*.
  U denotes the union of two events.
  *B* denotes event *B*.

## EXAMPLE 6.5

**Experiment:** What is the probability that on a single roll of a die the outcome will be a 3 or a 4?

**Answer:** $P(A \cup B) = .333$

**Solution:** This is a union question; the key word is "or". It asks for the probability of a 3 or a 4. The events are mutually exclusive, because on a single roll you can get a 3 or 4, but you cannot get them at the same time. Because they are mutually exclusive, use the special addition rule:

$$P(A \cup B) = P(A) + P(B)$$

Before calculating, identify the events. Assign $P(A)$ the probability of rolling a 3. Assign $P(B)$ the probability of rolling a 4. $P(A)$ and $P(B)$ are calculated by the original formula for calculating a probability: $P(A) = n(A) / n(S)$. There is one event in six possible outcomes that is a 3: $P(A) = 1/6$. $P(B)$ is found the same way; There is only one way to get a 4 from six possible outcomes, $P(B) = 1/6$.

The two probabilities are then added together. When performing calculations, show all steps.

$$P(A \cup B) = P(A) + P(B)$$
$$P(3 \cup 4) = P(3) + P(4)$$
$$= 1/6 + 1/6$$
$$= 2/6 = 1/3$$
$$= .333 \text{ (don't leave as a fraction)}$$

Note: If you are not sure which addition rule to use, remember that the original formula is always correct. Notice what happens if you used the original formula:

$$P(A \cup B) = P(A) + P(B) - P(A \cap B)$$
$$P(3 \cup 4) = P(3) + P(4) - 0$$
$$= 1/6 + 1/6 - 0$$
$$= 2/6 = 1/3$$
$$= .333$$

## CONTINGENCY TABLES AND UNIONS

**Contingency Probability Table**  A table representing probabilities of two variables and their events. The outcomes of a variable are overlapped with the outcomes of another variable. The intersections are referred to as cells.

A contingency probability table is another way of representing probabilities of two events. They are a convenient way to determine simple probabilities, unions, and intersections. In most computerized statistical programs, contingency tables are known as crosstabulations, or crosstabs. The outcomes of a variable are overlapped with the outcomes of another variable. For example, Table 6.1 represents 100 people who were asked their party identification and if they were registered.

### Table 6.1
### Contingency Table for Party Identifications and Voter Registration

| Registered ↓ Party I.D.→ | Republican | Independent | Democrat | Total |
|---|---|---|---|---|
| Yes | 22 | 28 | 26 | 76 |
| No | 2 | 16 | 6 | 24 |
| Total | 24 | 44 | 32 | 100 |

### EXAMPLE 6.6
**Experiment:** Use Table 6.1:
a. What is the probability that a person is registered to vote?
b. What is the probability that a person is a Republican?
c. What is the probability that a person is a Democrat?
d. What is the probability that a person is a Democrat or a Republican?
e. What is the probability that a person is not registered to vote?
f. What is the probability that a person is a registered voter or a Republican?
g. What is the probability that a person is not a registered voter or a Republican?

**Answer:**

a. $P$ (Reg.) = .76

b. $P$ (Rep.) = .24

c. $P$ (Dem.) = .32

d. $P$ (Dem. $\cup$ Rep.) = .56

e. $P$ (Not Reg.) = .24

f. $P$ (Reg. $\cup$ Rep.) = .78

g. $P$ (Not Reg. $\cup$ Rep.) = .46

**Solution:**

a. This is not a union, because the probability of only one event is desired. The probability of one event is calculated by dividing the number of elements in *(A)* by the number in the sample space: *P(A) = n(A) / n(S)*. Of the people surveyed, 76 reported they were registered. The probability that a person is registered to vote is 76 divided by the total in the sample space, 100.

$$P\ (A) = \frac{n(A)}{n(S)}$$

$$P\left(\text{reg. to vote}\right) = \frac{n\left(\text{reg.}\right)}{n\left(\text{sample space}\right)} = \frac{76}{100} = .76$$

b. This is not a union, because, as in part a, only one event occurs. It is calculated as in a. Of the 100 people surveyed, 24 reported they were Republican. The probability that a person is Republican is 24 divided by the total in the sample space.

$$P\ (A) = \frac{n(A)}{n(S)}$$

$$P\left(\text{Republican}\right) = \frac{n\left(\text{Rep.}\right)}{n\left(\text{sample space}\right)} = P\left(\text{Rep.}\right) = \frac{24}{100} = .24$$

c. This is also a single event question, as in parts a and b, only one event is involved. The probability is calculated as before. Of the 100 people surveyed, 32 said they were Democrats. The probability that a person is a Democrat is 32 divided by the total in the sample space.

$$P(A)\ = \frac{n(A)}{n(S)}$$

$$P\left(\text{Dem.}\right) = \frac{n\left(\text{Dem.}\right)}{n\left(\text{sample space}\right)} = \frac{32}{100} = .32$$

d.  The probability of two events makes this a union. Notice the key word, "or". The probability of the union of two events is the addition of the probabilities of the events minus the probability of those events that occur in both:

$$P(A \cup B) = P(A) + P(B) - P(A \cap B).$$

The probability that person is a Democrat is $P$ (Democrat) = $n$(Democrat)/$n$(sample space) = 32/100 = .32. The probability that a person is a Republican is $P$(Republican) = $n$ (Republican)/$n$ (sample space) = 24/100 = .24. There are no people who are both Democrats and Republicans, so the probability of their intersection is 0.

$$P(A \cup B) = P(A) + P(B) - P(A \cap B)$$
$$P(\text{Dem. or Rep.}) = P(\text{Dem.}) + P(\text{Rep.}) - P(\text{both Dem. and Rep.})$$
$$= .32 + .24 - 0 = .56$$

Notice the events are mutually exclusive. Mutually exclusive events share no elements. A person cannot be a Democrat and a Republican. The union of mutually exclusive events can be calculated with the special addition theorem:

$$P(A \cup B) = P(A) + P(B)$$
$$P(\text{Dem. or Rep.}) = P(\text{Dem.}) + P(\text{Rep.})$$
$$= .32 + .24 = .56$$

e.  As in parts a, b, and c, only one event is desired, so this is not a union. Of the 100 people surveyed 24 reported they were not registered to vote. The probability that a person is not registered to vote is calculated by dividing 24 by the total in the sample space, 100.

$$P (A) = \frac{n(A)}{n(S)}$$

$$P(\text{not reg. to vote}) = \frac{N(\text{not reg. to vote})}{N(\text{sample space})} = \frac{24}{100} = .24$$

f.  The probability of two events is required, so this involves a union. The events are not mutually exclusive, because there are elements in both events. It is similar to part d. But, in this case there are elements common to both events. The probability of the union of two events is the addition of the probabilities of the events minus that of any overlap that occurs:
$$P(A \cup B) = P(A) + P(B) - P(A \cap B).$$

The probability that a person is registered to vote is $P$(registered voter) = $n$ (registered voter) / $n$ (sample space) = 76/100 = .76. The probability that a person is a Republican is $P$ (Republican) = $n$ (Republican) / $n$ (sample space) = 24 / 100 = .24. The overlap occurs because 22 of the 100 people surveyed are registered to vote and are Republicans: 22/100 = .22. When performing the calculation, show all steps.

$$P(A \cup B) = P(A) + P(B) - P(A \cap B)$$
$$P(\text{reg. voter or Rep.}) = P(\text{reg. voter}) + P(\text{Rep.}) - P(\text{reg. voter and Rep.})$$
$$= .76 + .24 - .22 = .78$$

g.  As in part f, this is a union of two events that overlap. The events are not mutually exclusive, because there are some people who are not registered to vote and are Republican. Use the formula to calculate the probability of the union of two events, $P(A \cup B) = P(A) + P(B) - P(A \cap B)$.

The probability that a person is not registered to vote is $P$(not registered) = $n$ (not registered) / $n$ (sample space) = 24/100 = .24. The probability that a person is a Republican is $P$ (Republican) = $n$ (Republican) / $n$ (sample space) = 24/100 = .24.

However, 2 of the 100 surveyed report they are Republican and not registered to vote: $P$(Republican and not registered) = 2/100 = .02. When performing calculations, remember to show all steps.

$$P(A \cup B) = P(A) + P(B) - P(A \cap B)$$
$$P(\text{not reg. or Rep.}) = P(\text{not reg.}) + P(\text{Rep.}) - P(\text{nor reg. and Rep.})$$
$$= .24 + .24 - .02 = .46$$

**A LEARNING AID**
**CONTINGENCY TABLE**
A survey was taken in a state representative district in 2000. The district was predominantly Republican and was an area of high socioeconomic status. The purpose of the survey was to determine party identification and voters' opinion within this given district on the death penalty for murder. The following contingency table shows the results of this survey.

| Party I.D. ↓ Support → | **Death Penalty for Murder** | | | |
| --- | --- | --- | --- | --- |
| | Yes | Sometimes | No | Total |
| Republican | 59 | 14 | 10 | **83** |
| Independent | 28 | 4 | 10 | **42** |
| Democrat | 8 | 5 | 5 | **18** |
| **Total** | **95** | **23** | **25** | **143** |

## Step 1
### What is a Contingency Table?
A contingency table is a way of representing probabilities of two variables and their events. The cumulative reported survey data are sorted into cells, making it easier to see and calculate simple probabilities, unions, and intersections.

## Step 2
### What is a simple probability and how do we calculate it?
A simple probability is a number based on data gathered on a single event, which is calculated as $P(A) = n(A) / n(S)$. For example, what is the probability that a respondent to this survey was an independent?

$P$(Independent) equals $n$ (Independents) divided by $n$ (survey respondents), or the number in the sample-space. Calculated, this equals 42 reported respondents divided by 143 surveyed, which gives a probability of .29.

## Step 3
### What is the probability of the union of two events?
The probability of the union of two events is the probability that event $A$ or event $B$ will occur. For example, to find the probability that a survey respondent is a Democrat or a proponent of the death penalty, first use the formula for calculating a simple probability. Determine the probability of event $A$ and then of event $B$. Then decide if the events are mutually exclusive or if there is an intersection. These events do have elements in common, so they do intersect. Use the addition theorem to calculate this conditional probability. $P(A \cup B) = P(A) + P(B) - P(A \cap B) = P$(Democrat or proponent of the death penalty) = $P$(Democrat) + $P$(proponent) - $P$(Democrat and proponent) = $18/143 + 95/143 - 8/143 = .13 + .66 - .06 = .73$

# SECTION 3

## Complementary Probabilities

A complementary event is an event that isn't something else. That is, the complement of event *(A)* is everything that is not *(A)*. It is denoted by an event and the prime symbol, such as $P(A')$. While the complement of *(A)* may sometimes be obvious to the eye, it is safer to rely on a formula for the times when it isn't so obvious. For example, if the probability of a boy being born is .5, then the probability of a boy not being born is also .5. But what if the *P(A)* is .4, the *P(B)* is .4 and *P(C)* is .2. The probability of not being A, $P(A')$ is .6. But is it .6 simply because *(B)* and *(C)* add to .6? Not really, this may simply be a coincidence. If it is slightly changed, the approach may be faulty. If *P(A)* is .4, *P(B)* is .4 and *P(C)* is also .4, what is the probability of *(A')*? This time it can not be found by adding *(B)* and *(C)* because *(B)* and *(C)* add to .8. In Chapter 5 it was said that the union of an event and its complement must equal 1.0. Therefore, if *P(A)* is .4, its complement $P(A')$ can not be .8 because that would add to 1.2. Probabilities may not be more than 1.0. Therefore, the $P(A')$ is still .6. It is .6 because if the union $P(A \cup A') = 1$, then $P(A') = 1 - P(A)$. $1 - .4 = .6$.

The key word for a complement event is "not." Be sure that the word is asking for a complement and not simply a negative response. If the variable or question is a yes or no question, then the probability of "no" is simply the event "no." However, if a variable is asking for marital status such as single, married, or divorced, then not being married is a complement asking for everyone not in the category married (single or divorced).

**Complement** The set of all elements in the universal set that are not in a given set. The complement of set *A* is denoted by *A'*. Since the union of an event and its complement must equal the universal set, 1.0, the complement may be found by:

$$P(A') = 1 - P(A)$$

**EXAMPLE 6.7**
**Experiment:** Use Table 6.1 again:

### Table 6.1
### Contingency Table for Party Identifications and Voter Registration

| Registered ↓ Party I.D.→ | Republican | Independent | Democrat | Total |
|---|---|---|---|---|
| Yes | 22 | 28 | 26 | 76 |
| No | 2 | 16 | 6 | 24 |
| Total | 24 | 44 | 32 | 100 |

a. What is the probability that a person is not registered to vote?

b. What is the probability that a person is not an independent?

c. What is the probability that a person is a not Democrat?

**Answer:**

a. $P(\text{Reg}') = .24$

b. $P(\text{Ind}') = .56$

c. $P(\text{Dem}') = .68$

**Solution:**

a. This is not a complement, because the probability of not being registered is an actual category "not registered." It is a single event 24/100 or .24.

b. The probability of not being an independent is 1 – the probability of being an independent. $1 - P(\text{Ind}) = 1 - 44/100 = .56$.

c. The probability of not being a Democrat is $1 - P(\text{Dem})$. $1 - 32/100 = .68$.

# SECTION 4

## Conditional Probabilities

The study of **conditional probabilities** begins the transition into the intersection of two events. A conditional probability answers the question, if a given event is already known to have happened, what is the probability that another event will happen at the same time? For example, if identical twins are born and the first baby is a girl, what is the probability that the second baby will be a girl? Because they are identical and one is a girl, the second baby must also be a girl. The probability of the second baby being a girl is 1.0.

Key words in conditional probabilities are "if", "since", "given", "of those," "knowing", and "assuming". Any question where the probability of the second event is dependent on the conditions of the first event involves a conditional probability.

**Conditional Probability** Where event *B* has already occurred, the probability that event *A* will also occur. Conditional probability is denoted by *P* (*A*|*B*):

$$P(A \mid B) = \frac{P(A \cap B)}{P(B)}$$

The Conditional Probability if A is the known event is:

$$P(B \mid A) = \frac{P(A \cap B)}{P(A)}$$

In the formula, the probability of the intersection of the events is divided by the probability of event B. The events can be interchanged so the condition is placed on event B. Thus, $P(B|A) = P(A \cap B) / P(A)$. The probability of the event known to have happened is always the denominator. The formula is easily remembered by thinking of the conditional bar as a division or fraction sign; whatever is to the right of it is the event whose probability is in the denominator.

Remember, if events are mutually exclusive, there is no intersection. If there is no intersection, the events cannot occur at the same time. Since they cannot occur at the same time, there cannot be a conditional probability.

**EXAMPLE 6.8**

**Experiment:** If $P(A) = .6$, $P(B) = .4$, and $P(A \cap B) = .325$, what is $P(A|B)$?

**Answer:** $P(A|B) = .8125$

**Solution:** This is a conditional probability because the question asks for a conditional probability (represented by the upright bar). $P(A|B)$ can be read as, "Given that B has occurred, what is the probability that A will occur?" The events A and B are not mutually exclusive, because they intersect with a probability of .325. The conditional probability is determined by dividing the probability of the intersection of A and B by the probability of event B: .325 / .4 = .8125.

$$P(A|B) = \frac{P(A \cap B)}{P(B)} = \frac{.325}{.4} = .8125$$

**EXAMPLE 6.9**

**Experiment:** If $P(A) = .6$, $P(B) = .4$, and $P(A \cap B) = .325$, what is $P(B|A)$?

**Answer:** $= P(B|A) = .542$

**Solution:** This is a conditional probability, because the question asks for $P(B|A)$. The events are not mutually exclusive, because they intersect. The probability is determined by dividing the probability of the intersection of A and B by the probability of event B: .325/.6 = .542. Notice that the denominator in this problem is $P(A)$, the probability of the event to the right of the conditional bar.

$$P(B|A) = \frac{P(A \cap B)}{P(A)} = \frac{.326}{.6} = .542$$

Conditional probabilities are easy to calculate using a contingency table. Recall intersections are shown in the cells, where two events overlap. The totals on the outside represent totals for each event. Table 6.3 is a contingency probability table. Note that probabilities, not totals, are given in a contingency probability table.

### TABLE 6.3
### Contingency Probability Table for Party Identification and Voter Registration

|  | Rep. | Ind. | Dem. | Total |
|---|---|---|---|---|
| Registered ↓ Party → | | | | |
| Yes | 22/100 = .22 | 28/100 =.28 | 26/100 = .26 | **76/100 = .76** |
| No | 2/100 = .02 | 16/100 =.16 | 6/100 = .06 | **24/100 = .24** |
| Total | **24/100 = .24** | **44/100 =.44** | **32/100 = .32** | **100/100=1.0** |

Conditional probabilities are determined by finding the appropriate cell representing an intersection and dividing by the probability of the event that is already known to have occurred. For example, if it is known that a person is a Democrat, the probability that the person is registered is .26/.32 (the circled values in the table), or .8125. The probability of the intersection of the two events is .26, as shown in the cell where Democrats overlap with all those registered. Since it is known that the person is a Democrat, the probability of the intersection (.26) must be divided by the probability of being a Democrat (.32). Notice that the probability of a Democrat becomes the sample space.

### EXAMPLE 6.10
**Experiment:** Given a person is not registered, what is the probability that the person is an Independent? Use Table 6.3.

**Answer:** $P$ (Ind. | not registered) = .667

**Solution:** This is a conditional probability, because information is given that a person is not registered, thus limiting the sample space to only non-registered people. The events are not mutually exclusive, because there are people who are not registered and who are Independents. When performing calculations, show all steps.

$$P(A \mid B) = \frac{P(A \cap B)}{P(B)}$$

$$P(\text{Ind.} \mid \text{not reg.}) = \frac{P(\text{Ind.} \cap \text{not reg.})}{P(\text{not reg.})} = \frac{.16}{.24} = .667$$

**EXAMPLE 6.11**

**Experiment:** Of those registered to vote, what is the probability of a Republican? Use Table 6.3.

**Answer:** $P$ (Rep. | reg.) = .289

**Solution:** This is a conditional probability, because a person must first register before being considered a Republican. The sample space is limited to only registered people. The events are not mutually exclusive, because there are people who are registered and are Republicans. Divide the probability of the intersection of those who are registered and those who are Republicans by the probability of being registered. When performing calculations, show all steps.

$$P(A/B) = \frac{P(A \cap B)}{P(B)}$$

$$P(\text{Rep.} \mid \text{reg.}) = \frac{P(\text{Rep.} \cap \text{reg.})}{P(\text{reg.})} = \frac{.22}{.76} = .289$$

**A LEARNING AID**
**CONDITIONAL PROBABILITIES**

From Section 2, recall that the following survey results were obtained from a survey taken in 1990 in a state representative district. The purpose of the survey was to determine the constituents' party identification and their positions on the death penalty for murder. The contingency table shows the results of the survey.

### Death Penalty for Murder

| Party I.D. ↓   Support → | Yes | Sometimes | No | Total |
|---|---|---|---|---|
| Republican | 59 | 14 | 10 | 83 |
| Independent | 28 | 4 | 10 | 42 |
| Democrat | 8 | 5 | 5 | 18 |
| **Total** | **95** | **23** | **25** | **143** |

## Step 1
**What is conditional probability?**
Conditional probability refers to the conditions that exist with the intersection of two events. Examining event *A* and event *B*, you can determine the probability of event *B* occurring if you know that event *A* has already occurred. If the occurrence of event *B* is dependent on the condition of event *A*, then it is a conditional probability question.

## Step 2
**Can the probability of mutually exclusive events be conditional?**
No. Mutually exclusive events have no intersection. If there is no intersection, there is no evaluation of dependence between events. If there is no dependence on occurrence between events (no overlap), then there is no condition on their occurrence.

## Step 3
**Using the given table, what is the probability that a constituent respondent said yes to the death penalty for murder given the fact the constituent is a Republican?**
You know the constituent is a Republican. You want to find out, given this fact, the probability that the constituent also said yes in the survey. The formula for calculating this conditional probability is $P(B|A) = P(A \cap B) / P(A)$.

In calculating the conditional probability with this formula, the denominator will be the probability that a person is Republican, because the probability of the event that is known to have occurred is always the denominator. With this known, the calculation is as follows:

$$P(B \mid A) = \frac{P(A \cap B)}{P(A)}$$

$$P(\text{yes} \mid \text{Rep.}) = \frac{P(\text{yes and Rep.})}{P(\text{Rep.})}$$

$$= \frac{59/143}{83/143} = \frac{59}{83} = .711$$

**Note:** This answer means that given a constituent is a Republican, in this state representative district, the probability of a constituent also being in favor of the death penalty for murder is .711, which is 71.1%.

Had the condition shifted from Republican to registered, the formula would be accommodated by adjusting the denominator to registered voters and proceeding with calculations.

## SECTION 5

### Joint Probabilities

In the last section, the conditional probability formula required the probability of the intersection of the events. There are times, however, that the probability of the intersection is not given. The probability of the intersection can be found from other information. The probability of the intersection of two events is known as the joint probability. *Joint probability* is the probability that two events happen together. The key word for intersection, "and," is also the key word for joint probabilities. Other key words are "both," "together," "simultaneously," or "at the same time." Another key to remember is that because an intersection does not exist when events are mutually exclusive, mutually exclusive events have a joint probability of 0.

> **Joint Probability** The probability that two events happen at the same time. The joint probability of *A* and *B* is represented by *P (A ∩ B)*.

Before calculating joint probabilities, some information must be known about the relationship between the events. It must be determined whether the events are dependent or independent. Events are dependent when the occurrence of one event affects the occurrence of the second. If they are independent, they do not affect each other. For example, if someone goes into a store to buy milk, then the purchase depends on whether he or she has any money. If a woman is in labor delivering her second child, the sex of the baby is not dependent on the sex of her first child (unless they are identical twins). Another way to define the difference is to note that the events are dependent if one event precludes another from happening. One cannot buy milk without money. Buying milk depends on having money.

There is a mathematical test to take the guesswork out of deciding if two events are dependent or independent. It combines the idea of a simple probability and the conditional probability. Recall that a conditional probability involves the probability of an event given that something has already happened. If the something that has happened affects the event for which probability is being calculated, then the events are dependent. Thus, one can compare a probability of an event with its conditional probability given the other event. If the two values are equal, then the condition imposed by the conditional probability did not affect the event and they are independent. If the probabilities are not equal, then the events are dependent.

**If:**
$$P(A) = P(A \mid B) \quad \text{or} \quad P(B) = P(B \mid A) \quad \text{The Events are Independent.}$$
$$P(A) \neq P(A \mid B) \quad \text{or} \quad P(B) \neq P(B \mid A) \quad \text{The Events are Dependent.}$$

It is possible that a particular problem will not provide enough information to prove dependency mathematically. However, the researcher needs to make the decision before calculating the probability of the intersection. Once it is clear whether the events are independent or dependent, the probability of the intersection can be determined.

Before proceeding with the actual calculation of the probability of joint events, it is important to summarize the decisions that must be made:

1. Determine if the events are mutually exclusive. If they are not mutually exclusive, go to step 2. If they are, no joint probability can be calculated; the result will be 0.

2. Determine if the events are dependent or independent. If the events are dependent, then use the multiplication theorem for two dependent events. If the events are independent, then use the multiplication theorem for two independent events.

**Multiplication Theorem for Two Dependent Events**
$$P(A \cap B) = P(A) \cdot P(B/A)$$

The *multiplication theorem for two dependent events* requires the multiplication of the probability of event $A$ by the conditional probability of event $B$ given $A$. The conditional probability is used because it adjusts for the effect of $A$ on $B$.

**EXAMPLE 6.12**

**Experiment:** Seventy percent of the applicants to a law school are accepted into the program. Of those accepted, 40% complete the program. What is the probability that a randomly selected applicant will be both accepted into the program and complete the program?

**Answer:** $P(A \cap B) = .28$

**Solution:** This is a joint probability; notice the key words "both" and "and." It asks to find the overlap (intersection) of applicants accepted and completing the program. The events are not mutually exclusive, because some of the applicants are accepted and complete the program. The events are dependent. An applicant must first be admitted before completing the program. Another clue that they are dependent is that the problem gives the conditional probability by using the words of those accepted. Therefore, the multiplication theorem for two dependent events is used. (Note that the $P(B|A)$ is already given in the problem). When performing calculations, show all steps.

$$P(A \cap B) = P(A) \cdot P(B \mid A)$$
$$P(\text{accepted and complete}) = P(\text{accepted}) \cdot P(\text{complete} \mid \text{accepted})$$
$$= (.7)(.4) = .28$$

When two events are dependent, the conditional probability adjusts for the effect of the first event on the second. When events are independent, the first event has no effect on the second event. Conditional probability is not used. Recall that the mathematical test for dependency showed that if two events are independent, then the conditional probability equals the probability of the event: $P(B|A) = P(B)$. Because this is the case, when events are independent, the simple probability of the event can be substituted for conditional probability in the original formula for joint events.

**EXAMPLE 6.13**

**Experiment:** A graduate research assistant was writing her thesis and wanted to determine the probability that a person in the United States receives some form of entitlement program benefits and lives in a consolidated metropolitan statistical area (CMSA). She found that 40% of the population receives some form of entitlement benefits, and 75% live in a CMSA. What is the probability that a person receives benefits and lives in a CMSA?

**Answer:** $P(A \cap B) = .3$

**Solution:** This is a joint probability; notice the key word "and." The question asks to find the overlap (intersection) of those who received benefits and those living in a CMSA. The events are not mutually exclusive, because some people in the United States receive entitlement benefits and live in a CMSA. The events are independent; being an entitlement beneficiary does not affect whether a person lives in a CMSA.

Independence can also be determined by comparing the mathematical probabilities of *(A)* and *(A |B)*.

Because the events are independent, the multiplication rule for two independent events is used.

$$P(A \cap B) = P(A) \cdot P(B)$$
$$P(\text{benefits and CMSA}) = P(\text{benefits}) \cdot P(\text{CMSA})$$
$$= (40/100) \cdot (75/100) = (.4)(.75) = .3$$

**Note:** If it is difficult to determine if the events are independent or dependent and the mathematical test is not applicable, the multiplication rule for two dependent events can always be used. When in doubt, treat the events as dependent.

## A LEARNING AID
## JOINT PROBABILITIES

Using the same contingency table that was used for the Learning Aids in Sections 2 and 3, look at the differences between conditional probabilities and joint probabilities.

### Death Penalty for Murder

| Party I.D. ↓   Support → | Yes | Sometimes | No | Total |
|---|---|---|---|---|
| Republican | 59 | 14 | 10 | 83 |
| Independent | 28 | 4 | 10 | 42 |
| Democrat | 8 | 5 | 5 | 18 |
| Total | 95 | 23 | 25 | 143 |

**Step 1**
**What is the difference between conditional probability and joint probability?**
A conditional probability is the probability that given the occurrence of event *A*, event *B* will occur. The probability of the intersection is known. This is not the case with joint probability. The probability of the intersection is not known. To calculate joint probability is to calculate the probability that two events happen together, or simultaneously.

**Step 2**
**How does the calculation differ for conditional probability and joint probability?**

In Section 3, you learned to calculate conditional probability with the formula $P(B|A) = P(A \cap B) / P(A)$. This formula is used because event *A* is known and you want to find the probability of event *B*. You also learned that you could shift the condition from event *A* to event *B* and proceed with calculation. However, to calculate joint probability you must first test for independence or dependence. Based on these findings, you calculate using either the multiplication theorem for two dependent events, $P(A \cap B) = P(A) \cdot P(B|A)$, or the multiplication theorem for two independent events, $P(A \cap B) = P(A) \cdot P(B)$.

$$P(B \,|\, A) = \frac{P(A \cap B)}{P(A)}$$

$$P(\text{yes}\,|\,\text{Rep.}) = \frac{P(\text{yes and Rep.})}{P(\text{Rep.})}$$

$$= \frac{59/143}{83/143} = \frac{59}{83} = .711$$

**Step 3**
**What is the joint probability that a constituent will be both a Republican and be a proponent of the death penalty for murder?**

This question asks, "What is $P(\text{Rep} \cap \text{Yes})$?" To calculate this joint probability, the formula for dependent events can always be applied. If the events are in fact independent, the dependent calculation would still result in the same answer.

$$P(A \cap B) = P(A) \cdot P(B \mid A)$$
$$P(\text{Rep. and yes}) = P(\text{Rep.}) \cdot P(\text{yes} \mid \text{Rep.})$$

$$= P(\text{Rep.}) \cdot \left[ \frac{P(\text{Rep. and yes})}{P(\text{Rep.})} \right] = 83/143 \cdot \frac{59/143}{83/143} = .58 \cdot \left( \frac{.413}{.58} \right) = .58 \cdot .711 = .413$$

# SECTION 6

## Joint and Conditional Probabilities Using Tree Diagrams

Joint and conditional probabilities are easily calculated using tree diagrams. Each branch of the tree diagram shows where two events occur simultaneously. The ease of calculating joint probabilities comes from not having to question dependence or independence. If the tree diagram is drawn correctly, dependent effects have already been accounted for by adjustments of the probabilities in each part of the branch. The same is true for conditional probabilities, because conditional effects are also calculated into the branches. Thus, calculations for intersections are made by simply multiplying the probabilities of the parts of a branch. If more than one branch is required, then multiply across each branch and then add the branch products together.

It is important to understand sample space when drawing tree diagrams. The most crucial issue is understanding changes in the sample space when conducting an experiment. It is always necessary to question what is known as **replacement**.

**Replacement** Replacement occurs if, during a phase of an experiment, an element is withdrawn and then replaced in the original sample space. Each event during an experiment with replacement is independent.

**No Replacement** No replacement occurs if, during a phase of an experiment, an element is removed but is not replaced in the original sample space. The act of not replacing an element results in a change in the sample space of each event. The outcome of the second event is dependent on the outcome of the first event.

With replacement, the sample space remains the same. For example, suppose a person has five coins in his or her pocket. One coin is pulled out. The sample space contains five coins before the person withdraws one coin. If the withdrawn coin is replaced and then a coin is drawn again, the sample space of five coins remains the same for the second draw. But, if the first coin is not replaced, then the sample space does not remain the same. The first experiment has a sample space of five. The second has a sample space of four, reflecting the four coins that remain in the person's pocket.

The changes in the sample space can be reflected in a tree diagram. The changes in the sample space are the adjustments for dependent or conditional effects caused when replacement does not occur. When calculating probabilities using the formula $P(A) = n(A) / n(S)$, the changes in the sample space are reflected in the denominator, although the numerator may also be affected.

## EXAMPLE 6.14

**Experiment:** A bag contains 3 oranges and 4 apples. You pull out a piece of fruit and then pick a second piece of fruit out of the bag without replacing the first. What is the probability you will pick 2 oranges?

**Answer:** $P$ (Orange and Orange) = .143

**Solution:** To approach the solution to this experiment, first draw a tree diagram. Second, calculate the probabilities for the parts of the branches. Finally, label the branches. Adjust the second part of each branch to represent the change in the sample space. The denominator changes to 6 after draw 1; there are only 6 pieces of fruit left in the bag after the first draw. The numerators may change, depending on what was picked on the first draw. For example, for branch 1, the probability for the first part of the branch is 3/7 (fractions are used in the tree diagram to make the calculations easier). There are 3 oranges out of 7 pieces of fruit. The second part of the branch must adjust for what has happened in the first part of the branch. If you had 3 oranges and you drew an orange on the first draw, then you have only 2 oranges left out of a total of 6 pieces of fruit in the bag. The probability for the second part of the branch is 2/6.

| Pick 1 | Pick 2 | Branch |

```
                Pick 1          Pick 2        Branch

                                    2/6      O      1
                         O  <
                  3/7               4/6      A      2
             <
                  4/7               3/6      O      3
                         A  <
                                    3/6      A      4
```

Branch 1 contains the event that both picks result in an orange. The probabilities of the parts of branch 1 are multiplied. The probability of the first part of the branch, 3/7 is multiplied by the probability of the second part of the branch, 2/6. When performing calculations, show all steps. Final answers must be in decimal form (don't leave fractions).

$$P(O_1 \text{ and } O_2) = P(\text{orange, first draw}) \cdot P(\text{orange, second draw})$$
$$= (3/7)(2/6) = (.429)(.333) = .143$$

**EXAMPLE 6.15**

**Experiment:** There are 6 yellow marbles and 4 red marbles in a bag. You pick three marbles consecutively without replacement.
a. What is the probability of picking 3 red marbles?
b. What is the probability of picking a yellow, a red, and a red marble, in that order?
c. What is the probability of picking 3 yellow marbles?

**Answer:**
a. $P$ (R and R and R) = .033
b. $P$ (Y and R and R) = .1
c. $P$ (Y and Y and Y) = .1665

**Solution:** To approach the solution to this experiment, first draw a tree diagram. Second, calculate the probabilities for the parts of the branches. Third, label the branches. In step 2, be sure to adjust the second and third parts of each branch to represent the change in sample space. In the first phase of the experiment, there are 10 marbles in the bag. In the second phase of the experiment, there are 9 marbles left in the bag, because one marble was drawn and not replaced. In the third phase of the experiment, after two marbles are drawn and not replaced, there are only 8 marbles left in the bag. The sample space is the denominator and represents the total number of marbles in the bag at each phase of the experiment. The numerator may also change. Change in the numerator is based on the color of the marble drawn in each phase of the experiment. For example, if you have 6 yellow marbles in the bag and draw a yellow marble on the first draw, you now have 5 yellow marbles left in the bag out of the total of 9 marbles. If you draw a yellow and a yellow in the first and second draws, on the third draw you would have only 4 yellow marbles left out of the 8 marbles still in the bag.

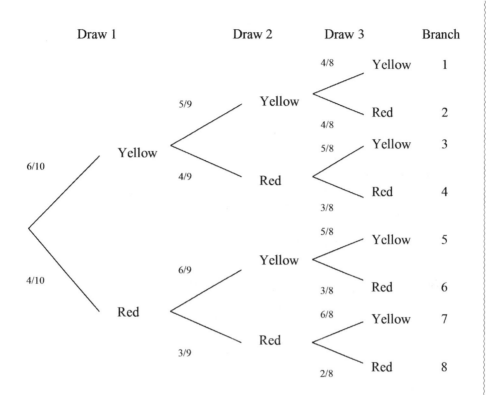

a. Picking three red marbles means that you pick a red marble on the first draw, a red marble on the second draw, and a red marble on the third draw. This event is shown in branch 8. The probability of branch 8 is found by multiplying the probabilities across the branch. That is, multiply the probability of drawing a red marble in the first draw by the probability of drawing a red marble in the second draw and then by the probability of drawing a red marble in the third draw. When performing calculations, show all steps.

$$P(R \cap R \cap R) = P(\text{red}) \cdot P(\text{red}) \cdot P(\text{red})$$
$$= (4/10)\,(3/9)\,(2/8) = (.4)\,(.333)\,(.25) = .033$$

b. The probability of drawing a yellow marble, then a red, and then another red is found by calculating the probability of branch 4. When performing calculations, a student should show all steps and circle the final answer.

$$P(Y \cap R \cap R) = P(\text{yellow}) \cdot P(\text{red}) \cdot P(\text{red})$$
$$= (6/10)\,(4/9)\,(3/8) = (.6)\,(.444)\,(.375) = .100$$

c. Drawing three yellow marbles means you pick a yellow on the first draw, a yellow on the second draw, and a yellow on the third draw. Branch 1 represents this event. When performing calculations, show all steps.

$$P(Y \cap Y \cap Y) = P(\text{yellow}) \cdot P(\text{yellow}) \cdot P(\text{yellow})$$
$$= (6/10) \, (5/9) \, (4/8) = (.6) \, (.555) \, (.5) = .167$$

**A LEARNING AID**
**JOINT AND CONDITIONAL PROBABILITIES USING TREE DIAGRAMS**

A friend of yours has 2 pencils, 2 blue pens, and 3 black pens in his school bag. You ask to borrow a writing instrument from your friend. What if he gave you a blue pen, but you need a black pen? If he does not put the blue pen back in the bag, what is the probability that he will pull out a black pen the second time?

**Step 1**

Draw and label a tree diagram. To draw the tree, begin with the trunk. There are three different events that may occur for any draw from the bag: pencil, blue pen, or black pen. Phase 1 of the experiment is the first time your friend draws from his bag. Phase 2 is the second time he draws from his bag. Calculate the probability of each part of each branch. To do this you must ask if replacement occurred during the experiment. If not, the sample space and each probability will change for each part of each branch. Replacement does not occur; your friend did not replace the first item drawn from the bag. Note the tree diagram and the probabilities for each part of each branch.

**Step 2**

Find the branch that represents the event that your friend drew a blue pen on his first draw and a black pen on his second draw. Branch 6 represents the event.

**Step 3**

This probability is a conditional probability because replacement did not occur. Because the sample space and probabilities are adjusted in the tree diagram to represent the conditions for each draw, the solution is found by multiplying probabilities across the branch.

**Step 4**
The probability of joint and conditional probabilities is found by multiplying across the branch that represents the event. The event in question reads: What is the probability that a black pen will be drawn given that a blue pen was drawn?

$$P(A \mid B) = P(\text{black pen} \mid \text{blue pen})$$
$$= 3/6$$
$$= .5$$

## SECTION 7

### Combining the Addition and Multiplication Theorems

There are times when the addition and multiplication theorems can be combined. Combining the rules of probability allows calculating the probability of two events occurring simultaneously, where at least one event has two or more outcomes or the events happen together several times. Both the addition (Section 2) and multiplication (Section 4) theorems are used. The multiplication rule is applied to the two events as they happen together. If they happen together several times, the multiplication rule for joint probabilities is applied to each as they happen. The addition rule for their union is applied to add together all the joint probabilities.

Combining the theorems is easy when using tree diagrams. Each branch represents the joint occurrences. Joint occurrences, or intersections, require the multiplication rule. If several branches fulfill the outcomes of one or both events, then the union is found by adding the probabilities of the branches. A very simple rule emerges when using tree diagrams for combined events: Multiply across branches and add down branches.

**Combining Theorems Using Tree Diagrams** Multiply across branches to obtain intersections as joint probabilities and add down branches to obtain unions.

**EXAMPLE 6.16**
**Experiment:** Observe the sex of the next two babies born at General Hospital. What is the probability that of the next two babies, only one will be a boy?

**Answer:** $P$ (only one boy) = .5

**Solution:** Draw a tree diagram. Assign probabilities to the parts of the branches and label each branch. This experiment happens to be independent. Note that the probabilities of each part of the branch remain the same. For example, for branch 1, the probability that the first baby is a boy is ½. If the first baby is a boy, the probability that the second baby is a boy is still ½. No adjustments are necessary.

| First Baby | Second Baby | Branch |
|---|---|---|

Only on branch 2 and branch 3 is just one boy born. No other branch has exactly one boy. Because two branches fulfill the event in question, the probabilities of each branch must be found by multiplying across the branch and then the probabilities of the two branches must be added together. Multiply across branch 2: ( ½ )( ½ ) = .25. Multiply across branch 3: ( ½ )( ½ ) = .25. Because both branches satisfy the condition that only one boy is born, the probabilities must be added: .25 + .25 = .5. When performing calculations, show all steps.

$$P(\text{only one boy}) = P(\text{B and G}) \text{ or } P(\text{G and B})$$
$$= (1/2 \cdot 1/2) + (1/2 \cdot 1/2)$$
$$= .25 + .25$$
$$= .5$$

One aid in calculating these kinds of probabilities is to remember the rule of multiplying across and adding down branches. The second aid is to draw the tree diagram correctly. Be sure to adjust the second phase of the tree if the sample space changes. Recall that when an experiment is conducted without replacement, the sample space usually changes.

This change affects the denominator and possibly the numerator when calculating probabilities using fractions. When replacement does not occur, a conditional probability results. Each phase of an experiment may depend on what happens in prior phases. Adjusting the numerators and denominators controls the conditional probabilities and allows the calculation of branch probabilities as if they are simple joint probabilities. If replacement does occur, the phases of the events are independent, and no adjustment is usually required.

## EXAMPLE 6.17

**Experiment:** A deck of playing cards has 52 cards, of which half are red and half are black. There are two red cards and two black cards for every number 2 through 10 and for every face card (jack, queen, king, and ace). Two cards are drawn without replacement. What is the probability that at least one card will be red?

**Answer:** $P$ (at least 1 red) = .755

**Solution:** Draw and label the tree diagram. Calculate the probabilities for the parts of the branches. Notice that the phases of the experiment are dependent, because there is no replacement of the first card drawn. When there is no replacement, the sample space changes. For the first phase, 52 cards are in hand, 26 red and 26 black. In the second phase, the denominators change to 51, since one card has been drawn. Each numerator is adjusted, depending on the color of the card from the first part of the branch. For example, if, in branch 1, a red card is originally drawn (26/52) in draw 2 there are only 25 red cards left from the total of 51 cards. In branch 2, if a red card was originally drawn in the first phase, all 26 black cards remain, but there are only 51 cards in all. Remember that the numerator and denominator may change when no replacement occurs.

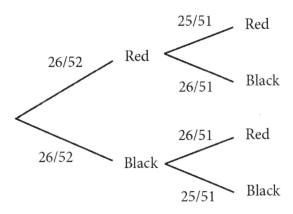

$$P(\text{at least 1 red}) = \left[(26/52)(25/51)\right] + \left[(26/52)(26/51)\right] + \left[(26/52)(26/51)\right] = .755$$

Branches 1, 2, and 3 all satisfy the event of drawing at least 1 red card when drawing 2 cards without replacement. You must find the probabilities of each branch and then add them together. Calculate the probability of each branch by multiplying across. Each of the three branch probabilities must then be added together. When performing calculations, show all steps.

## A LEARNING AID
## ADDITION AND MULTIPLICATION THEOREMS

In the Section 5 Learning Aid, a friend of yours has 2 pencils, 2 blue pens, and 3 black pens in his school bag. You need something with which to write. You ask to borrow something from your friend. He pulls one implement from his bag and then pulls another in a second draw. Calculate the probability that your friend drew 2 different colored pens.

## Step 1

Draw and label a tree diagram. To draw the tree, begin with the trunk. There (are three different events that may occur for any draw from the bag: pencil, blue pen, and black pen. Phase 1 of the experiment is the first time your friend draws from his bag. Phase 2 represents the second time he draws from his bag.

Calculate the probability for each part of each branch. Replacement does not occur, requiring you to adjust the sample space for each part of each branch.

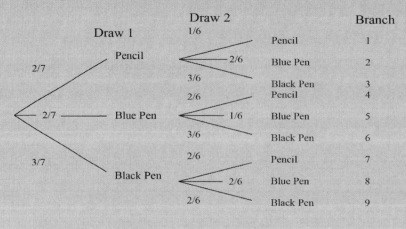

**Step 2**

Find the branch or branches representing the event that your friend drew two different-color pens. There are two different branches that represent the event. Branch 6 is the event that your friend pulled out a blue pen then a black pen. Branch 8 is the event he pulled out a black pen then a blue pen. Both branches must be used in calculating the probability that two different colored pens were drawn.

**Step 3**

This problem begins as a conditional probability treated as a joint probability, because you have already adjusted the probabilities of each part of each branch for the condition that no replacement occurred. But the problem also is a union of two events, since there are two different branches that represent two different colored pens being drawn.

**Step 4**

The probability of joint and conditional probabilities is found by multiplying across the branch that represents the event. You must do this for branches 6 and 8.

$$P(\text{branch 6}) = P(\text{blue pen}) \cdot P(\text{black pen})$$
$$= (2/7) \cdot (3/6) = (.2857) \cdot (.5) = .143$$

$$P(\text{branch 8}) = P(\text{black pen}) \cdot P(\text{blue pen})$$
$$= (3/7) \cdot (2/6) = (.429) \cdot (.333) = .143$$

**Step 5**

To calculate the union of the two events you must add probabilities. When two branches fulfill an event, add the probabilities of the two branches. Remember the rule to multiply across branches and add down branches. Add the probability of branch 6 to the probability of branch 8. The whole problem would look like this:

$$P(\text{two different colors drawn}) = P(\text{Blue} \cap \text{Black}) \cup P(\text{Black} \cap \text{Blue})$$
$$= P(\text{branch 6}) + P(\text{branch 8})$$
$$= \left[ (2/7)(3/6) \right] + \left[ (3/7)(2/6) \right]$$
$$= \left[ (.2857)(.51) \right] + \left[ (.429)(.333) \right]$$
$$= .143 + .143 = .286$$

## Probability Rules

All probabilities are between 0 and 1, inclusive. Never negative, never greater than 1.

The sum of all probabilities must equal 1.0 (100%).

There are four mathematical rules which apply to multiple event probabilities. The multiple event types are unions, complements, conditional, and joint.

| Type | Key word | Math rule | Symbol | Formula |
|---|---|---|---|---|
| Union | Or, either | Add | $\cup$ | $P(A \cup B) = P(A) + P(B) - P(A \cap B)$ |
| Complement | Not (be sure "not" or "no" isn't an actual event) | Subtract | $'$ | $P(A') = 1 - P(A)$ |
| Conditional | If, given, Knowing, Assuming, of those | Divide | $\mid$ | $P(B\mid A) = P(A \cap B) / P(A)$ |
| Joint, Intersections | And, both | Multiply | $\cap$ | $P(A \cap B) = P(A) \cdot P(B \mid A)$ |

# CHAPTER 6 IN REVIEW

6.1 Twenty-five out of 40 students in class are business majors.
   a. What is the probability that a randomly selected student will be a business major?
   b. If 10 consecutive selections resulted in a business major, is it more likely that the eleventh student will be a business major?

6.2 Twelve employees are randomly selected from an engineering department. Ten of the employees are men and 2 are women. Two employees are randomly selected from the sample with no replacement between the draws.
   a. Draw a tree diagram and label all branches and probabilities.
   b. What is the probability that there would be at least one woman?
   c. What is the probability that there will be no women?
   d. What is the probability that there will be two women?
   e. What is the probability that there will be exactly one man and one woman?

6.3     Seventy-five percent of students must take a statistics course. Of those required to take the course 80 percent complete the course with a passing grade. What is the probability that a randomly selected student must take statistics and complete the course with a passing grade?

6.4     Eight airport travelers are randomly selected to be rescreened due to increased security requirements. Five of the rescreened travelers were found with no violations while three were found with security breaches.
a. Draw a tree diagram with two selections and no replacement between selections. Note probabilities on all parts of the branches.
b. What is the probability that two travelers were with breaches?
c. What is the probability that at least one traveler was with a breach?
d. What is the probability that a second traveler had no violation after the first also had no violation?
e. What is the probability that a traveler selected on the first draw was with no violation?

6.5     If 36 percent of bureaucrats are in the Defense Department, 25 percent are in the Postal Service, 39 percent are in other agencies, and all agencies are mutually exclusive, what is the probability that a person randomly chosen is in the Postal Service and the Defense Department?

6.6     The following table represents 500 students at the University of Detroit.

| Gender ↓ | Marital Status→ | Single | Married | Divorced | Total |
|----------|-----------------|--------|---------|----------|-------|
| Males    |                 | 150    | 50      | 20       | 220   |
| Females  |                 | 210    | 40      | 30       | 280   |
| Total    |                 | 360    | 90      | 50       | 500   |

What is the probability that a randomly selected person is:
a. A male?
b. A divorced woman?
c. Female if a single person?
d. Single or married?
e. Not a divorced person?

6.7     Suppose a poll is taken to determine if voters support the President. The following data represent support and gender.

| Gender ↓ | Support→ | Favorable | Undecided | Unfavor-able | Total |
|---|---|---|---|---|---|
| Males | | 90 | 150 | 60 | 300 |
| Females | | 105 | 130 | 65 | 300 |
| Total | | 195 | 180 | 125 | 600 |

What is the probability that a person selected at random:
a. If a male, favors the President?
b. Is a male and is undecided?
c. Favors the President given that he/she is undecided?
d. Favors the President or is a female?

6.8　The new minimum wage bill has a 75 percent chance of passing if the Democrats win the election. The Democrats have a 50 percent chance of winning the election. What is the probability that the Democrats will win and the bill will pass?

6.9　Given that events $A$ and $B$ are mutually exclusive and $P(A)=0.4$ and $P(B)=0.3$, find:
a. $P(A$ and $B)$
b. $P(A|B)$
c. $P(A$ or $B)$
d. Are $A$ and $B$ independent?

6.10　A baseball player has hit 298 times out of the last 500 times at bat. What is the probability that she will hit the ball the next time at bat? If she hits the ball the next 10 times at bat (510), what is the probability that she will not hit the next time at bat?

6.11　If a coin flipped 6 times came up heads each time, what is the probability that on the seventh flip it will come up heads?

6.12　A study of college students shows that 8 out of 12 students prefer a PC computer system while 4 prefer a Mac. Randomly select two students with no replacement between selections:
a. Draw a tree diagram and place probabilities on each branch.
b. What is the probability that both would prefer a Mac?
c. What is the probability that at least one would prefer a Mac?
d. What is the probability that one would prefer a Mac and one a PC?
e. What is the probability that one would prefer a Mac after one who prefers a PC?

6.13 If a pair of identical twins is born and the first baby is a boy, what is the probability that the second baby is a boy?

6.14 Identical triplets are born.
   a. Draw a tree diagram showing the probabilities for all outcomes.
   b. If the first baby is a girl, what is the probability that the second baby is a girl?
   c. What is the probability that if the first baby is a girl, the third baby is a boy?

6.15 A survey was taken to determine whether students are for U.S. military action in Iraq. Twelve students were surveyed. Seven students were pro-war while 5 students were anti-war. With two draws and no replacement between draws:
   a. Draw a tree diagram of the two draws including the probabilities.
   b. What is the probability that a random selection would result in two students who were anti-war?
   c. What is the probability that a selection will result in two students who are pro-war?
   d. If the first student was pro-war, what is the probability that the second student would be anti-war?
   e. What is the probability that at least one student would be pro-war?

6.16 Given $P(A') = .2$, $P(B|A) = .6$, and $P(B|A') = .3$ and events are $A$, $A'$, $B$, and $B'$:
   a. Draw a tree diagram.
   b. What is $P(A \cap B)$?
   c. What is $P(A \cup A')$?
   d. What is $P(A' \cap B')$?
   e. What is $P(B'|A')$?

6.17 A survey of 100 U.S. senators shows the following results on a recent vote on a bill and the party identification of the senator.

| Party ↓     Vote → | Yes | No | Total |
|---|---|---|---|
| **Republican** | 28 | 12 | 40 |
| **Democrat** | 50 | 10 | 60 |
| **Total** | 78 | 22 | 100 |

   a. What is the probability that a senator chosen at random is a Republican?
   b. What is the probability that a senator chosen at random is a Democrat who voted for the bill?
   c. What is the probability that a senator chosen at random voted against the bill?
   d. What is the probability that a senator chosen at random is not a Republican?
   e. If the senator chosen is a Democrat, what is the probability he or she voted against the bill?

6.18  Presidents from George Washington to Bill Clinton have vetoed 15 percent of the bills passed by Congress. Of those vetoes, only 4 percent have been overridden by Congress. What is the probability that a bill will be vetoed by the President and overridden by Congress?

6.19  Given $P(A) = .3$, $P(B) = .5$, and $P(A \cap B) = .1$, find:
   a. $P(A \cup B)$
   b. $P(A \mid B)$
   c. $P(B')$
   d. $P(A')$

6.20  The president is about to nominate a justice for the Supreme Court. Let $A$ be the event that the person is African-American, let $B$ be the event that the person is Hispanic, let $C$ be the event that the person is female, and let $D$ be the event that the person is confirmed by the Senate. Describe, in words, the following events.
   a. $P(A \cup B)$
   b. $P(A \cap C)$
   c. $P(A')$
   d. $P(A \cap C \cap D)$
   e. $P(A \cap C \cap D')$

6.21  True or False?
   a. Probabilities can be positive or negative.
   b. The key word "and" indicates a union of two events.
   c. Dependent events require that the events are always related.
   d. Complementary events require the division rule.
   e. Intersections on a contingency table are found in the outside totals.

6.22  Eight out of every 10 online homes in the U.S. have switched to broadband high-speed internet. Two homes are randomly selected with no replacement between draws.
   a. Draw a tree diagram of the two draws including the probabilities.
   b. What is the probability that a selection would result in two broadband homes?
   c. What is the probability that a selection will result in no broadband?
   d. If the first is broadband, what is the probability that the second is not?
   e. What is the probability that at least one home is broadband?

6.23  Suppose a poll is taken to determine if voters support the new automobile insurance proposal on the upcoming election ballot. The following data represents the voters' preference for the proposal and residency.

| Support ↓ Residency→ | City | Suburb | Rural | Total |
|---|---|---|---|---|
| **Yes** | 70 | 200 | 30 | 300 |
| **No** | 110 | 50 | 40 | 200 |
| **Total** | **180** | **250** | **70** | **500** |

What is the probability that a person selected at random …
a. Supports the proposal?
b. Lives in the suburbs?
c. Lives in the suburbs and supports the proposal?
d. Does not live in the city?
e. Does not support the proposal given that the person lives in the city?

6.24 Ten students are randomly selected and asked if they will vote for the incumbent President. Five say yes, and three say no. Two students are randomly selected with no replacement between the selections.
a. Draw a tree diagram for the two draws and indicate all probabilities.
b. What is the probability that two students will say yes?
c. What is the probability that two will say no?
d. What is the probability that the selection ends up with a one yes and one no?
e. What is the probability that the second said yes after the first said no?

6.25 While testing the quality of 10 machines, a manufacturer notes that 4 machines pass quality inspections and 4 machines do not. A buyer randomly selects two machines (no replacement).
a. Describe the sample space with a tree diagram and assign probabilities to the branches.
b. What is the probability that the buyer selects two machines that did not pass the inspection?
c. What is the probability that the buyer selects one machine that passes the inspection and one that does not?
d. What is the probability that the buyer selects a machine that passed given that he already selected a machine that passed?

# 7 PROBABILITY DISTRIBUTIONS OF DISCRETE VARIABLES

SECTION 1  **Probability Distribution of a Discrete Random Variable**

SECTION 2  **Discrete Probability Function**

SECTION 3  **Mean and Standard Deviation of a Discrete Probability Distribution**

SECTION 4  **Binomial Probability Distribution**

SECTION 5  **Mean and Standard Deviation of a Binomial Distribution**

Now that the fundamentals of probabilities have been mastered, probabilities can be combined with frequency distributions. Recall that a relative frequency distribution (Chapter 2) is a distribution representing the occurrence of a response variable relative to the total number of occurrences. It is a proportional measure: the proportion of the occurrence of the response relative to the total. It is found by dividing the number of occurrences of the response variable by the total number of occurrences of the whole frequency distribution. The response variable is simply a response or a characteristic about a population or sample. In response to the question, "What is your religious preference?", a person may reply "Protestant," "Catholic," "Jewish," and so on. Each response has a frequency. To determine the relative frequency, the number of responses of a particular type is divided by the total number of responses. Recall a few basic rules that apply to a relative frequency distribution. First, frequency distributions represent discrete variables. Discrete variables are counts. Second, the relative proportion of a response variable in a distribution must be between 0 and 1.00, inclusive. Third, the relative proportions of all responses must have a sum of 1.00. The last two rules are referred to as properties of probabilities.

A relative frequency distribution used in predicting outcomes of an event becomes a probability experiment. The relative frequency distribution is then referred to as a probability distribution. The response variable is referred to as a random variable. The experiment is defined as observing the occurrence of a particular random variable.

## SECTION 1

### Probability Distribution of a Discrete Random Variable

Random variables are equivalent to response variables in a relative frequency distribution. The only difference is that the random variable is assigned a numerical value based on an event that is being observed. For example, instead of asking five people their religious preference, ask how many are Catholic. This way a response is given that has a numerical value. Of the five people asked, the possible number of Catholics could be 0, 1, 2, 3, 4, or 5. There could be no Catholics, one who is Catholic, two who are Catholic, and so forth. Each outcome is referred to as a random variable. Because each outcome represents a discrete count, each count is referred to as a *discrete random variable*.

> **Discrete Random Variable** A variable that assumes a numerical value for each outcome or element of the sample space. A random variable is represented by a capital letter, such as *X*, *Y*, or *Z*.

---

### EXAMPLE 7.1

**Experiment:** Observe the next 4 babies born at General Hospital. Note the number of girls born. List all the values of the random variable, a girl is born.

**Answer:** $x$ = girl is born, $x = 0, 1, 2, 3, 4$

**Solution:** This is a discrete variable, because the number of girls being born is a discrete count: 0, 1, 2, 3, . . . . The random variable is the event defined by the observation looking for the number of girls born. Always check to see if 0 is a valid value. It is possible that no girls are born. The nonoccurence of an event may be an event, with a value of 0.

---

A random variable is represented by any capital letter. A person walking down the street can be identified as $X$, $Q$, or any other capital letter. The value assigned to a random variable is represented by the corresponding lowercase letter. Thus, $X$ walks down the street and enters house $x$. $Q$ enters house $q$, and $D$ enters house $d$. If the value of a random variable is represented by a number, then it is usually stated with a lowercase letter, equal sign, and the number, such as $x = 0$.

---

### EXAMPLE 7.2

**Experiment:** The random variable is the number of girls being born out of the next 4 babies born at General Hospital. Describe each value of the random variable.

---

**Answer:**

$x = 0$: No girls are born.

$x = 1$: One girl is born.

$x = 2$: Two girls are born.

$x = 3$: Three girls are born.

$x = 4$: Four girls are born.

**Solution:** This is a discrete random variable, because it is a count of the number of girls being born. $x$ = girls being born, and the values of $x$ are 0, 1, 2, 3, 4. This problem differs from Example 7.1 by asking to describe the meaning of the values of the random variable.

The probability distribution begins by listing a frequency distribution for the random variable and its values. The frequency distribution can then be converted to a probability distribution. Assigning probabilities to values of a random variable is not always easy. Experiments can involve the three types of probabilities (experimental, theoretical, and subjective). Most of the problems presented in this text use theoretical examples, which allow for easy calculations of probabilities based on the understanding of how to combine sample spaces with frequency distributions. Many problems give enough information to allow easy calculation of the random variable values or their probabilities. The following steps should be used in presenting a probability distribution:

Step 1 State and define the discrete random variable $x$ (or any other letter).

Step 2 Prepare a frequency distribution with a column $x$ and its values below $x$.

Step 3 List a column for 1, the frequency at which each value of $x$ occurs.

Step 4 Calculate the relative frequency by dividing each frequency $x$ by the total number of occurrences found by adding all the $f$ values. That is, for each value of $x$, determine $f / \Sigma f$.

Step 5 Check to be sure all the rules of probability are met:

    a. All values of $x$ are represented.

    b. Each probability is greater than or equal to 0 and less than or equal to 1 $(0 \leq P(x) \leq 1)$.

    c. All probabilities of $x$ sum to 1: $\Sigma\{P(x) = 1\}$.

### EXAMPLE 7.3

**Experiment:** Observe the sex of the next two babies born at General Hospital. List the probability distribution for the number of boys born.

**Answer:**

Number of boys born at General Hospital

| $x$ | $f$ | $P(x)$ |
|-----|-----|--------|
| 0 | 1 | .25 |
| 1 | 2 | .50 |
| 2 | 1 | .25 |
| **Total** | | **1.00** |

**Solution:**

**Step 1**

This is a discrete variable, because the variable is a count of the boys born.

**Step 2**

Prepare the frequency distribution by listing $x$ and its value in the first column. The values of $x$ are 0, 1, and 2, where $x = 0$ represents no boys born; $x = 1$ represents one boy born; and $x = 2$ represents two boys born.

**Step 3**

List the frequency for each $x$ in a column labeled $f$. This example is a theoretical example. The sample space has four outcomes: $S = \{(B, B), (G, B), (B, G), (G, G)\}$. The frequency is determined by counting how many boys are in each outcome. There is one outcome with no boys, (G, G). There are two outcomes with one boy, (G, B) and (B, G). There is one outcome with two boys, (B, B).

**Step 4**

Calculate the relative frequency as the probability of each value of $X$. Divide the frequency of each $x$ by the total number of outcomes. For example: for $x = 0$, with a frequency of 1, the probability is ¼, or .25

| $x$ | $f$ | $f / \Sigma f$ | $P(x)$ |
|-----|-----|--------------|--------|
| 0 | 1 | 1/4 | .25 |
| 1 | 2 | 2/4 | .50 |
| 2 | 1 | 1/4 | .25 |
| | $\Sigma f=4$ | 4/4 | **1.00** |

**Step 5**

Check to be sure that no rules of probability of distribution have been violated.

a. Are all values of $x$ represented? Yes, there are no other possibilities except 0, 1, 2.

b. Are all probabilities between 0 and inclusive? Yes, each $x$ fulfills the requirement.

c. Do the probabilities of $x$ have a sum of 1? Yes, $.25 + .5 + .25 = 1.0$.

**A LEARNING AID**
**PROBABILITY DISTRIBUTIONS FOR DISCRETE RANDOM VARIABLES**

Observe the marital status of the next three people you see. List the probability distribution for the number of people who are married.

**Step 1**

This is a discrete variable, because the variable is a count of the number of people who are married among the next three that you observe. The discrete random variable is the number married. You can identify it as $X$: the number of people married. The values that $x$ can take on are represented by $x$.

**Step 2**

Prepare the frequency distribution by listing each $x$ and its value in the first column of the distribution. List the values of $x$. The values of $x$ are all the possible number of people who are married. None could be married, one could be married, two could be married, and all three could be married. Therefore,

| | |
|---|---|
| $x = 0$ | None are married. |
| $x = 1$ | One is married. |
| $x = 2$ | Two are married. |
| $x = 3$ | All three are married. |

**Step 3**

List the frequency for each $x$ in a column labeled $f$. Listing the sample space may help to determine how many times a particular value of $x$ may theoretically occur. Since the random variable is the number of people married, you can identify married and non-married people in the listing of the sample space. Represent married by M and non-married by N.

$S=$ {M, M, M), (M, M, N), (M, N, M), (M, N, N), (N, M, M), (N, M, N),
(N, N, M), (N, N, N)}

Now it is possible to count the frequency for each value of x. Looking at the
sample space, notice there is only one outcome where no one is married, three
outcomes where only one is married, three where two are married, and one
where all three people are married. The distribution should look like this:

| $x$ | $f$ |
|---|---|
| 0 | 1 |
| 1 | 3 |
| 2 | 3 |
| 3 | 1 |
| | $\Sigma f=8$ |

**Step 4**
Calculate the relative frequency as the probability of each value of x. Divide
the frequency of each x by the sum of $f$: $f / \Sigma f$. For $x = 0$, divide the frequency
of 1 by 8: 1 /8 = .125. You must do this for each value of x. The relative
frequency is the probability that x occurs, and it is placed in the table under
the label $P(x)$.

| $x$ | $f$ | $f / \Sigma f$ | $P(x)$ |
|---|---|---|---|
| 0 | 1 | 1 /8 | .125 |
| 1 | 3 | 3 /8 | .375 |
| 2 | 3 | 3 /8 | .375 |
| 3 | 1 | 1 /8 | .125 |
| | $\Sigma f=8$ | | **1.000** |

**Step 5**
Check to be sure that no rules of probabilities have been violated.
a. Are all values of x represented? Yes, the only values of x are 0, 1, 2, and 3.
b. Are all probabilities between 0 and 1 inclusive? Yes, each is greater than or
   equal to 0 and less than or equal to 1.0.
c. Do the probabilities of x have a sum of 1? Yes, $\Sigma P(x) = 1.000$.

# SECTION 2

## Discrete Probability Function

A *discrete probability function* is a statement that represents a discrete probability distribution. The discrete probability function assigns a probability to each value of the random variable. The rule may state a mathematical formula, which, when applied to each value of $x$, represents its probability. When the formula is applied to all values of $x$, a full distribution is represented.

> **Discrete Probability Function**  A rule that assigns a probability to every value of $x$, such as
>
> $$P(X) = \underline{\quad\quad} \quad \text{for } x = 0, 1, 2, \ldots$$

A probability function can be viewed as a shorthand notation that reflects a probability distribution. The rule, or formula, placed in the blank of the definition is any mathematical formula that allows the calculation of the probability for each $x$ cited. The mathematical formula serves no other purpose than for the calculation of the probability. If the formula states to divide each $x$ by 10 ($x/10$), then each value of $x$ is inserted in the numerator and divided by 10. Whatever the formula, each value of $x$ must be inserted to calculate its probability.

> **True Probability Function**  A probability function and its distribution meeting the two properties or rules governing probabilities. Property 1: Each probability must be between 0 and 1 inclusive; and Property 2, all outcomes must sum to 1.0.

Discrete probability functions are tested by calculating the probability of each $x$ and creating a probability distribution. The rules of probability and their distributions must still be met. Each probability must be between 0 and 1, inclusive. The probabilities must have a sum of 1.0. All values of $x$ must be represented.

---

### EXAMPLE 7.4

**Experiment:** Is the following a true discrete probability function?

$$P(Y) = \frac{2 + y}{3} \quad \text{for } y = 0, 1$$

**Answer:** No

---

**Solution:** Insert each value of $y$ into the formula. Calculate the probability and create a probability distribution. Check the distribution to be sure the rules of 1 probability are met. It must be assumed from the rule presented that all values of $y$ are included. Each probability falls between 0 and 1, inclusive. However, the sum of the probabilities is not 1.0; it is 1.667. All three rules must be fulfilled for this rule to be a true probability distribution. If any rule is not fulfilled, then the distribution violates the rules of probabilities. Therefore, the rule is not a true probability function.

| $y$ | $\dfrac{2+y}{3}$ | $P(y)$ |
|-----|------------------|--------|
| 0 | $\dfrac{2+0}{3} = \dfrac{2}{3}$ | .667 |
| 1 | $\dfrac{2+1}{3} = \dfrac{3}{3}$ | 1.000 |
| | | $\overline{1.667}$ |

## A LEARNING AID
## DISCRETE PROBABILITY FUNCTION

Determine if the following discrete probability distribution is true. Recall that a function is a mathematical rule that describes a distribution. The formula in the rule may differ for every distribution.

$$P(G) = \frac{g}{10} \quad \text{for } g = 1,2,3,4$$

**Step 1**
This is a discrete probability function, because it describes a distribution. It is discrete since the values of the random variable represent discrete counts. The rule must be calculated as a distribution to determine if it fulfills the two probability properties.

**Step 2**
Begin by preparing the distribution. List the values of $g$ in the first column. Label a second column with the function $g/10$. Label a third column as the probability $P(g)$.

| $g$ | $g/10$ | $P(g)$ |
|---|---|---|
| 1 | | |
| 2 | | |
| 3 | | |
| 4 | | |
| **Total** | | |

## Step 3

Insert each value of $g$ into the formula and place the result in the second column.

| $g$ | $g/10$ | $P(g)$ |
|---|---|---|
| 1 | 1/10 | |
| 2 | 2/10 | |
| 3 | 3/10 | |
| 4 | 4/10 | |
| **Total** | | |

## Step 4

Calculate the probability for each value of $g$ by rewriting the values. The probability in the second column as decimals. Be sure to perform each calculation separately. Place the calculated value in the third column, labeled $P(g)$. Sum the third column.

| $g$ | $g/10$ | $P(g)$ |
|---|---|---|
| 1 | 1/10 | .1 |
| 2 | 2/10 | .2 |
| 3 | 3/10 | .3 |
| 4 | 4/10 | .4 |
| **Total** | | **1.0** |

## Step 5

Check that all the rules of probabilities and their distributions are met:

a. Are all values of $g$ included? We must assume so, since no other information is given.

b. Is the probability for each $g$ between 0 and 1, inclusive? Yes, each value in the third column for each $g$ is greater than or equal to 0 and less than or equal to 1.

c. Do the probabilities have a sum of 1.0? Yes, note the total of 1.0. Since all the rules of probabilities are fulfilled, you can conclude that the probability function describing this distribution is true.

# SECTION 3

## Mean and Standard Deviation of a Discrete Probability Distribution

Now that probabilities have been combined with frequency distributions, add to them the rules of means, variances, and standard deviations. Whereas frequency distributions represent the relative frequency of the response variable $X$, probability distributions represent the expected relative frequency of a random variable $X$. The use of the word expected implies that the distribution is theoretical. It shows what will happen in the long run. An experiment may be carried out or observed. The observational probability may not equal the theoretical probability. The law of large numbers states that as the number of trials increase, the observational probability will approach the theoretical. This statement is true because theoretical probability represents the universal set, whereas the observational probability represents a sample. Thus, a probability distribution represents a theoretical population. Any descriptive statistic describing that distribution is known as a parameter. Recall that parameters are measures that describe populations and are represented by Greek symbols.

To calculate the mean of a probability distribution, it is important to remember the rules for calculating the mean of a frequency distribution. Recall that the mean of a frequency distribution required as the numerator each value of $X$ multiplied by its frequency. This multiplication was necessary to ensure that each value of $x$ was represented by its relative frequency. The formula can be altered slightly for a probability distribution. Note the adjustment of the formula for the mean of a frequency distribution:

$$\bar{x} = \frac{\sum xf}{\sum f}$$

The mean formula of the frequency distribution can be adjusted to represent the mean of a probability distribution. The mean of a probability distribution is found by replacing $f/\sum f$ with $P(x)$ and moving the $\sum$ and $x$. Change the symbol $\bar{x}$ to $\mu$ to indicate that the mean is now of a theoretical population.

**Mean of a Discrete Probability Distribution**

$$\mu = \sum [x \cdot P(x)]$$

where

$\Sigma$ is the summation of the product inside the parentheses for each value of $x$.

$x$ is each value of the random variable.

$P(x)$ is the probability of $x$.

The formula for the mean of a discrete probability distribution requires each value of $x$ to be multiplied by its probability. This multiplication occurs for each value. The products of these multiplications are then added together.

**EXAMPLE 7.5**

**Experiment:** A coin is tossed three times. Find the mean for the following probability distribution for the random variable $x$, the number of heads occurring.

| $x$ | $P(x)$ |
|-----|--------|
| 0 | .125 |
| 1 | .375 |
| 2 | .375 |
| 3 | .125 |
| | **1.000** |

**Answer:** $\mu = 1.5$

**Solution:** The mean is found by multiplying each $x$ by its probability and then adding all the products. The easiest way to solve is to form a column for the multiplication of each $x$ by its probability and then sum the column. The sum of the column is the mean. When performing the calculations, show all steps.

| $x$ | $P(x)$ | $x \cdot P(x)$ |
|-----|--------|----------------|
| 0 | .125 | .000 |
| 1 | .375 | .375 |
| 2 | .375 | .750 |
| 3 | .125 | .375 |
| | **1.000** | **1.500** |

$$\mu = \sum \left[ x \cdot P(x) \right] = 1.5$$

The variance and standard deviation of the probability distribution are also derived from the variance and standard deviation of the frequency distribution. Again, minor adjustments can be made. Recall the variance formula for a frequency distribution:

$$\sigma^2 = \frac{\sum x^2 f - \dfrac{\left( \sum xf \right)^2}{\sum f}}{\sum f - 1}$$

In the first part of the numerator, $\Sigma x^2 f$, $f$ is replaced by $P(x)$; that is, instead of multiplying $x^2$ by $f$, the new formula multiplies $x^2$ by $P(x)$. Brackets are used to ensure that the multiplication is done before the summation. Thus, $\Sigma x^2 f$ becomes $\Sigma [x^2 \cdot P(x)]$. The second part of the numerator has already been adjusted as the mean formula. The only adjustment to the mean formula is the squared term. Thus, $\Sigma x^2 f / \Sigma f$ becomes $\Sigma [x \cdot P(x)]^2$. The denominator is dropped and the numerator is put together, subtracting as in the original formula.

**Variance of a Discrete Probability Distribution**

$$\sigma^2 = \sum \left[ x^2 \cdot P(x) \right] - \sum \left[ x \cdot P(x) \right]^2$$

or

$$\sigma^2 = \sum \left[ x^2 \cdot P(x) \right] - \mu^2$$

Both formulas require that each value of $x$ be squared ($x^2$) and then multiplied by its probability. These products are then added. Subtracted from this single value is the squared sum of all the products of each $x$ and its probability. Both formulas give the same answer. Since the second part of the first formula equals the mean of a probability distribution, if the mean is already calculated, its value is inserted and squared. The most common mistake in using either formula is forgetting to square the mean.

The standard deviation of discrete probability distribution is the square root of its variance. Recall that taking the square root of the variance returns to the same unit of analysis that the problem uses in its original form. That is, if a probability distribution describes ages in years, the variance describes ages in squared years, but the standard deviation again uses years.

**Standard Deviation of a Discrete Probability Distribution**

$$\sigma = \sqrt{\sum \left[x^2 \cdot P(x)\right] - \sum \left[x \cdot P(x)\right]^2}$$

or

$$\sigma = \sqrt{\sigma^2}$$

## EXAMPLE 7.6

**Experiment:** A coin is tossed three times. Find the variance and standard deviation for the following probability distribution for the random variable $x$, the number of times a heads occurs.

| $x$ | $P(x)$ |
|-----|--------|
| 0 | .125 |
| 1 | .375 |
| 2 | .375 |
| 3 | .125 |
| **Total** | **1.000** |

**Answer:** $\sigma^2 = 0.75$; $\sigma = 0.87$

**Solution:** Start by creating columns that aid in the calculation. Columns for $x \cdot P(x)$, $x^2$, and $x^2 \cdot P(x)$ are all necessary for the formula. $x \cdot P(x)$ is the value of each $x$ multiplied by its probability (the same as in Example 7.5 for the mean). Sum this column for the second part of the formula. $x^2$ is the square of each value of $x$. $x^2 \cdot P(x)$ shows the multiplication of the previous column, $x^2$, by the probability of $x$, $P(x)$. Sum this column for the first part of the formula. When performing calculations, show all steps.

| $x$ | $P(x)$ | $x \cdot P(x)$ | $x^2$ | $x^2 \cdot P(x)$ |
|-----|--------|----------------|-------|------------------|
| 0 | .125 | .000 | 0 | .000 |
| 1 | .375 | .375 | 1 | .375 |
| 2 | .375 | .750 | 4 | 1.500 |
| 3 | .125 | .375 | 9 | 1.125 |
| **Total** | **1.000** | **1.500** | | **3.000** |

Variance is:

$$\sigma^2 = \sum \left[ x^2 \cdot P(x) \right] - \sum \left[ x \cdot P(x) \right]^2$$
$$= 3.0 - 1.5^2 = 3.0 - 2.25 = .75$$

Standard deviation is:

$$\sigma = \sqrt{\sigma^2}$$
$$= \sqrt{.75} = .866 = .87$$

**A LEARNING AID**
**MEANS AND STANDARD DEVIATIONS OF A PROBABILITY DISTRIBUTION**

On the basis of the past record of the local electric company, the probability of the number of reported electrical outages on an average day is represented by the following probability distribution.

Calculate the mean and standard deviation of the distribution by plugging $x$ values into $L_1$ and $P(x)$ values into $L_2$ by pressing STAT and with "Edit..." highlighted, press ENTER.

| $x$ | $P(x)$ |
|-----|--------|
| 0 | .01 |
| 1 | .04 |
| 2 | .15 |
| 3 | .25 |
| 4 | .30 |
| 5 | .25 |
| **Total** | **1.00** |

**Step 1**

This is a discrete probability distribution, because $X$ is the number of reported outages with values $(x)$ of 0, 1, 2, 3, 4, and 5. This is a true distribution because you must assume all values of $x$ are reported.

Each probability of each value of $x$ is between 0 and 1, inclusive. The probabilities have a sum of 1.0.

Enter the data in the calculator using STAT and then Edit. Enter the *x* values in $L_1$ and the probabilities in $L_2$.

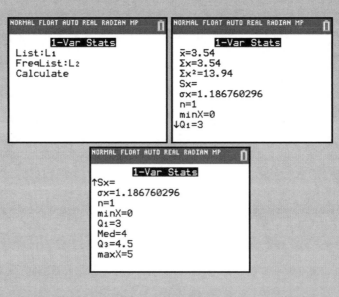

**Step 2**

Once these numbers have been plugged into the calculator, press the STAT button, arrow right to "CALC" and press the 1 button to select "1:1-Var Stats."

Adhere to the following settings, highlight "Calculate" and press ENTER. The results should appear as follows:

$$\mu = \sum \left[ x \cdot P(x) \right] = 3.54$$

$$\sigma x = \sqrt{ \sum \left[ x^2 \cdot P(x) \right] - \sum \left[ x \cdot P(x) \right]^2 } = 1.187$$

# SECTION 4

## Binomial Probability Distribution

A ***binomial probability distribution*** is a special kind of probability distribution. A binomial probability distribution of a discrete random variable has only two possible outcomes. Often, a probability distribution represents several outcomes of an experiment. Many times only one of the outcomes of an experiment is of interest. The chance of one thing happening is often asked. In this situation, what is really being asked is the probability that one outcome may happen compared to all the other possible outcomes. By dividing the outcomes into only two categories, a binomial distribution results. For example, in asking people their religious preference, several religions may be reported. There are times that it is important to know only how many people are Catholic. The reported religions could be divided into two groups: Catholic and non-Catholic. The two-group classification represents a binomial random variable.

There are several conditions necessary for using the binomial probability distribution. All the following conditions must be met:

> **Conditions for the Use of the Binomial Probability Distribution**
> 1. There is a fixed number of trials, *n*.
> 2. There are only two possible outcomes on each trial, a success and a failure.
> 3. The probability of success remains constant on all trials and is designated by *p*. The probability of failure remains constant and is designated by *q*.
> 4. The probabilities of success and failure must have a sum of 1.0: $p + q = 1.0$.
> 5. A success or failure on any trial is independent of a success or failure on any other trial.

Condition 1 requires that there be a fixed number of trials, designated by the symbol *n*. Trials refer to the number of experiments conducted. Flipping a coin 5 times means there are 5 trials. Watching the outcome of 4 elections means there are 4 trials. With fixed trials, it is known how many trials or experiments will be conducted.

Condition 2 states that only two outcomes are possible on each trial. If several outcomes result in an experiment, they can usually be grouped into two categories. The outcome that is of importance is defined as a success. All other outcomes are combined as the second outcome, or failure.

Condition 3 requires that the probability of success and the probability of failure remain constant on all trials. That is, if the probability of success is .1 on one trial, it must be .1 on all other trials. If *q* is .4 on one trial, it must be .4 on all others. Success is always represented by the symbol *p*, and failure is represented by *q*.

Condition 4 states that $p + q = 1.0$. The binomial distribution, as all probability distributions, must have a sum of 1.0. The probability of each outcome must be between 0 and 1, inclusive: $0 \leq P(x) \leq 1$. All outcomes must be defined as either a success or failure; therefore, the sum of their probabilities must equal 1.0. The probability of success, $p$, is often known in a problem. If $p$ is known, then $q$ can be found by subtracting $p$ from 1.0: $1 - p = q$. The opposite is also true where only $q$ is known: $1 - q = p$.

Condition 5 requires that all outcomes be independent. This is determined by asking if the outcome of one trial affects the outcome of another trial. The answer must be no for the trials to be independent. For example, getting heads on a flip of a coin does not affect whether the coin will land heads up again; the results of flipping a coin are independent.

When all the conditions for a binomial distribution are met, the calculations for creating the distribution can be done. The calculations and formula are often intimidating and cumbersome, but once a distribution is determined, a variety of probability questions can easily be answered. Unlike the probability distribution of Section 1, where the probability function or rule differed for every distribution, the binomial probability function always remains the same. The function must be applied to every value of the random variable. That is, the formula must be applied to every value of $x$. Collectively, the probabilities create the distribution.

### Binomial Probability Function

$$P(x) = \binom{n}{x} p^x q^{n-x}$$

where

$\binom{n}{x}$ is the binomial coefficient $= \dfrac{n!}{x!(n-x)!}$

$p$ is the probability of success.
$q$ is the probability of failure.
$x$ is the value of the random variable success.
$n$ is the number of trials.

The binomial coefficient requires the use of factorials, as indicated by the exclamation point. The factorial of any number is the product of it and all the integers of lesser value, down to 1. Therefore, $4! = 4 \cdot 3 \cdot 2 \cdot 1 = 24$, $3! = 3 \cdot 2 \cdot 1 = 6$, $2! = 2 \cdot 1 = 2$ and $1! = 1 \cdot 1 = 1$. It is very important to remember a special factorial that surprises most people: $0! = 1$.

As *n* increases, the binomial coefficient becomes more difficult to calculate. However, coefficient is the same as a combination learned in the last chapter and therefore, can be found using the TI 83/84 series calculators. The coefficient is only the first part of the formula needed when calculating the binomial probability. The coefficient is not a probability.

---

## EXAMPLE 7.7

**Experiment:** Observe the sex of the next two babies born at General Hospital. What is the probability distribution of the number of boys born?

**Answer:** $X$ = number of boys born at General Hospital

| *x* | *P(x)* |
|:---:|:---:|
| 0 | .25 |
| 1 | .50 |
| 2 | .25 |
| **Total** | **1.00** |

**Solution:** This is a binomial probability distribution, because it meets all the conditions of the binomial distribution.

Condition 1: There are *n* independent trials. Each baby born is a trial. If two babies are to be observed, *n*= 2.

Condition 2: There are two possible outcomes, as defined by the random variable that a boy is born.

Condition 3: The two outcomes are classified as success (a boy is born) and a failure (a boy is not born).

Condition 4: The probability of success and the probability of failure remain the same across all trials. The probability that the first baby born is a boy is .5. The probability that it is not a boy is also .5. The probabilities are the same for the sex of the second baby. The probability of success and failure add to 1.0, or $p + q = 1$.

Condition 5: The trials are independent. The probability that the first baby is a boy does not affect the probability that the second baby is a boy. The binomial function may now be applied to each value of $X$. Where there are 2 babies born, it is possible to have no boys, 1 boy, or 2 boys. Therefore, $x = 0, 1, 2$, where $n = 2$, $p = .5$, and $q = .5$ The probability distribution is calculated as follows:

$$P(0) = \binom{2}{0}(.5)^0 (.5)^{2-0} = \frac{2!}{1!(2-0)!}(1)(.25) = .25$$

$$P(1) = \binom{2}{1}(.5)^1 (.5)^{2-1} = \frac{2!}{1!(2-1)!}(1)(.25) = .50$$

$$P(2) = \binom{2}{2}(.5)^2 (.5)^{2-2} = \frac{2!}{2!(2-2)!}(.25)(1) = .25$$

The binomial probability distribution allows for easy manipulation of the probabilities to determine the probability of a number of events. Events can be defined in such a manner that the probability of one or more values of $x$ fulfills the event. When two or more values of $x$ fulfill an event, their probabilities are added. Some key words to look for are "less than," "less than or equal to," "greater than," "greater than or equal to," "not greater than," and "not more than." These key words usually require the addition of two or more probabilities.

If a binomial probability distribution has a random variable with values of 0, 1, 2, and 3, and one wishes to find the probability that an event occurs at 2 or more times, the probability of $x$ at 2 and of $x$ at 3 are added together. The notation for such an event is written $P(x \geq 2)$. Be careful with the definitions. If greater than $x$ is sought, then the value cited as $x$ is not included in the calculation. For example, to find the probability of $x$ greater than 2, $P(x > 2)$, requires adding the probability of $x = 3$ and all probabilities of $x$ values greater than 3. But if $P(x \geq 2)$ then the probability of $x = 2$ is also included, adding the probabilities of $x$ values of 2, 3, and all others greater. Recall the addition theorem (Chapter 6). When two or more outcomes make up an event, the probability of their union is the addition of the two (or more) probabilities minus the probability of their intersection. Binomial distributions do not involve intersections, because the outcomes are mutually exclusive events. The probability of unions is, thus, the sum of all the outcomes' probabilities.

### EXAMPLE 7.8

**Experiment:** Six members of congress are up for reelection. Each election is a toss-up. What is the probability distribution for the number of members winning reelection?

**Answer:** $X$ = number of members winning reelection

| x | P(x) |
|---|------|
| 0 | .016 |
| 1 | .093 |
| 2 | .236 |
| 3 | .313 |
| 4 | .236 |
| 5 | .093 |
| 6 | .016 |
| **Total** | **1.000** |

**Solution:** This is a binomial distribution, because all the conditions are fulfilled.

Condition 1: There are six elections. Each election represents a trial, so $n = 6$.

Condition 2: There are two possible outcomes: Success is winning the election, and failure is losing the election.

Condition 3: The probabilities of success and failure remain the same. Since each election is a toss-up (50/50 chance for each candidate in each election), $p = .5$ and $q = .5$.

Condition 4: $p + q = 1.0$. Here, $.5 + .5 = 1.0$.

Condition 5: Each election is independent. No election affects the outcome of any other election (this is assumed, because no other information is given). The binomial function must be applied to each value of $x$.

The random variable has values of 0, 1, 2, 3, 4, 5, and 6; $p = .5$; $q = .5$; $n = 6$.

$$P(0) = \binom{6}{0}(.5)^0 (.5)^{6-0} = 0.16$$

$$P(1) = \binom{6}{1}(.5)^1 (.5)^{6-1} = .093$$

$$P(2) = \binom{6}{2}(.5)^2 (.5)^{6-2} = .236$$

$$P(3) = \binom{6}{3}(.5)^3(.5)^{6-3} = .313$$

$$P(4) = \binom{6}{4}(.5)^4(.5)^{6-4} = .236$$

$$P(5) = \binom{6}{5}(.5)^5(.5)^{6-5} = .093$$

$$P(6) = \binom{6}{6}(.5)^6(.5)^{6-6} = .016$$

## EXAMPLE 7.9

**Experiment:** Using the binomial probability distribution from Example 7.8, congressional reelections, find the following:

a. The probability that three members will win reelection.
b. The probability that no more than three will win reelection.
c. The probability that more than four will win reelection.

**Answer:**
a. $P(x = 3) = .313$
b. $P(x \leq 3) = .656$
c. $P(x > 4) = .109$

**Solution:**
The TI-83/84 series calculators include the binomial probability functions. The binomial function includes two options. One option is to find the probability of a specific value of a random variable $X$. The specific value of $x$ is also written as $r$. So $P(x)$ is also written as $P(r)$. The second option finds the cumulative probability for $r$ (again, $r$ is the same as $x$) and fewer successes ($\leq$). Adjustments can be made to find the probabilities for $r$ and more successes. The two functions are binompdf for probability of a specific value $r$ and binomcdf for cumulative probability from 0 up to $r$. To enter the data, it is in the order of $(n, p, r)$ where $n$ is the number of trials, $p$ is the probability of success, and $r$ is the specific value of the random variable $X$.

a. The probability that three members will win reelection means that only the probability that $x = 3$ is sought. From the binomial probability distribution presented in Example 7.8, the probability is .313. To find this answer, begin by pressing the 2nd and then the VARS button, to select DISTR, which is written above it. Scroll down to binompdf(. Press ENTER. Determine the proper number of trials, probability of success, and $x$ value, then plug them into your calculator. Highlight "Paste" and press ENTER. Press ENTER again, and the calculator will display the numerical value.

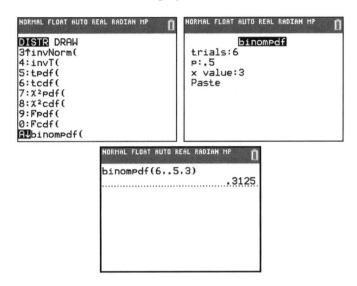

$$P(x = 3) = .313$$

b. The probability that no more than three will win reelection means that the probability of three or fewer is sought. This problem requires the use of the binomialcdf( function in your calculator, to give a probability that is cumulative from 0, to your $x$ value. Begin again by pressing the 2nd button and then the VARS button. Scroll down to binomialcdf(. Plug in the number of trials, the probability of success, and the $x$ value. Highlight "Paste" and press ENTER. Press ENTER again, and the calculator will display the numerical value.

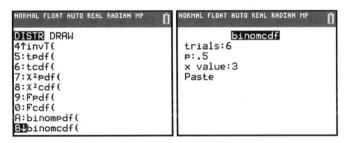

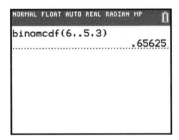

$$P(x \le 3) = P(0) + P(1) + P(2) + P(3) = .656$$

c. The probability that more than four will win also requires use of the addition theorem. The value of four is not asked for, because more than four is sought. Binomialcdf( is cumulative from 0, so to find the answer, which asks for a result "greater than four," use the binomialcdf( function with the *x* value as 4. Plug the *x* value along with the probability of success and number of trials into your calculator, highlight "Paste" and press ENTER. Press ENTER again for the numerical value. Considering the fact that binomialcdf( is cumulative from 0, and this question requires observing probabilities of outcomes greater than four, 1-binomialcdf( will give the correct answer. Press 1 and the subtraction button, then 2nd and the (-) button. Press ENTER and the results should appear as follows:

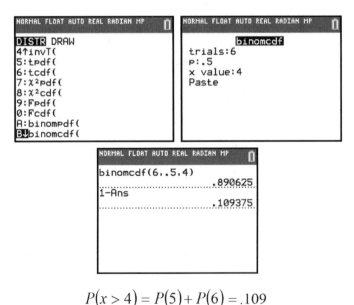

$$P(x > 4) = P(5) + P(6) = .109$$

## A LEARNING AID
## BINOMIAL PROBABILITY DISTRIBUTIONS

The governors of five states are meeting in Washington, D.C., to go before a congressional committee on crime problems across the nation. Each governor arrives separately by plane, and all planes arrive independently at 9 a.m. If the probability that each plane arrives on time is 0.4, what is the probability that at least three of the planes arrive on time?

### Step 1

This a binomial probability, because a binomial is a special kind of probability distribution that defines outcomes as one of two categories. These categories can be described as success and failure. In this example, success occurs when a plane arrives on time. Check to see that all the conditions for the binomial probability are met.

Condition 1: There is a fixed number of trials, n. In this example, $n$ is equal to 5. There are five governors arriving in Washington, so the arrival of each governor represents a trial.

Condition 2: There are only two outcomes, defined as success and failure. Success is a governor arriving on time. Failure is a governor not arriving on time.

Condition 3: The probabilities of $p$ and $q$ must remain constant. The probability of arriving on time is the same for each governor. The probability of not arriving on time is also the same for each governor.

Condition 4: Success *(p)* is stated as .4.

Since $p + q = 1.0$, subtract $p$ from 1.0 to find $q$: $1 - .4 = .6$, so $q = .6$.

Condition 5: The outcomes of each trial must be independent of those of all other trials. Each governor is arriving independently of all others. Therefore, arriving on time for any one governor does not affect any other governor's arrival time.

### Step 2

State the random variable, $X$, and its values, $x$. $X$ is "a governor arrives on time"; its values, $x$, are 0, 1, 2, 3, 4, and 5. No governors could arrive on time, or one, two, three, four, or five could arrive on time.

**Step 3**

Now you can go back to the original problem and state the event being asked. You were asked to find the probability that at least 3 of the planes arrived on time. At least 3 means 3 or more planes. Therefore, the event you are looking for is the union of 3, 4, and 5 on-time arrivals. Looking at probabilities in this direction requires utilizing the binomialcdf( function to observe the cumulative probability for events of on time arrival of 0, 1, 2, or 3 planes. Press the 2nd button, followed by pressing the VARS button, select binomialcdf(, adhere to the following settings, highlight "Paste" and press ENTER. Now press 1 and "—" then 2nd and the "(--)" button. Press ENTER again and the answer will be displayed.

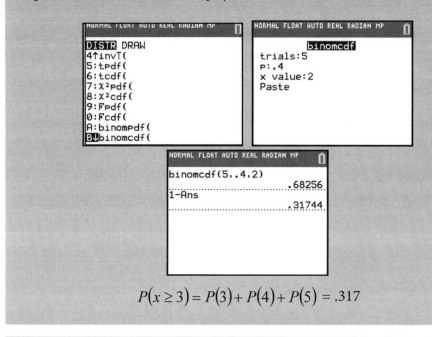

$$P(x \geq 3) = P(3) + P(4) + P(5) = .317$$

## SECTION 5

### Mean and Standard Deviation of a Binomial Distribution

As all probability distributions represent theoretical populations, so too does the binomial distribution. Remember, the binomial probability distribution is simply a special kind of probability distribution, and all statistics representing populations are known as parameters and are usually represented by Greek letters.

Binomial probability distributions also lend themselves to description by parameters. With all probability distributions, means and standard deviations of binomials represent theoretical populations. The mean of the binomial is also represented by the Greek letter $\mu$. The standard deviation of the binomial is represented by the Greek letter $\sigma$. The mean and standard deviation for a binomial probability distribution are easily calculated.

The formula for the mean of a binomial distribution is very easy. Recall the formula in Section 3 of this chapter for the mean of a probability distribution. It was quite lengthy and required each value of $x$ to be multiplied by its probability. Then all products were summed. The formula for the mean of a binomial probability distribution does not require each value of $x$ to be identified. Both the formula just presented and the formula presented in Section 3 calculate means for probability distributions. They will both result in the same answer any time the random variable $x$ fulfills the conditions of a binomial distribution. In fact, many of the examples in Section 2 were binomials. It may be wise to look back at Section 3 and calculate the means with the new formula to see that the same answers are obtained.

---

**Mean for a Binomial Probability Distribution**

$$\mu = n \cdot p$$

where
  $n$ is the number of independent trials.
  $p$ is the probability of success.

---

The mean for the binomial probability distribution requires that the number of independent trials, n, be multiplied by the probability of success, $p$. The only catch with this formula is to identify success correctly. Sometimes a question defines a problem in such a way that the probability of failure is sought. Be careful not to define failure as success when calculating the mean.

---

**EXAMPLE 7.10**

**Experiment:** Using the information from Example 7.5, calculate and compare the mean using the formula for a probability distribution given in Section 3 and the formula for a binomial probability distribution given here. A coin is tossed three times. Find the mean for the random variable $x$, the number of heads occurring.

**Answer:** $\mu = \Sigma[x \cdot P(x)] = 1.5, \quad \mu = n \cdot p = 1.5$

**Solution:** The mean for a probability distribution is found by multiplying each $x$ by its probability then adding all the products. Recall that the

---

probability of each *x* in a distribution must be found. Using the probability distribution from Example 7.5, the mean was found to be 1.5. When performing calculations, show all steps.

| *x* | *P(x)* | *x • P(x)* |
|-----|--------|------------|
| 0 | .125 | .000 |
| 1 | .375 | .375 |
| 2 | .375 | .750 |
| 3 | .125 | .375 |
| | **1.000** | **1.500** |

$$\mu = \sum [x \cdot P(x)] = 1.5$$

However, tossing a coin and observing heads is a binomial, and the mean for a binomial is much easier to calculate. All conditions of a binomial distribution are met: There are three trials ($n = 3$); there are only two possible outcomes, heads or no heads; the probability of heads is .5 and remains constant; the probability, *p*, of success (heads) is .5 and the probability of failure, *q*, is .5; .5 + .5 = 1.0; and each toss is independent of the other tosses. The binomial mean requires *n* to be multiplied by *p*. The number of trials is 3, representing each toss. The probability of success on any one toss is .5:

$$\mu = n \cdot p = 3 \cdot (5) = 1.5$$

The formula for the standard deviation of a binomial distribution is also easily calculated. It is the square root of the product of the number of trials, the probability of success, and the probability of failure.

**Standard Deviation for a Binomial Probability Distribution**

$$\sigma = \sqrt{n \cdot p \cdot q}$$

where
    *n* is the number of trials.
    *p* is the probability of success.
    *q* is the probability of failure.

The standard deviation is the square root of the number of trials multiplied by the probability of success and the probability of failure. As in the calculation of the mean for a binomial distribution, the standard deviation of a binomial distribution does not require the calculation of the full probability distribution. This makes the calculations easier and faster. The ease of these calculations makes the mean and standard deviation formulas preferred over the formulas in Section 3 when a probability distribution can be defined as a binomial probability distribution.

### EXAMPLE 7.12

**Experiment:** Six members of congress are up for reelection. Each election is a toss-up. What are the mean and standard deviation of the number of members winning reelection?

**Answer:** $\mu = 3$, $\sigma = 1.225$

**Solution:** This is a binomial. To summarize the conditions for a binomial, this problem has two possible outcomes: winning and not winning. There are six independent trials, representing the six members and their individual elections. The probability of success is a toss-up in any one election, which is a probability of .5 of success. The mean requires the product of $n$, the number of trials, and $p$, the probability of success. There are six independent trials. The chance of any one member winning has a probability of .5. Thus, $\mu = n \cdot p = 6$ (.5), or 3. The standard deviation is the square root of $n \cdot p \cdot q$. The probability of $q$ is $1 - p$. Because $p = .5$, $q$ is also .5 ($1 - .5 = .5$). When performing calculations, show all steps. $n = 6$, $p = .5$ and $q = .5$

$$\mu = n \cdot p = 6(.5) = 3$$
$$\sigma = \sqrt{n \cdot p \cdot q} = \sqrt{6(.5)(.5)} = \sqrt{1.5} = 1.225$$

### A LEARNING AID
### MEAN AND STANDARD DEVIATION OF BINOMIAL DISTRIBUTION

Use the same information in the Learning Aid for Section 4 to find the mean and the standard deviation of the number of planes that can be expected to arrive on time.

To summarize the information, five governors are meeting in Washington, DC. Each arrives separately and each arrival is independent of other arrivals. The probability that each plane will arrive on time is .4.

### Step 1

This is a binomial, because there are only two outcomes defined as success and failure. Success occurs when a plane arrives on time. Success, $p$, is set at

.4. Failure, $q$, is 1 minus success, or $1 - .4 = .6$. There are five trials ($n = 5$), and each is independent of the others.

**Step 2**
To find the mean, multiply the number of trials to the probability of success:

$$\mu = n \cdot p = (5)(.4) = 2$$

The mean for a binomial distribution is much easier to find than the mean for other probability distributions. The full probability distribution is not necessary.

**Step 3**
To find the standard deviation, first multiply the number of trials by the probability of success and the probability of failure. Second, take the square root of the product.

$$\sigma = \sqrt{n \cdot p \cdot q} = \sqrt{(5)(.4)(.6)} = \sqrt{1.2} = 1.095$$

## *CHAPTER 7 IN REVIEW*

7.1    Indicate yes or no if the following fulfill the requirements for a discrete probability function?

   a. $P(x) = \dfrac{x}{2 - x}$ for $x = 0,1$

   b. $P(G) = g - 1$ for $g = 0,1,2$

   c. $P(H) = \dfrac{h}{4}$ for $h = -2,0,2,4$

   d. $P(Q) = \dfrac{q + 2}{6}$ for $q = -1,0,1$

7.2    The probability making the basket for the leading NBA free throw shooter is .914. What is the expected number of baskets would we expect if he regularly attempts 12 a game?

7.3    If the probability of being a nursing student is .40, what is the probability that 4 of the next 5 students walking in to the library is a nursing student?

7.4    Ninety percent of the students in the class are not married. A sample of 20 students is taken. What is the probability that:

a. No more than 15 will not be married?

b. Exactly 15 will be married?

c. Exactly half will be not married?

d. All would be not married?

e. What are the expected mean and standard deviation of not being married?

7.5    Eighty percent of people arrested for illegal weapons possession are men while only 20 percent are women. If 50 arrestees are randomly selected, what is the probability that:

a. All 50 will be men?

b. Only 40 would be men?

c. There would be 15 women?

d. What are the expected mean and standard deviation of the number of men?

7.6    Thirty percent of medical malpractice cases were settled out of court, 68 percent were dismissed and 2 percent actually had jury verdicts. If 8 cases were examined, what is the probability that:

a. All were settled out of court?

b. None were settled out of court?

c. Exactly half were settled out of court?

d. No more than half were settled out of court?

e. What are the expected mean and standard deviation of settled cases?

7.7    Twenty percent of non-voters in the U.S. say that do not vote because they are too busy. Fifteen percent say they don't vote because of illness or emergency. Five percent say they are not interested. If 20 non-voters are randomly selected, what is the probability that:

a. All would say they are too busy?

b. No more than 2 would say they are too busy?

c. None would say they are too busy?

d. What are the expected mean and standard deviation of the number to say they are too busy?

7.8    If the probability of a cell phone network dropping a call is .15, what is the probability that all the next 10 calls will be dropped? That all will not be dropped?

7.9    Seventy percent of college students must take a statistics course. In a random sample of 50 students, what is the probability that:

a. Exactly half are required to take statistics?

b. That at least 25 must take statistics?

c. That no more than 30 must take statistics?

d. That all must take statistics?

e. What are the expected mean and standard deviation of students NOT taking statistics?

7.10 The probability that the entire class will show-up for class today is .75. If the class size is 30, what is the probability that:
a. No more than 25 will show-up?
b. At least 25 show up?
c. Exactly half will show up?
d. Less than half will show up?

7.11 In a recent year, 36 percent of bureaucrats worked in the Defense Department, 25 percent worked in the Postal Service, and 39 percent worked in all other agencies. In a random sample of six employees, what is the probability that:
a. Three work in the Defense Department?
b. Three work in the Postal Service?
c. What are the expected mean and standard deviation for the number working in the Defense Department?

7.12 Fifteen local politicians were charged with embezzling school tax monies. If the probability of being found guilty is .7, what is the probability that:
a. All 15 will be found guilty?
b. None will be found guilty?
c. At least 8 will be found guilty?
d. Exactly 10 will be found guilty?
e. What are the mean and standard deviation of the expected number of politicians that will be found guilty?

7.13 It is reported that only 20 percent of all car salespersons are women. In a survey of salespersons, 10 were asked their gender.
a. What is the probability that no more than one respondent was a female?
b. What is the probability that none of the respondents are female?
c. What is the probability that all are male?
d. What is the probability that at least 8 are male?
e. What are the mean and standard deviation of the number of females?

7.14 Twenty percent of full-time students drop out of a university. If a random sample of 6 students is taken, what is the probability that:
a. No more than 2 students will drop out of school?
b. Three students will drop out of school?
c. No students will drop out?
d. All students will drop out?
e. What are the mean and standard deviation of the number of students from the sample that will drop out of school?

7.15 Sixty percent of the population is overweight. If a sample of 12 people were taken, what is the probability that:

    a. Half of the people are overweight?
    b. No person is overweight?
    c. No more than 8 are overweight?
    d. At least 11 are overweight?
    e. What is the expected mean for the sample?

7.16  Fifty percent of American marriages end in divorce. If 12 married couples are randomly selected, what is the probability that:
    a. All would end in divorce?
    b. No more than 3 would end in divorce?
    c. Half would end in divorce?
    d. None would end in divorce?
    e. What are the expected mean and standard deviation of the number to end in divorce?

7.17  Former President George W. Bush's appointments to the Federal district courts consisted of 61 percent Protestant, 30 percent Catholic, and 8 percent Jewish appointees. In a random sample of 6 justices, list the probability distribution for the random variable of a Catholic being appointed.

7.18  If 75 percent of the public favors the death penalty for murderers, then what are the expected mean and standard deviation that favor the death penalty in a random sample of 20 people?

7.19  Of the babies born out of wedlock, 64 percent are born to African American females. In a random sample of 10 babies born out of wedlock, what is the probability that at least 6 were born to African American females?

7.20  Sixty percent of the criminal cases coming before Judge Demitra result in convictions. The judge will hear five independent cases tomorrow. What is each probability?
    a. Exactly 3 convictions
    b. No more than 3 convictions
    c. At least 3 convictions
    d. No convictions
    e. All convictions

7.21  In 2010, 28 percent of Americans lived in central cities, 47 percent lived in the suburbs, and 25 percent lived in non-metropolitan areas. A random sample of 8 people is taken.

   a. What is the probability that 6 lived in the central city?
   b. What is the probability that 6 lived in a suburb?
   c. What is the probability that 6 lived in a non-metropolitan area?
   d. Find the mean and standard deviation of the number of people expected to be in the suburbs.

7.22  Thirty-five percent of children in juvenile court receive probation. Of the next four cases, what is the probability that at least half will receive probation? What is the probability that all would receive probation?

7.23  If 85 percent of homes in the United States have a computer, what is the average number of homes that should have a computer in a random sample of 20 homes? What is the expected standard deviation?

7.24  Eighty percent of Americans claim that they are middle class. In a random sample of 14 Americans, what is the average number claiming to be middle class?

7.25  True or False?
   a. Binomials are continuous random variables.
   b. Binomials require two separate variables.
   c. Binomial probability distributions must sum to 1.0.
   d. Non-Binomial discrete probability distributions must sum to 1.0.
   e. The expected mean is represented by the Greek letter $\mu$.

# 8

# *NORMAL PROBABILITY DISTRIBUTIONS*

***SECTION 1*** **Continuous Random Variable**
***SECTION 2*** **Normal Probability Distributions: Concept and Calculation**
***SECTION 3*** **Normal Probability Table**
***SECTION 4*** **Calculating Normal Probabilities**
***SECTION 5*** **Normal Approximation of the Binomial Distribution**

Chapter 7 combined the concepts of frequency distributions of discrete variables with probabilities, creating discrete or binomial probability distributions. Discrete variables were described as counts. Recall that there is another kind of variable, which uses measurements instead of counts. Variables that use measures instead of counts are called continuous variables. Continuous variables typically measure distance, time, or temperature. Many of the social sciences also measure continuous concepts, such as the degree of support for a candidate, the income level of a group of people, or the degree of racial integration of a community. Any variable that uses measures instead of counts is a continuous variable.

This chapter combines the concept of a frequency distribution of a continuous variable with probabilities. The probability distribution of a continuous variable can take many shapes. One of the most common shapes of a continuous probability distribution is the bell-shaped distribution. The bell-shaped distribution is also known as the Gaussian, or normal, distribution.

The bell-shaped distribution reflects the probability distribution of continuous variables representing standard scores or $z$-scores. The $z$-score was first presented in Chapter 3. This chapter will extend the use of the $z$-score as a probability using a table in the appendix. Adjustments to the probabilities from the table may be necessary depending on what portion of the bell-shaped curve is desired. Essentially, probability questions are presented $P(x\ldots)$. The raw data is transformed into a $z$-score as familiar from Chapter 3. The $z$-score will be converted into a probability using Table A.3 and then adjusted as necessary.

$P(x\ldots)\rightarrow\rightarrow$Convert raw data $x$ into $z$-score$\rightarrow\rightarrow$
Convert $z$-score into Probability$\rightarrow\rightarrow$(adjust Prob if necessary)

# *Section 1*

## Continuous Random Variable

As binomials represented a discrete random variable, the normal bell-shaped curve represents continuous random variables. A ***continuous random variable*** is a random variable whose values are usually found by measuring. The probability distribution of the continuous random variable can take on many shapes. The most commonly described distribution is the normal, or bell-shaped, distribution. Although the calculations of the normal distribution are very difficult, the use of a table to determine probabilities for any normally distributed random variable is relatively easy.

**Continuous random variable** A variable that describes a measurement. It can take on an infinite number of values. When describing intervals, a continuous random variable can take on an infinite number of possible values in the interval.

Continuous random variables use measures instead of counts. They also can take on an infinite number of values. That is, the number of values a continuous random variable can have is limited only by the measuring device. For example, if a digital scale measures whole pounds, a person may weigh 175 lbs. However, another scale may measure in tenths of pounds, and the same person may weigh 175.4 lbs. On yet another scale, the person may weigh 175.49 lbs. It is obvious that weight is a continuous measurement whose values are limited only by the measuring device.

Continuous random variables often describe a measurement between two designated points. The interval between the points is continuous if the number of possible values is infinite. If the number of values between two points is infinite, then the random variable is continuous. If the number of values is finite, then the random variable is discrete. For example, counting the number of desks in a classroom between the first row and the last row is a discrete count between two designated points. The count is finite because the number of values is clearly represented by the number of desks. However, the distance between the desks in the first row and the desks in the second row is a continuous measurement. The distance between the two designated points is viewed as infinite, because the measuring device used can always be improved to give an infinite number of possibilities. A ruler marked in inches can be used, as well as one marked in quarter inches. A ruler can be improved to measure in smaller and smaller increments. Thus, it is said to have an infinite number of values.

**EXAMPLE 8.1**

**Experiment:** Determine if the following are discrete or continuous random variables:

a. Number of students in class with black hair
b. Time necessary to get from home to school
c. Change in the temperature of the room during 1 hour
d. Number of pencils sold in the bookstore in 1 day

**Answer:**

a. Discrete
b. Continuous
c. Continuous
d. Discrete

**Solution:**

a. The number of students in class with black hair is discrete, because it is a count. The values are represented by counting the number of students in the class with black hair.

b. The time necessary to get from home to school is continuous. Time is a continuous random variable, because it requires a measurement. Its measuring instrument is typically a watch, and the values the random variable can take on are limited only by the instrument.

c. As is time, temperature is a continuous random variable. The change in the temperature of a room must be measured with some sort of thermometer, whose values are limited by the thermometer itself. As technology is developed, thermometers will have fewer limitations.

d. The number of pencils sold in a day is discrete. To determine the number, one simply counts the number of pencils sold.

**A LEARNING AID**
**CONTINUOUS RANDOM VARIABLE**

You are asked to measure the change in your body's temperature between morning and night. Identify the three continuous variables involved in this experiment.

**Step 1**

Identify the events. There are three different events occurring: (1) measuring your temperature in the morning, (2) measuring your temperature at night, and (3) measuring the change in the temperature readings from morning to night.

**Step 2**
Address each event as a variable, noting whether the variable is continuous or discrete.

**Variable 1:** *Temperature in the morning.* Temperature is a measurement and is, therefore, continuous. Continuous variables measure; discrete variables count. Suppose your temperature is 98.0 in the morning. Your thermometer is the traditional type marked with .2° increments. In reality, you visually estimated your temperature; it looked closer to the 98.0 marking. But if you had a digital thermometer, it might have revealed your temperature to be closer to 98.1. Yet a third digital thermometer measuring in hundredths might reveal your temperature is 98.08. Every time the measuring device is improved, the measurement might change. Thus, the measurement is limited only by the measuring device.

**Variable 2:** *Temperature at night.* Again, temperature is a continuous measurement limited by the measuring device. Your traditional thermometer now reads 98.8, but the digital thermometer reads 98.7, and the other digital thermometer reads 98.77.

**Variable 3:** *Change of temperature from morning to night.* This variable is a measurement between two points. It is referred to as an interval. Not only are the two temperature readings continuous, so, too, is the distance between them. It is easy to comprehend the mathematical difference between 98.0 and 98.8 (an increase of .8). It may be a little more difficult to comprehend the continuous interval between these points, which is limited only by the measuring device. There are infinitely many possibilities in measuring intervals. One measuring device may be in tenths; another may be in hundredths. The distance between two points is a continuous variable.

# SECTION 2

## Normal Probability Distributions: Concept and Calculation

The normal probability distribution is yet another kind of probability distribution. Unlike those discussed in Chapter 7, the normal probability distribution describes the theoretical distribution of continuous data. Although the distribution could be described by a probability function, the calculations are much more difficult than the functions describing other probability distributions. However, there is a relatively easy way of calculating various probabilities using what is known as a standard $z$-score and a probability table found in Appendix A.3.

> **Normal Probability Distribution** A probability distribution describing continuous random variables. The distribution is plotted as a bell-shaped curve that is symmetric, with the mean, mode, and median in the center. It is also known as a normal curve.

The normal probability distribution can be plotted as a bell-shaped curve. The bell-shaped curve is a symmetric curve with its maximum height in the center and what are known as tails at either end. See Figure 8.1.

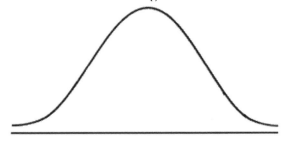

**FIGURE 8.1 The Normal Curve**

Many of the phenomena that social scientists study approximate the normal curve. For example, most Americans are ideologically middle of the road, or moderate. Americans pretty evenly disperse themselves around the middle, becoming more liberal on one side and more conservative on the other side. Both sides then almost consistently taper off equally in both directions as the numbers of people with increasingly liberal or conservative views diminish. This is illustrated in Figure 8.2.

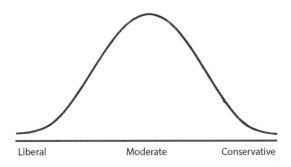

Liberal          Moderate          Conservative

**FIGURE 8.2**

The normal probability distribution has two parameters, $\mu$ and $\sigma$. Recall that the mean describes central tendency. All measures of central tendency are equal to the mean in a normal probability distribution. As expected by looking at the bell-shaped curve, the mean, mode, and median all occur in the center (Figure 8.3). Since the distribution is a probability distribution and is, therefore, theoretical, the mean represents a population and is represented by the symbol $\mu$.

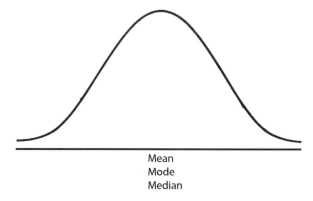

Mean
Mode
Median

**FIGURE 8.3**

The standard deviation, $\sigma$, describes dispersion around the mean. Recall that the standard deviation describes how far the average value of $x$ deviates from the mean. Standard deviations in a *normal probability distribution* may deviate both to the left and to the right of the mean.

**EXAMPLE 8.2**

**Experiment:** The height of a variety of delphinium flowers is normally distributed with a mean of 68 inches and a standard deviation of 2 inches. On a normal probability curve, place the mean value in its appropriate place and also show three standard deviations above and below the mean.

**Answer:**

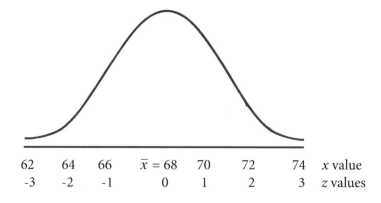

| 62 | 64 | 66 | $\bar{x} = 68$ | 70 | 72 | 74 | $x$ value |
| -3 | -2 | -1 | 0 | 1 | 2 | 3 | $z$ values |

**Solution:** Begin by drawing the curve. Place the mean in the center. Because the standard deviation is 2 inches, one standard deviation above the mean must be 68 + 2, or 70, inches. Two standard deviations above the mean is 72, and three is 74. To find the values corresponding to the standard deviations below the mean, repeatedly subtract 2 inches. One standard deviation below the mean equals 68 - 2, or 66, inches. Two standard deviations below the mean is 64, and three below the mean is 62. Notice that the distribution is normal; the heights of the flowers cluster around the mean, with other heights deviating almost equally in both directions. The highest point in the center of the curve represents where most of the flowers are clustered.

It would be very cumbersome to calculate a probability distribution for each population and for each mean and standard deviation. To make the task much easier, the random variable that the distribution describes can be transformed into a standard normal variable known as a standard score, standard $z$-score, or, simply, a $z$-score.

**Standard Normal Variable (standard score, z-score)** A standard score that transforms any normally distributed random variable into a distribution that has an expected mean, $\mu$, of 0 and whose standard deviation is 1. The formula for the transformation is:

$$z = \frac{x - \mu}{\sigma}$$

This formula allows the transformation of any random variable $X$ into a standard score. The actual values of the mean and standard deviation are not important on the distribution itself. The transformation adjusts all means to a standard score, 0, and all standard deviations to a standard score of 1. This transformation allows the comparison of several values of $x$ either from the same population or from different populations.

The standard score, $z$, can be either negative or positive. A negative score falls below the mean, whereas a positive $z$-score falls above the mean. Remember, the mean has a $z$-score of 0. Standard $z$-scores are simply standardized standard deviations. Typically, $z$-scores are rounded to two decimal places. The scores should be determined to at least three decimal places and rounded to two. A calculated score of 1.234 should be rounded to a $z$-score of 1.23.

**EXAMPLE 8.3**

**Experiment:** If the height of a variety of delphinium flowers is normally distributed with a mean of 68 inches and a standard deviation of 2 inches, what $z$-score would a flower have if it is 63 inches tall?

**Answer:** $z = -2.5$

**Solution:** This is a normal probability distribution because height is a continuous random variable (it is a measurement). Begin by calculating the $z$-score. The value of $\mu$, is given as 68 inches, and $\sigma$ is given as 2. The value of $x$ that you are given is 63. When performing calculations, show all work.

$$z = \frac{x - \mu}{\sigma}$$

$$= \frac{63 - 68}{2}$$

$$= \frac{-5}{2}$$

$$= -2.5$$

Be sure not to drop the negative sign. The negative sign means that the $z$-score is to the left of the mean. It may help to visualize the answer on the following distribution:

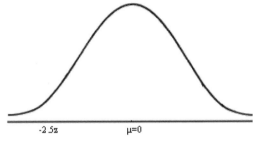

One of the most important uses of the standard $z$-score is in describing the probabilities associated with intervals between specific values of $z$. This is accomplished by first dividing the distribution in half and then calculating probabilities from the center of the distribution out to a specific point. The full distribution has a probability of 1, with each half having a probability of .5.

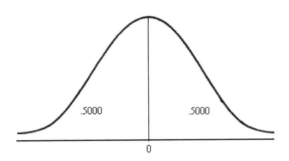

Before learning to transform $z$-scores into probabilities, it is important to summarize a few key points:

1. $z$-scores are not probabilities, but they can be translated into probabilities.
2. $z$-scores can be negative or positive. The sign indicates on which side of the curve a value falls relative to the mean, which is adjusted to 0.
3. $z$-scores are simply standardized standard deviations.
4. Probabilities can only be positive, ranging from 0 to 1.
5. The full curve represents a probability of 1. Each half is .5000.

## A LEARNING AID
## NORMAL PROBABILITY DISTRIBUTIONS

If the mean body temperature is 98.6° with a standard deviation of .4, what $z$-score would a person have if her body temperature is 98.1°?

**Step 1**
Determine if this is a continuous variable. Temperature is a continuous variable since it measures instead of counts.

**Step 2**
Decide if this is a normal probability distribution. Although you cannot be sure, continuous variables are typically described using a normal curve. Also, the question implies it is normally distributed, because it asks for the standard $z$-score.

**Step 3**
Calculate the $z$-score. The calculation requires an $x$ value representing the person's temperature; here, $x = 98.1$. The calculation also requires the mean and standard deviation. These values are given: $\mu = 98.6$, $\sigma = .4$. Therefore,

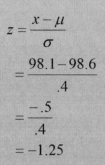

$$z = \frac{x - \mu}{\sigma}$$

$$= \frac{98.1 - 98.6}{.4}$$

$$= \frac{-.5}{.4}$$

$$= -1.25$$

**Step 4**

Interpret the result. The answer tells you the person's body temperature is below the mean at -1.25 standard $z$-scores. A standard $z$-score is a standardized standard deviation. It can be used to calculate probabilities or to compare values across populations with different means and standard deviations. The following curve represents the $z$-score in relation to the mean:

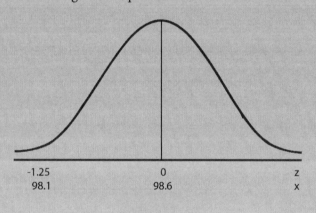

## SECTION 3

### Normal Probability Table

Table A.3 in Appendix A describes the probabilities associated with standard $z$-scores. It is important to become familiar with Table A.3, because it will also be used in several forthcoming chapters. Notice the curve at the top of Table A.3. The curve is a normal probability distribution that shows the mean, 0, at the center. The shaded area of the curve represents the area of the curve between the mean, 0, and $z$. This shaded area could be enlarged, reduced, or placed on the left of the curve, depending on the actual $z$-score. Notice the values of $z$ down the left of the page beginning with 0 and ending with 3.0. These values are given to one decimal place. To have two decimal places, the scores are combined with the $z$-scores across the top row of the table that represent second decimal places. For example, to find the probability for a z-score of 1.22, begin by going down the first column to 1.2. Then move over that row to the column corresponding to the second decimal place, .02 (see Table 8.1). The probability .3888, found at the intersection of the column and row, represents the z-score 1.22 (1.2 + .02 = 1.22).

**Table 8.1**
**Excerpt from Appendix Table A.3**

| z | 0.00 | 0.01 | 0.02 |
|---|------|------|------|
| ↓ |      |      | ...... |
| ↓ |      |      | ...... |
| 1.2 | →→ | →→ | .3888 |

The numbers in the body of the table are probabilities associated with the area of the curve from the mean 0 to a specific z-score. All probabilities read from the mean out to a specific place. Negative z-scores are found by symmetry. The negative sign of a z-score represents the side of the curve on which the probability falls; it does not make the probability itself negative.

**EXAMPLE 8.4**
**Experiment:** Find and interpret the area of the curve associated with a z-score of 2.12.

**Answer:** $P(0 \le z \le 2.12) = .4830$. The probability associated with the area from $\mu$ to 2.12 is .4830.

**Solution:** Begin with Table A.3. Find $z = 2.10$ in the first column and 0.02 across the top row. The value at the intersection of the column and row is .4830. Placing the value on a curve helps visualize the area found.

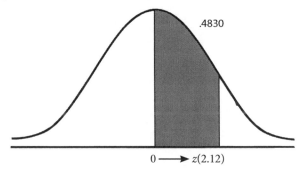

**EXAMPLE 8.5**

**Experiment:** Find and interpret the probability associated with the area of the curve for a *z*-score of -3.06.

**Answer:** $P(z = -3.06) = .4989$; the probability associated with the area of the curve from the mean to the *z*-score -3.06 is .4989.

**Solution:** Beginning with Table A.3, find the *z*-score of 3.0 in the first column and 0.06 in the top row. Find their intersection, which is the probability .4989. Remember that the curve is symmetric. The negative *z*-score value shows that the area of the curve is to the left of the mean. The *z*-score can be negative but a probability is never negative. Find the probability of a negative *z*-score in the same way you find that of a positive one. However, place the negative score and its probability to the left of the mean, as in the following curve:

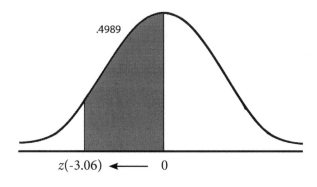

.4989

$z(-3.06) \longleftarrow 0$

Remember, the table describes the probability associated with the area of the curve from 0 to a *z*-score. To find the probability of the area of the curve beyond a specified point, subtraction is required. Remember, each side of the curve is associated with a probability of .5. If the probability of the area of the curve from the mean 0 to a specific point is known and if the probability of the whole curve is known, the probability beyond a specified point can be found by subtraction. Since the probability distribution of the normal curve is based on two symmetric halves of the curve, most answers can be found by subtracting from .5. For example, if the probability associated with the area from the mean 0 to a *z*-score of 1.52 is .4357 (see Table A.3), the probability associated with the area beyond the *z* of 1.52 is found by subtracting .4357 from .5. That is, the probability associated with the area beyond 1.52 is .5 - .4357 = .0643. The notation for this probability is $P(z \geq 1.52) = .0643$.

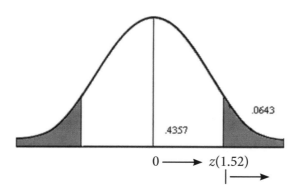

**EXAMPLE 8.6**
**Experiment:** Find $P(z \leq -.38)$

**Answer:** $P(z \leq -.38) = .3520$

**Solution:** Begin by looking up .3 in the left column of Table A.3. Read across the top row to .08 to find the second decimal place. You should find the value .1480 at the intersection. Remember, the negative sign shows that you are concerned with the left of the curve. Also notice that you are looking for the area of the curve to the left of the z-score -.38. Because the probability .1480 is from 0 to -.38 and you know that the whole side of the curve is .5, you can subtract .1480 from .5 to find the probability associated with the remaining portion of the area. It is the probability associated with the following shaded area of the curve that you are asked to find.

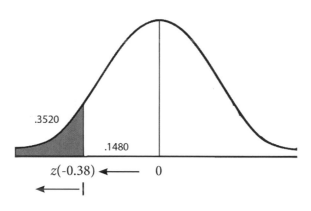

A question involving combinations of areas could be asked. It is usually helpful to draw and shade the area of the curve under consideration. The visual helps place negative signs and decide whether it is necessary to subtract the probability from .5 or make any other adjustments. There are times when it may be necessary to add a probability to .5 or to add two probabilities together. Remember, even when adding probabilities, the final probability is always between 0 and 1, inclusive.

**EXAMPLE 8.7**

**Experiment:** Find $P( z \geq -.38)$

**Answer:** $P( z \geq -.38) = .6480$

**Solution:** Find the probability associated with -.38 from Table A.3. The value at which .30 and .08 intersect is .1480. Placing the information on the curve and shading the desired area allows you to see whether you need to do any subtractions or additions. Notice that part of what you want is the area associated with the curve from the mean, 0, to -.38. This area has a probability of .1480. But you also want all the area of the curve to the right of -.38. This includes the whole second half of the curve. The probability associated with half of the curve is .5000. In this case, you want to add .1480 to .5000 to obtain the probability of .6480. The rule is to add anytime you cross the center.

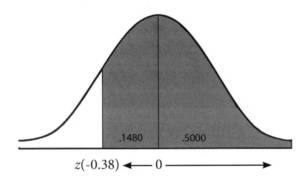

$z(-0.38) \longleftarrow 0 \longrightarrow$

**EXAMPLE 8.8**

**Experiment:** Find $P (.60 \leq z \leq 1.5)$

**Answer:** $P (.60 \leq z \leq 1.5) = .2075$

**Solution:** You must treat the two *z*-scores separately before finding the probability between them. First, find the probability from 0 to .60. Table A.3 shows a probability of .2257 for $z = .60$. The *z*-score of 1.5 has a probability of .4332. You are asked to find the probability associated with the area between these two $z$ values. To do this, subtract the smaller probability from the larger. The logic of this is that since both probabilities read from the mean to a specific point, you can subtract the smaller probability from the larger to leave only the area between them. Again, it is always recommended that you illustrate the area of the curve that you want to find.

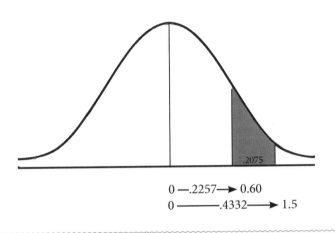

$$0 \text{ —.2257} \rightarrow 0.60$$
$$0 \text{ —————.4332} \rightarrow 1.5$$

Table A.3 reports the probability associated with the area of the curve from the mean 0 to a $z$-score. The shaded areas on the normal curve in Figure 8.4 illustrate the possible adjustments needed to the reported probability values from Table A.3. The $z$-scores 1.0 and -1.0 are used as illustration.

## Four Rules Emerge

**Rule 1.** A probability for the area between 0 and $z$ is the value from Table A.3. This includes a probability statement that asks for a value equal to $x$, which is transformed into $z$. That is, $P(x = ...)$ transformed into $P(z = 1.0) = .3413$.

**Rule 2.** When the probability of a tail is needed, find the probability from Table A.3 and subtract it from .5000, leaving the difference as the tail probability. For example, $P(z > 1.0) = (.5000 - .3413) = .1587$.

**Rule 3.** When the area needed is between two positive $z$ values or between two negative $z$ values, often referred to as a slice or a sliver, then find the probabilities of both $z$ values from Table A.3 and subtract the smaller probability from the larger. (Remember, although $z$ values may be positive or negative, probabilities are always positive). For example, $P(1.0 \leq z \leq 2.0) = .4772 - .3413 = .1359$.

**Rule 4.** Any time the area needed crosses over the center of the curve, the probabilities of the two sections are added. That may mean adding two values from Table A.3 or adding one value from the table to .5000 when half of the curve is needed. For example, $P(-1.00 \leq z \leq 1.00) = .3413 + .3413 = .6826$. Also, $P(z < 1.00) = .5000 + .3413 = .8413$.

The following curves illustrate these rules:

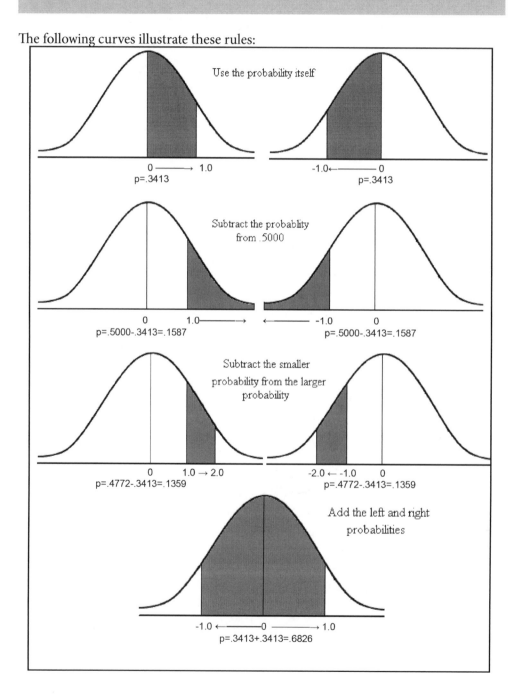

# *SECTION 4*

## Calculating Normal Probabilities

### PUTTING IT ALL TOGETHER

The transformation of raw data to a $z$-score allows the $z$-score to be transformed into a probability. The probabilities are then understood and may be compared to other probabilities. The process begins by identifying a random variable as a continuous variable. The probability statement for $x$ is stated, such as $P(x = 4)$. The value 4 can be transformed into a $z$-score by completing the $z$ calculation. The resulting $z$-score is then placed on a curve to visualize the area needed. The $z$-score is transformed into a probability by using Table A.3. The probability value from the table may need to be adjusted according to the area needed on the curve (such as adding two values, adding to .5000, or subtracting from .5000).

### EXAMPLE 8.9

**Experiment:** The average life expectancy of African American males in the United States is 67.6 years with a standard deviation of .82. What is the probability that a randomly selected African American male will live beyond 70?

**Answer:** $P(x > 70) = .0017$

**Solution:** The variable life expectancy is measured in years. Years is a continuous variable. The probability of continuous variables is measured by the normal curve. State the probability question. The question asks the probability that a African American male will live beyond age 70, therefore, $P(x > 70)$. Next, transform the 70 into a $z$-score. The mean is stated as 67.6 with a standard deviation of .82. The resulting calculation of $z$ is 2.93. Be sure to round correctly to two digits to the right of the decimal.

$$z = \frac{x - \mu}{\sigma} = 2.93$$

When solving using the table, place the $z$-score on a curve. 2.93 is in the right half of the curve with 0 in the center. Since the original question asks for "beyond" or greater, shade the area of the curve to the right of 2.93. This shaded area is referred to as the tail. Next, transform the $z$-score into a probability. Using Table A.3, 2.93 is found by going down the left column to 2.9 and across the top row to .03. The probability .4983 is in the intersection.

Finally, .4983 needs to be adjusted since it is the probability of the curve from 0 out to the z of 2.93. You want the area from 2.93 out to the tail. To get the probability of the tail, subtract .4983 from .5000. The remaining section, .0017 is the final answer for the probability of a black male living beyond age 70.

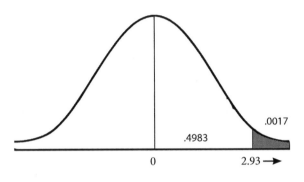

The TI-83/84 calculators include the calculation for the normal distribution. The functions include identifying the probability for a normal random variable to between two *x* values, or identifying the *x* value for a given cumulative probability. These functions are found by entering 2nd and DISTR (above the VARS key).The first procedure is ***normalcdf(*** for the probability and the second procedure is ***invNorm(*** for *x* value.

The general syntax for finding the probability of a normal random variable between values *a* and *b* is normalcdf(*a*, *b*, *μ*, *σ*).

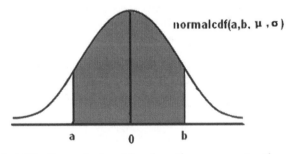

To calculate a probability for *X* to be either less than or greater than a value, an adjustment is needed using E99 (found by pressing 2nd and EE which is above the comma key and then typing 99) or –E99 (found by pressing (–) 2nd and EE which is above the comma key and then typing 99). The E99 is used to find probabilities above the *x* value. The –E99 is used to find probabilities below the *x* value.

For $P(X < b)$, use normalcdf(-E99, *b*, *μ*, *σ*).

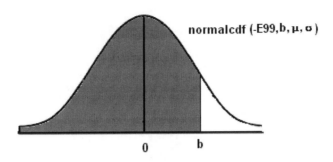

To find $P(X > a)$, use normalcdf(a, E99, $\mu$, $\sigma$).

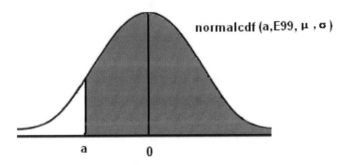

**Inverse:** Now, let us try the inverse where we are looking for the $x$ value corresponding to a given probability. Earlier in the chapter we described this as $x = \mu + \sigma z$. To find $x$ by hand, you had to transform the probability to a $z$-score and then do the math. To find it on the calculator, the probability is used and its transformation is automatically done (you get to skip a step!). To find the $x$ value corresponding to the cumulative probability $p$, the syntax invNorm($p$, $\mu$, $\sigma$) is used. That is, you enter the probability (to the left of a value), the mean, and the standard deviation.

Assume that the heights of delphinium plants are normally distributed with mean height of 68 inches, and a standard deviation of 2 inches. If a delphinium is randomly selected in a garden, what are the following probabilities?
a. A delphinium is at most 70 inches tall.
b. A delphinium's height is between 63 and 72 inches.
c. A delphinium is taller than 65 inches.
d. For what height are 90 percent of delphiniums below?

**Solution:**

a. Let $X$ be the heights of delphinium plants measured in inches, then $X \approx N(68,2)$
   The probability that a randomly selected plant is at most 70 inches tall is denoted

by $P(x \le 70)$. Press 2nd DISTR. Scroll down to or press the two button to select "2:normalcdf(" Enter the data. After the values are entered, highlight "Paste" and press ENTER twice. The answer should appear as .8413447404.

$$P(X \le 70) = .841$$

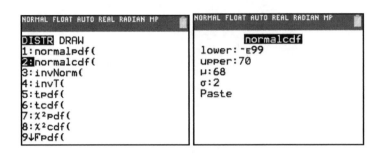

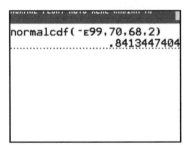

b. The probability that a randomly selected plant between 63 and 72 inches tall can be denoted by $P(63 \le X \le 72)$. This is the area of the normal curve between 63 and 72. Press 2nd DISTR. Scroll down to 2: normalcdf( and press ENTER or press the 2 button to select it. Enter the data. After the values are entered, highlight "Paste" and press ENTER twice. The answer should appear as follows:

$$P(63 \le X \le 72) = .971$$

c. The probability that a randomly selected plant is taller than 65 inches can be denoted by $P(X > 65)$. Press 2nd DISTR. Scroll down to 2: normalcdf( and press ENTER. Enter the data in the settings screen. After the data are entered, highlight "Paste" and press ENTER. It should appear as normalcdf(65, E99, 68, 2). Press ENTER again and the answer should appear as .9331927713.

$$P(X > 65) = .933$$

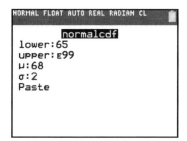 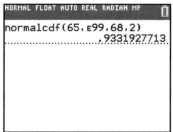

d. Let $H$ be the height that 90 percent of delphiniums are below, this would mean $P(X \leq H) = .90$. Press 2nd DISTR. Scroll down to 3: invNorm( and press ENTER or select the function by pressing the 3 button. Enter the data in the settings screen, highlight "Paste" and press ENTER twice. The screen will display 70.56310313. Conclude that $H = 70.6$ inches or 90 percent of delphiniums are at most 70.6 inches tall.

 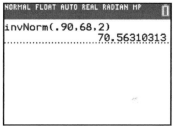

## WORKING IT IN REVERSE: FINDING *X* FROM *Z*

There are times that a probability is known or sought and the actual $z$-score or original value is not known. For example, a student may want to know what score on a final exam will yield a certain grade in the course. In this situation, the actual score is desired. If information about the class is available and a particular percentile ranking is known (the percentage that will give the desired grade), then it is possible to work backward using the normal curve. Algebraically, the $z$-score formula is rewritten so that the value $x$ is isolated on one side of the formula. To find the value $x$, the $z$-score must first be determined. It is usually easiest to translate the desired probability into a $z$-score by drawing and shading the normal curve and reading Table A.3. For example, for a student to be in the top 10 percent of the class, the probability can be found by rewriting 10 percent as a probability and then working with the normal curve and Table A.3. Percentages are rewritten as probabilities by moving the decimal to the left two places. Thus, 10 percent gives a probability of .1000. The top of .1000 of a normal curve is seen in the shaded area of the curve.

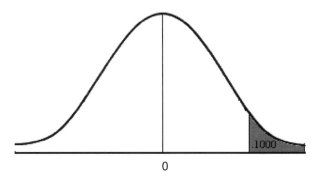

0

Because the normal curve is symmetric, with 0 in its center, the probability associated with the right half of the curve is .5. If .1000 is the value of the area outside of the curve near the tail, .4000 must be the value of the area under the remaining inner portion of the right half of the curve.

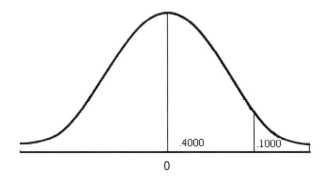

0

The probability reported in Table A.3 for the normal curve reads from the mean to a specific point. To find the point that is associated with the probability .4000, find .4000 in the body of Table A.3. The closest probability in the table is .3997. Read across the row and up the column to find the z-score. The z-score associated with the probability .3997 is 1.28.

> **Calculate *x* from a probability or z-score** To find the *x* value from a probability, the probability must be turned into a z-score and then calculated using the formula:
>
> $$x = \mu + \sigma z$$

The following steps summarize the procedure in finding a z-score when a probability or percentile is given:
1. Draw and shade a curve to visualize the area desired.
2. Rewrite the percent or percentile as a probability.
3. Adjust the probability if necessary.

4. Use Table A.3 to find the probability or the nearest probability reported.
5. Use Table A.3 to find the *z*-score associated with the probability.
6. If the lower limit is needed, use the z-score as negative in the formula. If the upper limit is needed, use the z-score as a positive value. Notice Example 8.10 below. It asks for the fewest days, therefore, use the z-score as negative.

Once the *z*-score is obtained, the value can be inserted into the formula:
$$x = \mu + \sigma z \text{ to find the value of } x.$$

Note: If using TI 83/84 calculator function 3:invNorm, the lower limit uses the probability value to the left of the area that is wanted. The upper limit uses the probability 1- the area of the right tail. In Example 8.10, the shaded area is .4750. The left tail area is .5000-.4750 =.025. However, if the right area is needed, the value for the area is 1-.025, or .975.

---

### EXAMPLE 8.10

**Experiment:** The local cable company is installing cable in your area. You are told that the time required is a normally distributed $\mu = 24.6$ days, and $\sigma = 3$ days. You are planning to buy a new TV. You don't want to buy the TV until you are 95 percent sure that the installation is completed. What is the fewest number of days you should wait before buying the TV?

**Answer:** $x = 18.72$ days

**Solution:** Time is a continuous variable and thus is normally distributed. The problem asks you to find the value of $x$, the number of days to wait before buying a TV. To find the value of $x$ you must find the mean and add to it the standard deviation multiplied by $z$.

Begin by finding $z$. The $z$-score can be found by using Table A.3 to translate the probability given in the problem into a $z$-score. The problem states that you want to be 95 percent sure that the installation is completed before buying the TV. Using the normal probability curve, the probability of .9500 is split on the left and right of the mean. This is done, because it is possible that the installation is done before normally expected or after normally expected. Half of the .9500, or .4750, is to the right of the mean, and the other half of .9500, or .4750, is to the left of the mean. Since this problem only requires looking at the minimum number of days, you must consider the area of .025 which is to the left of the shaded area on the curve. This can be solved by using the invNorm( function. Press the 2$^{ND}$ button, followed by pressing VARS. Press three to select "3: invNorm". Adhere to the following settings, highlight "Paste" and press ENTER twice.

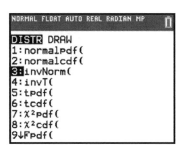

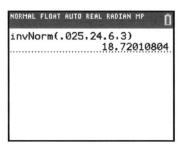

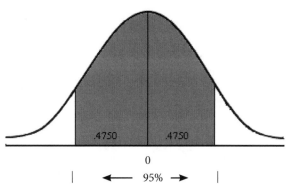

The probability .4750 is associated with the $z$-score of 1.96. Using Table A.3, $z = 1.96$ is found by looking through all the probabilities and finding the probability closest to .4750. After locating the closest probability, read up and over to the columns to find the associated $z$-score. The equation for $x$ requires the mean and standard deviation: $\mu$ was given as 24.6 and $\sigma$ as 3.

$$x = \mu + \sigma\, z$$
$$= 24.6 + 3(-1.96)$$
$$= 24.6 + -5.88$$
$$= 18.72$$

# *SECTION 5*
## Normal Approximation of the Binomial Distribution

The binomial probability distribution was introduced in Chapter 7. Recall that the binomial probability distribution describes probabilities for discrete variables. Also recall that the calculations for binomial probabilities become very difficult as $n$ increases. In fact, calculating the binomial coefficient is difficult if $n$ is much larger than 8 or 9. Table A.2 in Appendix A gives binomial coefficients up to $n = 20$. Rarely would one want to continue using the binomial formula for large samples. Fortunately, there is a method of approximating binomial probability by the normal probability distribution. The normal approximation of the binomial becomes closer to the actual binomial probability as $n$ increases.

The approximation is based on two principles. The first principle is the law of large numbers. As the number of trials increases, the observational probability approaches the theoretical. Although the binomial distribution is theoretical, the distribution differs for each random variable and is very much affected by $n$. The effect that the sample size has on the probability is signified by the inclusion of $n$ in the binomial probability function.

The second principle that explains why the normal distribution can approximate the binomial is that all samples taken repeatedly from a population will appear to be normally distributed regardless of the original appearance of the population. This principle is discussed in more detail in Chapter 9. The important idea here is that repeated observations of a discrete variable will appear normal even though the original population may not be normally distributed.

The following histogram shows a binomial distribution illustrated as a histogram. For this distribution, $n = 8$ and $p = .5$. The histogram resembles a normal distribution. If the corners of the bars were smoothed, the distribution would resemble a normal distribution even more. Notice the normal curve is superimposed over a binomial distribution. There are portions of the bars of the histogram that fall outside the normal curve, but other portions of the bars fall inside the curve. An adjustment must occur that will balance the overestimation with the underestimation. This adjustment is needed because of the two types of random variables. The binomial distribution represents a discrete random variable, whereas the normal probability distribution represents a continuous random variable.

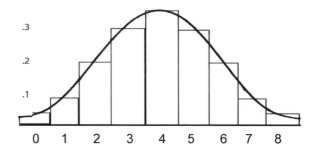

The actual process of approximating the binomial distribution with the normal distribution begins with an adjustment of the value of the random variable. Pay special attention to the bars of the histogram. The value of a discrete random variable actually occurs in the center of the bar. Because of the approximation, any probability needed that includes a bar must be adjusted to include the whole bar. For example, if the probability for the bar representing the value of 6 is required, the bar includes the values from 5.5 to 6.5. Because the normal curve describes the probability associated with areas of the curve, the probability of a discrete value 6 must include the area of the curve from 5.5 to 6.5.

> When using the normal distribution as an approximation of the binomial distribution, the value x must always be adjusted by
> $$x \pm .5$$

The value of $x$ may be adjusted in several different ways. If the probability of a specific value $x$ is desired, two probabilities must be calculated, one for the lower edge of the bar and one for the higher edge of the bar.

$$P(x = 6) = P(5.5 < x < 6.5)$$

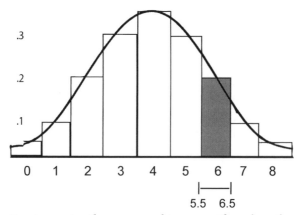

If the area in question is greater than or equal to a specific value, the value $x$ must be adjusted to include the lower edge of the bar. This is accomplished by subtracting .5 from $x$.

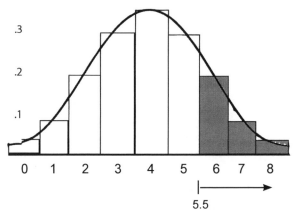

Alternatively, if the area in question is less than or equal to a specific value, the value $x$ must be adjusted to include the higher edge of the bar. This is accomplished by adding .5 to the value $x$. See Figure 8.10.

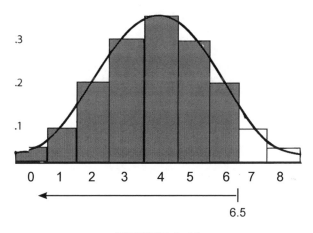

**FIGURE 8.10**

The rule is that if any portion of a bar is desired, then the whole bar must be included. This also means that when a value is excluded, such as in cases where the probability of an area is greater than or less than some value, the whole bar must be excluded. Again, drawing and shading a curve usually helps visualize the necessary adjustment.

**EXAMPLE 8.11**
**Experiment:** Restate the following discrete probabilities as required by the normal approximation of the binomial.

a. $P(x \leq 2)$     c. $P(x = 2)$

b. $P(x > 1)$     d. $P(x < 2)$

**Answer:**

 a. $P(x \leq 2.5)$      c. $P(1.5 < x < 2.5)$

 b. $P(x > 1.5)$      d. $P(x < 1.5)$

**Solution:**

a. The discrete probability for $(x \leq 2)$ means that the area includes 2 and below. To include 2 means that the whole bar representing 2 must be included in the calculation. The value 2 is adjusted by adding .5 so the upper edge of the bar is included. Because any distribution can be used to represent this, the distribution presented earlier is used. Notice the shaded area is the area in question.

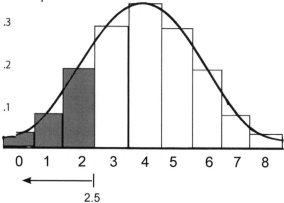

b. The probability for the area greater than 1 does not include the bar representing 1. Greater than means everything larger than 1, which means 2 or more. The bar representing 2 begins at 1.5. Notice the shaded area of the curve.

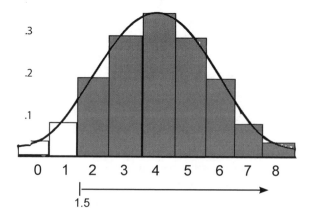

c. The probability that $x$ is equal to 2 requires only the probability of the bar representing 2. The bar representing 2 has two edges; the lower edge begins at 1.5, and the upper edge ends at 2.5. These two values are used in any calculations for the area of the curve representing the value of 2.

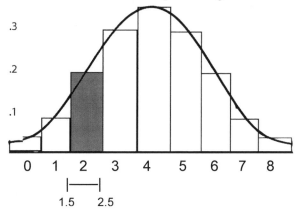

d. The probability of the area of the curve less than 2 does not include the bar representing 2. To have included the bar for 2, the problem would have read "less than or equal to 2." Because the bar representing 2 must be excluded, the desired area begins at 1.5.

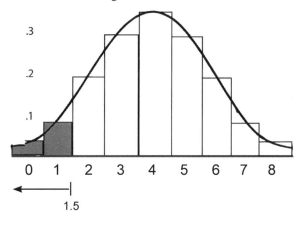

Once the adjustment of the random variable has been completed, the calculation of its probability proceeds as if the random variable were continuous. Recall that the calculation for the standard score $z$ requires the population mean and the population standard deviation. If these parameters are not readily available, they must be calculated using the process discussed in Chapter 7.

The mean of the binomial is found by multiplying the number of trials by the probability of success. Caution about how the problem defines success is required. If the problem states what appears to be a failure and asks for the probability of the apparent failure, the failure is usually treated as a success.

## The Mean and Standard Deviation of the Binomial Probability Distribution

$$\mu = n \cdot p$$

$$\sigma = \sqrt{n \cdot p \cdot q}$$

where
  $n$ stands for the number of trials.
  $p$ stands for the probability of success.
  $q$ stands for the probability of failure.

The standard deviation is the square root of the product of the number of trials, the probability of success, and the probability of failure.

After the adjustment is made for the random variable and the mean and standard deviation are known or calculated, the $z$-score can then be calculated just as it was in the last section. The $z$-score is calculated by subtracting the population mean from the value $x$ (adjusted) and then dividing by the population standard deviation.

### EXAMPLE 8.12

**Experiment:** A government agency reported that 10 percent of all applicants are not truthful on their applications. What is the probability that in a random sample of 20 applicants, no more than 3 were not truthful on their applications?

**Answer:** $P(x \leq 3.5) = .8686$

**Solution:** This is a discrete random variable. The random variable is a count of people. Counts are discrete variables. This is a binomial random variable, because all the conditions of the binomial exist. Briefly, only two outcomes are possible, success and failure. The sample is random, allowing for independent trials. However, an $n$ value of 20 complicates the binomial calculations. Binomials can be approximated using the normal distribution.

The first step is to state the problem and adjust $x$. The normal approximation of the binomial always requires $x$ to be adjusted by 2.5. Drawing a histogram usually helps visualize the adjustment. The problem asks for everything lower than a value of 3 but not more than 3. Three itself is a valid value. The bar in the following partial histogram representing 3 illustrates that .5 must be added to 3 to obtain the whole bar. The probability statement is also stated after the histogram.

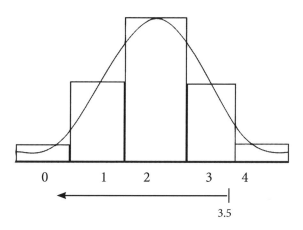

$$P\,(x \le 3) = P\,(x \le 3.5)$$

The next step is to find the mean and the standard deviation of the binomial distribution in order to calculate the $z$-score. The mean is the number of cases multiplied by the probability of success. Even though the experiment seems to state a failure (not being truthful on an application), it also asks for the probability of that same event. Therefore, not being truthful will be looked at as the success. The number of cases, $n$, is stated as 20. A random sample of 20 people is taken. The probability of success, not being truthful, is .1, because 10 percent of people are reported not to be truthful. A percentage is rewritten as a probability by moving the decimal to the left two places, so 10% = .1. The mean is then calculated as follows:

$$\mu = n \cdot p = 20(.1) = 2$$

The standard deviation is the square root of the product of the number of cases, the probability of success, and the probability of failure. The probability of failure is found by subtracting the probability of success from 1.0. The probability of failure is 1 - .1 = .9. The standard deviation is

$$\sigma = \sqrt{n \cdot p \cdot q} = \sqrt{(20(.1)(.9)} = \sqrt{1.8} = 1.34$$

The next step is to calculate the $z$-score; $z$ is calculated by subtracting the mean from $x$ and dividing by the standard deviation.

$$z = \frac{x - \mu}{\sigma} = \frac{3.5\text{-}2}{1.34} = \frac{1.5}{1.34} = 1.12$$

The final step is to transform the $z$-score into a probability and make any adjustments necessary. The transformation is done by looking up the $z$-score in Table A.3 and finding its associated probability. If you look up the $z$-score 1.12, you will find the probability .3686. The adjustment necessary is to add .5 to the probability to represent the area of the curve to the left of 1.12 and the entire left side of the curve. Visualizing the area by using a curve usually helps.

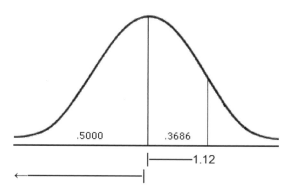

$$P(x \le 3.5) = P(z \le 1.12)$$
$$= .5000 + .3686$$
$$= .8686$$

## A LEARNING AID
## NORMAL APPROXIMATION OF THE BINOMIAL DISTRIBUTION
At the present time, incumbency advantage for House members seeking reelection is 92 percent. This means that a member is 92 percent certain of winning reelection. What is the probability that in a random sample of 50 House members, 44 or more will win reelection?

### Step 1
Determine if this is a discrete or continuous variable. Counting the number of members winning reelection is a discrete variable. Discrete variables are counts, whereas continuous variables are measures.

### Step 2
This discrete variable is also a binomial variable, because the conditions for a binomial discrete variable exist. Briefly, there are two outcomes, winning or losing; 50 independent trials; a probability of success of .92 (92 percent); and a probability of failure of .08 ($q = 1 - p$). Because the binomial experiment

requires a large $n$ (50), it is possible to approximate the distribution using the normal curve.

**Step 3**

State the probability of interest. The question asks for the probability that 44 or more members will win. But when using the normal approximation of the binomial, you must adjust $x$ to represent the inclusion or exclusion of the whole bar. In this case, 44 is desired as a possible value. To include 44, the lower edge of the bar representing 44 must be used. The lower edge of the bar for 44 is 43.5. Therefore,

$$P(x \geq 44) = P(x \geq 43.5)$$

**Step 4**

To calculate $z$, first calculate the mean and standard deviation. These parameters of the binomial are easily calculated. Note the information needed:

$$n = 50, p = .92, \text{ and } q = .08.$$

$$\mu = n \cdot p \qquad\qquad \sigma = \sqrt{n \cdot p \cdot q}$$
$$= 50(.92) \qquad\qquad = \sqrt{50(.92)(.08)}$$
$$= 46 \qquad\qquad\quad = \sqrt{3.68}$$
$$\qquad\qquad\qquad = 1.92$$

**Step 5**

Calculate $z$. Note the information needed: $x = 43.5$, $\mu = 46$, and $\sigma = 1.92$.

$$z = \frac{x - \mu}{\sigma} = \frac{43.5\text{-}46}{1.92} = \frac{\text{-}2.5}{1.92} = \text{-}1.30$$

**Step 6**

Find the probability associated with -1.30. Table A.3 gives the probability .4032 for a $z$ of 1.30. The negative $z$-score denotes the area of the curve to the left of center.

**Step 7**

Adjust the probability to represent the portion of the curve desired. Drawing the normal curve may help visualize the adjustment. The probability statement $P(x \geq 43.5)$ can now read as a $z$ statement $P(z \geq \text{-}1.30)$. The probability associated with -1.30 involves the area of the curve from 0 left to

-1.30 as well as the entire right half of the curve. The right half of the curve has a probability .5000, which must be added to .4032.

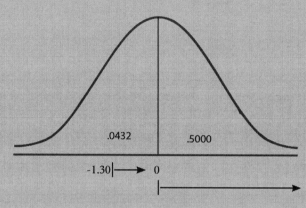

.0432       .5000

-1.30 ⟶ 0

**Step 8**
Restate the final answer. The probability that 44 or more House members in a sample of 50 will win reelection is .9032.

$$P(x \geq 43.5) = .9032$$

# *CHAPTER 8 IN REVIEW*

8.1    Find the area of the normal curve that lies between the following $z$-scores:

     a. $z = 0$ to $z = 1.85$          d. $z = 0$ to $z = -.89$

     b. $z = 0$ to $z = 1.42$          e. $z = 0$ to $z = -3.80$

     c. $z = 0$ to $z = .14$           f. $z = 0$ to $z = -1.66$

8.2    Find the area of the normal curve that lies between the following $z$-scores:

     a. $z = -1.94$ to $z = 1.94$      d. $z = 2.00$ to $z = 3.00$

     b. $z = -1.12$ to $z = 2.42$      e. $z = -.40$ to $z = -.49$

     c. $z = -.89$ to $z = 3.56$       f. $z = -1.96$ to $z = 2.96$

8.3    Find the following probabilities:

     a. $P(z > 1.96)$            d. $P(z < 1.96)$

     b. $P(z > .96)$             e. $P(z < .49)$

     c. $P(z > 3.00)$            f. $P(z < 1.00)$

8.4    Find the following probabilities:

    a. $P(-2.59 < z < -1.81)$          d. $P(-.75 < z < 1.79)$

    b. $P(-2.57 < z < -.75)$          e. $P(-1.00 < z < 2.00)$

    c. $P(-.95 < z < -.12)$          f. $P(-1.96 < z < 2.45)$

8.5    What is the probability that $z$ is greater than 0?

8.6    What is the probability associated with the area of the curve between the following $z$-scores?

    a. -1 and 1

    b. -2 and 2

    c. -3 and 3

8.7    Find the $z$-score associated with the shaded area of each curve.

a.

b.
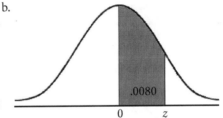

c.
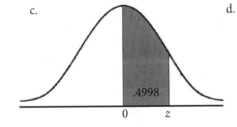

d.
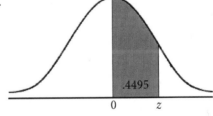

8.8    Find the *z*-score associated with the shaded area of each curve.

a.

b.
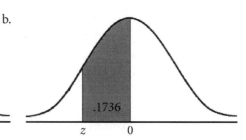

c.
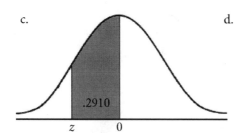

d.
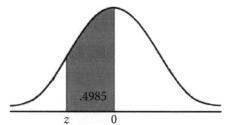

8.9    Find the *z*-score associated with the shaded area of each curve.

a.
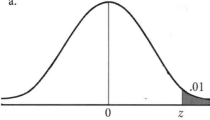

b.
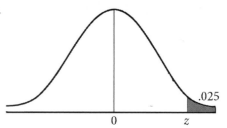

c.
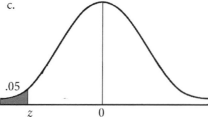

d.
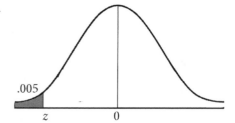

8.10 Find the *z*-score associated with the shaded area of each curve.

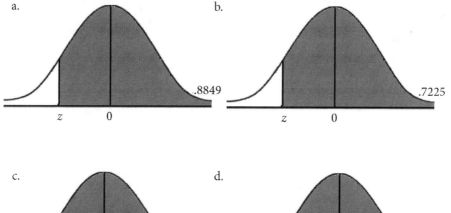

8.11 The average length of a bill passed by Congress is now 10.8 pages, with a standard deviation of 1.8. Find the probability that a randomly selected bill is between 11 and 12 pages.

8.12 The percentage of eligible voters voting in presidential elections is normally distributed with a mean of 52 and standard deviation of 2. In a randomly selected election, what is the probability that the percentage of eligible voters is:
a. Between 50 and 53?        c. Less than 50?
b. Greater than 52?          d. Greater than 53?

8.13 The number of burglaries per year in South Lyon is normally distributed with an average of 52 with a standard deviation of 5. What is the probability that a randomly selected year produces:
a. Between 50 and 54?        c. Less than 54?
b. More than 54?           d. Less than 50?

8.14 Where affirmative action programs are used in law-school admissions, the average minority enrollments average 8.3 percent with a standard deviation of 2 percent. What is the probability that a randomly selected law school would have a minority enrollment:

a. More than 7 percent?          d. Between 7 and 10 percent?
b. More than 9 percent?          e. Less than 7 percent?
c. Between 9 and 10 percent?     f. Exactly 8.3 percent?

8.15  The average credit card debt is currently $15,000 (15) with a standard deviation of 5,000 (5). What is the probability that (use single digits):
a. A person will have a debt of more than 18 thousand dollars?
b. A person will have a debt more than 12.5 thousand?
c. A person will have a debt less than 10 thousand?
d. A person will have a debt between 14 and 16 thousand?

8.16  The average credit card interest rate is now at 14.95 percent with a standard deviation of 3 percent. What is the probability that a card has a rate:
a. Above 12%?          c. Between 13 and 16%?
b. Below 12%?          d. Between 15 and 18%?

8.17  The salaries of teachers in the West Bloomfield Public School District are normally distributed with a mean of $53.5 thousand with a standard deviation of 5.5. What is the probability that a randomly selected teacher will have a salary…
a. Above 53.5?          c. Above 60?
b. Below 50?            d. Between 54 and 60%?

8.18  The lifetime of a computer is normally distributed with a mean of 3.5 years and a standard deviation of 1.2 years. What is the probability that a randomly selected computer would have a lifetime of:
a. 3 to 5 years?
b. Less than 4 years?
c. More than 4.5 years?
d. 6 years?

8.19  If a brand of low-fat popcorn has a mean of 3 grams of fat with a standard deviation of .65, what is the probability that a randomly selected bag contains less than 2 grams of fat?

8.20  The number of viewers of the recent summer Olympic games average 109 million with a standard deviation of .85. What is the probability that next year's Super Bowl will have more than 111 million viewers?

8.21  The average cost of the 2015 Super Bowl ticket was $3,985 with a standard deviation of $1,225. What is the probability that a person paid more than $3,000?

8.22   Find the *x* value for a *z*-score of 2.25 with a mean of 500 and a standard deviation of 75.

8.23   Suzy is moving into her new apartment. She is told that the time required to turn on the electricity is a normally distributed with a mean of 2 days, and $\sigma = 1.5$ days. Suzy doesn't want to move in until the electricity is turned on. If she waits until she is 95 percent sure, how many days should she wait before moving in?

8.24   Antonio wants to buy a new computer online. He is told that the specific computer he wants will take an average of 5 business days for delivery with a standard deviation of .5. How many days should he expect to wait if he wants to be 90 percent sure of the delivery? How many days if he wants to be 95 percent sure?

8.25   If the average amount of caloric intake for individuals in a region is normally distributed with a mean of 2,192 calories, a standard deviation of 138, and a *z*-score of 1.96, what is the value of *x*?

8.26   The average monthly increase of gasoline in the city was 14 cents per gallon with a standard deviation of 3. What is the probability that a randomly selected gas station increased by 16 cents per gallon?

8.27   Of college graduates, 18.4 percent smoke cigarettes. What is the probability that more than 56 smoke from a sample of 280 graduates?

8.28   If 40 percent of the employees of the university favor going on strike, what is the probability that at least 5 of the 8 employees in the Registrar's Office will favor going on strike? Use the normal approximation of the binomial.

8.29   A study was conducted on the effects of incarceration in state prisons. It was found that 10 percent of prisoners are helped by their prison experience, 60 percent of prisoners are harmed, and 30 percent are unaffected. Out of 100 prisoners, what is the probability that more than 15 are helped by their prison experience? Use the normal approximation of the binomial.

8.30   If 30 percent of urban youth are arrested before they reach the age of 18, what is the probability that in a family of 8 children, fewer than 3 children will be arrested before they are 18? Use the normal approximation of the binomial.

# 9

# SAMPLING DISTRIBUTIONS

*SECTION 1* **Sampling Distributions**
*SECTION 2* **Central Limit Theorem**

As noted in Chapter 1, one of the most important aspects of doing research is obtaining data. Although the ideal situation may be to observe every element of a population, there are times when every element cannot or should not be used. When the whole population cannot or should not be studied, samples are usually taken. It is possible to describe a population after studying a sample drawn from that same population. Chapter 1 addressed some sampling techniques and errors. This chapter will address another form of sampling that will result in a distribution of the sample information. The distribution will take on a probability distribution that is normal and bell-shaped, enabling the application of *z*-scores. The *z*-score application allows us to calculate probabilities similar to what was done in Chapter 8, with some slight adjustments.

To overview what was addressed in Chapter 8, a probability question was asked concerning a continuous variable. The raw data was converted into a *z*-score which was then converted into a probability and possibly adjusted for tail sections, cross-overs, etc... This chapter will also ask a probability question but of a sample for the distribution that occurs from the sampling. The sample mean will be questioned. The sample mean is converted into a *z*-score that is then converted into a probability and possibly adjusted for tail sections, cross-overs, etc. The *z*-score calculation will be slightly adjusted to accomplish the conversion.

Chapter 8: *P(x...)*→→Convert *x* into *z*-score→→
Convert *z*-score into Probability→→Table A.4
adjust Prob if necessary

Chapter 9: *P(x-bar...)*→→Convert *x* into *z*-score→→
Convert *z*-score into Probability→→Table A.4
adjust Prob if necessary

---

## SECTION 1

### Sampling Distributions

Although the key to sampling is to make the sample representative of the population, it is unrealistic to believe that every sample will yield information that perfectly matches the population. One way of reducing the possible error resulting in using a sample is to increase the size of the sample. Recall that the law of large numbers states that as the number of casts increase, the observational probability approaches the theoretical probability. A researcher must determine the cost and benefit of increasing the sample size to achieve a reduction in the sampling error. There are times when it may not be possible or may be too costly.

Another way to reduce the error resulting from using a sample is to conduct several samples. Also, based on the law of large numbers, collecting several small samples may balance any biases found in any one sample. Information such as means and standard deviations of one sample can be compared to those of other samples. Conducting several samples is referred to as ***repeated sampling***.

**Repeated Sampling**  Obtaining several samples from the same population.

### EXAMPLE 9.1
**Experiment:** Using a Venn diagram, illustrate a repeated sample of the average age of students at your school. Use four samples of 10 students, and arbitrarily assign means to each sample.

**Answer:**

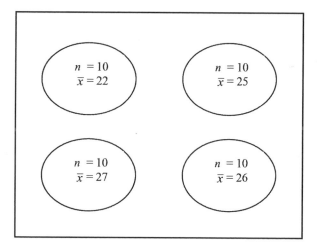

Because the goal remains selecting a sample that represents the population, repeated sampling helps to create a set of unbiased samples that can be compared and combined to represent the population. The mean of one sample can be calculated and then compared to the mean of another sample. When all possible samples are taken, their means can be recorded and presented in a frequency distribution. This frequency distribution is transformed into a probability distribution. The probability of a specific sample mean occurring can be calculated and presented in a probability distribution, along with the probabilities of other means of samples of the same size. For example, if a class of five has students of age 18, 19, 20, 21, and 22, a sample of two would not necessarily be representative of the whole class and might cause a large error in inferring about the population. However, several samples of two could be taken and compared to each other to better describe the population. A list of all possible combinations of two can be made, along with the mean for each sample.

| Sample | Mean |
|--------|------|
| (18, 19) | 18.5 |
| (18, 20) | 19.0 |
| (18, 21) | 19.5 |
| (18, 22) | 20.0 |
| (19, 18) | 18.5 |
| (19, 20) | 19.5 |
| (19, 21) | 20.0 |
| (19, 22) | 20.5 |
| (20, 18) | 19.0 |
| (20, 19) | 19.5 |
| (20, 21) | 20.5 |
| (20, 22) | 21.0 |
| (21, 18) | 19.5 |
| (21, 19) | 20.0 |
| (21, 20) | 20.5 |
| (21, 22) | 21.5 |
| (22, 18) | 20.0 |
| (22, 19) | 20.5 |
| (22, 20) | 21.1 |
| (22, 21) | 21.5 |

A distribution of the sample means can be created by counting the number of times each of the sample means occurs. Because there are 20 possible sample combinations, the probability of each sample mean can be determined by dividing the number of occurrences of each mean by 20. This is referred to as a sampling distribution. See Table 9.1

### TABLE 9.1
### Sampling Distribution of Mean Ages for Sample Size = 2

| Sample Mean | Frequency | Probability |
|-------------|-----------|-------------|
| 18.5 | 2 | 2/20 = .1 |
| 19.0 | 2 | 2/20 = .1 |
| 19.5 | 4 | 4/20 = .2 |

| | | |
|---|---|---|
| 20.0 | 4 | 4/20 = .2 |
| 20.5 | 4 | 4/20 = .2 |
| 21.0 | 2 | 2/20 = .1 |
| 21.5 | 2 | 2/20 = .1 |
| **Total** | **20** | **1.00** |

As with all probability distributions, sampling distributions of the mean must meet the conditions required to make the distribution true. Recall from previous chapters that all probabilities must be no less than 0 and no more than 1 *(0 ≤ P ≤ 1)*, and all probabilities associated with an event must have a sum of 1.0. The sample statistic is known as $\mu_{\bar{x}}$ .

---

**EXAMPLE 9.2**

**Experiment:** Using a sample of size three, illustrate the sampling distribution of the mean for 1, 2, 3, 4.

**Answer:** Sampling distribution; Sample size = 3.

| Sample Mean | Frequency | Probability |
|---|---|---|
| 2.00 | 6 | .25 |
| 2.33 | 6 | .25 |
| 2.67 | 6 | .25 |
| 3.00 | 6 | .25 |
| **Total** | **24** | **1.00** |

**Solution:** All combinations of three digits must be listed so that the mean of each sample combination can be calculated.

| Combination | Mean |
|---|---|
| (1, 2, 3) | 2.00 |
| (1, 2, 4) | 2.33 |
| (1, 3, 2) | 2.00 |
| (1, 3, 4) | 2.67 |
| (1, 4, 2) | 2.33 |
| (1, 4, 3) | 2.67 |
| (2, 1, 3) | 2.00 |
| (2, 1, 4) | 2.33 |
| (2, 3, 1) | 2.00 |
| (2, 3, 4) | 3.00 |

---

| | |
|---|---|
| (2, 4, 1) | 2.33 |
| (2, 4, 3) | 3.00 |
| (3, 1, 2) | 2.00 |
| (3, 1, 4) | 2.67 |
| (3, 2, 1) | 2.00 |
| (3, 2, 4) | 3.00 |
| (3, 4, 1) | 2.67 |
| (3, 4, 2) | 3.00 |
| (4, 1, 2) | 2.33 |
| (4, 1, 3) | 2.67 |
| (4, 2, 1) | 2.33 |
| (4, 2, 3) | 3.00 |
| (4, 3, 1) | 2.67 |
| (4, 3, 2) | 3.00 |

There are 24 sample combinations. As the mean of each combination is calculated, only four different values appear: 2.00, 2.33, 2.67, and 3.00. A count of each of these values reveals each mean occurs six times. The sampling distribution presented as the answer records only the four different values of the mean, the number of times each occurred (usually omitted but presented for learning purposes), and the probability of that mean occurring. The probability is calculated by dividing the numbers of times each mean occurred by 24 total occurrences. Recall the probability formula, $P(A) = n(A)/n$. In this example, since each of the four means occurs 6 times, the probability of each is 6/24, or .25. The conditions of a probability distribution exist: Each probability of .25 is between 0 and 1 and the sum of all the probabilities is 1.0.

Something interesting happens when the theory of sampling distributions is combined with the theory of random sampling. A sampling distribution of sample means of a random sample has characteristics of the normal distribution. The mean of the sample means of the same sample size n approaches a normal distribution as sample size increases. Notice the distributions in Figure 9.1. As a sampling distribution of the mean moves from a sample size of 2 to a sample size of 5, the distribution begins to look like a normal distribution.

Sampling distribution of $\overline{x}$ when $n = 2$     **Figure 9.1**     Sampling distribution of $\overline{x}$ when $n = 5$

Values of $x$            Values of $x$

The sampling distribution will always approach a normal distribution regardless of the shape of the probability distribution of the original population. If the random variable $X$ of the population is itself normally distributed (as in the case of heights of an adult population), then the means of a sample of any size, including 1, will be normally distributed. If the distribution of the random variable $X$ of a population is skewed or even U-shaped, sample means of size 20 or more will approach the normal distribution. The general rule is that a sample of size 30 is nearly always considered large enough to use the normal distribution.

The sampling distribution of the mean is a theoretical probability distribution and, as such, has an expected mean value and standard deviation. Because the distribution is characteristic of the normal distribution, the expected value of the mean can be estimated by the mean value of the population; that is, the mean of the sample means is estimated by the mean of the population. The estimate is referred to as the sampling mean, or the mean of the means.

**Sampling Mean** The expected value of the mean of the sample means if random samples of size $n$ are drawn from a population.

$$\mu_{\bar{x}} = \mu$$

where

$\mu_{\bar{x}}$ is the sampling mean (mean of the sample means).
$\mu$ is the population mean.

The Greek letter $\mu$, a population parameter, represents the theoretical distribution. The subscript $\bar{x}$ represents the sample means. Putting the two together, $\mu_{\bar{x}}$ represents the mean of the **sampling distribution of the sample means**, which is known as the **sampling mean**.

**EXAMPLE 9.3**
**Experiment:** The population mean of the age of students at the community college is 25 years. The following Venn diagram represents four samples of 10 students. Illustrate the sampling mean.

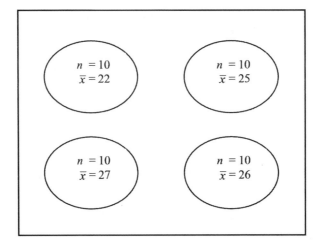

**Answer:** $\mu_{\bar{x}} = 25$

**Solution:** The sampling mean is the mean of the sample means. Since it is equivalent to the population mean, calculating it is not even necessary. That is, since the population mean, $\mu$, is given as 25, the sampling mean is equal to $\mu$ and is therefore 25. However, illustrating the concept may provide a better understanding. Add the sample means and divide by 4, the number of samples.

$$\mu_{\bar{x}} = 22 + 25 + 27 + 26 = 100$$
$$= 100/4$$
$$= 25$$

## EXAMPLE 9.4

**Experiment:** Suppose the average age of patients seeing Dr. Martinez is 35 with a standard deviation of 6. What is the expected value of sample means when the ages of five patients are sampled?

**Answer:** $\mu_{\bar{x}} = 35$

**Solution:** The mean of the sample means, or the sampling mean, is always estimated to be equal to the mean of the population. This is true of all populations. Because the original population mean is given as 35, the mean of samples is likely to be 35.

The variability of the sampling distribution is more complicated than the mean. Variances and standard deviations are not normally distributed and become difficult to estimate when a sample size is small. Recall that the standard deviation depends on sample size. Repeated sampling increases the dependency on sample size. Any estimation of the standard deviation of the sample mean requires an adjustment when samples are small. The adjusted standard deviation becomes known as the standard error of the mean.

**Standard Error of the Mean** Standard deviation of the sampling distribution of the sample means. It is calculated as

$$\sigma_{\bar{x}} = \frac{\sigma}{\sqrt{n}}$$

where

$\sigma_{\bar{x}}$ represents the standard error.
$\sigma$ represents the population standard deviation.
$n$ represents the sample size.

Greek letters are used, because these parameters represent a theoretical probability distribution. The Greek letter $\sigma$ represents the standard deviation of the population, and the subscript $\bar{x}$ represents a sample mean; thus, $\sigma_{\bar{x}}$ is the standard deviation of the sample mean, which is known as the standard error.

**EXAMPLE 9.5**

**Experiment:** Suppose the average age of patients seeing Dr. Martinez is 35 with a standard deviation of 6. What is the standard error of the sample means when the ages of five patients are sampled?

**Answer:** $\sigma_{\bar{x}} = 2.68$

**Solution:** The standard error is the standard deviation of the sample means- that is, the variability between the sample means. Because the standard deviation depends on sample size, it must be adjusted to compensate for the repeated sampling of size 5. Although the mean of the means is simply equal to the population mean, the standard deviation of the means is the standard deviation of the population divided by the square root of the sample size. The population standard deviation is given as 6 ($\sigma = 6$) whereas the sample size is given as 5 ($n = 5$). The standard error is

$$\sigma_{\bar{x}} = \frac{\sigma}{\sqrt{n}}$$

$$= \frac{6}{\sqrt{5}}$$

$$= 2.68$$

## A LEARNING AID
## SAMPLING DISTRIBUTIONS

The numbers 2, 3, 4, 5, 6, and 7 have a mean of 4.5 and a standard deviation of 1.71. Find the probability distribution of samples of size 2. What is the expected mean of the sample means and the expected standard error?

**Step 1**

A probability distribution for sample means is known as a sampling distribution. A sampling distribution lists all possible sample means of a specific size with the probability of each occurring. Begin by finding all the possible samples of size 2. Listing each and finding the sample mean of each will help create the sampling distribution. The following is a list of each possible sample of size 2 with the mean of each sample.

| Sample | Mean | Sample | Mean | Sample | Mean |
|--------|------|--------|------|--------|------|
| (2, 3) | 2.5 | (4, 2) | 3.0 | (6, 2) | 4.0 |
| (2, 4) | 3.0 | (4, 3) | 3.5 | (6, 3) | 4.5 |
| (2, 5) | 3.5 | (4, 5) | 4.5 | (6, 4) | 5.0 |
| (2, 6) | 4.0 | (4, 6) | 5.0 | (6, 5) | 5.5 |
| (2, 7) | 4.5 | (4, 7) | 5.5 | (6, 7) | 6.5 |
| (3, 2) | 2.5 | (5, 2) | 3.5 | (7, 2) | 4.5 |
| (3, 3) | 3.5 | (5, 3) | 4.0 | (7, 3) | 5.0 |
| (3, 4) | 4.0 | (5, 4) | 4.5 | (7, 4) | 5.5 |
| (3, 5) | 4.5 | (5, 6) | 5.5 | (7, 5) | 6.0 |
| (3, 6) | 5.0 | (5, 7) | 6.0 | (7, 6) | 6.5 |

**Step 2**

There are 30-different samples of size 2 that can be found. The 30 samples produce 9 different sample means: 2.5, 3.0, 3.5, 4.0, 4.5, 5.0, 5.5, 6.0, and 6.5. The frequency of each sample mean can be listed in a frequency distribution, which can then be redone as a probability distribution. List each possible sample mean and the number of times it occurred. Divide each frequency by 30 (the total number of occurrences) to obtain its probability.

| Sample Mean | Frequency | Probability |
|:---:|:---:|:---:|
| 2.5 | 2 | .067 |
| 3.0 | 2 | .067 |
| 3.5 | 4 | .133 |
| 4.0 | 4 | .133 |
| 4.5 | 6 | .200 |
| 5.0 | 4 | .133 |
| 5.5 | 4 | .133 |
| 6.0 | 2 | .067 |
| 6.5 | 2 | .067 |

**Step 3**

The expected mean of the sample means is known as the sampling mean and is estimated to be equal to the population mean. The original problem stated that the population mean is 4.5; therefore, the estimated sampling mean is 4.5. The standard error is really the standard deviation of the sampling means and is equal to the standard deviation of the population divided by the square root of the sample size, $n$. Thus, the estimated mean and the standard error are:

$$\mu_{\bar{x}} = \mu \qquad\qquad \sigma_{\bar{x}} = \sigma/\sqrt{n}$$
$$= 4.5 \qquad\qquad = 1.71/\sqrt{2}$$
$$= 1.21$$

# SECTION 2

## Central Limit Theorem

Combining the information from the previous sections results in a theorem known as the ***central limit theorem***. The central limit theorem is applied to sampling distributions approaching the normal distribution, where the mean of the sample means equals the population mean and the standard deviation of the sample means is the standard error.

**Central Limit Theorem** If random samples are taken from a population with a mean $\mu$ and a standard deviation, $\sigma$, the sampling distribution approaches the normal probability distribution.

1. Samples must be of equal size.

2. $\mu_{\bar{x}} = \mu$

3. $\sigma_{\bar{x}} = \dfrac{\sigma}{\sqrt{n}}$

The central limit theorem combines sampling distributions with the $z$-score of the normal distribution. Because the central limit theorem requires that a sampling distribution approach the normal distribution, with the means equal and a standard error based on the standard deviation, the $z$-score representing the normal distribution can be adjusted to reflect a sampling distribution.

## $z$-Score for Sampling Distributions

$$z = \frac{\bar{x} - \mu}{\sigma / \sqrt{n}}$$

The central limit theorem is of great use because it describes all types of sampling distributions, regardless of the shape of the original population. Because the mean from a large sample will have a normal probability distribution, the adjusted $z$ calculation becomes one of the most common tests of sample means.

### EXAMPLE 9.6

**Experiment:** Suppose the probability distribution of incomes in the United States is skewed to the right with a mean of $20,000 and a standard deviation of $8,000. If a random sample of 100 people is taken from the U.S. population, what will be the shape of the sampling distribution of the sample means?

**Answer:** A normal, bell-shaped distribution.

**Solution:** According to the central limit theorem, the probability distribution of sample means will be a normal probability distribution. This is true regardless of the fact that the original population is skewed. Notice the two distributions:

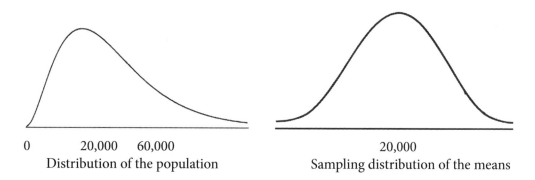

| 0 | 20,000 | 60,000 | 20,000 |
Distribution of the population  Sampling distribution of the means

It is very important to understand the difference between the $z$-score calculation presented in Chapter 8 and the adjusted calculation presented for sampling distributions. The $z$-score calculation of Chapter 8 is applied when finding the probability of one element of a population. For example, finding the probability of a cantaloupe in a farmer's field (one cantaloupe from a whole field) having a specific weight is to find the probability of one element of a population. In the calculation $(x - \mu)/\sigma$, the population mean is subtracted from one element or value of the random variable. The adjusted $z$-score calculation, $(\bar{x} - \mu_{\bar{x}})/\sigma_{\bar{x}}$ using a sampling distribution gives the probability of a value of a sample mean (not one element) from all possible sample means. The value of the mean of means must be subtracted from a value of one specific sample mean. For example, to find the probability of a mean of a sample of 10 cantaloupes after the mean of all samples of 10 has been estimated is to find the probability of a value of a sample mean from the sampling mean.

The process of applying the new $z$-score calculation is the same as in Chapter 8. The first step is to identify the probability statement. The probability statement requires the notation of the sample mean and a value. For example, a problem may require finding the probability that a sample mean is less than 10. The statement is written $P(\bar{x} < 10)$. The second step is to calculate the $z$-score using its adjusted formula.

The $z$-score formula when a sample mean is involved is the adjusted formula $(\bar{x} - \mu_{\bar{x}})/\sigma_{\bar{x}}$. Use the value from the probability statement as the value represented by $\bar{x}$. The mean of the means is estimated as the population mean. Thus $\mu_{\bar{x}} = \mu$. The standard error requires the population standard deviation to be divided by the square root of $n$, the number of cases in the sample. The actual computational formula is

$$z = \frac{\bar{x} - \mu}{\sigma/\sqrt{n}}$$

The third step is to transform the calculated $z$-score into a probability using Table A.3. The value related to the $z$-score is written as a probability by rounding the $z$-score to two decimal places. The value found by reading the intersection of the appropriate left column and top row represents the probability of the z-score. The final step is to place the probability on a normal curve and make any adjustments the problem may require. Drawing and shading a curve usually helps visualize whether adjustments are required. To find the area on the outside tails of the curve, the probability found in Table A.3 must be subtracted from .5000. To find the area in the center of the curve that overlaps parts of both sides, the probabilities found in Table A.3 must be added. There are times when adding and subtracting may be required. Interpreting the probability is the same as in earlier chapters. A probability approaching 1.0 is very strong and means an event is likely to occur. A probability approaching 0.0 is very weak and means the event is not likely to occur. Probabilities range from 0.0 to 1.0, inclusive. Probabilities are never negative.

Remember that the z-score itself is the standardized value of the random variable. It measures the number of standardized standard deviations a value is from the mean, where the mean is adjusted to 0. Watch for checks that may signal errors. For example, if a sampling mean is 5 and a sample value is 7, the z-score must be positive and the z-score is placed on the right side of the curve. A negative z-score is placed on the left side of the curve, but its probability is still positive. Also remember that there may be times when the area needed involves both sides of the curve. A probability statement may ask for the area between two sample means (for example, $P(10 < \bar{x} < 15)$). A calculation for each sample value is needed before each z-score is transformed into a probability and is placed on a curve. Shading the areas of the curve or using arrows helps visualize how probabilities need to be adjusted.

---

## EXAMPLE 9.7

**Experiment:** Suppose the probability distribution of incomes in the United States is skewed to the right with a mean of $20,000 and a standard deviation of $8,000. What is the probability that a sample of 10 would produce a sample mean less than $25,000?

**Answer:** $P(\bar{x} < 25,000) = .9756$

**Solution:** Begin by asking if this is a normal distribution. Income is a continuous variable and its sampling distribution approximates a normal distribution regardless of the shape of the original population. The key words in the problem implying this is a sampling distribution are "a sample of 10." The process begins by stating the probability question. The problem requires the probability that a sample mean is less than 25,000. A sample mean is represented by z, therefore, the probability statement is $P(\bar{x} < 25,000)$.

The calculation of the $z$-score involves the adjusted formula that reflects the use of a sampling distribution. Remember $\mu_{\bar{x}} = \mu$ and the standard error equals the standard deviation divided by the square root of the sample size. The following information is found in the wording of the original problem:

$\bar{x} = 25,000$, $\mu = 20,000$, $\sigma = 8,000$, and $n = 10$.

$$z = \frac{\bar{x} - \mu}{\sigma/\sqrt{n}} = \frac{25,000 - 20,000}{8000/\sqrt{10}}$$

$$= \frac{5,000}{2,532.65}$$

$$= 1.97$$

A calculated $z$-score transforms the original sample value to standard-scores. It shows that a sample mean of 25,000 is 1.97 standardized standard deviations above the sampling mean of 20,000. The $z$-score must be transformed into a probability using Table A.3. The $z$-score 1.97 yields a probability of .4756. This may not be the final answer. The probability must be considered in terms of the curve to determine if any adjustments are needed. In the following curve, the area needed is not only that represented by .4756 but also the entire other half of the curve. Half of the curve has a probability of .5000. The probability of the curve from 1.97 to 0 must be added to the probability of the left half of the curve.

Therefore, the probability from 1.97 through the left half of the curve is .4756 + .5000, or .9756. A probability of .9756 is very high and suggests that a sample of incomes producing a mean of less than $25,000 is very likely.

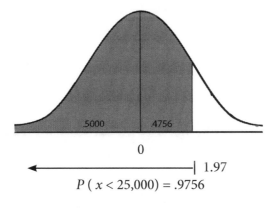

$$P(x < 25,000) = .9756$$

Probabilities for the sampling mean using the central limit theorem (CLT) can be calculated using the TI-83/84 calculators. There are many different ways to obtain answers. The most important point is to understand what you are looking for. Here we introduce one of the methods that can be used in later chapters too.

To find a probability that involves CLT, such as finding the probability of a sample mean to be in certain range, use the following steps: Press STAT. Scroll to TESTS, 1:Z-Test…and press ENTER. Highlight STATs, and enter the data as indicated such as mean, standard deviation, sample mean, and $n$. Highlight the desired direction, < if you are looking for $P(\bar{x} < a)$ or > if you are looking for $P(\bar{x} > b)$. Scroll down to Calculate and hit ENTER. The screen will display $z$ and p, where $z$ will be the $z$-score corresponding to the value entered for the sample mean and $p$ is the desired probability.

---

## EXAMPLE 9.8

**Experiment:** A package of powdered sugar at the grocery store indicates the weight is 16 oz ($\pm 1$ oz.) Assume that the weight of the powdered sugar is normally distributed with a mean of 16 oz and standard deviation of 1 oz. What is the probability that a sample of 10 packages of powdered sugar will produce a sample mean weight less than 15 oz?

**Answer:** $P(\bar{x} < 15) = P(z < -3.16) = 7.83 \times 10^{-4} \approx .00078$

**Solution:** Identify the desired probability. Let $\bar{x}$ be the sample mean weight of 10 packages of pastas and look for $P(\bar{x} < 15)$. The $\mu = 16$ and $\sigma = 1$.

To solve this problem, utilizing a TI calculator, first press the STAT button. Scroll right to TESTS, and with "1:Z-Test…" highlighted, press ENTER.

In the Z-Test screen, be sure that "Stats" is highlighted and blinking. If it is not, scroll to it and press the ENTER button.
Proceed to enter the data in the calculator as follows.

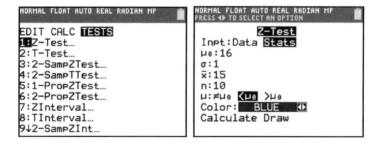

$\mu_0 :$ 16   This is the population mean.

$\sigma :$ 1   This is either the standard deviation.

$\bar{x} :$ 15   This is the value the of the sample mean.

$n :$ 10   This is the sample size.

$\mu :$ <   Highlight the < and press ENTER to select it. The selection of the

sign here depends on the probability being sought. If looking for $P(\bar{x} < a)$, <
must be highlighted.

Once the Stats are entered, scroll down to highlight "Calculate" and press
ENTER.

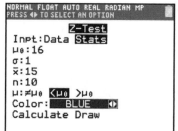
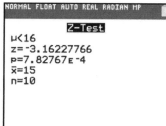

The result screen should indicate that the $Z = -3.16$ and $P = 7.827$ E-4. Keep in
mind that this notation means to move the decimal left 4 decimal places.

Thus, the answer is: $P(\bar{x} < 15) = P(z < -3.16) = 7.83 \times 10^{-4} \approx .00078$

## A LEARNING AID
## CENTRAL LIMIT THEOREM (CLT)

Suppose the daily sales at the local delicatessen average $600, with a standard
deviation of $50. What is the probability that a sample of 10 randomly
selected days produces a sample mean above $650?

### Step 1

Identify the problem as a sampling distribution. The variable, money, is a
continuous variable with a normal distribution whose sampling distribution
is also normally distributed. The central limit theorem states that the
distribution will approach the normal distribution when samples are taken
in the case where the mean of the means is equal to the population mean and
the standard error is equal to the population standard deviation divided by
the square root of the number of cases sampled. This problem asks about the
probability of a sample mean, thus qualifying as a sampling distribution.

**Step 2**

Identify the probability statement. The problem asks for the probability of a sample mean above (greater than) 650. The statement is written $P(\bar{x} > 650)$.

**Step 3**

Calculate the $z$-score using Z-Test function in a TI-83/84 calculator. The population mean, $\mu$, is given as 600, the standard deviation is $\sigma = 50$, the number of cases is $n = 10$, and the sample mean is $\bar{x} = 650$.

Begin by pressing the STAT button, followed by scrolling right to TESTS, and pressing 1 to select "1:Z-Test..." With Stats selected under the settings screen of this test, plug in the given information. Highlight "Calculate" and press the ENTER button to display the results.

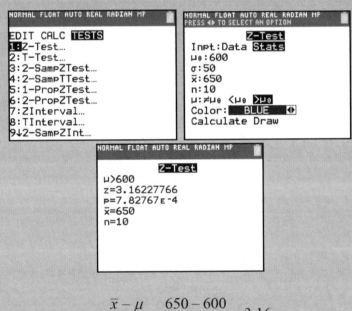

$$z = \frac{\bar{x} - \mu}{\sigma/\sqrt{n}} = \frac{650 - 600}{50/\sqrt{10}} = 3.16$$

**Step 4**

Interpret the results. The probability .0008 represents the probability that a sample of 10 daily sales would produce a mean greater than $650. Because .0008 is very small, it can be said that such a sample mean is very unlikely to occur.

# CHAPTER 9 IN REVIEW

9.1 Find the sampling distribution of means of samples of size 2 from the population 2, 4, 6, 8. Does it meet the requirements of a true probability distribution?

9.2 The ages of employees in the Registrar's Office are 20, 25, 30, and 40. Find the probability distribution of samples of size 2.

9.3 Find the probabilities associated with the following $z$-scores:

a. $z = 1.25$        d. $z = 0.67$

b. $z = -1.25$      e. $z = -3.12$

c. $-.67$ to $-2.12$     f. 1.34 to 2.00

9.4 Find the probabilities associated with the area of the curve between the following $z$-scores:

a. $-.67$ to $.67$      d. $-2.00$ to $2.00$

b. $-2.12$ to $1.33$    e. $-1.50$ to $1.29$

c. 0 to $-2.00$       f. 1.29 to 1.99

9.5 A survey was taken on the annual per capita spending for children's toys in industrialized nations. The annual spending per capita averages $88.20 with a standard deviation of $28.31. What is the probability that a sample mean from 10 countries would:
a. Spend $70?
b. Spend $90?
c. Spend between $70 and $90?
d. Spend between $90 and $100?

9.6 The salaries of teachers in the West Bloomfield Public School District are normally distributed with a mean of $53.5 thousand with a standard deviation of 5.5. What is the probability that a sample of 20 teachers will have a salary:
     a. Above 53.5?         c. Above 55?
     b. Below 50?           d. Between 54 and 55?

9.7 Subscribers in a health care plan visited the clinic on average 4.6 times a year with a standard deviation of 2.0. An interviewer sampled 36 subscribers on a specific day. What is the probability that these subscribers had a sample mean of fewer than 5 visits a year?

9.8 The lifetime of a computer is normally distributed with a mean of 4.5 years and a standard deviation of 1.2. What is the probability that a randomly selected computer would have a lifetime of:
a. 4 to 5 years?
b. Less than 4 years?
c. If 10 computers are randomly selected, what is the probability that the sample mean will be greater than 5 years?
d. If 10 computers are randomly selected, what is the probability that the sample mean will be less than 6 years?

9.9 The percentage of Americans with diabetes is normally distributed with a mean of 20 and a standard deviation of 1.75. What is the probability that a sample of 10 Americans will produce a sample mean of 25 percent?

9.10 Business travelers are on the road an average of 10 days a month, with a standard deviation of three days. What is the sampling mean and standard error for a sample of 40 business travelers?

9.11 A cigarette company claims that smokers smoke a mean of 8.5 cigarettes a day, with a standard deviation of 6 cigarettes.
a. What is the expected sampling mean of a sample of 25 smokers?
b. What is the standard error of the sample?
c. What is the probability that the sample of 25 will produce a mean of smoking not more than 10 cigarettes a day?

9.12 In 2014, the highest paid CEOs in U.S. companies have an average salary of $70.05 million with a standard deviation of 30.38 million. What is the probability that a sample of 10 would have a mean less than $50 million?

9.13 If Ms. Armstrong spends an average 44.1 hours a week in her office with a standard deviation of 4.2, what is the probability that a sample of 10 weeks will produce a mean less than 40 hours?

9.14 The average credit card debt is currently averaging $15,000 (15) with a standard deviation of 5,000 (5). What is the probability that (use single digits):
a. Mrs. Yono will have a debt of more than 9 thousand dollars?
b. Mr. Lopez will have a debt more than 8 thousand?
c. A sample of 20 people will have a debt less than 12 thousand?
d. A sample of 20 people will have a debt between 14 and 16 thousand?

9.15 The mean weight of employees at the oil-distribution center is 178 pounds with a standard deviation of 12.5.

a. What is the probability that Mr. Gomez, an employee at the company, weighs more than 200 lbs?

b. What is the probability that a random sample of 30 employees will produce a sample mean greater than 200 lbs?

c. Explain why the answers in a and b are not the same.

9.16 A population is normally distributed with a mean of 100 and a standard deviation of 16. What is the probability that a sample of 40 will produce a sample mean between 95 and 105?

9.17 Students spend on average 12.5 hours a week studying for a statistics course with a standard deviation of 4. If a sample of 30 students is taken, what is the:

a. Expected mean of a sample of 30 students?

b. Standard error of the mean for the sample?

c. Probability they would spend more than 12.5 hours studying?

d. Probability they would spend less than 12.5 hours studying?

e. Probability they would spend less than 13 hours studying?

f. Probability they would spend more than 13 hours studying?

9.18 The average length of a bill passed by Congress is now 10.8 pages, with a standard deviation of 1.8. What is the expected sampling mean and standard error for a sample of 30 bills?

9.19 The expected number of absences in a school year for college students is 8.9 and the standard deviation is 2.0 days.

a. What is the expected sampling mean for absences of a randomly selected group of 30 college students?

b. What is the standard error for absences of the sample?

c. What is the probability that the mean of the random sample of 40 college students will be more than 9.4 days?

9.20 A professor believes students cheat on average 5 times a semester, with a standard deviation of 3. What is the probability that your class of 30 students will have a sample mean for cheating less than 6 times a semester?

9.21 True or False?

a. Probabilities are never negative.

b. To find the area of the normal curve on the outside of the tail, the probability is added to .5000.

c. A $z$-score represents a standardized mean.

d. The calculation of the standard error is equal to the population standard deviation.

9.22 True or False?
   a. A sampling distribution of means approaches a normal curve regardless of the shape of the distribution of the original population.
   b. The sampling mean equals the population mean.
   c. The probability of half the normal curve is equal to .5.
   d. The area of the normal curve from a negative $z$-score to a positive $z$-score requires adding the corresponding probabilities.

9.23 The average salary of a new first round draft choice in men's professional basketball is $1.3 million with a standard deviation of .5. What is the probability that a randomly selected recruit:
   a. Will be paid more than $1.5 million?
   b. Will be paid more than $.5 million?
   c. If 10 recruits are randomly selected, what is the probability that the sample mean will be between $1.1 and $1.4 million?
   d. If 10 recruits are randomly selected, what is the probability that the sample mean will be between $1.4 and $1.5 million?
   e. If 10 recruits are randomly selected, what is the probability that the sample mean will be less than $1.3 million?

9.24 The percent of births to mothers with less than 12 years of education in the top cities with the highest rates averages 39.3 with a standard deviation of 4.1. What is the probability that:
   a. A city will have a rate less than 40?
   b. A city will have a rate more than 40?
   c. If 6 cities are selected, that the sample mean will be less than 40?
   d. If 6 cities are selected, that the sample mean will be more than 40?

9.25 The number of pages in a doctoral dissertation is normally distributed with an average of 350 pages and a standard deviation of 125. What is the probability that a randomly selected dissertation will have …
   a. More than 400 pages?
   b. Less than 400 pages?
   c. If a sample of 30 dissertations is taken, what is the probability that the sample mean will be greater than 350 pages?
   d. In the sample of 30 dissertations, what is the probability that the sample mean will be between 400 and 425 pages?

9.26 Suppose the average number of points scored in an NFL football game is normally distributed with $\mu = 21.7$ and $\sigma = 4$. What is the probability that a sample of 12 games would produce a mean between 20 and 23 points?

9.27  The average cost of a 30-second TV commercial in the summer Olympics was $4.5 million with a standard deviation of .5. What is the probability that a sample of 15 30-second commercials costs more than $4 million?

9.28  From June until September, the average temperature in Athens, Greece is 35° C (95° F) with a standard deviation of 6° C. If a random sample of 25 days is taken, what is the probability that the average would be more than 30° C?

9.29  According to the U.S. Census Bureau, the average percent of single-parent households in developed countries for 2008 is 21.7% with a standard deviation of 5 percent. What is the probability that a sample of 10 random developed countries has an average above 23?

9.30  The average student debt for students graduating with their bachelor's degree from a four-year university in 2014 was $30,000 with a standard deviation of $8,000. What is the probability that a sample of 30 students would have an average debt of less than $33,000?

# 10 | INFERENTIAL STATISTICS

SECTION 1  **The Null and Alternative Hypotheses**
SECTION 2  **Hypothesis Testing Using the Classical Approach for One Population Mean**
SECTION 3  **Hypothesis Testing Using P-Values for One Population Mean**
SECTION 4  **Confidence Interval for One Population Mean**

Probabilities and sampling distributions, as presented in previous chapters, determine the likelihood of an event occurring when information is known about the population. However, information about the population may not be known or be able to be determined. For example, can all the fish in Lake Michigan be measured to determine their average length? Though some may answer yes, such a project seems almost impossible, and the consequences would be severe. Sampling distributions require that every fish be measured and that the mean of several samples be estimated by the population mean. But if the population mean cannot be determined, a sampling mean has little use.

Inferential statistics works in the opposite fashion. Instead of predicting sample information from a population, inferential statistics predicts population information from a sample. More importantly, decisions can be made about various hypotheses that may lead to accepting or discarding policies, behavior, and even theories. The goal is to make inferences (thus the name inferential statistics) about a population using sample data. Most inferences are based on one or two samples, usually concerning the mean, variances, and the binomial probability $p$.

---

## SECTION 1

### The Null and Alternative Hypotheses

Inferential statistics allow testing of hypotheses, which leads to theory building. The nature of theory building does not allow a theory to be proven absolutely; such is also the case with hypotheses. The rule is that theories and hypotheses can be disproved but cannot be proven. Hypotheses must be accepted as true until such time that they are proven false. A theory or hypothesis cannot be proven at all times in all situations. But when tested, if the theory fails, it is clear that it is not true.

Consider, for example, the theory that the sun will rise in the east and will set in the west. There is no way to test today what will happen tomorrow; a scientist cannot guarantee the theory that the sun will rise in the east tomorrow and every day for eternity. Yet, the theory that the sun will rise tomorrow in the east and set in the west remains an accepted theory until such time that it can be proven to be false—until it does not rise in the east and set in the west.

Another example of testing hypotheses involves the theory that the world was flat. By the laws of theory and hypothesis testing, the theory must be accepted as true until proven otherwise. Christopher Columbus, among others, doubted the theory and set out to prove that the world was not flat. It was only when Columbus presented irrefutable proof that the world was not flat that the theory could be rejected for the new theory—the world is round.

Inferential statistics usually begins with testing hypotheses about the differences between the value of samples and the estimated value of the population. It is the science of making decisions about the descriptive statistics that have been collected from a population or from a sample. A population parameter is usually hypothesized and compared to a sample statistic. Hypotheses are divided into two categories: null and alternative.

> **Null Hypothesis**  A statement that there is no difference between the hypothesized value of the population and a sample statistic. It carries the benefit of the doubt. It is denoted by $H_O$.

The **null hypothesis** states that there is no difference between the hypothesized population parameter and the value of a sample statistic. It is the hypothesis that is tested and is denoted by $H_O$. It gets its name from the fact that it states there is no difference between the population and the sample other than what can be reasonably attributed to chance. It is also the hypothesis that must be proven false before it can be rejected. This means that the null hypothesis must be favored in the case of doubt. It must be accepted as true until there is definite evidence showing it to be false.

> **Alternative Hypothesis**  A statement that the value of the population parameter is different from that specified by the null hypothesis. It challenges the null as not true. It carries the burden of proof and is denoted by $H_I$ or $H_a$.

The **alternative hypothesis** is a statement that the value of the population parameter is different than that stated in the null hypothesis. The alternative hypothesis carries the burden of proof. It is denoted by $H_I$ or $H_a$. If the alternative hypothesis is found to be true, then the null hypothesis can be rejected.

In verifying scientific hypotheses, the burden of proof falls on the alternative hypothesis. It is the one that must be proven. The null hypothesis is accepted as true until such time that an alternative hypothesis disproves it. Again, the null hypothesis is given the benefit of the doubt and must be disproved. It can be rejected only when an alternative hypothesis is used to disprove it.

In the example of the theory about the sun rising every day, the null hypothesis is that the sun will rise in the east and set in the west. It must be accepted as true until tested and proven false. An alternative hypothesis must challenge the theory. It could state that tomorrow the sun will not rise in the east and set in the west. If, in the test, the sun does not rise in the east and set in the west, then the null hypothesis can be rejected in favor of the alternative. If the test supports the original theory set out in the null hypothesis, then the theory again passes the test; although not proven false, it is not proven that it will always be true. It has passed only this particular challenge.

In the theory about the Earth, the null hypothesis states that the Earth is flat. The alternative hypothesis states that the Earth is not flat, it is round. The null hypothesis was tested, and it failed causing it to be rejected. The alternative hypothesis then replaces the null hypothesis as the theory until such time that a new challenge can prove otherwise.

---

**EXAMPLE 10.1**

**Experiment:** It is a premise of the U.S. legal system that a person is innocent until proven guilty. A person is being brought to trial for first-degree murder. What are the null and alternative hypotheses?

**Answer:**

$H_0$: The person is innocent.
$H_1$: The person is not innocent.

**Solution:** The premise that all are innocent until proven guilty is a claim for the population. That this particular person is innocent until proven guilty is then the sample from the population. The null hypothesis makes a comparison between the sample and the population and states that there is no difference. Therefore, the person must be said to be innocent until proven guilty. The alternative hypothesis must challenge the null hypothesis. The alternative states that there is a difference between the sample and the population. Therefore, the person is not innocent; the person is guilty.

---

Hypotheses are usually stated with symbols and values as opposed to words. Usually a value of a parameter is in question. For example, the director of fisheries claims that the average length of fish in Lake Michigan is 3.5 in. An angler thinks the average length of fish is not 3.5. The parameter in question is the population mean, $\mu$, the length of all fish in Lake Michigan. The value in question is 3.5. The null hypothesis is the statement from the director of fisheries, $H_0$: $\mu = 3.5$. The null hypothesis always contains an equal sign (including $\leq$ and $\geq$). The angler questions the null hypothesis; this claim becomes the alternative hypothesis and is written $H_1: \mu \neq 3.5$.

### Format of Hypotheses

$H_0$: Parameter $(=, \geq, \leq)$ Value

$H_1$: Parameter $(\neq, <, >)$ Value

There are only three possible symbols for the null hypothesis and three for the alternative hypothesis (Table 10.1). When in doubt, the symbols can be used as a cue in determining which statement is the null hypothesis. Note that symbols are also paired. For example if the $H_0$ contains $\leq$, $H_1$ must be $>$.

### TABLE 10.1

| Hypothesis | Symbols | Parameters |
|:---:|:---:|:---:|
| $H_0$ | $=, \geq, \leq$ | $\mu, \sigma^2, \sigma, \rho$ |
| $H_1$ | $\neq, <, >$ | $\mu, \sigma^2, \sigma, \rho$ |

For example: The mean age of students at U of D is 29 is written:

$$H_0: \mu = 29$$
$$H_1: \mu \neq 29$$

Another example is: The standard deviation in heights of men is 3 inches:

$$H_0: \sigma = 3$$
$$H_1: \sigma \neq 3$$

Another requirement in determining the null and alternative hypotheses is to question the authority of the person making a claim. When a claim is offered by someone of authority, there is usually no reason to doubt that claim. The claim usually becomes the null hypothesis, based on the idea that the null hypothesis carries the benefit of the doubt. Since the null hypothesis always shows equality between the sample statistic and the population parameter, any claim involving equal to (=), greater than or equal to ($\geq$), or less than or equal to ($\leq$) becomes the null hypothesis. Any other claim, involving not equal to ($\neq$), less than (<), or greater than (>), becomes the alternative hypothesis.

### EXAMPLE 10.2

**Experiment:** The owner of the local cable television company claims the average cable bill is \$44.95, with a standard deviation of 4.50. A cable subscriber believes the mean may be correct but thinks the standard deviation is greater than 4.50. State the null and alternative hypotheses.

**Answer:** $H_0: \sigma \leq 4.50$, $H_1: \sigma > 4.50$

**Solution:** Begin by identifying the parameter. There are four choices for the parameter: $\mu$, $\sigma^2$, $\sigma$, $\rho$. The mean is stated but is not in question. The subscriber is questioning the standard deviation, $\sigma$. Next, the null hypothesis must be identified. There are two ways of identifying the null statement. The first is to consider the authority of the two individuals. The owner has the information needed to calculate the standard deviation for cable subscribers. There is probably no reason to doubt the owner. Also, the owner's claim includes an equal sign. The owner claims the standard deviation is (is equal to) 4.50. The null hypothesis carries the benefit of the doubt until someone can prove it false. The subscriber's claim becomes the alternative hypothesis and must prove the information from the owner is incorrect. The subscriber carries the burden of proof. The subscriber does not just think the owner's claim of 4.50 is wrong; the subscriber thinks it is wrong in a particular direction, greater than 4.50. The greater than sign ($>$) is needed with the alternative hypothesis, so the null hypothesis symbol must be equal to or less than ($\leq$). Thus, a test may be conducted to determine if the subscriber's challenge is correct. He or she would be correct only if a value greater than 4.50 is found. If a value equal to or less than 4.50 is found, then the original null hypothesis still stands.

As important as stating the hypothesis correctly is making the correct decision to accept the null hypothesis or to reject it when a test is conducted. For example, suppose a hypothesis is really true, but the test is not conducted correctly (perhaps the sample is not a random sample). The decision to reject the hypothesis because of the sample test would be an error. There are four different decisions that can be made, two correct decisions and two incorrect decisions. The two correct decisions are to accept the null hypothesis when it is true or to reject it when it is false. There are two kinds of errors that can occur in incorrectly deciding the status of the hypotheses, type I error and type II error.

A type I error is committed when the researcher incorrectly rejects the null hypothesis based on a test when the null hypothesis is actually true. A type II error occurs when the null hypothesis is incorrectly accepted to be true based on a test when it is actually false. The seriousness of each error changes from hypothesis to hypothesis. Which error is more serious must be decided by the researcher. Because the null hypothesis is the one to favor in case of doubt, it should be stated in such a way as to make the more serious error avoidable. Table 10.2 summarizes the situation.

**TABLE 10.2**

|  | $H_o$ **is really true** | $H_o$ **is really false** |
|---|---|---|
| **Test results in accepting** $H_o$ **as true** | Correct decision I | Type II error $\beta$ |

| Test results in rejecting $H_O$ as false | Type I error $\alpha$ | Correct decision II |
|---|---|---|

The following example is not written in the traditional statistical format of a hypothesis but as a narrative to illustrate the types of errors.

---

**EXAMPLE 10.3**

**Experiment:** A women is diagnosed by her doctor as having breast cancer. State the null and alternative hypotheses in words (not symbols). Describe the errors. Which error is more serious?

**Answer:**
$H_O$: Woman does not have cancer
$H_i$: Woman does have cancer

Type I error $(\alpha)$: She does not have cancer but a test incorrectly shows she does.

Type II error $(\beta)$: She has cancer but a test incorrectly shows she does not.

Most serious error: Type II, $\beta$

**Solution:** $H_O$ states that she does not have cancer, because that was her condition prior to going to the doctor. Theoretically, there is no difference in her health prior to or after she goes to the doctor. Although she may have questioned her health before she visited the doctor, there is no proof that anything specifically is wrong. The benefit of the doubt goes to the null hypothesis. The $H_i$ states that she has cancer, a claim by the doctor that requires conclusive proof. The type I correct decision is that she does not have cancer; further tests correctly support this by being negative. The type II correct decision is that further tests show correctly that she has cancer and she accepts treatment. The type I error is that she does not have cancer but for some reason further tests incorrectly suggest she does. The type II error is that she does have cancer but further tests suggest that she does not. The most serious error must, therefore, be the type II error, because its consequences are fatal. That is, in a type I error she would be treated as if she has cancer—perhaps with surgery or chemotherapy. As severe as unnecessary treatment is for a non-existing disease, more severe is no treatment at all for a patient who has a fatal disease. The type II error, in this case, would probably result in the death of the woman; therefore, it is the more severe error that needs to be avoided.

---

In a world of certainty, errors would not be of concern. Statisticians would always predict accurately what would or would not happen. But the world is not one of certainty. In the real world people make mistakes. These mistakes can be costly, even deadly. The only way errors can be reduced is to observe the whole universe of events. Generally speaking, testing every object in a universe cannot, and sometimes should not, be done. Large samples increase the cost of doing research. Smaller samples are often as useful and are more manageable but can increase the chance of error. A solution is to assign a probability to the error, which can be adjusted to avoid the more serious error. For example, often a person wants to be 95% sure he or she is correct, which means there will be a 5% chance he or she is incorrect. Adjusting the risks of being correct and incorrect may reduce the chance of serious error. Most researchers attempt this balance by using smaller samples and assigning probabilities to errors by defining the hypotheses in such a way that the more serious error is the type I error. The error is then controlled by adjusting the acceptable *level of significance* associated with the type I error. This means the level of significance is the probability of committing a type I error when testing the null hypothesis.

> **Level of Significance** The probability of committing a type I error (the probability of rejecting $H_O$ when it is actually true). The level of significance is represented by the Greek letter $\alpha$ (alpha).

The most common levels set for $\alpha$ are .01, .05, .025, and .1. When the type I error is not so grave, a higher $\alpha$ level, such as .05, is acceptable. This would mean that 95% of the benefit of doubt would rest upon the null hypothesis, and 5% would go to the probability of being wrong. If the consequence of the type I error is critical, then a smaller $\alpha$ would add extra certainty that an incorrect hypothesis would not be mistakenly accepted as correct.

The probability of committing a type I error is represented by the first letter in the Greek alphabet, **alpha** ($\alpha$). The probability of committing a type II error is represented by the second letter in the Greek alphabet, **beta** ($\beta$). Alpha and beta can be thought of as opposites. As one increases, the other decreases. This text will not directly use or calculate beta but will avoid type II errors by increasing or decreasing alpha appropriately. When a type II error is the more serious error, alpha is set large so that beta is reduced. When the type I error is more serious, alpha is set low.

$$\alpha \uparrow \beta \downarrow \qquad\qquad \alpha \downarrow \beta \uparrow$$

**EXAMPLE 10.4**
**Experiment:** An electrician is told by the building manager that the electrical power to the building is off. Which error is more serious, type I or type II? At what level should alpha be set?

**Answer:** Type II error; $\alpha$ should be large, perhaps .05.

**Solution:** A type I error may occur if the electrical power is off but the electrician believes it is on. Nothing serious would occur by making this mistake. A type II error occurs if the electrical power is on but the electrician believes it is off. This is a serious error, because the electrician may be electrocuted if he or she attempts to repair any wiring. Alpha represents the probability of committing a type I error; if $\alpha$ is set high, the probability of a type II error is reduced. A type II error should be avoided.

## A LEARNING AID
## THE NULL HYPOTHESIS

Suppose the local bakery claims that the mean weight of a loaf of bread is 14 oz. A customer believes that the mean weight is less than 14 oz. State the hypotheses and describe the errors.

### Step 1

State the null hypothesis. The null hypothesis is found by considering the authority of the bakery claiming the mean weight of bread is 14 oz. The bakery has access to information about weight, and the customer probably does not. Also, the bakery's claim includes an equal sign. The null hypothesis is affected by the customer's claim that the mean weight is less than 14. The challenge of less than 14 forces the null hypothesis to become not only equal to 14 but also greater than 14. The null hypothesis is believed to be true until proven false.

### Step 2

State the alternative hypothesis. The alternative hypothesis challenges the null hypothesis and carries the burden of proof. The customer's claim must prove the bakery's claim false. The customer is not viewed as the authority, nor does the claim contain an equal sign. The customer's claim is that the mean is less than 14 and reads:

$$H_0: \mu \geq 14$$
$$H_1: \mu < 14$$

### Step 3

Describe the errors. A type I error is incorrectly rejecting a null hypothesis. This would be the case if a test of the weights of a sample leads to a decision that the mean weight of all the bread is less than 14 oz. A type II error is incorrectly accepting a null hypothesis when really it is false. A type II error would occur if a test of weights of the bread leads to a decision to accept the bakery's claim when the claim is really false. Neither error is extremely serious. The type I error may result in losing a customer because he or she might think the bakery is overcharging for the bread. The type II error could result in a complaint to the Department of Agriculture and other government agencies that, one hopes, would conduct further tests to discover if the bakery does indeed sell less than 14 oz. loaves. The type II error could be the more serious error and should be avoided.

# SECTION 2

## Hypothesis Testing for 1 Sample/Population Mean Using *z*

The process of testing and deciding whether to reject hypotheses can be very systematic. A series of six steps is detailed and then reviewed and integrated at the end of this section. Each step is important and cannot be overlooked. These steps are applicable to many types of data and to testing of different parameters. Therefore, they must be followed, with slight alterations, for most of the rest of the text.

To briefly overview the classical approach, a hypothesis is stated. The parameter (for example, the mean) is converted into a *z*-score by using the $\alpha$ level of significance. The sample information is also converted into a *z*-score by using the formula presented in Chapter 9. Both *z*-scores are compared and a decision is made to either ***reject or fail to reject the null hypothesis***.

Population $\rightarrow\alpha \rightarrow$*z-score*

$\rightarrow\rightarrow$compare *z*-scores to make a decision

Sample$\rightarrow\rightarrow\rightarrow\rightarrow$*z-score*

## Step 1
The first step is to state the hypotheses. The null and alternative hypotheses must be stated in appropriate form. Recall that the null hypothesis must carry the benefit of the doubt and must be assumed to be true until the alternative hypothesis proves it wrong. The null hypothesis always involves an equal sign (=), less than or equal to sign ($\leq$), or greater than or equal to sign ($\geq$). The alternative hypothesis carries the burden of proof and directly challenges the null hypothesis. The alternative hypothesis never involves an equal sign, but instead may be written with $\neq$, $<$, or $>$.

## Step 2
The second step in hypothesis testing is to establish the test criteria. The test criteria allow one to determine the level of significance—the type I error. The criteria also determine the exact test to be performed that will challenge the null hypothesis

and the values of a test that may result in the rejection of the null hypothesis. The test criteria have four specific concerns. The first concern is to specify the level of significance, alpha, or the probability of committing a type I error. The second is to determine the *test statistic* that will be applied to the sample information. The third concern of the *test criteria* is to determine the critical region, which will specify the range of values that will not fall within an acceptable distance of the population parameter. The fourth and final concern is to determine the *critical value* that will note the decision line dividing the critical region from the non-critical region. Each concern is further discussed below.

---

**Test Criteria**
Four considerations leading to the actual test of the null hypothesis:

1. Setting the level of significance.
2. Identifying the test statistic.
3. Determining the critical region.
4. Determining the critical value.

---

The level of significance, alpha, is the probability of committing a type I error. Typically, a problem states the alpha level as part of a claim challenging a null hypothesis. The alpha level specifies how much error is acceptable. If alpha is not stated, then one must decide how much risk will be allowed by rejecting a potentially true hypothesis. If a type I error appears more severe than a type II error, then alpha should be set low. If a type II error is more serious, then alpha should be set high so that beta is reduced.

The test statistic is the random variable, and its probability distribution is used to compare the sample statistic to the hypothesized population parameter. Thus far, only the test statistic $z$ has been described with its normal probability distribution. In later sections and chapters, different test statistics will be used to calculate means of very small samples, variances between one and two samples, and proportions representing the binomial distribution. Probability distributions representing $t$, $F$, and $\chi^2$ will be added to the choice of the test statistic. When the $z$-score is used for means of large samples, the central limit theorem is applied in the same fashion as in Chapter 9.

---

**Test Statistic** The random variable used to calculate and compare the sample statistic to the hypothesized population parameter. The test statistics used in this book are $z$, $t$, $\chi^2$, and $F$.

**Criteria for Using $z$ As the Test Statistic**
1. Testing or estimating $\mu$ with a normal distribution.
2. $n$ (the sample size) is greater than 30.
3. $\sigma$ (the standard deviation of the population) is given or known.

---

The critical region is an area of the probability distribution that will lead to rejecting the null hypothesis if the calculated test statistic value falls within it. A sample rarely results in a value exactly equal to the value specified in the null hypothesis. A value "close enough" to the specified is usually accepted. For example, suppose that the average age of students at school is 27 years. The null hypothesis would state that the mean of a sample of students' ages must be 27. If a sample mean results in 26.5, should it be accepted as close enough to 27 to be considered correct? The answer is probably yes. If the sample produces a mean of 27.5, should it also be accepted as close enough? Again, the answer is probably yes. But what if the sample produces a mean of 20? Should 20 be considered close enough? The answer is probably not. One of the considerations in hypothesis testing is the acknowledgment that a specified value of the null hypothesis will have a range of values that will be considered close enough to be correct. Determination of how large the range will be is a critical question. The "close-enough" area is referred to as the non-critical region, whereas the values outside the range is the critical region.

**Non-Critical Region = Close Enough     Critical Region = Rejection Area**

The process of establishing the critical region begins by drawing the appropriate distribution for the test statistic. For example, the bell-shaped normal distribution is drawn for the test statistic $z$. The next step is to review the null and alternative hypotheses. Most people concentrate on the alternative hypothesis in determining where to draw the critical region. If the alternative hypothesis states the parameter is not equal to a hypothesized value, the critical region will be divided in half and appropriately placed on the two ends of the distribution. That is, if an alternative hypothesis states a mean is not equal to 27 ($H_1$: $\mu \neq 27$), an accepted range of values below and above the mean will be identified, as shown in Figure 10.1. Any values beyond those values will be considered in the critical region. When the critical region is divided, falling in both tails of the curve, it is referred to as a ***two-tailed test***.

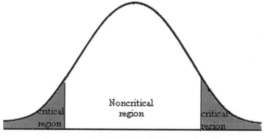

**FIGURE 10.1**

**Two-tailed Test** A test used when a critical region is divided, with half of its area on both ends of the probability distribution. This test occurs when $H_1$ indicates a parameter is not equal to the hypothesized value.

**EXAMPLE 10.5**

**Experiment:** A candy company claims an average box of jellybeans contains 40 candies. A disgruntled consumer claims the mean is incorrect. If $H_O$ is $\mu = 40$ and $H_I$ is $\mu \neq 40$, identify the location of the critical region.

**Answer:**

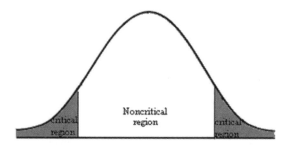

**Solution:** Draw the normal curve, which represents the test statistic $z$. The critical regions are indicated by the alternative hypothesis, because it contains a not equal to ($\neq$) sign. The critical region must be divided, with half of its area in the left tail and half in the right tail. This is a two-tailed test situation.

There are times when the critical region may fall in only one tail of a probability distribution. Sometimes a concern arises that the hypothesized value is underestimated. The alternative hypothesis then would contain a greater than sign (>). Sometimes the hypothesized value is overestimated, which results in an alternative hypothesis containing a less than sign (<). In either case, the critical area falls on one side, the side that the alternative hypothesis indicates. When the critical region falls to only one side, the related test is called a ***one-tailed test***. See Figure 10.2.

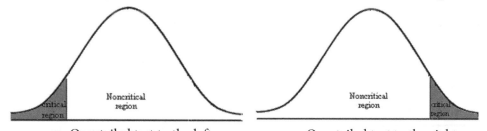

One-tailed test to the left        One-tailed test to the right

**Figure 10.2**

**One-tailed Test** The test used when a critical region falls on only one side of a probability distribution. This occurs when $H_I$ involves less than (<) or greater than (>).

Because many statistics books write the null hypothesis only with an equal sign, the alternative hypothesis can best indicate whether a test is one-tailed or two-tailed. The following chart should be used to determine the placement of the critical region.

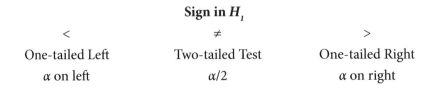

**Sign in $H_1$**

| $<$ | $\neq$ | $>$ |
|---|---|---|
| One-tailed Left | Two-tailed Test | One-tailed Right |
| $\alpha$ on left | $\alpha/2$ | $\alpha$ on right |

**EXAMPLE 10.6**
**Experiment:** A candy company claims an average box of jellybeans contains 40 candies. A disgruntled consumer not only believes the mean is incorrect but thinks it is less than 40. He claims that his boxes are always short of 40 candies. If $H_O$ is $\mu \geq 40$ and $H_1$ is $\mu < 40$, draw and identify the location of the critical region.

**Answer:**

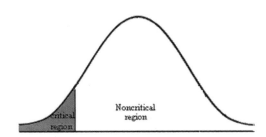

Noncritical region

Critical region

**Solution:** Draw a normal curve, which represents the test statistic $z$. The alternative hypothesis states the mean is less than 40. When $H_1$ is less than ($<$), the critical region is in the left tail of the distribution. If, when tested, a mean is found to be greater than 40, perhaps even as high as 100, the null hypothesis would stand, because the consumer challenges the mean only as being less than 40. The area to the left of the mean is the only area with values that could result in rejecting the null hypothesis.

The fourth consideration of the test criteria is the critical value. Thus far, the critical region has been drawn only to illustrate where the critical region falls with no values assigned to the dividing line. The critical value is the value in the critical region that divides the critical from the non-critical areas. Its value will be compared with the calculated value, which is found in the next step. The critical value is included in the critical region. When a two-tailed test is conducted, there is a critical value representing each critical region.

> **Critical Value** The value of the critical region used to compare with the calculated test statistic. It is the value that divides the area that will be used later to reject or fail to reject the null hypothesis.

The critical value reflects values that are not considered close enough to the hypothesized mean. For example, what sample mean of ages of students in one class would be acceptable as close enough if the population mean is hypothesized at 27? Is 26 close enough? Is 25 close enough? The critical value not only reflects what is close enough, but it does so as a value of the test statistic. Thus far, it does so as a $z$-score after the hypothesized mean is transformed into the standard $z$-score, 0.

To find the critical value, begin by noting the level of significance. Place the alpha on the curve in its appropriate tail. If the critical region is one-tailed, simply place the probability of alpha in the critical region. If the test is two-tailed, alpha must be divided by 2 before placing each half in the separate critical regions. For example, if alpha is .05, in a one-tailed test the value .05 is placed in the critical region; for a two-tailed test, .05 must be divided by 2, and .025 (.05/2 = .025) is placed in the left critical region and .025 is placed in the right critical region. See Figure 10.3.

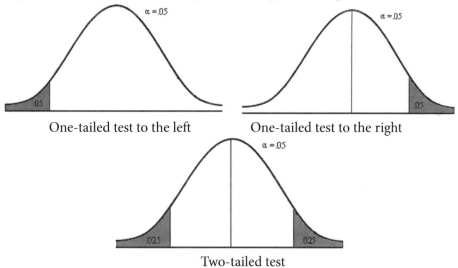

One-tailed test to the left      One-tailed test to the right

Two-tailed test

**FIGURE 10.3**

If alpha notes the probability of the critical region, then the area of the curve not represented by alpha is that of the non-critical region. For the normal curve, the probability of half of the curve is .5000. The value associated with the non-critical region is easily found by subtracting the probability of the critical region from .5000. That is, .5000 - .01 is the value of the non-critical region for one-tailed tests and .5000 - $\alpha/2$ is the value for two-tailed tests. For example, if alpha for a one-tailed test is .05, then probability associated with the non-critical region is .5000 - .05, or .4500. See Figure 10.4.

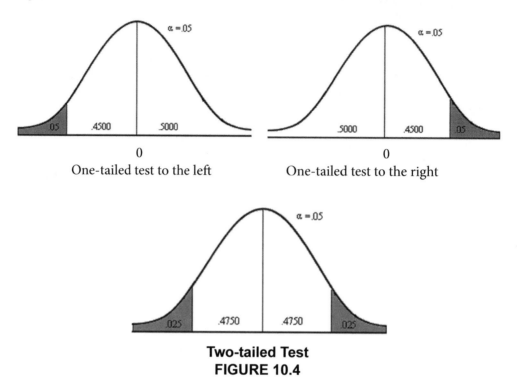

One-tailed test to the left      One-tailed test to the right

**Two-tailed Test**
**FIGURE 10.4**

Finally, the critical value itself is found by using Table A.3 in Appendix A and finding the $z$-score that corresponds to the probability of the non-critical region. Table A.3 is now read in reverse, as compared to its use in earlier chapters. The probability of the non-critical region is matched as closely as possible to a probability in the body of the table. The critical value is found by tracing over and up to the $z$-score on the outside of the table. For example, if a one-tailed non-critical region is represented by .4900 (thus, $\alpha$ is .01, and .5000 - .01 = .4900), .4900 is closest to the probability of .4901 in Table A.3:

| $z$ | $\rightarrow\rightarrow$ | $\rightarrow\rightarrow$ | $\rightarrow\rightarrow$ | **0.03** |
|---|---|---|---|---|
| ↓ | | | | ↓ |
| ↓ | | | | ↓ |
| ↓ | | | | .4871 |
| **2.3** | **.4893** | **.4896** | **.4898** | **.4901** |

To the left of .4901 is the $z$-score 2.3, and at the top of the column is the $z$-score 0.03. These two scores are added, reflecting a $z$-score of 2.33 associated with the probability .4901. The $z$-score 2.33 is the critical value dividing the critical region from the non-critical region. Any calculated value falling in the critical region will lead to a decision to reject the null hypothesis. Remember: when working specifically with $z$-scores, $z$ critical values to the left of the mean are negative numbers.

**EXAMPLE 10.7**

**Experiment:** Find the critical value for the alternative hypothesis if the mean is less than 10; ($\alpha = .025$).

**Answer:** -1.96

**Solution:** The critical value cannot be determined until the critical region is set. The critical region is guided by the alternative hypothesis, which requires only values less than the mean, 10. The test is a one-tailed $z$ test to the left, because the alternative hypothesis questions the mean and denotes less than ($<$). The normal curve is drawn. Alpha is placed in the critical region in the left tail. Because .025 is the probability of the alpha, the area of the non-critical region is found by subtracting .025 from .5000, the probability of half a normal curve. The probability associated with the non-critical region is .5000 - .025 or .4750.

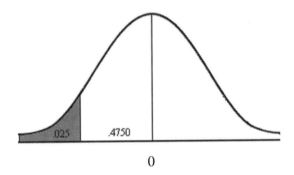

Using Table A.3, .4750 is found in the middle of the table. Across the row from .4750 is the $z$-score 1.9; up the column from .4750 is the score 0.06. The critical value is the $z$-score of -1.96 (the negative sign is needed because the area falls to the left of the mean).

| $z$ | $\rightarrow\rightarrow$ | $\rightarrow\rightarrow$ | $\rightarrow\rightarrow$ | **0.06** |
|-----|--------------------------|--------------------------|--------------------------|----------|
| $\downarrow$ | | | | $\downarrow$ |
| $\downarrow$ | | | | $\downarrow$ |
| $\downarrow$ | | | | .4686 |
| **1.9** | .4732 | .4738 | .4744 | .4750 |

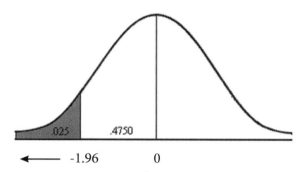

## Step 3

Once the hypotheses are stated and all test criteria are found, the calculation of the test statistic occurs. The test involves the calculation of the sample information offered as a challenge to the null hypothesis. In other words the information from a sample is transformed into the form taken by the probability distribution so that it can be compared to the test criteria. The calculated value is placed on the curve. If it falls in the critical region, it is said to have provided sufficient proof to reject the null hypothesis. The calculation used is specific to the test statistic. So far only the test statistic $z$ has been used, but later sections will use other tests, including $t$, $F$, and $\chi2$. The $z$ normal curve is used when testing a mean with a large sample size defined as $n > 30$, and where the standard deviation of the population $\sigma$ is known or given. The value of $z$ is calculated using the formula given in Chapter 9.

**The Calculation of z**
**When Testing Means That Are Normally Distributed**

$$z = \frac{\bar{x} - \mu}{\sigma / \sqrt{n}}$$

Step 4 in hypothesis testing is placing the calculated value from above on the curve that was drawn in step 2. The placement of the calculated value is in relationship to the critical value already placed on the curve. Usually the calculated value is distinguished from the critical by using an asterisk for the calculated value. This step is simply placing the value on the curve.

The next step of hypothesis testing is step 5 and involves making a decision. There are only two decisions that can be made. The decision is either to reject the null hypothesis or to fail to reject the null hypothesis. The decision is based on the placement of the calculated value.

**Decision:**
**Reject** $H_O$ When the calculated test statistic falls in the critical region.
**Fail to Reject** $H_O$ When the calculated test statistic falls in the non-critical region.

If the calculated value is in the critical region, then the decision must be to reject the null hypothesis. The null hypothesis is rejected only when the sample information falls outside the area defined as non-critical. That is, if the sample information is not close enough to the hypothesized value, then the null hypothesis cannot be accepted as true. Although the null hypothesis is said to have been proven false, the alternative hypothesis is not necessarily proven true. The null hypothesis can be rejected in favor of the alternative, but then the alternative will itself eventually be tested.

If the value of the test statistic is found to be within the non-critical region, then the decision is to fail to reject the null hypothesis. The understanding of this decision is that the test of the sample produced values considered to be close enough to the hypothesized value to be viewed as the same. The sample test does not necessarily prove the null true, but at least it does not prove it false. Perhaps another test will prove the null hypothesis wrong. Perhaps a different level of significance would also prove the null hypothesis wrong. But until such time as the null hypothesis is proven wrong, it is assumed to be true. Notice the words "fail to reject the null hypothesis." The null hypothesis is not accepted or proven correct; it is only not proven false. Do not use different wording.

Step 6 is the final step in hypothesis testing and is the interpretation of the results. Once the decision is made, it must be applied to the original problem. Recall that the testing process transformed all information into the standardized values using $z$-scores or other test statistics. The original values must be recalled to understand the application of the decision. The decision to reject the null hypothesis or to fail to reject the null hypothesis should be interpreted by restating the null hypothesis, using the words in the original problem. Because the decision is based on a specific level of significance, the alpha should also be restated. For example, the answer might be: there is sufficient evidence to reject the null hypothesis that the mean length of fish in the river is equal to 3 inches at the .05 level of significance.

To review, there are several steps in testing hypotheses using the classical approach. The specific test statistic will differ from problem to problem, but the other steps remain very similar.

**Steps in Hypothesis Testing Using the Classical Approach**
1. State $H_O$ and $H_1$.
2. Identify the test criteria:
   a. Level of significance, $\alpha$
   b. Test statistic ($z$, $t$, $\chi^2$, $F$)
   c. Critical Region:
      (1) One-tailed test
      (2) Two-tailed test ($\alpha/2$)
   d. Critical value
3. Calculate the test statistic.
4. Place the calculated value on a distribution curve.
5. Make a decision:
   a. Fail to reject $H_O$
   b. Reject $H_O$
6. Interpret the results.

## EXAMPLE 10.8

**Experiment:** A farmer claims that the mean weight of the turkeys on the farm is 10.2 pounds, with a standard deviation of 2. An employee believes the mean weight is more than 10.2 lbs. To test this claim, a random sample of 100 turkeys is taken. The sample produces a mean of 10.6. Does the sample provide sufficient evidence to reject the null hypothesis at the .05 level of significance?

**Answer:** Yes, there is sufficient evidence at the .05 level of significance to reject the farmer's claim that the mean weight of the turkeys is 10.2 lbs.

**Solution:**
**Step 1**
State the hypothesis. The null hypothesis is the claim from the farmer. This claim carries the benefit of the doubt and includes an equal sign. The null assumes there is no difference between a sample and a population until a difference can be proven. The employee's claim is the alternative hypothesis, since the employee is challenging the farmer's claim. The employee claims the mean is greater than 10.2. If a sample produces a mean equal to or less than 10.2, the null hypothesis will stand and the employee's claim falls. Writing these claims in symbols produces the following:

$$H_O : \mu \leq 10.2$$
$$H_1 : \mu > 10.2$$

**Step 2**

Identify the test criteria. Begin by identifying the level of significance. The problem clearly states to use a level of significance, alpha, of .05. The test statistic that should be used is the *z* distribution, which represents normally distributed means with larger sample size and the standard deviation of the population *σ* is given. The critical region must be set in the right tail, so a one-tailed test is used. This choice is guided by the alternative hypothesis, because the area of concern in the employee's challenge involves only values greater than the mean. The critical value is found by placing the alpha level on the normal curve in the critical region and finding the probability of the non-critical region. When using the normal curve, this is done by subtracting alpha from .5000. The non-critical probability can be transformed into a *z*-score by using Table A.3. Therefore, .5000 - .05 = .4500. The probability .4500 is the *z*-score 1.645 (reading from Table A.3.) The *z*-score 1.645 is the value at the beginning of the critical region it will fall in the critical region.

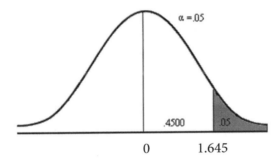

**Step 3**

Calculate the test statistic, which is identified as *z*. Using the following information, the *z*-score is calculated: $\bar{x} = 10.6$, $\mu = 10.2$, $\sigma = 2$, and $n = 100$.

$$z = \frac{\bar{x} - \mu}{\sigma/\sqrt{n}} = \frac{10.6 - 10.2}{2/\sqrt{100}}$$

$$= \frac{.4}{2/10}$$

$$= 2.00$$

**Step 4**

Place the calculated $z$-score on the normal curve and compare it to the critical value.

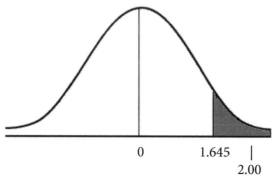

$$0 \qquad 1.645 \quad |$$
$$2.00$$

**Step 5**

Make the decision concerning the null hypothesis. Notice that the calculated value 2.0 is within the critical region, which begins at 1.645. The decision to reject $H_O$ is made whenever the calculated value falls within the critical region.

Reject $H_O$

**Step 6**

Interpret the decision. To reject the null hypothesis is interpreted as follows: There is sufficient proof, at the .05 level, to allow us to reject the null hypothesis. Therefore, the farmer's claim that the mean weight of turkeys is 10.2 lbs is not accepted as true. The employee provides sufficient evidence that the mean weight of turkeys is greater than 10.2 lbs.

# SECTION 3

## Hypothesis Testing Using *P*-Values

With the invention of the computer came a new approach to hypothesis testing. Computers go one step further than the classical approach by computing the test statistic as a value known as a *P*-value. The *P*-value is a probability representing the level of significance at which the test statistic becomes significant provided the null hypothesis is true. In other words, the *P*-value is the probability of obtaining a sample value at least as extreme as the value reported in the sample challenging the null hypothesis. Whereas the classical approach converted information into $z$-scores to compare, the *P*-value approach converts the information into probabilities.

Population →$\alpha$ →Probability

Sample→*z-score*→Probability

→→ compare *probabilities* to make a decision

**P-value (Also known as prob-value or probability value)** The smallest level of significance for the sample test statistic at which it becomes significant, provided the null hypothesis is true. *P* is considered significant when it is less than or equal to the *type I* error, $\alpha$.

The *P*-value is the point at which a sample statistic is more extreme, toward the tails of a probability curve, than the sample information challenging the null hypothesis. It is the point at which the test statistic is considered significant, leading to rejecting the null hypothesis. If the type I error value, alpha, is in the region representing the *P*-value, then the null hypothesis must be rejected.

| **One-tailed Left** | **Two-tailed** | **One-tailed Right** |
|:---:|:---:|:---:|
| $P(z < z^*)$ | $P(z < z^*) + P(z > z^*)$ | $P(z > z^*)$ |

where

z represents values that are more extreme than the calculated z* value.
z* is the calculated value.

Hypothesis testing using the *P*-value begins much like the classical approach.

Step 1 is to identify the null and alternative hypotheses.

Step 2 is to identify two aspects of the test criteria: the level of significance and the test statistic. The level of significance is usually offered as $\alpha$ in the problem. The test statistic must be determined by reviewing the parameter noted in the hypotheses (so far, only normally distributed means have been tested using *z*-scores). The critical value and the critical region are not needed in the *P*-value approach.

Step 3 is to calculate the test statistic exactly as done in the classical approach:

$$z = \frac{\bar{x} - \mu}{\sigma/\sqrt{n}}$$

Step 4 is to calculate the *P*-value. If using the tables in the appendix, calculated value of the test statistic is transformed into a probability and adjusted as needed. For the normal curve, a calculated *z*-score is transformed into a probability using Table A.3.

The adjustment needed is to find the area of the curve from the calculated $z$ to the tail of the curve. This adjustment is accomplished by subtracting the $z$-score's probability from .5000, the probability of half of the normal curve. The probability for the tail is the $P$-value if the test is a one-tailed test. For example, a one-tailed test to the right for a calculated $z$-score 2.12 produces a $P$-value of .0170. Referring to Table A.3, the $z$-score 2.12 has a probability of .4830. The probability .4830 is the area of the curve from 0 to 2.12. The area from 2.12 to the end of the tail is needed. Because half of the curve is associated with a probability .5000, subtracting .4830 produces a $P$-value .0170. See Figure 10.5.

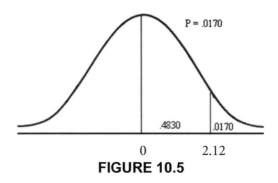

**FIGURE 10.5**

A two-tailed test requires that the probabilities of both tails be calculated and added to produce the $P$-value. Because the normal curve is symmetric, the test statistic $z$ is placed on both sides of the mean, with the left value carrying a negative sign. The probability of the $z$-score is found in Table A.3 and adjusted to represent the area from $z$ out to the end of the tails. The probabilities of the tails are then added. For example, a two-tailed test with a calculated $z$-score 2.12 produces a $P$-value .0340. The $z$-score 2.12 must be read as 2.12 and -2.12. Table A.3 gives the probability of all $z$-scores regardless of sign. The $z$-scores 2.12 and - 2.12 represent the probability .4830. For the right tail, the area from 2.12 is found by subtracting .4830 from .5000, which gives .0170. For the left tail, the area from -2.12 is also found by subtracting .4830 from .5000, which gives .0170. Thus, the probability that a test statistic is significant is found by adding .0170 to .0170. The $P$-value is .0340. See Figure 10.6.

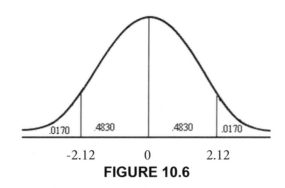

**FIGURE 10.6**

$$P\text{-value} = .0170 + .0170 = .0340$$

However, the tables can be avoided by using the TI-83/84 calculators. The *P*-value is found on the result screen simply as $P = \ldots$ Be sure to move the decimal if there is a scientific notation. All *P*-values must fall between 0 and 1. In fact, the *P*-values should be comparable to alpha levels. Since the curves read *P*-values from the right (values near 0) to the left (values near 1), any left-tailed *P*-values .5 or greater need to be subtracted from 1.0.

For example, the calculator for a right-tailed test may report a *P* as .001, but with the same data will report a left-tailed value as $P = .999$. Since these are the same data, the .999 is the way the calculator indicates it was in the left-tail. The real answer for *P* to compare to alpha is found by subtracting .999 from 1.0 (the entire curve), leaving .001 as *P*.

Step 5 is to make a decision concerning the null hypothesis. The decision requires the comparison of the *P*-value to the alpha level. If the probability of committing a type I error is in the tail whose values are considered significant, then the decision is to reject the null hypothesis. If the point where values are significant is greater than the probability of a type I error, the decision is to fail to reject the null hypothesis. In other words, if the *P*-value is less than or equal to alpha, then the null hypothesis must be rejected. If the *P*-value is greater than alpha, then the decision is to fail to reject the null hypothesis.

> **$P \leq \alpha$**    **Reject $H_o$**
> **$P > \alpha$**    **Fail to reject $H_o$**

Step 6 is to interpret the decision using the original information from the problem. The decision to reject the null hypothesis implies there is sufficient evidence to reject the null hypothesis at a specified level of significance. A decision to fail to reject the null hypothesis also depends on the specific level of significance.

**Steps in Hypothesis Testing using the *P*-Value Approach**
1. State $H_o$ and $H_1$
2. Identify the test criteria
   a. Level of significance, $\alpha$
   b. Test statistic $(z, t, \chi^2, F)$
3. Calculate the test statistic
4. Identify the *P*-value.

5. Make a decision:
    a. If $P > \alpha$,  Fail to Reject $H_o$
    b. If $P \leq \alpha$,  Reject $H_o$
6. Interpret the results.

## EXAMPLE 10.9

**Experiment:** A farmer claims that the mean weight of turkeys on the farm is 10.2 lbs, with a standard deviation of 2. An employee believes the mean weight is more than 10.2 lbs. To test this claim, a random sample of 100 turkeys is taken. The sample produces a mean of 10.6. Using the *P*-value approach, does the sample provide sufficient evidence to reject the null hypothesis at the .05 level of significance?

**Answer:** Yes, there is sufficient evidence at the .05 level of significance to reject the farmer's claim that the mean weight of the turkeys is 10.2 lbs.

**Solution:**
**Step 1**
State the hypothesis. Notice the farmer's claim contains an equal sign, as required by the null hypothesis. The employee believes the mean weight of turkeys is more than 10.2 lbs. The employee's challenge is a one-directional alternative hypothesis, concerned only with values greater than 10.2. If a sample produces a mean equal to or less than 10.2, then the null hypothesis will stand, and the employee's challenge will fail. Writing these claims symbolically gives:

$$H_O : \mu \leq 10.2$$
$$H_I : \mu > 10.2$$

**Step 2**
Identify the level of significance and the test statistic. The level of significance is given as .05. The test statistic for means of sampling distributions normally distributed is the *z*-score. The test is a one-tailed test to the right, as determined by the alternative hypothesis challenging the mean, which contains greater than (>).

**Step 3**
Calculate the test statistic, *z*, along with the *P*-value by utilizing the *z* test function on a calculator. Press STAT, scroll right to TESTS and select "1:Z-Test" by pressing ENTER. Under the settings screen of *Z*-Tests, plug in the proper information, with "Inpt" set to Stats. Be sure the correct alternative hypothesis is selected. Scroll down to highlight "Calculate" and press ENTER. The results of the test should appear as follows.

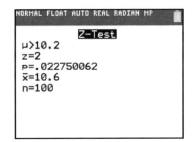

$$z = \frac{\bar{x} - \mu}{\sigma/\sqrt{n}} = \frac{10.6 - 10.2}{2/\sqrt{100}} = 2.00$$

**Step 4**

Note that the calculated *P*-value is reported as "p =..." on the calculator result screen.

$$P\text{-value} = .0228$$

**Step 5**

Compare the *P*-value to alpha and make a decision about the null hypothesis. If *P* is greater than $\alpha$, then the decision is to fail to reject the null hypothesis. If *P* is less than or equal to $\alpha$, the decision is to reject the null hypothesis. *P* at .0228 is less than $\alpha$ at .05, so the decision is reject the null hypothesis.

$$P(.0228) \leq \alpha(.05) \quad \text{Reject } H_o$$

**Step 6**

Interpret the decision. Rejecting the null hypothesis is interpreted using the original problem: There is sufficient proof, at the .05 level, to allow rejecting the null hypothesis; therefore, the farmer's claim that the mean weight of turkeys is 10.2 lbs. is not accepted as true. The employee provides sufficient evidence that the mean weight of turkeys is not 10.2 lbs. and is probably greater than 10.2 lbs.

## EXAMPLE 10.10

**Experiment:** A company tells its customers that ordering products online is the quickest way to receive them. They told the customers that it takes an average of 15 days with a standard deviation of 2 days to receive an order. To convince the new customers, a manager randomly chose 40 returns and found that they received their orders on average in 16 days. Is there sufficient evidence to convince the new customers at a significance level of 0.05? Assume that the time to receive the product is normally distributed.

**Answer:** There is sufficient evidence at the .05 level of significance to conclude that the average time to receive a product from an online order is not 15 days.

**Solution:**
**Step 1**
State the hypotheses. The null hypothesis contends that the mean equals 15. The statement includes an equal sign, which must be placed in the null hypothesis. The alternative hypothesis is the challenge presented by the manager. Because the manager does not specify whether the mean is too high or too low, the statement simply implies the average is not equal to 15. It is the manager's burden to prove the exchange wrong. Writing the hypotheses in symbols gives:

$$H_o : \mu = 15$$
$$H_i: \; \mu \neq 15$$

**Step 2**
The significance level is $\alpha = 0.05$. This is a two-tailed test because of the not-equal sign in the alternative hypothesis. Since this is a normal distribution testing a population mean with a large sample size and a known standard deviation, the test statistic is the standard normal calculated by a $z$-score.

**Step 3**
Calculate the test statistic value. Press STAT, scroll across to TESTS, and down to 1:Z-Test...press ENTER. Enter the data. Once completed, highlight "Calculate" and press ENTER. The results should appear as follows.

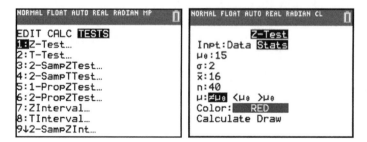

The *P*-value is found by transforming the test statistic 3.16 into a probability. Note that a negative *z*-score represents a value below the mean, but its probability is not negative. Identify the *P*-value noted above as: *p* = .001565534, rounded to .0016.

The *P*-value must be compared to the original alpha to make a decision about the null hypothesis. Compare the *P*- value .0016 to the alpha, .05. Because *P* is less than *α*, reject the null hypothesis.

$$P(.0016) \le \alpha(.05) \qquad \text{Reject } H_O$$

Rejecting the null hypothesis suggests there is sufficient proof at the .01 level of significance that the average time to receive a product from an online order is not 15 days.

---

### A LEARNING AID
### *P*-Value for 1 Sample/Population Mean Using *z*

A potato chip factory packages bags of chips that weigh an average of 4 oz, with a standard deviation of .62 oz. The Bureau of Weights and Measures randomly selects 30 bags, measures their contents, and reports a sample mean of 4.2. Using the *P*-value approach, does the sample provide sufficient evidence to conclude that the potato chip company cheats its customers ($\alpha = .02$)?

### Step 1
State the hypotheses. The potato chip company claims the mean is 4 oz. A claim including an equal sign (=) becomes the null hypothesis. The bureau challenges the factory's claim. Since the bureau does not specify where the mean may be, its challenge is simply that the mean is not equal to ($\neq$) 4 oz.

$$H_o: \mu = 4 \quad H_i: \mu \neq 4$$

**Step 2**

Identify the level of significance and the test statistic. The level of significance is the alpha ($\alpha$) value of .02 reported. The test statistic $z$ must be used for normally distributed means with a large sample space ($n > 30$) and the standard deviation of the population $\sigma$ is known. The test is a two-tailed test, because the alternative hypothesis contains a not equal to sign ($\neq$).

**Step 3**

Calculate the test statistic and $P$-value, using the information provided: $\bar{x} = 4.2$, $\mu = 4$, $\sigma = .62$, and $n = 30$.

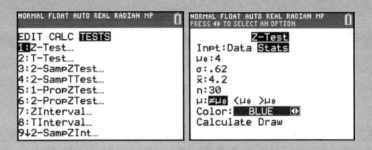

Press STAT, scroll right to "TESTS" and press ENTER to select "1:Z-Test…". With the "Stats" option selected, plug in the following information, highlight "Calculate and press ENTER.

The results will appear as follows:

$$z = \frac{\bar{x} - \mu}{\sigma / \sqrt{n}} = \frac{4.2 - 4}{.62 / \sqrt{30}} = 1.77$$

**Step 4**

Identify the $P$-value from the result screen your calculator.

**Step 5**
Compare the *P*-value to alpha and make a decision about the null hypothesis. If the *P*-value is less than or equal to alpha, the decision is to reject the null hypothesis. If *P* is greater than alpha, then the decision is to fail to reject the null hypothesis. The *P*-value of .0773 is greater than the alpha. The decision must be to fail to reject $H_O$.

$$P(.0773) > \alpha(.02) \qquad \text{Fail to reject } H_O$$

**Step 6**
Interpret the results. Failing to reject the null hypothesis implies the bureau's check on the weights of potato chip bags produced a mean close enough to confirm the factory's claim. In other words, there is not sufficient evidence at the .02 level of significance to reject the factory's claim that the mean weight of a bag of potato chips is 4 oz.

# SECTION 4

## Confidence Intervals

The introduction explains that inferential statistics predict population parameters from sample information. Sections 1 through 3 showed how to test population information using sample statistics. However, there are times that the population information is not known. For example, a light bulb manufacturer would not test every bulb to determine the average life of a bulb. There would not be bulbs left to sell. Even testing repeated samples may be very costly. But whether one or several samples are tested, the manufacturer really has no definite population mean. Sample data can be used to predict population parameters. A population parameter can be estimated from sample data by establishing a range of values where the parameter may lie. The range of values is called a ***confidence interval***.

**Confidence Interval** Estimating a population parameter from sample statistics given a specified level of confidence. It is the algebraic manipulation of the *z*-score calculation.

Recall how, in Chapter 9, one estimated the sampling mean given a population mean. A standard error was also estimated given a standard deviation and the sample size. Turning the rules around and combining information from the earlier sections of this chapter, one has the ability to estimate the population mean given a sample mean. An interval in which the population mean will fall can be calculated based on sample information. The term confidence interval implies there is an interval or range of values where the mean will fall given a particular degree of confidence. The interval is estimated using the sampling information and the degree of certainty that seems adequate given the risk of error.

The central limit theorem describes a distribution where the mean of a sampling distribution is equal to the population mean ($\mu_{\bar{x}} = \mu$). If this statement is true, then it is possible to reverse the rule allowing the mean to be estimated by the sampling mean ($\mu = \mu_{\bar{x}}$).

Logically, if the mean is not determined, then the mean of all sample means is also not likely to be determined. Using one sample to estimate the population mean increases the chance of error. However, one sample mean is a good place to begin. The estimate using a sample mean as the point of departure to determine a range of values in which the population mean will fall is referred to as a ***point estimate***.

> **Point Estimate** The sample statistic used to estimate the population parameter. When estimating the parameter $\mu$, the point estimate is the sample statistic $\bar{x}$.

The point estimate can be used for any sample statistic estimating a population parameter. When estimating $\mu$, $\bar{x}$ is the point estimate. When estimating $\sigma$, s is the point estimate. For example, if the length of all fish in Lake Michigan cannot be determined and repeated sampling is impractical, one sample mean may be sufficient as a starting place. If a sample mean is 3.5 inches, then the point of estimation begins at 3.5 inches.

An interval encasing the point estimate can be determined. The population mean can be expected to occur within this interval. The interval is split, with half of the range of values to the right of the point estimate and half to the left. The size of the range depends on the level of confidence that is to be allowed. The level of confidence establishes the probability that the population parameter will fall inside the range of values set by the sample statistic. The ***level of confidence*** is also referred to as the degree of confidence reflecting the level of certainty desired.

> **Level of Confidence** The probability that a parameter is contained in the confidence interval established around a sample statistic. It is also known as a confidence coefficient and is *1 − α*.

The of confidence can be understood as the probability of being correct. It is the opposite of alpha, which is the probability of being wrong. Therefore, because alpha is often given in a problem, the degree of confidence is determined by subtracting alpha from 1.0. Because the most common alpha levels are .05, .01, and .1, the most common levels of confidence are .95, .99, and .90. In other words, one typically wishes to be 95%, 99%, or 90% sure the population parameter will be in the estimated range.

Calculating the probability for the level of confidence is similar to finding the critical value in a hypothesis test. Whether alpha ($\alpha$) or a confidence level percentage is given, the probability must be found for the normal curve from 0 out to where the confidence ends and the alpha level begins. Since a range of values below and above the point estimate is required, all confidence intervals can be understood as two-tailed. See Figure 10.7.

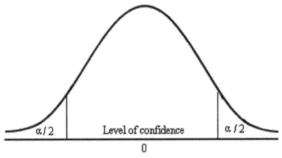

**FIGURE 10.7**

The level of confidence must be transformed into a probability and then into a $z$-score. Confidence levels are reported as percentages, which are easily transformed into probabilities by dropping the percent sign (%) and moving the decimal to the left two places. For example, a 95% confidence interval becomes a probability of .95. Half of .95 (.95/2 = .4750) is above the point estimate, and half is below. The probability of half the level, .4750, is transformed into a $z$-score using Table A.3 in Appendix A. The $z$ value 1.96 is denoted by $z(\alpha/2)$, which will be the upper limit of the curve, setting the boundary for the range of values in the interval. The left limit has a negative sign, reflecting the area of the curve below the point estimator. The probability .4750 left of the center is associated with the negative $z$-score - 1.96. The subscript ($\alpha/2$) is used to reflect the two-tailed alpha level, indicating that $\alpha$ must be divided by 2 to find the $z$ value for the half of the range above the mean and the half of the range below. Alpha is the opposite of the confidence level; thus, either can be found when the other is given. See Figure 10.8.

$1-\alpha$ = confidence level          1- confidence level = $\alpha$

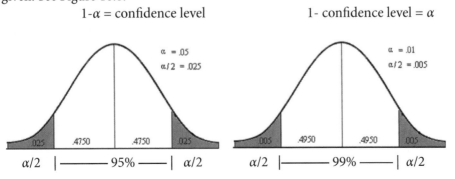

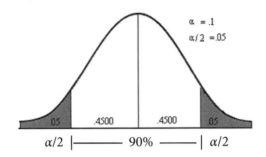

$\alpha/2 \; |\!\!-\!\!-\!\!-\!\!-\!\!-\!\!- \; 90\% \; -\!\!-\!\!-\!\!-\!\!-\!\!-| \; \alpha/2$

**FIGURE 10.8**

| Level of Confidence | $\alpha$ | $\alpha/2$ | Critical Value |
|:---:|:---:|:---:|:---:|
| 99% | .01 | .01/2 = .005 | 2.58 |
| 98% | .02 | .02/2 = .01 | 2.33 |
| 95% | .05 | .05/2 = .025 | 1.96 |
| 90% | .10 | .10/2 = .05 | 1.645 |

Combining the concepts of the point estimator and the level of confidence results in an interval, or range of values, where the parameter should fall. Precision is lost when using an interval instead of a point estimator, but confidence is gained. The calculation of the confidence interval for normally distributed means with large sample size is an algebraic manipulation of the $z$-score calculation for the central limit theorem. Instead of finding the probability of the $z$-score, the probability of the $z$-score is inserted in the formula and the population mean is estimated.

$$z = \frac{\bar{x} - \mu}{\sigma/\sqrt{n}} \qquad E_\mu = \bar{x} \pm z_{(\alpha/\,2)} \frac{\sigma}{\sqrt{n}}$$

**Formula for a Confidence Interval
with a Normally Distributed Mean with $n > 30$ and $\sigma$ known**

$$E_\mu = \bar{x} + z_{(\alpha/\,2)} \frac{\sigma}{\sqrt{n}} \text{ and } E_\mu = \bar{x} - z_{(\alpha/\,2)} \frac{\sigma}{\sqrt{n}}$$

where
$E_\mu$ is the estimate of the population mean.
$\bar{x}$ is the sample mean, also known as the point estimator.
$z_{(\alpha/2)}$ is the $z$ value reflecting the level of confidence.
$\sigma$ is the standard deviation of the population.
$n$ is the sample size.

The point estimate is understood as the sample mean, where half of the interval is to the right and half is to the left. The values in the right half of the interval are calculated using the formula that involves adding to the sample mean. The values to the left of the interval are calculated using the formula that involves subtraction from the sample mean.

The formula for calculating the confidence interval requires the multiplication of $z(\alpha/2)$ (found in the earlier stage) by the standard error. The value $z(\alpha/2)$ reflects the probability of being correct. The value is inserted into the formula without any further manipulation (that is, it is not multiplied by $\alpha/2$). The product of $z$ and the standard error is added to the sample mean and is the upper limit of the interval. The lower limit is found by subtracting the product of $z$ and the standard error from the sample mean. The final interval is noted by stating the values with the parameter in the middle:

$$(\text{Lower limit} < \mu < \text{Upper limit})$$

It is important to understand that an interval depends on a specific sample. If a different sample mean is used as a point estimate, then the range of values estimating the population mean will change. Also, if the degree of confidence or the alpha level changes, so will the range of values in the interval. Decreasing the level of confidence decreases the range of values.

---

**Steps in Calculating a Confidence Interval when Using Tables**
1. Identify the level of confidence (90%, 95%, 99%).
2. Identify the test statistic ($z$, $t$, $\chi^2$, or $F$).
3. Determine the critical value with $\alpha/2$.
4. Calculate the interval.
5. State the interval.

---

### EXAMPLE 10.11

**Experiment:** In order to determine the mean grocery store bill for shoppers at Big Market Warehouse Grocers, a random sample of 50 shoppers is selected and analyzed. The mean bill is $47.80. Assuming the standard deviation of the population is $16.91, find the 95% confidence interval for the mean grocery bill.

**Answer:** $E\mu = (\$43.11 < \mu < \$52.49)$

**Solution:** The problem requires a 95% confidence interval for the population mean. The sample size is relatively large at 50 and money, as a continuous variable, is normally distributed. The $z$-score is the test statistic for normally distributed means of large samples. Begin by identifying the point estimate.

The point estimate is the sample mean $47.80 used to estimate the range of values encasing the population mean. The level of confidence must be identified and transformed into a z-score. A confidence of 95% is given. Dividing 95% by 2 gives 47.50%. Drop the percent sign and move the decimal to the left two places, and 47.50% becomes the probability of .4750. Using Table A.3 in Appendix A shows the probability .4750 is associated with a z-score of 1.96. The value 1.96 represents the boundary of values above the point estimate. The lower z-score is -1.96, representing the area of the curve below the point estimate. The value 1.96 will be used in the calculation of the interval to represent $z(\alpha/2)$.

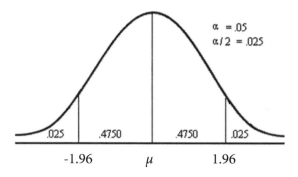

The next step is to calculate the interval. The calculation of the interval requires the following information: $\bar{x}$ = 47.80, $\sigma$ = 16.91, $n$ = 50, and $z(\alpha/2) = 1.96$

$$E_\mu = \bar{x} + z_{(\alpha/2)} \frac{\sigma}{\sqrt{n}} \qquad\qquad E_\mu = \bar{x} - z_{(\alpha/2)} \frac{\sigma}{\sqrt{n}}$$

$$= 47.80 + 1.96 \frac{16.91}{\sqrt{50}} \qquad\qquad = 47.80 - 1.96 \frac{16.91}{\sqrt{50}}$$

$$= 47.80 + 1.96(2.39) \qquad\qquad = 47.80 - 1.96(2.39)$$

$$= 47.80 + 4.69 \qquad\qquad\qquad = 47.80 - 4.69$$

$$= 52.49 \qquad\qquad\qquad\qquad = 43.11$$

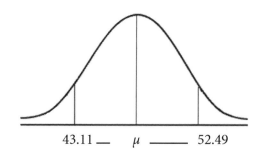

The confidence interval estimating the range of values where the population mean should fall has a lower boundary of 43.11 and an upper boundary of $52.49. Therefore, with 95% confidence, the mean grocery bill is between $43.11 and $52.49.

$$(\$43.11 < \mu < \$52.49)$$

---

**Steps in Calculating a Confidence Interval when Using the TI Calculator**
1. Identify the level of confidence (C-level) (90%, 95%, 99%).
2. Identify the test statistic ($z$, $t$, $x^2$, or $F$).
3. Calculate the interval.
4. State the interval.

---

A confidence interval is very similar to hypothesis testing in that the same criteria are employed to determine which test statistic should be used. Instead of a "test," the calculator will note an "interval." That is, press STAT, scroll across to TESTS, and down to the needed interval. For a $z$ interval, it will be number 7 or "7:Z Interval".

---

**EXAMPLE 10.12**

**Experiment:** Repeat Example 10.13 using a confidence interval of 99% and the TI-83/84 calculator.

**Answer:** $E\mu = (\$41.64 < \mu < 53.96)$

**Solution:** The difference between this problem and the previous is the level of significance. This problem requires a 99% confidence interval. A larger confidence interval increases the range of values, because you want to be more sure that the range includes the population mean. Begin by identifying the sample mean, $47.80, as the point estimate.

The next step is to calculate the interval. The calculation of the interval requires the following information: $\bar{x} = 47.80$, $\sigma = 16.91$, $n = 50$, and the level of confidence is 99% noted as .99.

Begin by pressing STAT. Scroll right to TESTS and press 7 to select "7: ZInterval…" Plug the required information into the settings screen, highlight "Calculate" and press ENTER. Through this process, the results should appear as follows:

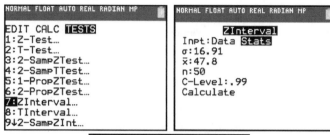

$$E_\mu = \bar{x} + z_{(\alpha/2)} \frac{\sigma}{\sqrt{n}} \qquad\qquad E_\mu = \bar{x} - z_{(\alpha/2)} \frac{\sigma}{\sqrt{n}}$$

$$=53.96 \qquad\qquad\qquad =41.64$$

The confidence interval estimating the range of values in which the population mean should fall has a lower boundary of 41.64 and an upper boundary of 53.96. Therefore, with 99% confidence, the mean grocery bill is between $41.64 and $53.96.

| | |
|---|---|
| 99% confidence interval | ($41.64 < \mu < $53.96) |
| 95% confidence interval | ($43.11 < \mu < $52.49) |

**A LEARNING AID**
**CONFIDENCE INTERVAL FOR THE MEAN**
Considering the difficulty of finding the average body temperature of the world's population, construct a 90% confidence interval for the mean body temperature using a sample of 50 people that produces a sample mean of 98.7. (Assume a population standard deviation of .4.)

**Step 1**

The problem asks for a confidence interval that estimates the mean body temperature of all the people in the world. The central limit theorem allows estimating a population mean using a sample mean known as the point estimator. The sample size is considered large (50), and the variable temperature is a continuous variable. The test statistic for continuous means of large samples is the $z$-score.

**Step 2**

Identify the level of confidence. The level of confidence is the probability that a parameter is contained in the confidence interval. The problem identifies the confidence level as 90%. A 90% value involves a probability of .90 that the parameter is included in the interval.

**Step 3**

Calculate the confidence interval. The calculation of the interval requires the following information: $\bar{x} = 98.7$, $\sigma = .4$, and $n = 50$, and the level of confidence is .90. The calculation is a confidence interval representing the $z$ statistic for normally distributed means.

Upper Limit

$$E_\mu = \bar{x} + z_{(\alpha/2)} \frac{\sigma}{\sqrt{n}}$$

$$= 98.8$$

Lower Limit

$$E_\mu = \bar{x} - z_{(\alpha/2)} \frac{\sigma}{\sqrt{n}}$$

$$= 98.6$$

Calculating the interval can be performed by utilizing a TI-83/84 calculator. Begin by pressing the STAT button, scrolling right to TESTS, followed by pressing 7 to select "7:ZInterval…" A settings screen will appear. Be sure "Stats" is selected and fill in the information according to the question. Highlight "Calculate" and press ENTER. The following results will appear:

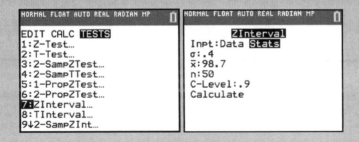

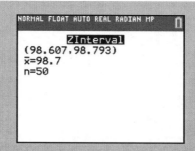

**Step 4**

Identify and interpret the interval. The lower limit of the interval begins at 98.6; the upper limit ends at 98.8. Thus, with 90% certainty, the mean body temperature for the world's population should fall between 98.6 and 98.8.

$$E\mu = (98.6 < \mu < 98.8)$$

---

## CHAPTER 10 IN REVIEW

10.1    Find the critical *z* value associated with the shaded area of each curve.

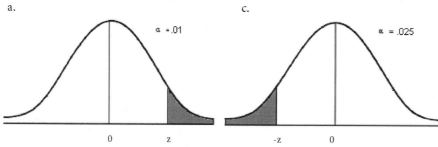

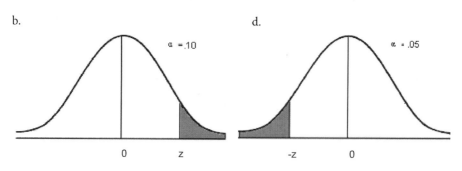

10.2    Find the critical *z* values associated with the shaded areas of each curve.

a.

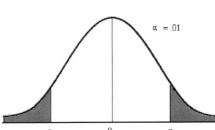

c.

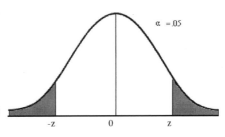

b.

d.

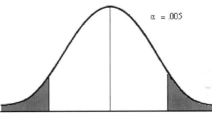

10.3 Using the correct format, state the null and alternative hypotheses.
   a. The mean sodium in a soda is at least 25 mg.
   b. The mean commute for employees is less than 30 minutes.
   c. The mean mortgage is more than $175,000.
   d. The mean weight of babies is 7.2 lbs.
   e. The mean cost of a new car is no more than $18,560.

10.4 If the null hypothesis is that a man's foot does not need to be amputated due to a possible staph infection, which of the errors, $\alpha$ or $\beta$, is more serious? Why?

10.5 Identify whether the following hypotheses are one-tailed to the left, one-tailed to the right, or two-tailed:
   a. $H_0: \mu \le 3$             $H_1: \mu > 3$
   b. $H_0: \mu = 275$          $H_1: \mu \ne 275$
   c. $H_0: \sigma \le 2.1$         $H_1: \sigma > 2.1$
   d. $H_0: \sigma \ge .4$          $H_1: \sigma < .4$
   e. $H_0: \sigma^2 = 19$        $H_1: \sigma^2 \ne 19$
   f. $H_0: \mu \ge 2$             $H_1: \mu < 2$

10.6 The average percentage of sunny days per year in the U.S. is 81.2 with a standard deviation of 5.26. The average percentage of sunny days in the top 40 cities is 84.3. Is there a significant difference in the average percentage of sunny days between the U.S. total and the 40 top cities? Use $\alpha = .05$.

10.7 Test the claim that average game attendance for home baseball games of the St. Louis Cardinals is 43,853. A sample of 50 home games produced a mean of 44,102. The population standard deviation is 625. Use $\alpha = .05$.

10.8 Southern Florida is known as the "Lightning Capital" of the U.S. It averages 25.1 lightning strikes per year per square mile with a standard deviation of 5.25. A meteorologist believes the number of strikes has increased. Using a sample of the last 40 years with 26.5 strikes, does there seem to be a significant increase? Use $\alpha = .01$.

10.9 The average miles per gallon (MPG) for a 2015 Mercedes 350 GLK is advertised at 20 MPG with a standard deviation of 2. A random sample of 40 GLK owners produced a mean of 21.1. Does the sample suggest that the advertised mean is too low? Test at the .005 level.

10.10 An ulcer medicine claims that each tablet contains an average of 300 milligrams (mg), with a standard deviation of 11 mg. Test whether a sample of 60 tablets producing a mean of 304 mg significantly exceeds the claimed mean. Use a level of significance of .01.

10.11 Describe the errors involved in a car manufacturer's claim that the driver's side-impact airbag was tested and approved. Which error is the most serious?

10.12 Describe the decision concerning the following *P*-values.
a. $P = .024$, $\alpha = .05$      d. $P = .013$, $\alpha = .01$
b. $P = .01$, $\alpha = .02$      e. $P = .05$, $\alpha = .01$
c. $P = .005$, $\alpha = .005$      f. $P = .215$, $\alpha = .025$

10.13 Estimate at 90% certainty the average cost of college textbooks using a sample of 40 books producing an average of $165. The population standard deviation is $50.

10.14 On average, a person loses about 70 hairs a day with a standard deviation of 30. Test the claim that the average is greater than 70 using a sample of 100 people who lost an average of 75 hairs per person. Use $\alpha = .05$.

10.15 A 12 oz. can of soda contains an average 135 calories and a standard deviation of 14.5. Test to see if the mean is accurate based on a sample of 40 cans with a mean of 133 calories. Use $\alpha = .01$.

10.16 Estimate with 99 percent certainty the mean amount of stream pollution in the Rouge River using a sample of 100 units producing 122 milliliters of pollution; $\sigma = 14$.

10.17 Calculate a confidence interval for the mean amount of credit card balance per year per household given a sample of 100 households with a sample mean of $9,100. The population standard deviation is $5,000 and $\alpha = .05$.

10.18 Conduct a 90 percent confidence interval for the average monthly one bedroom apartment rent using a sample of 32 apartments with a mean of $675; $\sigma = 52.5$.

10.19 True or False?
   a. Increasing the percentage for the confidence interval decreases the range of values of the interval.
   b. If $P \leq \alpha$, the decision is to reject the null hypothesis.
   c. The critical region is determined by the sign in the null hypothesis.
   d. A two-tailed test has only one critical region to the right.
   e. Theories must be accepted as true until proven false.
   f. The null hypothesis carries the burden of proof.

10.20 Farmington Park claims that their emergency response time averages 3.7 minutes with a standard deviation of 1.75. Test the claim that the response time is higher using a sample of 50 calls averaging 4.3 minutes. $\alpha = .05$.

10.21 The average monthly cellphone bill for individual customers in the U.S. in 2015 was $71 with a standard deviation of 14. A sample of 50 cellphone customers produced a mean of $85. Is the sample significantly greater? Test at the .05 level.

10.22 New York City has the busiest subway system in the U.S. with a weekly average number of passengers of 4.6 million and a standard deviation of 1.1 million. Test whether a sample of 50 days producing a mean of 4.8 million is significantly greater using the significance level of .025.

10.23 The Apollo Cafe in Greektown claims that the average lunch customer spends 19 minutes ordering and eating her food with a standard deviation of 3.1. A customer thinks that the time to order and eat exceeds that claimed by the restaurant. She samples 40 customers which produces a mean of 20.1 minutes. Test with $\alpha = .005$.

10.24 The Spicy Spoon Restaurant has an automatic hamburger patty machine. The manufacturer had designed the machine so each patty weighs .25 lb, with a standard deviation of .10 lb. To test the equipment, 50 hamburgers were prepared and found to have a mean weight of .27 lb. Test, at $\alpha = .01$, that the weight is not more than .25 lb.

10.25 Hartsfield Atlanta International Airport is the busiest airport in the U.S. averaging 2,603 planes a day with a standard deviation of 100. A traffic controller believes that the average exceeds 2,603. She collected information using a sample of 51 days and found that the mean number of planes is 2,650. Is there enough evidence to suggest she may be correct? $\alpha=.01$

10.26 The average CEO of a large U.S. company made $70.05 million last year with a standard deviation of $10.38 million. Test whether a sample of 50 CEOs with an average salary of $72 million is significantly higher at the .05 level?

# 11

# *t*-TEST FOR ONE POPULATION MEAN

*SECTION 1*  **The *t* Distribution**
*SECTION 2*  **Hypothesis Test: Classical Approach for Mean Using *t***
*SECTION 3*  **Hypothesis Test: *P-Value* for Mean Using *t***
*SECTION 4*  **Confidence Interval for One Mean**

The central limit theorem presented in previous chapters is used when testing means of large samples when the population standard deviation $\sigma$ is known. It is very unusual to have access to the population standard deviation when a population mean must be estimated. Samples are often small or not normally distributed. When a random variable is not fully normally distributed, when sample size is small, or when the population standard deviation is unknown, a *z* test cannot be performed. If any of the conditions for the normal distribution are absent when testing a mean, a Student *t* distribution can be used. The Student *t* distribution is a common test used in statistical analysis. Social scientists, behavioral scientists, and health scientists are often confronted with testing situations where samples are small and where the population standard deviation is unknown.

---

## SECTION 1

### The *t* Distribution

The *Student t* distribution is a probability distribution similar to the normal curve. The **t *distribution*** is a probability distribution that depicts sampling means. It has several characteristics similar to the normal *z* distribution. The *t* distribution is symmetric, its mean is 0, and its variance is greater than 1 but decreases towards 1 as *n* increases. The *t* distribution looks very much like the *z* distribution, but if overlaid, *t* appears less peaked (flatter) than *z*. The tails of *t* are thicker than those for *z*. In other words, *t* is shorter and fatter than *z*. See Figure 11 .1.

As with *z*, *t* values to the left of the mean 0 are negative, whereas *t* values to the right are positive. Unlike *z*, the table in Appendix A for *t* values gives actual critical values instead of probabilities.

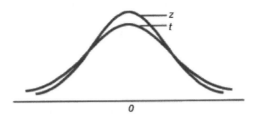

**Figure 11.1**

***Student t Distribution (t test)*** A distribution representing means of one population, where:
    1. The random variable is not normally distributed.
    2. Sample size is small, $n \leq 30$, and/or,
    3. The population standard deviation $\sigma$ is unknown.

Although there are several differences between $z$ and t, some differences require special emphasis. A major difference lies in the calculation of the test statistic. The $t$ test statistic is calculated by substituting the sample standard deviation for the unknown population standard deviation in the standard error estimate. Note the $z$ and $t$ formulas:

$$z = \frac{\bar{x} - \mu}{\sigma / \sqrt{n}} \quad t = \frac{\bar{x} - \mu}{s / \sqrt{n}}$$

Another difference between $z$ and $t$ relates to the sample size. The $t$ distribution estimates the population standard deviation $\sigma$ with the sample standard deviation s. Because s is subject to sampling error and depends on sample size, the $t$ distribution becomes a series of distributions. The distribution applied to any population depends on the sample size. A different distribution exists for every $n$ from 2 through infinity. The smaller the $n$, the shorter the $t$ curve. As sample size increases, the $t$ curve resembles the $z$ curve.

---

## SECTION 2

### Hypothesis Test: Classical Approach for Mean Using *t*

The classical approach for testing means of small samples using $t$ follows the same steps presented in Chapter 10 for $z$. The $t$ distribution will be used for testing means for small samples where $n$ is less than or equal to 30 ($n \leq 30$) or where the population standard deviation $\sigma$ is unknown.

Population $\rightarrow \alpha \rightarrow$ *t-score*

$\rightarrow \rightarrow$ compare *t-scores* to make a decision

Sample $\rightarrow \rightarrow \rightarrow \rightarrow$ *t-score*

The first step in the classical approach requires stating the null and alternative hypotheses. The statement of the hypotheses for *t* is the same as in testing for *z*. That is, the null hypothesis, $H_O$ requires the notation of the parameter $\mu$, a mathematical symbol =, ≤, or ≥, and a specified value. The alternative hypothesis, $H_I$ includes the same parameter and value but uses a contrasting mathematical symbol, ≠, >, or <. That is:

If $H_O$ is $\mu = 0$, then $H_I$ is $\mu \neq 0$.
If $H_O$ is $\mu \leq 3$, then $H_I$ is $\mu > 3$.
If $H_O$ is $\mu \geq 27$, then $H_I$ is $\mu < 27$.

The second step in hypothesis testing is to identify the test criteria. The test criteria include the level of significance, the test statistic, the critical region, and the critical value. The level of significance is usually given in the problem as alpha ($\alpha$). If alpha is not known, then the level of significance is determined based on the seriousness of a type I error. The test statistic is determined by deciding which test to conduct. The test statistics include $z$, $t$, $\chi 2$, $F$. Thus far, only $z$ and $t$ have been described. The $z$ test statistic is used when sample means are normally distributed, the sample size is greater than 30, and $\sigma$ is known. The $t$ test statistic is used when sample size is less than or equal to (≤) 30 and/or $\sigma$ is unknown.

**Criteria for Using *t* as the Test Statistic for One Population Mean**
1. Testing or estimating $\mu$.
2. $n$ (the sample size) is less than or equal to 30 and/or,
3. $\sigma$ (the standard deviation of the population) is not given or known.

The critical region is determined by considering the alternative hypothesis to decide if the test is one-tailed to the left, two-tailed, or one-tailed to the right. Recall that a one-tailed test to the left requires an alternative hypothesis involving less than. A two-tailed test requires the alternative hypothesis to involve not equal to, and a right-tailed test requires the alternative hypothesis to involve greater than.

| Test | Sign in $H_I$ |
|------|------|
| One-tailed left | < |
| Two- tailed | ≠ |
| One-tailed right | > |

The critical values are found in Table A.4. To find the critical value, the degrees of freedom and alpha level must be known. One-tailed values are found simply by reading down Table A.4 to the appropriate number of degrees of freedom (calculated as $n - 1$) and across to alpha. Values for one-tailed to the left are negative. Two-tailed tests require alpha to be divided by 2 ($\alpha/2$) before Table A.4 can be used. The right tail in a two-tailed test is the value reported with the appropriate *df* and $\alpha/2$. Because *t* is symmetric, the left-tail value is the same value as used for the right tail, but it is negative to reflect its position below (to the left of) the mean 0.

To find the appropriate *t* distribution for a given population, the sample size is used to find the number of degrees of freedom. The concept of degrees of freedom is very complicated, although it can be partially understood as the number of values in a sample that are independent of others. For the purpose of the *t* test, the number of degrees of freedom (denoted by *df*) is $n - 1$, and it determines which of the several *t* distributions should be used.

> **Degree of Freedom** for *t* test when testing one population mean
> $$df = n - 1$$

In addition to being used to find the appropriate distribution, degrees of freedom and the level of significance, $\alpha$, are used to find critical values for hypothesis testing and confidence intervals. Recall that alpha is the probability of committing a type I error, rejecting a true hypothesis. Table A.4 represents critical values of *t*. Table A.4 must be read using the degrees of freedom, the level of significance, alpha, and information about whether the distribution is one-tailed or two-tailed. Alpha levels appear across the top row, and degrees of freedom appear down the left column. The *t* notation representing the critical value is written with a subscript showing *df* and $\alpha$. For example, if $n = 30$ and $\alpha = .05$, $df = 30 - 1$, or 29, and *t* is denoted by $t(df,\alpha)$ or $t(29,.05)$. The critical *t* value 29 at .05 equals 1.699.

| *df* | | Alpha |
|---|---|---|
| | | **.05** |
| 1 | | ...... |
| ...... | | ...... |
| 29 | → → → → | 1.699 |

Other right-tailed *t* critical values are noted on the curve in Figure 11.3.

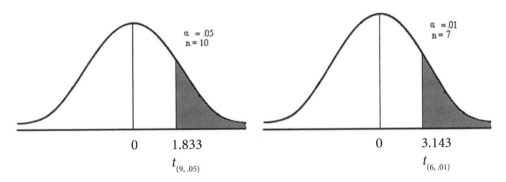

**FIGURE 11.3**

Left-tailed $t$ values are indicated in two different ways. Some people use $1 - \alpha$ to imply left-tailed $t$ values. For example, if $\alpha = .05$ and $df = 20$, a right-tailed test would be indicated by $t(20, .05)$, and a left-tailed value would be indicated as $t(20, .95)$. In this text left-tailed $t$ values are shown using right-tailed notations preceded by a negative sign. The negative sign is a reminder that the $t$ value must also be negative, representing values less than the mean, 0. For example, a right-tailed notation is shown as $t(20, .05)$, and the corresponding left-tailed notation is $-t(20, .05)$. As with $z$, left-tailed $t$ critical values are negative. See Figure 11.4.

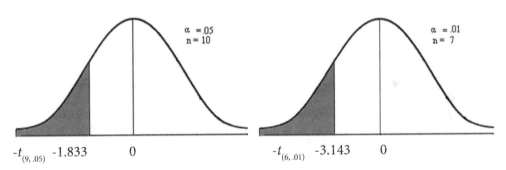

**FIGURE 11.4**

**EXAMPLE 11.1**
**Experiment:** Find the $t$ critical values for the following notations.

a. $t_{(27, .025)}$        b. $t_{(14, .05)}$        c. $t_{(16, .01)}$

d. $-t_{(8, .025)}$        e. $-t_{(12, .05)}$        f. $-t_{(29, .10)}$

**Answers:**

a. 2.052        b. 1.761        c. 2.584

d. -2.306        e. -1.782        f. -1.311

**Solution:** Table A.4 gives *t* critical values using degrees of freedom and levels of significance. The *t* notations are in the form of *t(df,α)*. The values in a, b, and c are for right-tailed tests, because no alteration of the notation occurred. Right-tailed values require moving down to the appropriate number of degrees of freedom and then across to the appropriate alpha level. The values reported in the table are the critical values and need no adjustments. The values in d, e, and f are for the left side of the curve because all three have a negative sign. The critical values are found the same way as the right-tailed values-by tracing down to the appropriate number of degrees of freedom and then across to the appropriate alpha. The only difference is that the answers in d, e, and f must also be preceded by a negative sign, because they represent an area below the mean.

## EXAMPLE 11.2

**Experiment:** Find the *t* critical values for the following two-tailed tests.

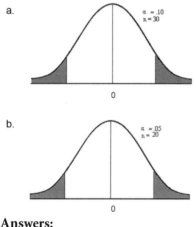

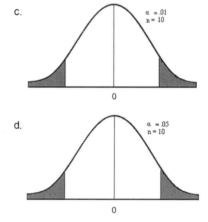

**Answers:**
- a. -1.699 and 1.699
- b. -2.093 and 2.093
- c. -3.250 and 3.250
- d. -2.262 and 2.262

**Solution:** All four curves are two-tailed and contain half of the critical region to the right of the mean and half to the left. Critical values for *t* are found by determining the degrees of freedom and alpha. Degrees of freedom are equal to *n* - 1. All four curves report the sample size *n*; thus, the degrees of freedom for the first curve are 30 - 1, for the second, 20 - 1, and for the third and fourth, 10 - 1. Alpha in a two-tailed test must be divided by 2 before finding the critical values. Therefore, the notations describing the curves are as follows.

a. $-t_{(29, .1/2)}$, and $t_{(29, .1/2)}$

b. $-t_{(19, .05/2)}$ and $t_{(19, .05/2)}$

c. $-t_{(29, .01/2)}$ and $t_{(29, .01/2)}$

d. $-t_{(9, .05/2)}$ and $t_{(9, .05/2)}$

Once the notations are found, the critical values are determined by reading Table A.4. For part a. $-t(29, .1/2)$ and $t(29, .1/2)$, trace down to 29 and across to .1/2, or .05. The value 1.699 is found. Because the distribution is symmetric, a value of -1.699 represents the left tail in a two-tailed test. For b. $-t(19, .05/2)$ and $t(19, .05/2)$, the value is found by tracing down to 19 and across to .05/2, or .025. The value 2.093 represents the right tail and -2.093 represents the left tail. In the third case, c., $- t(9, .01/2)$ and $t(9, .01/2)$ the value is found by tracing down to 9 and across to .01/2, or .005. Both values, 3.250 and -3.250, must be used for a two-tailed test. Finally in d., $-t(9, .05/2)$ and $t(9, .05/2)$ are found by tracing down to 9 and across to .05/2, or .025. The values 2.262 and -2.262 are used.

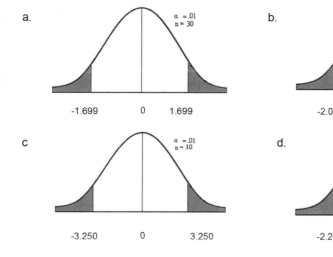

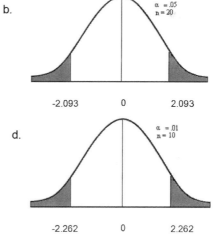

The third step in hypothesis testing using the classical approach is to calculate the test statistic. The calculation of the $t$ statistic is similar to $z$, but the sample standard deviation $s$ replaces the unknown population standard deviation $\sigma$.

### Calculation of the Test Statistic *t* for One Population Mean

$$t = \frac{\bar{x} - \mu}{s/\sqrt{n}}$$

where
- $\bar{x}$ is the sample mean
- $\mu$ is the population mean
- $s$ is the sample standard deviation
- $n$ is the sample size

The fourth step in hypothesis testing requires the placement of the calculated value on the curve to compare it to the critical value. Step 5 is the decision to reject the null hypothesis or to fail to reject the null hypothesis. Rejection of the null hypothesis must occur when the calculated value falls within the critical region. Failing to reject the null hypothesis should occur when the calculated value does not fall within the critical region. The critical regions are determined in step 2. See figures below.

The fifth step in hypothesis testing is to apply the decision to the problem: The decision to reject $H_O$ or fail to reject $H_O$ must be interpreted using the information in the original problem. The rejecting of $H_O$ means that the sample data provided sufficient evidence at the tested level of significance to reject the claim of the null hypothesis. Failing to reject $H_O$ means the sample did not provide sufficient evidence to disprove the null hypothesis. Failing to reject $H_O$ does not prove the null hypothesis correct. It simply does not prove it false.

Recall the steps in hypothesis testing as reviewed here and as presented in Chapter 10. Each step must be completed. The only major differences thus far are in calculating the test statistic $t$ and using the $t$ distribution table in Appendix A for the critical value.

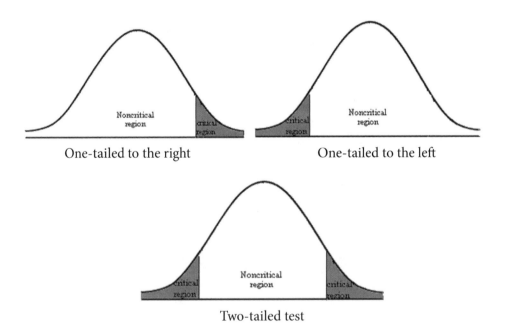

One-tailed to the right     One-tailed to the left

Two-tailed test

**Steps in Hypothesis Testing Using the Classical Approach**

1. State $H_o$ and $H_1$.
2. Identify the test criteria:
   a. Level of significance, $\alpha$
   b. Test statistic ($z$, $t$, $\chi^2$, $F$)
   c. Critical Region
      (1) One-tailed test
      (2) Two-tailed test ($\alpha/2$)
   d. Critical value:
3. Calculate the test statistic.
4. Place the calculated value on a distribution curve.
5. Make a decision:
   a. Fail to reject $H_o$
   b. Reject $H_o$
6. Interpret the results.

## EXAMPLE 11.3

**Experiment:** The camp coordinators at the ABC summer camp program claim the average age of students attending their camp is 12 years. A teenage boy thinks the average age is less than that and hopes to prove the camp coordinators wrong so he can convince his parents not to send him to summer camp. The boy conducts a survey of the ages of 30 boys at camp last year. The sample mean is 10.9 with a standard deviation of 1.4. Conduct a hypothesis test using the classical approach with an alpha of .05.

**Answer:** Reject $H_o$. The sample provides sufficient evidence at the .05 level of significance to reject the claim that the average age of children at the summer camp is 12 years old. The test suggests that the average age is less than 12.

**Solution:** The problem clearly asks for a classical hypothesis test.

**Step 1**

In hypothesis testing, first state the null and alternative hypotheses. The null hypothesis is the claim by the camp coordinators that the mean age of children is 12 years. The alternative hypothesis is the challenge by the teenage boy, who claims the mean age of children at camp is less than 12 years. Because the alternative hypothesis is less than, the null hypothesis becomes not only equal to but also greater than. The parameter in question is the mean, and the value challenged is 12 years. The hypotheses are:

$$H_O: \mu \geq 12$$
$$H_I: \mu < 12$$

**Step 2**

Identify the test criteria. The test criteria include the level of significance, test statistic, critical region, and critical value. The level of significance is given as alpha = .05. The test statistic is the *t* test, because the sample size is small at 30 (*t* is used when $n \leq 30$) and/or the population standard deviation $\sigma$ is unknown. Either of these conditions (small sample size or $\sigma$ unknown) is sufficient reason to use *t*. The critical region is to the left, because the < sign in the alternative hypothesis denotes a one-tailed test to the left. The critical value is found using Table A.4. Critical values for *t* require the degrees of freedom and alpha. The degrees of freedom are equal to $n$ - 1. Table A.4 is read by going down the left column to the appropriate number of degrees of freedom and across to the appropriate alpha level. This is a left-tailed test in which $n = 30$, $df = 30$ - 1, or 29, and alpha = .05. The notation and critical value are $-t(29, .05) = -1.699$.

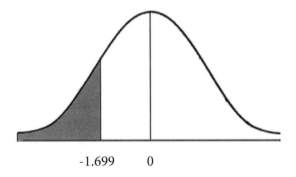

-1.699     0

**Step 3**

Calculation of the test statistic. The information needed for the calculation is: $n = 30$, $\mu = 12$, $\bar{x} = 10.9$, and $s = 1.4$. The *t* calculation is as follows:

$$t = \frac{\bar{x} - \mu}{s/\sqrt{n}} = \frac{10.9 - 12}{1.4/\sqrt{30}} = \frac{-1.1}{.255} = -4.31$$

**Step 4**

Place the calculated value, -4.31, on the curve representing the distribution. Notice -4.31 falls to the left of the critical value, - 1.699.

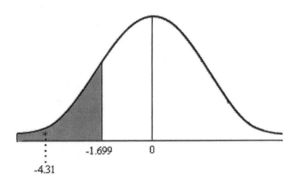

**Step 5**

Decide to reject $H_O$ or fail to reject $H_O$. Here, the decision is to reject $H_O$ because the calculated value -4.31 falls in the critical region, left of the critical value, - 1.699.

**Step 6**

Interpret the decision using the original problem. Rejecting the null hypothesis suggests that the sample provides sufficient evidence that the mean age of children at the camp is not equal to 12 years. There is sufficient proof at the .05 level of significance that the mean age of children is less than 12 years. It would seem that the teenage boy may have a pretty good argument not to go to the camp.

**A LEARNING AID**

**Classical Testing for *t* One Population Mean**

The admissions officer at a university believes that recent applicants have lower mean scores on the English placement test than past students. The mean of past students is 65. Twenty-five students were selected; their mean was 60 and standard deviation was 9. Can it be concluded that today's students have lower test scores? Use $\alpha = .05$.

**Step 1**

State the hypothesis. The classical approach for all test statistics begins by stating the null and alternative hypotheses. The null hypothesis carries the benefit of the doubt. A challenge to the null hypothesis carries the burden of proof. The mean of past students becomes the parameter used in the hypotheses. The admissions officer challenging the mean claims the mean is less than 65. A claim challenging a null hypothesis that also carries a less than

(<) sign must be placed in the alternative hypothesis. A less than (<) sign in the alternative hypothesis requires a greater than or equal to (≥) sign in the null hypothesis. The parameter is a population mean ($\mu$) with a value 65. State the hypotheses.

$$H_0: \mu \geq 65 \qquad H_i: \mu < 65$$

**Step 2**
Determine the test criteria. The first test criteria is the level of significance, alpha. Alpha is stated as .05. Select a test statistic from $z$, $t$, $\chi^2$, and $F$. Choose the $t$ distribution because the sample size is small ($n \leq 30$) and the population standard deviation $\sigma$ is unknown. Either of these conditions is sufficient to require the use of $t$.

The test is a left-tailed test, as determined by the direction of the sign in the alternative hypothesis. When the alternative hypothesis is less than (<), the test is one-tailed to the left. Add a negative sign to left-tailed $t$ critical values. Write the critical value using degrees of freedom and alpha. Degrees of freedom $(df)$ for $t$ are calculated as $n - 1$. The sample of 25 students produces $df = 25 - 1$, or 24. Alpha is .05. Alpha does not need to be divided in this problem because it is not a two-tailed test. State the notation:

$$-t(df, \alpha) = -t(24..05)$$

Using Table A.4, trace down to 24 degrees of freedom and across to .05. The value in the intersection is the critical value. You should find a value of 1.711. Add a negative sign to represent the left tail of the curve. The critical value separating the critical region from the non critical region is - 1.711.

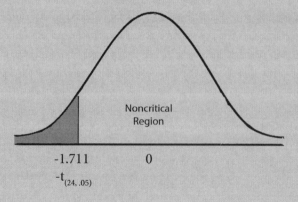

**Step 3**

Calculate the test statistic. The test statistic for $t$ uses the sample standard deviation instead of the unknown population standard deviation. The sample of 25 produced a sample mean of 60 and a sample standard deviation of 9; calculate $t$: $\mu = 65$, $\bar{x} = 60$, $s = 9$, and $n = 25$.

$$t = \frac{\bar{x} - \mu}{s/\sqrt{n}} = \frac{60 - 65}{9/\sqrt{25}} = \frac{-5}{1.8} = -2.78$$

**Step 4**

Place the calculated test statistic on the distribution curve. The calculated value -2.78 is placed to the left of the critical value, - 1.711.

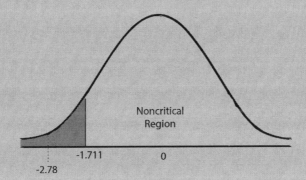

**Step 5**

Make a decision. Reject the null hypothesis, because the calculated value -2.78 falls within the critical region.

Reject $H_O$

**Step 6**

Interpret the results. Apply the decision to the original question presented in the experiment. The question is to determine if it can be concluded that today's students have lower test scores than past students. The decision to reject the null hypothesis suggests that the answer to the question is yes. Based on this sample of 25 students at the .05 level of significance, there is sufficient evidence to suggest that the sores of today's students are significantly lower than scores of past students.

The test only suggests the scores are significantly lower than 65. It does not indicate the average of the scores is 60. The rejection of the null hypothesis merely indicates it is false, not that any other assertion is correct.

# SECTION 3

## Hypothesis Test: *P*-Value for Mean Using *t*

The prob-value, or *P*-value, approach to hypothesis testing takes the classical approach one step further by transforming the calculated value into a probability and comparing the probability to an alpha level. *P*-values, whether for *z*, *t*, or other test statistics, are probabilities that measure the level of significance at which the test statistic becomes significant provided the null hypothesis is true. Because *P*-values and alphas are probabilities, each compared to the other leads to decisions about the null hypothesis.

Population →$\alpha$ →Probability

→→compare probabilities to make a decision

Sample→*t-score*→Probability

Computerized statistical programs typically report calculated *t* values with an associated *P*-value. The calculated *t* value may be used to conduct a classical hypothesis test, and the *P*-value may be used to conduct a *P*-value hypothesis test. The classical approach requires identification of the test criteria, including the critical region and critical value. Usually a statistics book or *t* distribution table is necessary to determine the critical value. When such tools are not readily available, the *P*-value test allows the same conclusions to be drawn.

When a *P*-value is offered by a computerized program or by another source, a comparison of the *P*-value with the alpha level is necessary. If the *P*-value is less than or equal to $\alpha$, then the null hypothesis should be rejected. If the *P*-value is greater than $\alpha$, the null hypothesis should fail to be rejected.

A complete hypothesis test using the *P*-value approach is much like the classical approach for *t* and the *P*-value approach for *z*. The six steps identified for *z* in Chapter 10 are repeated here for *t*. Step 1 is to identify the null and alternative hypotheses. Step 2 is to determine two aspects of the test criteria, the level of significance and the test statistic. The level of significance is either given as $\alpha$ in the problem or must be determined by considering the seriousness of a type I error-that is, rejecting a true hypothesis. The test statistic must be determined by reviewing the parameter in the hypotheses. The only parameter used in testing so far is the population mean, $\mu$, allowing for the use of only *z* or *t* test statistics. The *t* statistic is used with samples having an *n* of 30 or less and/or when $\sigma$ is unknown. Step 3 is to calculate the test statistic. The calculation for the *t* test statistic is

$$t = \frac{\bar{x} - \mu}{s/\sqrt{n}}$$

Step 4 is identifying the *P*-value. If using the table version the transformation of *t* is slightly different than for *z*. The *z*-score required finding a probability in the *z* table, subtracting it from .5000, and adjusting it as necessary. The *t* score also requires consulting the appendix, but the *t* table instead. In addition to knowing the alpha, to find the probability for *t*, the degrees of freedom for the sample are also necessary. The *P*-value for *t* is determined by noting the calculated value from step 3 with the degrees of freedom from step 2. Using Table A.4, trace down to the appropriate number of degrees of freedom. Read across all the values of that row, finding the value closest to the calculated value. The value in the table nearest to the calculated value serves as a guide to the probability used as the *P*-value. The *P*-value is the alpha level associated with the column where the value closest to the calculated value is found. For example, if the calculated value in step 3 equals 1.76 for a sample of 17 with *df* = 16 (17 - 1 = 16), the *P*-value is .05. Find the *P*-value of .05 by moving down to the number of degrees of freedom, 16, across to the value 1.746, which is nearest to the calculated value 1.76, and up to the alpha value of .05 associated with the column where 1.746 is found at 16 degrees of freedom.

| Degrees of Freedom | | Alpha | | |
|---|---|---|---|---|
| | .01 | .025 | .05 | |
| 1 | ..... | ..... | ..... | ↑ |
| 2 | ..... | ..... | ..... | ↑ |
| .... | ..... | ..... | ..... | ↑ |
| 16 | → | → | → | 1.746 |

**P- value(1.76, *df* 16) = .05**

If using the TI series calculators, the *P*-value approach described above is bypassed as the *P*-value is noted on the result screen. Simply remember that if the test is a left-tailed test, the *P*-value will appear on the result screen often with .9 numbers. *P*-values, as with alpha notations, often use .9 numbers to indicate they are left-tailed values. The technical answer is to subtract the number from 1.0. That is, a .95 *P*-value on the calculator is really 1.0 - .95, which is .05. The answer would be .05.

The next step in *P*-value testing requires comparing the *P*-value to alpha and making a decision about the hypothesis. The rule for the decision using *P*-values remains constant for all test statistics. If the *P*-value is less than or equal to alpha, then reject the null hypothesis. If the *P*-value is greater than alpha, then fail to reject the null hypothesis.

**Decisions Using *P-Values***
$P \leq \alpha$  Reject $H_o$
$P > \alpha$  Fail to reject $H_o$

The final step is to interpret the decision. Rejecting the null hypothesis suggests that the sample provided sufficient statistical proof that the null hypothesis is not true. It is important to remember that rejecting the null hypothesis does not suggest that the sample information is true or that the new parameter is represented by the sample statistic. Likewise, failing to reject the null hypothesis suggests only that the sample does not provide sufficient evidence to challenge the null hypothesis. Failing to reject the null hypothesis does not prove it to be correct or true but shows only that it withstood this specific test.

**Steps in Hypothesis Testing using the *P*-Value Approach**
(Using the Calculator)
1. State $H_o$ and $H_1$.
2. Identify the test criteria:
    a. Level of significance, $\alpha$
    b. Test statistic ($z, t, \chi^2, F$)
3. Calculate the test statistic.
4. Identify the *P-value*.
5. Make a decision:
    a. If $P > \alpha$,  Fail to Reject $H_o$
    b. If $P \leq \alpha$,  Reject $H_o$
6. Interpret the results.

**EXAMPLE 11.5**
**Experiment:** It is argued that the risk of complications in pregnancy is increased as the age of the mother increases. The mean age of mothers for all pregnancies is 27.8 years. Case histories of 25 pregnancies where complications occurred at Mercy Hospital reveal the mean age of mothers to be 29.75 years, with a standard deviation of 3.2. Using the *P*-value approach, does the sample provide sufficient evidence to support the assertion that the risk of complications in pregnancy increases with the age of the mother? Use $\alpha = .025$.

**Answer:** Yes, there is sufficient evidence to suggest that complications in pregnancy increase with the age of the mother.

**Solution:** There are six steps in hypothesis testing using the *P*-value approach:

State the hypothesis, identity the test criteria, calculate the test statistic, calculate the *P*-value, make a decision, and interpret the results.

**Step 1**
The hypothesis concerns the mean age of pregnancy. The mean is the parameter for the population, with a value of 27.8 years. The mathematical symbol referred to in the experiment is greater than (>), which is found in the statement that the risk of complications increases as the age of the mother increases. The symbol > is allowed only in the alternative hypothesis. Also, the statement about the relationship of complications to age is suggested as an argument. The alternative hypothesis argues or challenges the null hypothesis. If the alternative symbol is >, then the null symbol must be ≤. State the hypotheses.

$$H_O : \mu \le 27.8 \qquad H_i : \mu > 27.8$$

**Step 2**
The test criteria for *P*-value testing require identification of the test statistic and level of confidence. The test statistic is *t*. Use the *t* distribution for a sample of 25 where the population standard deviation is unknown. The level of significance is given as .025.

**Step 3**
Calculate the test statistic. The calculation of *t* requires the following information derived from the experiment: $\mu = 27.8$, $\overline{x} = 29.75$, $s = 3.2$, and $n = 25$.

After determining the proper null and alternative hypotheses, begin performing the T-Test in a TI-83 or 84 calculator by pressing the STAT button, scrolling right to "TESTS" and pressing 2 in order to select "2:TTest…". Under the settings screen of the T-Test, be sure "Stats" is selected and proceed to plug in the information given in the problem, along with the alternative hypothesis. Once completed, highlight "Calculate" and press the ENTER button. The results will appear.

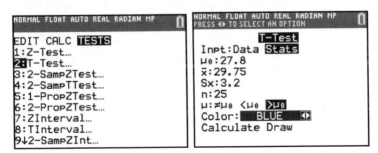

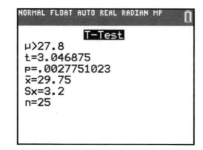

$$t = \frac{\bar{x} - \mu}{s/\sqrt{n}} = \frac{29.75 - 27.8}{3.2/\sqrt{25}} = 3.047$$

**Step 4**
Identify the *P*-value. It appears on the result screen as *P* = .0027751023 which rounds to .0028.

**Step 5**
Compare the *P*-value to the original alpha given in the experiment. If $P \leq \alpha$, then reject the null hypothesis. If $P > \alpha$, then fail to reject the null hypothesis. *P* at .0028 is less than $\alpha$ at .025; therefore, reject the null hypothesis.

$$P\text{-value}(.0028) \leq \alpha(.025) \qquad \text{Reject } H_O$$

**Step 6**
Interpret the results. Rejecting the null hypothesis suggests there is sufficient evidence provided by this sample of 25 at the .025 level of significance that the risk of complications in pregnancies is related to the age of the mother. As the age of the mother increases, so, too, does the risk of complications.

**A LEARNING AID**
***t* TESTING USING *P*-VALUE Approach for One Population Mean**
A random sample of nine students who used a computer to type a term paper showed that the mean number of typing errors was 7.8, with a standard deviation of 3.0. It had been predicted that the average number of errors would be 9.0. Using the *P*-value approach, do these results show, at the .05 level of significance, that the mean number of errors is actually different from 9.0?

## Step 1

State the hypotheses. The null hypothesis is contained in the sentence asking whether the mean number of errors is different from the predicted 9.0. If the mean is different, it is not equal to the given value. The not equal to symbol ($\neq$) is allowed only in the alternative hypothesis. Because the mathematical symbols in hypotheses are paired, if the alternative is not equal to, then the null must be equal to. State the hypotheses.

$$H_o: \mu = 9.0 \qquad H_1: \mu \neq 9.0$$

## Step 2

Identify the test criteria. The test criteria for $P$-value testing include the level of significance and test statistic. The level of significance is given as .05. The test statistic is $t$. Use $t$ when testing for means with small sample sizes and/or when the population standard deviation is unknown.

## Step 3

Calculate the test statistic and $P$-Value. The following information is derived from the problem: $n = 9$, $\bar{x} = 7.8$, $s = 3.0$, and $\mu = 9.0$ and is used in the settings screen of a T-Test on a calculator. After determining the proper null and alternative hypotheses, begin performing the T-Test in a TI-83 or 84 calculator by pressing the STAT button, scrolling right to "TESTS" and pressing 2 in order to select "2:TTest…". Under the settings screen of the T-Test, be sure "Stats" is selected and proceed to plug in the information given in the problem, along with the alternative hypothesis. Once completed, highlight "Calculate" and press the ENTER button. The results will appear.

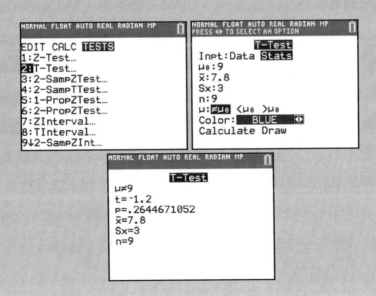

$$t = \frac{\bar{x} - \mu}{s/\sqrt{n}} = \frac{7.8 - 9.0}{3.0/\sqrt{9}} = -1.2$$

**Step 4**
Identify the *P*-value from the result screen. Rounded to 4 digits to the right of the decimal, *P* is .2645.

**Step 5**
Make a decision. Compare the *P*-value to the original alpha presented in the problem. If *P* is less than or equal to alpha, then reject the null hypothesis. If *P* is greater than alpha, then fail to reject null hypothesis. The *P*-value of .2645 is greater than alpha (.05); therefore, fail to reject the null hypothesis.

$$P\text{-value}(.2645) > \alpha(.05) \qquad \text{Fail to reject } H_O$$

**Step 6**
Interpret the results. Due to the decision to fail to reject the null hypothesis, there is not sufficient evidence at this particular level of significance to reject the mean. Applying this interpretation to the problem, the sample of nine students does not provide sufficient evidence at the .05 level of significance that the mean number of errors is different than the predicted 9 errors.

# SECTION 4

## Confidence Interval for *t for One Mean*

Testing population parameters using sample information is only one aspect of inferential statistics. A second aspect of inferential statistic is estimating population parameters from sample statistics. Testing and estimating can be viewed as opposite sides of the same coin. Testing allows a researcher to determine if a sample statistic is within a given range around the parameter. Estimating allows a researcher to determine the parameter within a given range around a sample statistic. A population parameter can be estimated from sample data using the technique known as confidence intervals. Recall the definition of a confidence interval presented in Chapter 10.

**Confidence Interval** Estimating a population parameter from sample statistics given a specified level of confidence.

A confidence interval establishes a range of values around the sample information where the population parameter will fall given a particular degree of confidence. The sample statistic used as the point of departure to determine the range of values for the interval is known as the point estimate.

> **Point Estimate** The sample statistic used to estimate the population parameter' When estimating the parameter, $\mu$, the point estimate is the sample statistic $\overline{x}$.

The degree of confidence, or level of confidence, establishes the probability that the population parameter will fall inside the range of values set by the point estimate. Recall that Chapter 10 presents the concept of the level of confidence as the opposite of alpha. Alpha is the probability of committing an error; the level of confidence is the probability of being correct. The level of confidence is usually stated as a percentage. To be 90% sure the population parameter falls within a range around the point estimate, the level of confidence must be 90 and alpha must be .10. Alpha and the level of confidence must have a sum of 1.0.

Unlike Chapter 10, where the level of confidence is transformed into a probability and then into a $z$ score, confidence intervals for $t$ require transforming the level of confidence directly into a $t$ value by using the degrees of freedom and alpha divided by 2. Remember that all confidence intervals are two-tailed, requiring dividing alpha by 2. Also remember that $t$ values are dependent on sample size, described as degrees of freedom and equal to $n$ - 1. Identify the degrees of freedom and the alpha level, $\alpha/2$ if using Table A.4. Go down to the appropriate degrees of freedom and across to the value under the correct alpha level. The critical value found in the intersection is denoted by $t(df, \alpha/2)$. Use this value to calculate the confidence interval.

If using the TI calculator, the confidence interval requires only a few pieces of information. It requires the sample mean, sample standard deviation (or population if given), sample size n, and the C-Level (confidence level). The calculation will be performed resulting in both the upper and lower limits of the interval.

The calculation of the confidence interval for means normally distributed with small samples ($n \leq 30$) is similar to z, but the population standard deviation, $\sigma$, is substituted with the sample standard deviation $s$.

**Formula for a Confidence Interval with a Mean Normally Distributed
with a Small Sample Size ($n \le 30$) and/or $\sigma$ Unknown**

$$E_{\mu} = \bar{x} + t_{(df, \alpha/2)} \frac{s}{\sqrt{n}} \text{ and } E_{\mu} = \bar{x} - t_{(df, \alpha/2)} \frac{s}{\sqrt{n}}$$

where

$E_{\mu}$ is the estimate of the population mean.

$\bar{x}$ is the sample mean, known as the point estimate.

$t_{(df, \alpha/2)}$ is the critical value found in Table A.4.

$s$ is the sample standard deviation.

$n$ is the sample size.

As in the case of other procedures, there are several steps that help organize the calculation and interpretation of the confidence interval.

**Steps in Calculating a Confidence Interval Using Tables**

**1.** Identify the level of confidence (90%, 95%, 99%).

**2.** Identify the test statistic ($z$, $t$, $\chi^2$, or $F$).

**3.** Determine the critical value with $\alpha/2$.

**4.** Calculate the interval.

**5.** State the interval.

Step 1 identifies the problem as a confidence interval and the level of confidence. Key words are interval, confidence, or estimate. The level of confidence is also usually cited within the statement as "estimate with 90% confidence" or "calculate a 90% interval." Questions asking for a confidence interval for the mean would not cite a population mean, $\mu$ value.

Step 2 is to identify the test statistic. Thus far, $z$ and $t$ have been described. Use $z$ for normally distributed means with large samples and where the standard deviation of the population is known. Use $t$ for normally distributed means with small samples ($n \le 30$) or when the population standard deviation is unknown.

Step 3 is to calculate the confidence interval. The TI series calculators result screen will report both the lower and upper limit of the interval. If doing the calculation by hand, the critical value would need to be found using a table and the calculation must be performed twice to establish the lower and upper limits of the range. The formulas are essentially the same; one formula subtracts a value from the point estimate and the other formula adds a value to it. The $t$ calculation is

$$E_\mu = \bar{x} + t_{(df,\alpha/2)} \frac{s}{\sqrt{n}} \text{ and } E_\mu = \bar{x} - t_{(df,\alpha/2)} \frac{s}{\sqrt{n}}$$

Step 4 is restating the interval in the appropriate format. The notation for an interval places the parameter inside the lower and upper limit of the values calculated in step 4. The parameter $\mu$ is used for the $t$ statistic.

$$E\mu = (\text{Lower limit} < \mu < \text{Upper limit})$$

**Steps in Calculating a Confidence Interval Using the Calculator**
1. Identify the level of confidence (90%, 95%, 99%).
2. Identify the test statistic ($z$, $t$, $\chi2$, or $F$).
3. Enter the data.
4. State the interval.

The approach to confidence intervals using the TI-83/84 calculators is very similar to using the table version. The biggest difference is that the critical value is not needed on the calculator. Needed information is only the sample mean, sample standard deviation, sample size, and the confidence interval.

**EXAMPLE 11.7**
**Experiment:** Find the 90% confidence interval for the mean age of the members of the U.S. Congress using a sample of 25 whose mean age is 54 years, with a standard deviation of 2.5 years.

**Answer:** 90% confidence interval: $(53.14 < \mu < 54.86)$

**Solution:** Begin by identifying the experiment as a confidence interval. The statement clearly asks for a confidence interval. The level of confidence is given at 90%. A 90% level of confidence means that the true population parameter should fall in the range of values 90% of the time. Stated another way, the probability of being correct is .9.

Use the $t$ statistic for the problem, because the sample size is small and the population standard deviation is unknown. Either of these conditions is sufficient to require the use of $t$.

To calculate the interval, the following information is necessary: $\bar{x} = 54$, $s = 2.5$, $n = 25$, and C-level (confidence level) .90. Using a calculator, begin by pressing the STAT button, scrolling over to "TESTS," followed by pressing the number 8 to select "8:TInterval…" With "Stats" selected in the settings screen, plug in the data given in the problem. Scroll down to highlight "Calculate" and press ENTER. The results will appear.

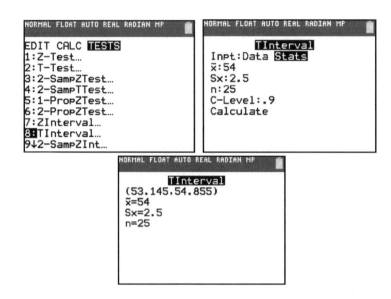

$$E_\mu = \bar{x} - t_{(df,\alpha/2)}\frac{s}{\sqrt{n}} \quad \text{and} \quad E_\mu = \bar{x} + t_{(df,\alpha/2)}\frac{s}{\sqrt{n}}$$

$$= 53.145 \qquad\qquad\qquad = 54.855$$

The lower limit of the interval is 53.145, and the upper limit is 54.855. Based on this sample, with 90% confidence, the mean age of all members of Congress ranges from 53.145 years to 54.855 years.

$$E\mu = (53.145 < \mu < 54.855)$$

**A LEARNING AID**
**CONFIDENCE INTERVALS FOR $t$ ONE POPULATION MEAN**
A sample of 30 teenage mothers shows that they have a lifetime average of 5.4 children, with a standard deviation of 1.2. Find the 95% confidence interval for the mean number of children born to all teenage mothers.

**Step 1**

Identify the level of confidence. The problem requires a 95% confidence interval. The level of confidence estimates the probability that the parameter will be contained in the range established around the sample statistic.

**Step 2**

Identify the test statistic. The $t$ statistic is necessary, because the mean is estimated using a sample of 30 and/or where the population standard deviation is unknown. If the sample size was larger and the population standard deviation was known, then the test statistic would be $z$.

**Step 3**

Calculate the confidence interval. The $t$ confidence interval uses the sample mean as the point estimate for the population mean. The necessary information for the calculation is $\overline{x} = 5.4$, $s = 1.2$, $n = 30$, and C-Level 95% = .95.

On a TI-83/84 calculator, begin by pressing the STAT button, scrolling over to "TESTS," followed by pressing the number 8 to select "8:TInterval…" With "Stats" selected in the settings screen, plug in the data given in the problem. Scroll down to highlight "Calculate" and press ENTER. The results will appear.

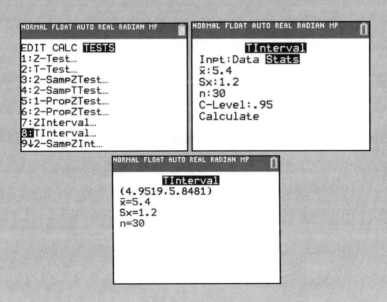

$$E_\mu = \bar{x} - t_{(df,\alpha/2)} \frac{s}{\sqrt{n}} \quad \text{and} \quad E_\mu = \bar{x} + t_{(df,\alpha/2)} \frac{s}{\sqrt{n}}$$
$$= 4.952 \qquad\qquad\qquad = 5.848$$

**Step 4**
State the interval. The lower limit of the interval is 4.95 and the upper limit is 5.85. This suggests that, based on this sample, with 95% confidence, the mean number of children born to all teenage mothers ranges from 4.952 to 5.848.

$$E\mu = (4.952 < \mu < 5.848)$$

## CHAPTER 11 IN REVIEW

11.1 Find the *t* critical values for mean testing associated with the shaded area of each curve.

a.

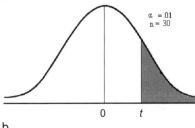

c.

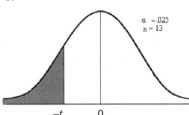

b.

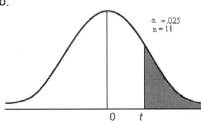

d.

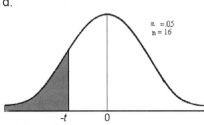

11.2 Find the *t* critical values for mean testing associated with the shaded areas of each curve.

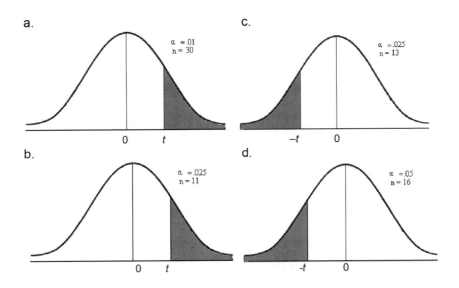

11.3  Using the correct format, state both the null and alternative hypotheses.
a. The mean cost of a hotel room per night is at least $200.
b. The mean number of calculations for the world's fastest computer is more than 280 trillion per second.
c The mean price of a new smart phone is more than $199.
d. The mean cost of a Rolls Royce Phantom Coupe is $440,000.
e. The mean cost of dinner at a world class restaurant is at least $125.

11.4  Find the *t* critical values suggested by the given data.
a. $H_O: \mu = 12$; $H_I: \mu \neq 12$; $n = 27$, $\alpha = .05$
b. $H_O: \mu \leq 500$; $H_I: \mu > 500$; $n = 17$, $\alpha = .10$
c. $H_O: \mu \geq 10.75$; $H_I: \mu < 10.75$; $n = 29$, $\alpha = .01$
d. $H_O: \mu = 75$ $H_I: \mu \neq 75$; $n = 24$, $\alpha = .05$
e. $H_O: \mu \geq 98.4$; $H_I: \mu < 98.4$; $n = 12$, $\alpha = .05$

11.5  Using the appropriate format, state both the null and alternative hypotheses.
a. Hershey sells an average of 395 million chocolate bars a year.
b. Americans spend at least $123 per person per year on toys.
c. The mean cost of a textbook is greater than $135.00.
d. An average of 180 million boxes of Cheerios is sold every year.
e. The mean IQ of students is greater than 110.

11.6  The average rushing totals for the 2014 NFL offensive players per game is 113.34 yards. A sample of the top 10 rushers is 130.5 yards with a standard deviation of 21.37. Test whether the sample is significantly greater than the claim using $\alpha$ .05.

11.7 The 2014 season average for professional golfers in the PGA is 71.355. Test if the average is correct using a sample of the top 5 players averaging 69.196 with a standard deviation of .383. Use $\alpha = .10$.

11.8 The average height of New York City's skyscrapers is 261 meters. An architect challenges this average. She takes a sample of 20 buildings producing a mean of 289 meters with a standard deviation of 40. Use a 5 percent level of significance.

11.9 For each of 12 hospitals, the cost of a surgery per patient was found. The 12 hospitals have a mean cost of $12,033 and a standard deviation of $1,245. At the .05 level of significance, test the claim of a patient who complains that the mean costs for all such surgeries exceeds $11,800.

11.10 A random sample of 31 industrial countries produces a mean per capita GDP of $32,600, with a standard deviation of $870. At the .02 significance level, test a researcher's claim that the mean per capita GNP is significantly less than $33,000.

11.11 An airport supervisor randomly selects 20 planes of the same model and tests them to determine the distance they require for takeoff. The 20 planes produce a sample mean of 678 meters and a standard deviation 30. At the .01 level of significance, test the claim that the mean distance for all such planes is more than 650 m.

11.12 Calculate the 90 percent confidence interval for the mean number of years to finish a Ph.D. after a baccalaureate degree. A sample of 30 professors produces a mean time of 8.2 years with a standard deviation 1.6.

11.13 The average ostrich egg weighs 4.1 pounds. A researcher believes this is too high. He samples 20 eggs and finds a mean of 3.7 with a standard deviation of .35. Test the claim at alpha = .05.

11.14 Test the claim that Toyota sells 35,666 Camrys per month. A sample of 10 months produced a mean of 35,225 and a standard deviation of 450; let $\alpha = .05$.

11.15 The total value of art by the world's most successful artists averages at least $4 billion. A museum appraiser believes the value is less and samples the 5 most successful artists whose values average $3.729 billion with a standard deviation of .323. Test using $\alpha = .01$.

11.16 Describe the decision concerning the following *P*-values:

a. $P = .04$, $\alpha = .05$      d. $P = .013$, $\alpha = .01$
b. $P = .05$, $\alpha = .02$      e. $P = .025$, $\alpha = .01$
c. $P = .005$, $\alpha = .005$      f. $P = .015$, $\alpha = .025$

11.17 Determine if Mrs. Welton's 3rd grade class scored significantly higher on the annual math assessment test given to all 3rd grade students in the state. Mrs. Welton's class of 23 students scored an average of 535 on the math portion of the test with a standard deviation of 20. The state average is 527. Test at $\alpha = .05$.

11.18 The average salary of a leading Hollywood actor is $18 million. Test the accuracy of this claim with a sample of 10 actors who earned an average of $21 million with a standard deviation of $4 million. Use $\alpha = .05$.

11.19 Estimate, with 95 percent certainty, the average infant mortality rate of the world given a sample of 25 countries whose mean infant mortality rate is 91.2, with standard deviation 15.7.

11.20 Estimate, with 90 percent certainty, the mean number of pounds of household garbage produced per week using a sample of 24 houses whose mean is 15.9 lbs, with standard deviation 2.34.

11.21 True or False?
   a. If the alpha level is .05, the level of confidence is 90 percent.
   b. The $t$ confidence interval is used when estimating a population with a sample less than or equal to 30 when the population standard deviation is unknown.
   c. If $P > \alpha$, then the decision is to reject the null hypothesis.
   d. If $df = 29$ and a calculated value is 1.7, the $P$-value is 2.054.
   e. If the calculated value falls to the right of a right-tailed critical value, the decision is to reject the null hypothesis.
   f. The $t$ test can be used for testing variances and standard deviations.

11.22 A report notes that 22.7 percent of Hispanics entering college indicate they are interested in the STEM fields (science, technology, engineering, and mathematics). A sample of 50 entering Hispanic students produces a mean of 21.5 with a standard deviation of 2.75. Test that the sample is substantially lower than the report using $\alpha = .01$.

11.23 A local cable company claims that the average cost of a cable bill is no more than $78.50 per month. A consumer advocacy group challenges this, claiming the bills are, on average, higher. Test at the .1 level a sample of 33 households whose mean is $81.32 and standard deviation is $4.14.

11.24 Calculate the 95 percent confidence interval for the percent change in apartment rent over a 1-year period using a sample of 32 with a mean change of 1.5 and a standard deviation of 0.69.

11.25 According to insurers, the average annual cost of medical malpractice insurance for an obstetrician in Las Vegas is $100,000. An obstetrician believes the figure is much higher and tests using the medical malpractice insurance cost from 20 of his colleagues. Their average payment is $108,000 with a standard deviation of $9,000. Test the insurer's claim using the sample at a .01 level of significance.

11.26 Since last year at the same time, national sales for women's and girls' apparel have declined an average of .81 percent with a standard deviation of .32. A sample of 30 stores reports an average decline of 1.0 percent. Do the data show a significant difference in sales at the .10 level?

11.27 The average cost of car insurance in the U.S. is currently at $150 a month (without taking into consideration other factors such as age and gender). To test the claim, 50 drivers were randomly selected in Michigan producing an average of $174.76 and a standard deviation of $35. Test using alpha at .05.

11.28 During the last several decades, improved nutrition has resulted not only in increases in height and weight, but also in shoe size. A report notes that the average American women's shoe size is now size 8.75. To test the claim that there is no difference in the shoe size average, a survey was done with 100 American women whose shoe size averaged size 9 with a standard deviation of 1.75. Test at the .10 level of significance.

# 12

# OTHER ONE POPULATION TESTS

*SECTION 1* **Hypothesis Test: Classical Approach for a Variance Using Chi-Square**

*SECTION 2* **Hypothesis Test: *P*-Value for a Variance Using Chi-Square**

*SECTION 3* **Confidence Interval for a Population Variance Using Chi-Square**

*SECTION 4* **Hypothesis Test: Classical Approach for a Proportion Using *z***

*SECTION 5* **Hypothesis Test: *P*-value Approach for a Proportion Using *z***

*SECTION 6* **Hypothesis Test: Classical Approach for Correlation between Two Variables Using *t***

*SECTION 7* **Hypothesis Test: *P*-Value Approach for Correlation between Two Variables Using *t***

In the last few chapters, hypothesis testing and estimations on population mean for one population was performed. The normal curve, $z$, and the $t$ distribution are typically used for testing population means. This chapter presents tests on other parameters such as a variance, correlation between two variables and proportions. The process for testing hypotheses for these other parameters remains the same as with means, while the hypotheses, and the calculations of test statistics, and the distributions could be different. There are three different procedures presented in this chapter. The first is the testing and estimating of a variance. The distribution used in this procedure is called a ***Chi-square*** distribution. The test statistic Chi-Square is also used for testing and estimating a standard deviation since a standard deviation can easily be converted into a variance by squaring. The second test statistic presented in this chapter is the test for a proportion. Proportion testing is also adjusted for probabilities and percentages. The test on a proportion is a modification of the *z-score* presented in earlier chapters. Finally, the third procedure in this chapter is the test for a correlation. Correlation testing uses a modification of the *t-test* presented in the last chapter.

To review, there are several steps in testing hypotheses using the classical approach. *P*-value steps will be reviewed later in this chapter. The specific test statistic and distribution used will differ from problem to problem, but the other steps remain very similar.

**Steps in Hypothesis Testing Using the Classical Approach**
1. State $H_o$ and $H_1$.
2. Identify the test criteria:
   a. Level of significance, $\alpha$
   b. Test statistic ($z$, $t$, $\chi^2$, $F$)
   c. Critical Region:
      (1) One-tailed test
      (2) Two-tailed test ($\alpha/2$)
   d. Critical value
3. Calculate the test statistic.
4. Place the calculated value on a distribution curve.
5. Make a decision:
   a. Fail to reject $H_o$
   b. Reject $H_o$
6. Interpret the results.

# SECTION 1

## Hypothesis Test: Classical Approach for a Variance Using Chi-Square

There are many situations when a variance or a standard deviation must be tested or estimated. For example, while a potato chip company considers purchasing a new filling machine for their chips, the average weight and the consistency of all bags of potato chips filled by this machine must be important factors of concern. Although mean weight is important, the manufacturer does not want customers in stores shaking bags to feel the fullness of the bag of chips. The consistency of the fill can be measured by the variance and standard deviation. In testing the population means, symmetric distributions were used. However, a new distribution that is skewed to the right will be introduced to test a claim about the population variance.

Under the assumption that the population resembles a normal distribution, sample variances are represented in a distribution curve that is skewed to the right. A right-skewed distribution has extreme values to the right, pulling the tail of the distribution toward the right. See Figure 12.1.

The right-skewed distribution representing sample variances is known as the Chi-square distribution. Chi is the Greek letter $\chi$ (pronounced as "ki," as in the ki in kite). The square represents the square of the variance. Thus, Chi-square is written $\chi^2$.

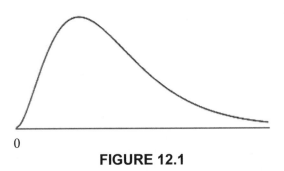

0

**FIGURE 12.1**

**Chi-Square Distribution, $\chi^2$**
A distribution representing sample variances of one population
  1. $\chi^2$ is nonsymmetrical, skewed to the right.
  2. $\chi^2$ is nonnegative, greater than or equal to 0.

Unlike the symmetric $z$ and $t$ distributions, Chi-square is not symmetric but is skewed to the right. The mean, mode, and median are neither centered nor placed together. The mode is to the left, the median is slightly to the right of the mode, and the mean is pulled further to the right. Recall that extreme values pull the mean in their direction. With extreme values to the right, the mean is pulled to the right. See Figure 12.2

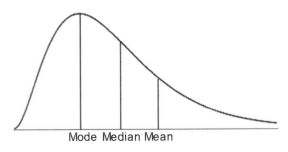

Mode Median Mean

**FIGURE 12.2**

Because Chi-square is nonsymmetrical, the values lower than the mean are not found by adding a negative sign to left-tailed values. Chi-square values are never negative. Chi-square begins at 0. A value less than 0 is impossible, because $\chi^2$ is a distribution representing variances. Variances are never less than 0. Recall that variance measures the dispersion of values around the mean. If all values are equal to the mean, then the variance is 0.

The classical approach for testing a variance using $\chi^2$ follows the same steps as for $z$ and $t$. The six steps in the classical approach begin with stating the hypotheses. Recall that hypotheses include a population parameter, a mathematical symbol, and a numerical value. Chi-square tests variances and standard deviations. The parameter for the population variance, $\sigma^2$, or the parameter for the population standard deviation, $\sigma$, must be included in the hypotheses. Do not use the mean symbol, $\mu$, when testing for $\chi^2$. Essentially, the population information is converted into a Chi-square value, the sample information is converted into a Chi-square value, and the Chi-square values are compared to make the decision to reject or fail to reject the null hypothesis.

Population $\rightarrow \alpha \rightarrow \chi^2$-*score*

$\rightarrow \rightarrow$ compare $\chi^2$-*scores* to make a

Sample $\rightarrow \rightarrow \rightarrow \rightarrow \chi^2$-*score*

decision

The three choices of the mathematical symbol for the null hypothesis are $=$, $\leq$, and $\geq$. The null hypothesis carries the benefit of the doubt and must be proven false before it can be rejected. The alternative hypothesis carries a contrasting symbol, $\neq$, $>$, or $<$. That is, if the null hypothesis is $=$, then the alternative hypothesis must be $\neq$. The alternative hypothesis carries the burden of proof and challenges the null hypothesis.

The value included in the hypothesis is determined by the experiment. It is either the stated or expected population variance or population standard deviation. Be careful to observe if the experiment tests the variance or the standard deviation. Hypothesis for variances could be stated as:

$$\text{If } H_O \text{ is } \sigma^2 = 9 \qquad \text{then } H_I \text{ is } \sigma^2 \neq 9$$
$$\text{If } H_O \text{ is } \sigma^2 \leq 4 \qquad \text{then } H_I \text{ is } \sigma^2 > 4$$
$$\text{If } H_O \text{ is } \sigma^2 \geq 5 \qquad \text{then } H_I \text{ is } \sigma^2 < 5$$

Hypothesis for standard deviations could be stated as:

$$\text{If } H_O \text{ is } \sigma = 3 \qquad \text{then } H_I \text{ is } \sigma \neq 3$$
$$\text{If } H_O \text{ is } \sigma \leq 16 \qquad \text{then } H_I \text{ is } \sigma > 16$$
$$\text{If } H_O \text{ is } \sigma \geq 25 \qquad \text{then } H_I \text{ is } \sigma < 25$$

The second step in hypothesis testing is to identify the test criteria. The test criteria include the level of significance, the test statistic, the critical region, and the critical value. The level of significance, or alpha, is usually given in the problem. If alpha is not stated, it must be determined based on the seriousness of a type I error-that is, rejecting a true hypothesis. The test statistic is determined by deciding which test to conduct. Chi-square is used for testing a variance or standard deviation. The critical region is determined by considering the alternative hypothesis to decide if the test is one-tailed to the left, two-tailed, or one-tailed to the right. Remember to use the following symbols found in the alternative hypothesis to determine the placement of the critical region.

| Sign in $H_1$ | Test |
|:---:|:---:|
| < | One-tailed left |
| ≠ | Two-tailed ($\alpha/2$) |
| > | One-tailed right |

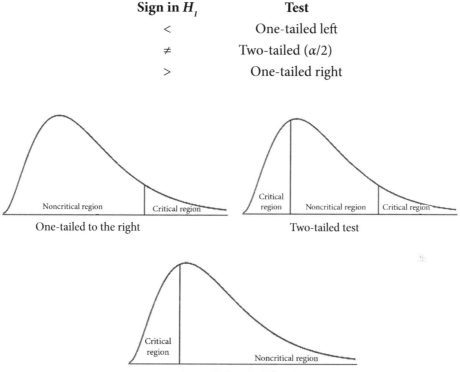

One-tailed to the right

Two-tailed test

One-tailed to the left

The Chi-square distribution is dependent on sample size. As does $t$, $x^2$ has a different distribution for every sample size. Each distribution represents the sample size through the concept of the degrees of freedom. The degrees of freedom for $x^2$ are found as $n$ - 1.

### Degrees of Freedom for $x^2$
$$df = n - 1$$

The $x^2$ critical values for hypothesis testing and confidence intervals are found in Table A.5 of Appendix A. Critical values for $x^2$ require degrees of freedom and alpha. Notice there are alphas reported in Table A.5 with values such as .99 and .95. Since $x^2$ is not symmetric, critical values for the left tail are not negative. Left-tailed $x^2$ values are reported under alphas adjusted for the left side of the distribution curve. Subtracting alpha from 1.0 makes the adjustment when the critical region is in the left tail. That is, if alpha is .05, a left-tail value is reported in Table A.5 under the column alpha .95 (1 - .05 = .95). An alpha of .025 is reported as a left-tail value under alpha = .975 (1 - .025 = .975). For a two-tailed test at alpha = .05, .05 is divided by 2, with critical values found under the alphas .025 for the right tail and .975 for the left (.05/2 = .025; 1 - .025 = .975).

The $\chi^2$ notation uses the subscripts ($df$, $\alpha$) for one-tailed tests and ($df$, $\alpha/2$) for two-tailed tests. To read Table A.5, move down the left column to the appropriate number of degrees of freedom and across to the appropriate alpha. The value found in the intersection of the number of degrees of freedom and alpha is the critical value.

---

**EXAMPLE 12.1**

**Experiment:** Find the critical values for the following notations:

a. $\chi^2$ (12, .05)        d. $\chi^2$ (40, .99)

b. $\chi^2$ (21, .025)        e. $\chi^2$ (6, .95)

c. $\chi^2$ (8, .005)        f. $\chi^2$ (16, .90)

**Answer:**

a. 21.026        d. 22.164

b. 35.479        e. 1.635

c. 21.955        f. 9.312

**Solution:** Table A.5 in the appendix gives $\chi^2$ critical values using degrees of freedom and levels of significance. The $\chi^2$ notations in *a, b,* and *c* are for right-tailed tests, because no alteration of the notation occurred. Right-tailed values require tracing *down* to the appropriate number of degrees of freedom and then *across* to the appropriate alpha level. The values reported in the table are the critical values. Notations *d, e,* and *f* are values for the left side of the curve, because all three have large alpha values. These alpha values were obtained by subtracting a typical alpha, such as .01, .05, or .10, from 1.0. Left-tailed critical values are found the same way as right-tailed values-by tracing *down* to the appropriate number of degrees of freedom and then *across* to the appropriate alpha.

---

**EXAMPLE 12.2**

**Experiment:** Find the $\chi^2$ critical values for the following two-tailed tests:

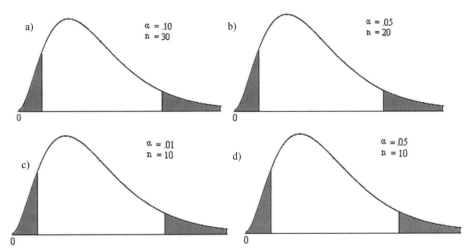

**Answer:**

a. $\chi^2_{(29, .95)} = 17.708$ and $\chi^2_{(29, .05)} = 42.557$

b. $\chi^2_{(19, .975)} = 8.907$ and $\chi^2_{(19, .025)} = 32.852$

c. $\chi^2_{(9, .995)}$ and $\chi^2_{(9, .005)} = 1.735$ and $23.589$

d. $\chi^2_{(9, .975)}$ and $\chi^2_{(9, .025)} = 2.700$ and $19.023$

**Solution:** Chi-square critical values are found in Table A.5. Chi-square distributions differ for every sample size. Therefore, degrees of freedom ($n$ - 1) are needed in addition to the alpha level. The four curves presented are all two tailed. As with all two-tailed distributions, alpha must be divided by 2 before reading from the tables in the appendix. Right two-tailed values are indicated $df$ and $\alpha/2$. Read down to the appropriate number of degrees of freedom and over to the divided alpha value. Left two-tailed values require $df$ and 1 - $\alpha/2$. Because the Chi-square distribution is not symmetric, left-tail values require a separate set of alpha columns representing the left side of the curve.

Given that $n = 30$ and $\alpha = 0.10$, it can be concluded that $df = 30-1 = 29$, $\alpha/2 = 0.05$, and $1-\alpha/2 = 0.95$. So the critical values would be found from that table by reading the degrees of freedom and the area to the right of the value. $\chi^2_{(29, .95)} = 17.708$ and $\chi^2_{(29, .05)} = 42.557$

Given that $n = 20$ and $\alpha = 0.05$, it can be concluded that $df = 20-1 = 19$, $\alpha/2 = 0.025$, and $1-\alpha/2 = 0.975$. So the critical values would be found from that table by reading the degrees of freedom and the area to the right of the value. $\chi^2_{(19, .975)} = 8.907$ and $\chi^2_{(19, .005)} = 32.852$

Given that $n = 10$ and $\alpha = 0.01$, it can be concluded that $df = 10\text{-}1 = 9$, $\alpha/2 = 0.005$, and $1\text{-}\alpha/2 = 0.995$. So the critical values would be found from that table by reading the degrees of freedom and the area to the right of the value.

$\chi^2_{(9,\,.995)} = 1.735$ and $\chi^2_{(29,\,.005)} = 23.589$

Given that $n = 10$ and $\alpha = 0.05$, it can be concluded that $df = 10\text{-}1 = 9$, $\alpha/2 = 0.025$, and $1\text{-}\alpha/2 = 0.975$. So the critical values would be found from that table by reading the degrees of freedom and the area to the right of the value.

$\chi^2_{(9,\,.95)} = 2.700$ and $\chi^2_{(9,\,.05)} = 19.023$

The third step in hypothesis testing using the classical approach is the calculation of the test statistic. In the calculation of the $\chi^2$ statistic, the sample variance is multiplied by $n - 1$ and then divided by the population variance. Pay attention to the problem that if a variance or a standard deviation is given. If a variance is given, place the value in the formula. If a standard deviation is given, the value must be squared. The standard deviation squared equals the variance.

**Calculation for the Test Statistic χ2**

$$\chi^2 = \frac{(n-1)s^2}{\sigma^2}$$

where
  $n$ is the sample size.
  $s^2$ is the sample variance.
  $\sigma^2$ is the population variance.

**EXAMPLE 12.3**

**Experiment:** Calculate the $\chi^2$ test statistic for a sample of 20 if the sample variance is 5 and the population variance is 8.

**Answer:** $\chi^2 = 11.875$

**Solution:** Identify the information given in the experiment. Chi-square requires $n$, $s^2$, and $\sigma^2$. Sample size, $n$, is 20. The sample variance, $s^2$, is 5, and the population variance, $\sigma^2$, is 8. Place these values in the formula and calculate $\chi^2$.

$$\chi^2 = \frac{(n-1)s^2}{\sigma^2} = \frac{(20-1)5}{8} = \frac{(19)5}{8} = \frac{95}{8} = 11.875$$

**EXAMPLE 12.4**

**Experiment:** Calculate the $\chi^2$ test statistic for a sample of 30 if the sample standard deviation is 9 and the population standard deviation is 11.

**Answer:** $\chi^2 = 19.413$

**Solution:** Determine the information given in the experiment. Chi-square requires $n$, $s^2$, and $\sigma^2$. Sample size, $n$, is 30. The sample variance is not given, but it can be calculated by squaring the sample standard deviation. Therefore, the sample standard deviation, 9, and the population standard deviation, 11, must be placed in the formula with the square notation.

$$\chi^2 = \frac{(n-1)s^2}{\sigma^2} = \frac{(30-1)9^2}{11^2} = \frac{(29)81}{121} = \frac{2349}{121} = 19.413$$

The fourth step in hypothesis testing using the classical approach is to place the calculated value on the curve and compare it to the critical value. Step 5 involves deciding whether to reject or not to reject the null hypothesis. Reject the null hypothesis when the calculated value falls in the critical region. Fail to reject the null hypothesis when the calculated value falls in the non-critical region.

The fifth step in hypothesis testing is to apply the decision to the problem. Narratively interpret the information provided in the original experiment as the decision is applied. That is, restate the null hypothesis narratively with explanation as to failing to reject or rejecting it.

**EXAMPLE 12.5**

**Experiment:** Test the null hypothesis $\sigma = 5$ using a sample of 25 with a sample standard deviation 3; $\alpha = .10$. Use the classical approach.

**Answer:** Reject the null hypothesis. There is sufficient evidence to reject the null hypothesis that the standard deviation is equal to 5.

**Solution:** The null hypothesis is already stated: $\sigma = 5$. The alternative hypothesis must include the contrasting mathematical sign; therefore, the alternative hypothesis is $\sigma \neq 5$. State the hypotheses.

$$H_o: \sigma = 5$$
$$H_1: \sigma \neq 5$$

The test criteria begin with identifying the level of significance, alpha. Alpha is given as .10. The test statistic is $\chi^2$. The $z$ and $t$ distributions cannot be used when testing a standard deviation or a variance. Chi-square represents the skewed distribution of variances and standard deviations. The critical region is two-tailed. A two-tailed test occurs when the alternative hypothesis includes the $\neq$ sign. All two-tailed tests require dividing alpha by 2, placing half of the critical region on each side of the distribution. Because $\alpha = .10$, alpha divided by 2 is .05. The .05 is the area for the right tail. Since $\chi^2$ is not symmetric, subtracting .05 from 1 determines the area for the left tail. The critical area for the left tail is 1 - .05, or .95. The degrees of freedom are $n$ - 1, or 24. The $\chi^2$ notations are:

$$\chi^2_{(24,\,.05)} \text{ and } \chi^2_{(24,\,.95)}$$

Use Table A.5 to find critical values for $\chi^2$. For the right tail, read down to 24 degrees of freedom and across to alpha = .05. The $\chi^2_{(24,\,.05)} = 36.415$ value found in the intersection is the critical value for the right tail. The left-tail value is found by reading down to 24 degrees of freedom and across to alpha = .95. The critical value for the left tail is $\chi^2_{(24,\,.95)} = 13.848$.

| Degrees of Freedom | | Alpha .95 | | .05 |
|---|---|---|---|---|
| ….. | | | | |
| ….. | | | | |
| 24 | →→ | 13.848 | →→ | 36.415 |

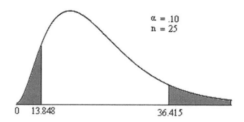

Calculate the test statistic. The calculated $\chi^2$ value requires the following information: $n = 25$, $\sigma = 5$, and $s = 3$. Notice that 5 and 3 are values representing standard deviations and not variances. The $\chi^2$ formula requires the variance, which is obtained by squaring the standard deviation.

$$\chi^2 = \frac{(n-1)s^2}{\sigma^2} = \frac{(25-1)3^2}{5^2} = 8.640$$

Place the calculated value 8.640 on the distribution curve. Comparing 8.640 to the critical values already placed on the curve determine its placement.

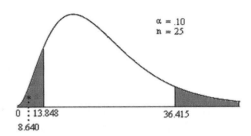

0 : 13.848          36.415
8.640

The next step is to decide to reject or not to reject the null hypothesis. If the calculated value falls in the critical region, as it does here, the decision is to reject the null hypothesis.

$$\text{Reject } H_o$$

The final step is to interpret the decision. Rejecting the null hypothesis suggests that there is sufficient proof based on this sample at this level of significance that the null hypothesis is incorrect. Because the original experiment did not explain what the test is, the interpretation is limited to the following: There is sufficient evidence at the .10 level of significance to reject the null hypothesis that the standard deviation is equal to 5.

## EXAMPLE 12.6

**Experiment:** Test the claim that the variance in body temperature is not greater than 1.2° (degree squared) using a sample of 51 patients producing a sample variance of 1.9 degrees squared; use $\alpha = .10$.

**Answer:** Reject the null hypothesis. There is sufficient evidence at the .10 level of significance to reject the null hypothesis that the variance in body temperature is not greater than 1.2° (degree squared).

**Solution:** State the hypotheses. The null hypothesis is already derived from the statement that the variance in body temperature is no greater than 1.2° (degree squared). The key words are "not greater than". The symbol for not greater than is ≤, and it must be placed in the null hypothesis. The symbol for the alternative hypothesis is the contrasting mathematical sign; therefore, the alternative hypothesis involves >. The parameter is $\sigma^2$, the population variance.

$$H_o: \sigma^2 \leq 1.2$$
$$H_1: \sigma^2 > 1.2$$

The test criteria begin with identifying the level of significance, alpha. Alpha is given as .10. The test statistic is $\chi^2$. Chi-square represents the skewed distribution of variances and standard deviations. The critical region is one-tailed to the right as guided by the > sign in the alternative hypothesis. The degrees of freedom for Chi-square are $n$ - 1, or 50. At alpha = .10 and 50 degrees of freedom, the $\chi^2$ notation is

$$\chi^2_{(50, .10)}$$

Use Table A.5 to find critical values for $\chi^2$. Move down to 50 degrees of freedom and over to alpha = .10. The $\chi^2_{(50, .10)}$ = 63.167 value found in the intersection is the critical value.

| Degrees of Freedom | | | | Alpha .10 |
|---|---|---|---|---|
| ….. | | | | |
| ….. | | | | |
| 50 | $\rightarrow\rightarrow$ | $\rightarrow\rightarrow$ | $\rightarrow\rightarrow$ | 63.167 |

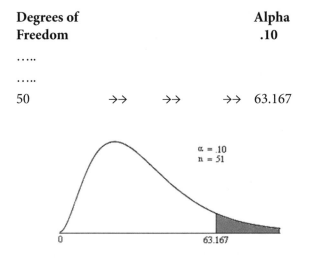

Calculate the test statistic. The calculated $\chi^2$ value requires the following information: $n = 51$, $\sigma^2 = 1.2$, and $s^2 = 1.9$. Notice that 1.2 and 1.9 are values representing variances and not standard deviations. The $\chi^2$ formula requires the variance; there is no need to square the variances again.

$$\chi^2 = \frac{(n-1)s^2}{\sigma^2} = \frac{(51-1)1.9}{1.2} = 79.167$$

Place the calculated value, 79.167, on the distribution curve. Its placement is determined by comparing 79.167 to the critical value already placed on the curve.

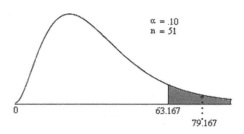

The next step is to make a decision. If the calculated value falls in the critical region, as it does here, the decision is to reject the null hypothesis.

Reject $H_O$

The final step is to interpret the decision. Rejecting the null hypothesis suggests that there is sufficient proof based on this sample at this level of significance that the null hypothesis is incorrect. There is sufficient evidence at the .10 level of significance to reject the null hypothesis that the variance in body temperature is no more than 1.2° (degree squared).

**A LEARNING AID**
**CLASSICAL TESTING FOR CHI-SQUARE**
It was estimated that the variance for final exam scores of all students taking statistics in one school was 81. It was hoped that the adoption of a new textbook would reduce this number. After a semester of using the new book, a random sample of 31 students' final exam scores were found to have a sample variance of 64. Is there strong evidence to believe that the students using the new textbook will perform more consistently than before? That is, is there enough evidence to support the claim that the variance of students' final exam scores using the new text book is smaller the 81? Use alpha 0.10.

**Step 1**
State the hypotheses. The parameter in question is the population variance, $\sigma^2$. The direction of the challenge is smaller, which means less than. A less than sign (<) can go only in the alternative hypothesis. If the alternative is less than, then the null hypothesis is greater than or equal to. The hypotheses are written:

$$H_o: \sigma^2 \geq 81 \quad \text{and} \quad H_1: \sigma^2 < 81$$

**Step 2**

Identify the test criteria. The test criteria begin with identifying the level of significance, alpha. Alpha is noted as .10. The test statistic is Chi-square. Chi-square tests for one variance or standard deviation. If a null hypothesis includes $\sigma^2$ or $\sigma$, the test statistic is Chi-square. The critical region is to the left, because the alternative hypothesis contains a less than sign. The critical value is determined by the degrees of freedom and alpha. The degrees of freedom are $n - 1 = 31-1 = 30$. Since this is a left-tailed test, $\alpha = 0.1$ represents the area under the curve to the left of the critical value. In order to find the critical value from the table, an area to the right of the critical value is needed. Since the entire area under the curve is 1, the area to the right of the critical value must be $1-0.1 = 0.9$. Reading from Table A.5 trace down to 30 *df* and *across* to the alpha value of .90. The critical value is $\chi^2_{(30, .90)} = 20.599$.

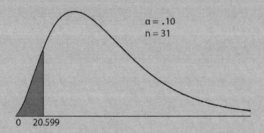

**Step 3**

Calculate the test statistic. The calculation requires $\sigma^2 = 81$, $s^2 = 64$, and $n = 31$.

$$\chi^2 = \frac{(n-1)s^2}{\sigma^2} = \frac{(31-1)64}{81} = 23.704$$

**Step 4**

Place the calculated value on the distribution. Note that the calculated value, 23.704, falls slightly to the right of the critical value, 20.599.

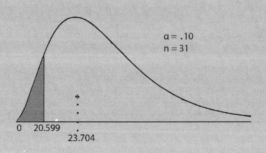

**Step 5**
Make a decision. The calculated value does not fall in the critical region. The decision is to fail to reject the null.

Fail to Reject $H_o$

**Step 6**
Interpret the results. A decision that fails to reject the null hypothesis suggests that this sample does not provide sufficient evidence to challenge the null successfully. Applying the decision directly to the experiment, the interpretation is as follows: There is insufficient evidence, at the .10 level of significance, to reject the null hypothesis. There is not enough evidence to claim that students using new textbook could perform more consistently than before.

---

# SECTION 2

## Hypothesis Test: *P*-Value for a Variance Using Chi-Square

The *P*-value approach to hypothesis testing takes the classical approach one step further by transforming the calculated value into a probability and comparing the probability to an alpha level. *P*-values, whether for $\chi^2$, $z$, $t$, or other test statistics, are probabilities presenting the level of significance at which the test statistic becomes significant provided the null hypothesis is true. Because *P*-values and alphas are probabilities, one compared to the other leads to decisions about the null hypothesis.

Population $\rightarrow \alpha \rightarrow$ Probability

$\rightarrow \rightarrow$ compare *probabilities* to make a decision

Sample $\rightarrow \chi^2$-*score* $\rightarrow$ Probability

Computerized statistical programs typically report calculated $\chi^2$ values with an associated *P*-value. The calculated value may be used to conduct a classical hypothesis test, whereas the *P*-value may be used to conduct a *P*-value hypothesis test. When a *P*-value is offered by a computerized program or by another source, a comparison of the *P*-value with the alpha level is necessary. If the *P*-value is less than or equal to $\alpha$, then the null hypothesis is rejected. The null hypothesis fails to be rejected if the *P*-value is greater than $\alpha$.

A complete hypothesis test using the *P*-value approach for $\chi^2$ is like the *P*-value approach for $t$. The six steps identified for $t$ in Chapter 11 are repeated here for $\chi^2$.

Unfortunately the TI-83/84 calculator does not calculate this particular Chi-square. Therefore, an adjusted approach is needed.

---

**Steps in Hypothesis Testing Using the *P*-Value Approach**
The TI 83/83 calculator does not have this version of the Chi-square statistic.

1. State $H_o$ and $H_1$.
2. Identify the test criteria:
    a. Level of significance, $\alpha$
    b. Test statistic ($z$, $t$, $\chi^2$, $F$)
3. Calculate the test statistic.
4. Transform the test statistic to the *P-value*:
    a. One-tailed test
    b. Two-tailed test (multiply *P* by 2)
5. Make a decision:
    a. If $P > \alpha$, Fail to reject $H_o$
    b. If $P \leq \alpha$, Reject $H_o$
6. Interpret the results.

---

The first step in *P*-value testing is to identify the null and alternative hypotheses. Step 2 is to determine two aspects of the test criteria, the level of significance and the test statistic. The level of significance is usually given as $\alpha$ in the problem or must be determined by considering the acceptance of a *type I* error—that is, rejecting a true hypothesis. The test statistic must be determined by reviewing the parameter in the hypotheses. The parameters used in testing so far are the population mean $\mu$, the population variance $\sigma^2$, and the population standard deviation $\sigma$. When the mean is tested, the test statistic is $z$ or $t$. When the population variance or the population standard deviation is tested, the test statistic is $\chi^2$. Step 3 is to calculate the test statistic. The calculation for $\chi^2$ is:

$$\chi^2 = \frac{(n-1)s^2}{\sigma^2}$$

Step 4 involves finding the probability associated with the calculated test statistic. The transformation of $\chi^2$ is exactly like $t$. The alpha levels reported in Table A.5 are used as estimates of *P*-values. The *P*-value for $\chi^2$ is determined by noting the calculated value from step 3 with the degrees of freedom from step 2. Using Table A.5, move *down* to the appropriate degrees of freedom. Read across all the values of that row, finding the value closest to the calculated value. The value in the table closest to the calculated value serves as a guide to the probability used as the *P*-value. The *P*-value is the alpha level associated with the column in which the value closest to the calculated value is found. For example, if the value calculated in step 3 equals 26.272 for a sample of 19 with 18 (19 - 1 = 18) degrees of freedom, then the *P*-value, if it is a right-tailed test, is .10. The *P*-value .10 is found by moving *down* to 18 degrees of freedom, *across* to the value 25.989, which is closest to the calculated value 26.272, and up to the alpha value .10 associated with the column in which 25.989 is found.

| Degrees of Freedom | | Alpha | |
|---|---|---|---|
| | | .10 | .05 |
| 1 | | ↑ | |
| ….. | | ↑ | |
| ….. | | ↑ | |
| 18 | →→ | 25.989 | |

$$P\text{-Value}_{(26.272,\ \text{at df }18)} = .10$$

Because only a few alpha levels are reported in Table A.5, $\chi^2$ $P$-value estimates tend to fall between two reported alphas. If the calculated value falls between two critical values, then use both alpha values to denote the range of values within which the $P$-value lies. For example, if a calculated $\chi^2$ value in step 3 equals 31.023 for a sample of 23, which has 22 degrees of freedom, the $\chi^2$ $P$-value ranges from .05 to .10. Both values become the $P$-values and are compared to the original alpha in making a decision about the hypothesis. The $P$-value for a $\chi^2$ calculated value of 31.023 is found by moving down the $\chi^2$ table to 22 degrees of freedom, over to the closest value, and up to the alpha levels. The values closest to 31.023 at 22 $df$ are 33.924 and 30.813. Tracing up the columns, 33.924 is associated with an alpha of .05, and 30.813 is associated with .10. The $P$-value falls between .05 and .10.

| Degrees of Freedom | | Alpha | |
|---|---|---|---|
| | .10 ←←← | →→→ .05 | |
| 1 | | | |
| ….. | | | |
| ….. | | | |
| 22 | 30.813 ←←← | →→→ 33.924 | |

$$0.05 < P\text{-Value}_{(31.023,\ \text{at df }22)} < 0.1$$

Remember that a two-tailed test requires the $P$-value to be multiplied by 2 before comparing it to alpha. It is important to be aware of the left-tailed alpha values reported in Table A.5. Remember that left-tailed alphas such as .90 and .95 are related to alphas of .10 and .05, respectively. Left-tailed alphas are found by subtracting the given alpha from 1.0. Reversing this process, subtracting left-tailed alpha from 1.0 results in the original right-tailed alpha. Therefore, if a one-tailed alpha representing the $P$-value is found to be .995, then the $P$-value is 1 - .995, or .005. If a two-tailed alpha representing the $P$-value is .995, then the $P$-value is 2 (1 - .995), or 2(.005) = .01.

The next step in *P*-value testing requires comparing the *P*-value to alpha and making a decision about the hypothesis. The rule for the decision using *P*-values remains constant for all test statistics, whether $\chi^2$, *z*, or *t*. If the *P*-value is less than or equal to alpha, then the null hypothesis is rejected. If the *P*-value is greater than alpha, then the null hypothesis fails to be rejected.

---

### Decisions Using *P*-Values
$P \le \alpha$  Reject $H_o$
$P > \alpha$  Fail to reject $H_o$

---

The final step is interpreting the decision. It is important to remember that rejecting the null hypothesis does not suggest that the sample information is true or that the new parameter is represented by the sample statistic. Likewise, failing to reject the null hypothesis suggests only that the sample does not provide sufficient evidence to challenge the null hypothesis.

---

### EXAMPLE 12.8

**Experiment:** Test the null hypothesis $\sigma = 5$ using the *P*-value approach. Use a sample of 25 with a sample standard deviation 3. Let $\alpha = .10$.

**Answer:** Reject the null hypothesis. There is sufficient evidence at the .10 level of significance to reject the null hypothesis that the standard deviation equals 5.

**Solution:** There are six steps in hypothesis testing using the *P*-value approach: State the hypothesis, identify the test criteria, calculate the test statistic, calculate the *P*-value, make a decision, and interpret the results. The experiment states the null hypothesis as $\sigma = 5$. The alternative hypothesis must challenge the null hypothesis by containing the contrasting mathematical symbol. If the null hypothesis is equal to, then the alternative hypothesis is not equal to. The parameter is sigma, $\sigma$, representing the population standard deviation. State the hypotheses:

$$H_o: \sigma = 5 \qquad H_i: \sigma \ne 5$$

The test criteria for *P*-value testing require identification of the test statistic and level of confidence. The test statistic for standard deviation or variance is Chi-square. The level of significance is given as .10.

The third step in using the *P*-value approach is to calculate the test statistic. The calculation for $\chi^2$ requires the following information derived from the experiment: $\sigma = 5$, $s = 3$, and $n = 25$. Notice the formula actually requires the population variance and sample variance. The experiment reports standard deviations. Standard deviations become variances by squaring them. Calculate the $\chi^2$ value.

$$\chi^2 = \frac{(n-1)s^2}{\sigma^2} = \frac{(25-1)3^2}{5^2} = 8.640$$

Transform the calculated $\chi^2$ value into a probability using Table A.5. The *P*-value for the $\chi^2$ statistic is determined by moving *down* the degrees of freedom column, *across* to the value closest to the calculated value, and up to the alpha associated with that column. The degrees of freedom are 25 - 1, or 24. The calculated value is 8.64. Trace *down* to *df* 24. Reading *across* this row only, notice the closest value to 8.64 is 9.886. Trace up the column where 9.886 is located and find the alpha .995. This means that the area to the right of the critical value is at least .995. This makes the left tail area to be smaller than 1-.995 = .005. Since this is a two-tailed test, the *P*-value is two times of the tailed value. It could be concluded that *P*-value<0.01

| **Degrees of Freedom** | | | | **Alpha .995** |
|---|---|---|---|---|
| ….. | | | | ↑ |
| ….. | | | | ↑ |
| 24 | →→ | →→ | →→ | 9.886 |

$$1 - .995 = .005 \qquad .005 \bullet 2 = .01$$
$$P_{(8.640 \ at \ df \ 24)} = < .01$$

Compare the *P*-value to the original alpha given in the experiment. If $P \leq \alpha$, then reject the null hypothesis. If $P > \alpha$, then fail to reject the null hypothesis.

$$P_{(.01)} \leq \alpha_{(.10)} \qquad \text{Reject } H_o$$

The final step in *P*-value testing is interpreting the results. Rejecting the null hypothesis suggests that there is sufficient evidence provided by this sample of 25 at the .10 level of significance that the standard deviation is not equal to 5.

## EXAMPLE 12.9

**Experiment:** A computer software program reports a calculated $\chi^2$ value 27.204 with a P-value .10. What decision can be made for a one-tailed to the right hypothesis test at a $\alpha = .05$?

**Answer:** Fail to reject $H_o$.

**Solution:** Computer software programs often report P-values representing the level of significance at which the test statistic becomes significant. When a P-value is given, proceed directly to step 5 in hypothesis testing. The determination of the calculated value and its transformation into a probability are already represented in the P-value. Simply compare the P-value to alpha and make a decision. If the P-value is less than or equal to alpha, then reject the null hypothesis. If P is greater than alpha, fail to reject the null hypothesis. In this experiment, P at .10 is greater than alpha at .05. Fail to reject the null hypothesis.

$$P_{(.10)} > \alpha_{(.05)} \qquad \text{Fail to Reject } H_o$$

## A LEARNING AID
## CHI-SQUARE TESTING USING *P*-VALUES

It is reported that the standard deviation of life expectancy at birth for all countries in the world is 5.32 years. A researcher believes that this number is too low. He collected information from a sample of 31 countries producing) a standard deviation of 6.31. Does the sample provide sufficient evidence to support the researcher's suspicion that the standard deviation of life expectancy for all countries in the world is greater than 5.32 years ($\alpha = .05$)?

### Step 1

Identify the null and alternative hypotheses. The hypothesis statement is contained in the last sentence, where a challenge is asserted that the standard deviation ($\sigma$) is greater than 5.32 years. Because the null hypothesis must always contain an equal sign, the greater than (>) symbol must be placed in the alternative hypothesis. The null hypothesis will include the equal sign as well as the less than sign; therefore, the hypotheses are:

$$H_o: \sigma \le 5.32 \qquad H_i: \sigma > 5.32$$

**Step 2**
Identify the level of significance and the test statistic. The level of significance is reported as alpha = .05. Chi-square must be the test statistic since the standard deviation is in question. The $z$ and $t$ distributions are reserved for testing means, whereas $\chi^2$ tests for a variance or standard deviation.

**Step 3**
Calculate the test statistic. Chi-square requires the following information derived from the problem: $n = 31$, $s = 6.31$, and $\sigma = 5.32$. Notice the values for $\sigma$ and $s$ are standard deviations and they must be squared in the calculation. Calculate $\chi^2$:

$$\chi^2 = \frac{(n-1)s^2}{\sigma^2} = \frac{(31-1)6.31^2}{5.32^2} = \frac{(30)39.816}{28.302} = \frac{1194.483}{28.302} = 42.204$$

**Step 4**
Transform the calculated value into a probability using Table A.5. The $P$-value is the alpha associated with the nearest critical value that has the same degrees of freedom as the calculated value (42.204). The degrees of freedom for $\chi^2$ are $n$ - 1, or 30. Trace along the row for 30 $df$ and find the value nearest to 42.204. The value 42.204 falls between two values, 40.256 and 43.773. The alphas associated with both critical values are reported as the $P$-value. In other words, the $P$-value for 42.204 at 30 $df$ is greater than .05 but less than .10.

| Degrees of Freedom | Alpha | |
|---|---|---|
| | .10 ←←← | →→→ .05 |
| 1 | | |
| ..... | | |
| ..... | | |
| 30 | 40.256 ←←← | →→→ 43.773 |

$$0.05 < P\text{-Value}_{(42.204,\text{ at df } 30)} < 0.1$$

**Step 5**
Compare the $P$-value to the original alpha and make a decision. If the $P$-value is greater than alpha, fail to reject the null hypothesis. If the $P$-value is less than or equal to alpha, then reject the null hypothesis. The $P$-value for the calculated value 42.204 is between .05 and .10, whereas the alpha is .05. Although it appears the $P$-value is equal to alpha since both contain the value .05, the $P$-value is actually understood to be greater than .05 but less than .10.

Therefore, the *P*-value is greater than .05, and because alpha is .05, the *P*-value is greater than alpha. The decision is to fail to reject the null hypothesis.

$$(.05 < P < .10) > \alpha_{(.05)} \quad \text{Fail to Reject } H_o$$

**Step 6**
Interpret the results. The decision to fail to reject the null hypothesis suggests that the sample does not successfully challenge the null. The sample information collected by the researcher did not provide sufficient evidence to support his claim that the standard deviation of life expectancy at birth for all countries in the world is greater than 5.32 years.

# SECTION 3

## Confidence Interval for a Population Variance Using Chi-Square

A confidence interval for estimating a population variance or standard deviation is calculated using the Chi-square test statistic. Recall that a population parameter can be estimated from sample data using a confidence interval. The confidence interval using $\chi^2$ distribution establishes a range of values around a sample variance or standard deviation. Recall the definition of a confidence interval.

**Confidence Interval** Interval estimates of a population parameter from sample statistics for a given specified level of confidence.

A confidence interval establishes a range of values around the sample information where the population parameter will fall for a given particular degree of confidence. The sample statistic used as the point of departure to determine the range of values for the interval is known as the point estimate. The point estimate for calculated confidence intervals using Chi-square is the sample variance or sample standard deviation.

The degree of confidence, or level of confidence, establishes the probability that the population parameter will fall inside the range of values set by the point estimate. Recall that Chapter 10 presents the concept of the level of confidence as the opposite of alpha. Alpha is the probability of committing an error, and the level of confidence is the probability of being correct. The level of confidence is usually given as a percentage. If a researcher wishes to be 90% certain that the population parameter falls within a range around the point estimate, the level of confidence is .90 and alpha is .10. Alpha and the level of confidence must have a sum of 1.0. Confidence intervals for $\chi^2$ are found the same way as confidence intervals for *t*. Chi-square requires transforming the level of confidence directly into a $\chi^2$ critical value by using the degrees of freedom and alpha divided by 2. *Remember that all confidence intervals are two-tailed, requiring that alpha be divided by 2.* Chi-square critical values are dependent on the sample size, which determines degrees of freedom, or *n* - 1. Identify the degrees of freedom and the alpha level, $\alpha/2$. Use Table A.5. Go *down* to the appropriate degrees of freedom and *across* to the value under the correct alpha level. The critical values to construct a confidence interval for the variance or the standard deviation will be $\chi^2_{(df,\,\alpha/2)}$ and $\chi^2_{(df,\,1-\alpha/2)}$. Retain this value for the calculation of the confidence interval.

---

### EXAMPLE 12.10

**Experiment:** Find the critical values associated with a 95% confidence interval to construct a confidence interval for the population variance where $n = 41$.

**Answer:** $\chi^2_{(40,\,.025)} = 59.342$ and $\chi^2_{(40,\,.975)} = 24.433$

**Solution:** Critical values for $\chi^2$ are found in Table A.5. Alpha and degrees of freedom are required for $\chi^2$ critical values. If a 95% (.95) confidence level is required, alpha is 5%, or .05. All confidence intervals are two-tailed. Divide alpha by 2 so that half of the probability of an error is on both sides of the point estimate. Alpha divided by two is .05/2, or .025. The degrees of freedom are *n* - 1, or 41 - 1 = 40. Using Table A.5, go *down* the *df* 40 and *across* to the $\alpha/2$ value, .025. The value $\chi^2_{(40,\,.025)} = 59.342$ is found in the intersection and is the critical value to be placed in the calculation of the confidence interval. The value of $\chi^2_{(40,\,.975)} = 24.433$ can be found in a similar fashion.

The calculation of the confidence interval for a population variance or population standard deviation is Chi-square.

---

### The Chi-Square Confidence Interval Formula for Estimating a Population Variance

$$E_\sigma^2 = \frac{(n-1)s^2}{\chi^2_{(df,\,\alpha/2)}} < \sigma^2 < \frac{(n-1)s^2}{\chi^2_{(df,\,1-\alpha/2)}}$$

where
    *n* is the sample size
    $s^2$ is the sample variance, known as the point estimate
    $\chi 2(df,\,\alpha/2)$ is the critical right-tailed value found in Table A.5
    $\chi 2(df,\,1-\alpha/2)$ is the critical left-tailed found in Table A.5

An adjustment is necessary for calculating a confidence interval estimating a standard deviation. The preceding formula will result in estimating a variance. Recall from earlier chapters that the square root of the variance is the standard deviation. When a standard deviation is estimated, take the square root of the variance formula just presented.

To find the confidence interval for the standard deviation $\sigma$, the formula becomes

$$E_\sigma = \sqrt{\frac{(n-1)s^2}{\chi^2_{(df,\alpha/2)}}} < \sigma < \sqrt{\frac{(n-1)s^2}{\chi^2_{(df,1-\alpha/2)}}}$$

Following are the steps to calculate the confidence interval:

### Steps in Calculating a Confidence Interval
1. Identify the level of confidence (90%, 95%, 99%).
2. Identify the test statistic ($z$, $t$, $\chi^2$, or $F$).
3. Determine the critical value with $\alpha/2$.
4. Calculate the interval.
5. State the interval.

Step 1 identifies the problem as a confidence interval and the level of confidence. Key words to keep in mind are "interval", "confidence", and "estimate". Also, the level of confidence is usually given within the statement, such as "estimate with 90% confidence" or "calculate a 90% interval."

Step 2 is to identify the test statistic. Thus far, $z$, $t$, and $\chi^2$ have been described. Use $z$ for normally distributed means with large samples and where the standard deviation of the population is known. Use $t$ for normally distributed means with small samples ($n \leq 30$) or when the population standard deviation is unknown. Use $\chi^2$ for one population variance or standard deviation.

Step 3 determines the critical values. The $\chi^2$ statistic requires the degrees of freedom and an alpha level. The degrees of freedom are equal to $n - 1$. Alpha is determined by subtracting the level of confidence from 1. If a 90% level of confidence is desired, then alpha is $1 - .9$, or .10. *All alphas must be divided by 2 when calculating a confidence interval.* Use Table A.5. For the right-tailed critical value, go *down* to the degrees of freedom and *across* to the alpha column. The value in the intersections is the critical value. The left-tailed critical value requires subtracting the divided alpha from 1.0. Left-tailed $\chi^2$ values are reported in separate columns in Table A.5. The values are found the same way as right-tailed values except by using the left-tailed alphas.

Subtract the divided alpha from 1, go *down* to the degrees of freedom and *across* to the alpha column. Retain these values for the calculation in step 4.

Step 4 calculates the confidence interval. The calculation must be performed twice to establish the lower limit of the range and the upper limit of the range. The formulas are essentially the same; in one formula the numerator is divided by a right-tailed critical value and in the other, the numerator is divided by a left-tailed critical value. The confidence interval for the variance is:

$$E_{\sigma}^2 = \frac{(n-1)s^2}{\chi^2_{(df,\alpha/2)}} < \sigma^2 < \frac{(n-1)s^2}{\chi^2_{(df,1-\alpha/2)}}$$

The confidence interval for the standard deviation is:

$$E_{\sigma} = \sqrt{\frac{(n-1)s^2}{\chi^2_{(df,\alpha/2)}}} < \sigma < \sqrt{\frac{(n-1)s^2}{\chi^2_{(df,1-\alpha/2)}}}$$

Step 5 restates the calculated values in the appropriate format for reporting confidence intervals. The notation for an interval places the parameter inside the lower and upper limit of the values calculated in step 4. The parameter of $\sigma^2$ is the population variance, whereas $\sigma$ is the population standard deviation.

$$E_{\sigma}^2 = \textbf{(Lower limit} < \sigma^2 < \textbf{Upper limit)}$$
$$E_{\sigma} = \textbf{(Lower limit} < \sigma < \textbf{Upper limit)}$$

---

**EXAMPLE 12.11**

**Experiment:** Find the 90% confidence interval for the variance in the heights (in inches) of elementary aged students using a sample of 51 with a variance of 25.

**Answer:** 90% confidence interval for variance: $(18.517 < \sigma^2 < 35.957)$

**Solution:** Begin by identifying the experiment as a confidence interval. The statement asks for a confidence interval. The level of confidence is given at 90%. A 90% level of confidence means that the population parameter should fall in the range of values 90% of the time with a 10% error, 5% on both sides of the point estimator.

Use the $\chi^2$ statistic for the problem, because it asks for an estimate of population variance. Two critical values must be determined for a Chi-square

---

confidence interval. Both critical values require the degrees of freedom and alpha. The degrees of freedoms is $n-1 = 50$. The confidence level given by the problem is .90, this leads to the conclusion that $\alpha = 1-.90 = 0.1$. Therefore $\alpha/2 = 0.05$ and $1-\alpha/2 = 0.95$. The two critical values needed will be $\chi^2_{(50, .05)} = 67.505$ and $\chi^2_{(50, .95)} = 34.764$.

Alpha must be determined by subtracting the level of confidence from 1: $1 - .9 = .10$. Alpha divided by 2 is $.10/2$, or $.05$. The right-tailed critical value is found in Table A.5. Go *down* to 50 degrees of freedom and *across* to an alpha ($\alpha/2$) of .05. The value 67.505 is found in the intersection.

$$\chi^2_{(50, .05)} = 67.505$$

The left-tailed critical value is found by subtracting the divided alpha from 1.0. Therefore, the left-tailed critical value for a divided alpha of .05 is .95 ($1.0 - .05 = .95$). Move *down* to 50 degrees of freedom and *across* to the column of values under an alpha of .95. The critical value 34.764 is found in the intersection.

$$\chi^2_{(50, .95)} = 34.764.$$

To calculate the interval, the following information is necessary: $s^2 = 25$, $n = 51$, $\chi^2_{(50, .05)} = 67.505$, and $\chi^2_{(50, .95)} = 34.764$.

$$\frac{(n-1)s^2}{\chi^2_{(df, \alpha/2)}} < \sigma^2 < \frac{(n-1)s^2}{\chi^2_{(df, 1-\alpha/2)}}$$

$$\frac{(51-1)25}{67.505} < \sigma^2 < \frac{(51-1)25}{34.764}$$

$$18.517 < \sigma^2 < 35.957$$

The lower limit of the interval is 18.517 and the upper limit is 35.957. This suggests that with 90% confidence, the variance of heights (in inches) for elementary students is between 18.517 and 35.957.

## A LEARNING AID
## CONFIDENCE INTERVALS FOR A VARIANCE

Calculate the 95% confidence interval for the variance in the Graduate Records Exam (GRE) taken by the students admitted to the graduate schools at University of Michigan in 2015 scores from a sample of 41 randomly selected students producing a variance of 223.96.

**Step 1**
Identify the level of confidence. The level of confidence is the probability the parameter will be contained in the interval. The experiment requires a 95% level of confidence suggesting that the parameter should fall in the range of values 95% of the time with a 5% error. To write 95% as a probability, drop the percent sign and move the decimal two places to the left (.95).

**Step 2**
Use Chi-square when estimating one population variance or standard deviation. Notice the experiment does not estimate a mean, which would require $z$ or $t$.

**Step 3**
Determine the critical value with $\alpha/2$. Because Chi-square is not symmetric, two critical values must be determined for the left and right tails. Critical values for $\chi^2$ require degrees of freedom and alpha. Degrees of freedom are $n - 1 = 41 - 1 = 40$. The confidence level given by the problem is .95, this leads to the conclusion that $\alpha = 1 - .95 = 0.05$. Therefore $\alpha/2 = 0.025$ and $1-\alpha/2 = 0.975$. The two critical values needed will be $\chi^2_{(40, .025)} = 59.342$ and $\chi^2_{(40, .975)} = 24.433$.

$$\chi^2_{(40, .025)} = 59.342 \qquad \chi^2_{(40, .975)} = 24.433$$

**Step 4**
Calculate the interval. The following information is necessary for estimating a variance with Chi-square: $n = 41$, $s^2 = 223.96$, $\chi^2_{(40, .025)} = 59.242$ and $\chi^2_{(40, .975)} = 24.433$.

$$E_\sigma^2 = \frac{(n-1)s^2}{\chi^2_{(40, .025)}} < \sigma^2 < \frac{(n-1)s^2}{\chi^2_{(40, .975)}}$$

$$\frac{(41-1)223.96}{59.342} < \sigma^2 < \frac{(41-1)223.96}{24.433}$$

$$150.962 < \sigma^2 < 366.652$$

**Step 5**
State the interval. The lower limit of the interval is 150.962 and the upper limit is 366.652. This suggests that with 95% confidence, the variance in GRE scores is between 150.962 and 366.652. The interval notation is:

$$E_\sigma^2 = (150.962 < \sigma^2 < 366.652)$$

# SECTION 4

## Hypothesis Test: Classical Approach for a Proportion Using *z*

While testing a mean or variance is extremely common, many situations such as polls and questioners will involve proportions or percentages of the population. It is not difficult to modify the hypothesis test to test the population proportion.

Hypothesis testing for a population proportion requires the conditions for a binomial experiment, which is introduced in Chapter 7. These conditions state that there are a fixed number of trials, each independent from the other. The probability of success in each trial stays a constant denoted as $p$, while $q = 1 - p$ represents the probability of failure in each trial. Also recall that the binomial mean is $\mu = np$, and the standard deviation is found $\sigma = \sqrt{n \cdot p \cdot q}$. Adding the information that was addressed in Chapter 8, it is understood that a binomial distribution with a large sample can be approximated by a normal distribution. Therefore, putting this all together, proportions, percentages, or probabilities that follow the conditions of a binomial may be tested using the normal curve, or *z-score*.

To briefly overview the classical approach: A hypothesis is stated. The parameter (for example, the mean) is converted into a *z-score* by using the $\alpha$ level of significance. The sample information is also converted into a *z-score*. Both *z-scores* are compared and a decision is made to either reject or fail to reject the null hypothesis.

Population $\rightarrow \alpha \rightarrow$ *z-score*

$\rightarrow \rightarrow$ compare *z-scores* to make a decision

Sample $\rightarrow \rightarrow \rightarrow \rightarrow$ *z-score*

The first step is to state the hypotheses. The null and alternative hypotheses must be stated in appropriate form. Recall that the null hypothesis must carry the benefit of the doubt and must be assumed to be true until the alternative hypothesis proves it wrong. The null hypothesis always involves an equal sign (=), less than or equal to sign ($\leq$), or greater than or equal to sign ($\geq$). The alternative hypothesis carries the burden of proof and directly challenges the null hypothesis. The alternative hypothesis never involves an equal sign, but instead may be written with $\neq$, $<$, or $>$.

If $H_o$ is $p = 0.1$,  then $H_1$ is $p \neq 0.1$.

If $H_o$ is $p \leq 0.3$,  then $H_1$ is $p > 0.3$.

If $H_o$ is $p \geq 0.27$,  then $H_1$ is $p < 0.27$.

The second step in hypothesis testing is to establish the test criteria. The test criteria allow one to determine the level of significance, the *type I* error. The criteria also determine the exact test to be performed that will challenge the null hypothesis and the values of a test that may result in the rejection of the null hypothesis. The test criteria have four specific concerns. The first concern is to specify the level of significance, alpha, or the probability of committing a *type I* error. The second is to determine the test statistic that will be applied to the sample information. The third concern of the test criteria is to determine the critical region, which will specify the range of values that will not fall within an acceptable distance of the population parameter. The fourth and final concern is to determine the critical value(s) that divides the critical region from the non-critical region. Each concern is further discussed below.

> **Test Criteria**
> Four considerations leading to the actual test of the null hypothesis:
> 1. Setting the level of significance
> 2. Identifying the test statistic.
> 3. Determining the critical region.
> 4. Determining the critical value.

The level of significance, alpha, is the probability of committing a *type I* error. Typically, a problem states the alpha level as part of a claim challenging a null hypothesis. The alpha level specifies how much error is acceptable.

The test statistic is the random variable, and its probability distribution is used to compare the sample statistic to the hypothesized population parameter. When testing proportions or percentages, the $z$ score is used.

The critical region is an area of the probability distribution that will lead to rejecting the null hypothesis if the calculated test statistic value falls within it. A sample rarely results in a value exactly equal to the value specified in the null hypothesis. A value "close enough" to the specified is usually accepted. Following is a summary of criteria used in other tests to determine the critical regions

### Sign in $H_1$

| $<$ | $\neq$ | $>$ |
|---|---|---|
| One-tailed left | Two-tailed test | One-tailed right |
| Critical region is on the left tail of the curve | Critical regions are on the both tails with area $\alpha/2$ | Critical region is on the right tail of the curve |

Finally, the critical value itself is found by using Table A.3 in Appendix A and finding the *z* score that corresponds to the probability of the non-critical region. Table A.3 is now read in reverse. That is, the probability of the non-critical region is matched as closely as possible to a probability in the body of the table. The critical value is found by tracing over and up to the *z* score on the outside of the table. For example, if a one-tailed non-critical region is represented by .4900 (thus, $\alpha$ is .01, and .5000 - .01 = .4900), .4900 is closest to the probability of .4901 in Table A.3:

To the left of .4901 is the *z* score 2.3, and at the top of the column is the z score 0.03. These two scores are added, reflecting a *z* score of 2.33 associated with the probability .4901. The *z* score 2.33 is the critical value dividing the critical region from the non-critical region. Any calculated value falling in the critical region will lead to a decision to reject the null hypothesis. Remember: when working specifically with *z* scores, *z* critical values to the left of the mean are negative numbers.

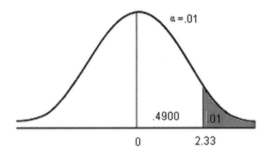

Note: The most commonly used critical values for *z* are listed in the footnote of Table A.3. Use the footnote when applicable and avoid all the above descriptions to find the critical value.

Calculate the test statistic. The test statistic for testing a proportion, probability, or percentage is *z*, however the calculation differs from the other *z* calculations already presented in the text.

The following are the steps to develop a test statistic for testing the proportion. The original *z-score* formula is represented below, followed by the adjustments for the binomial mean and standard deviation, finally leading to the application of the use of the *p* and *q* for the proportion test.

Original calculation $z = \dfrac{x - \mu}{\sigma}$ leads to $z = \dfrac{x - np}{\sqrt{npq}}$ and finally $z = \dfrac{\hat{p} - p}{\sqrt{\dfrac{pq}{n}}}$

## Test Statistic for Testing One Population Proportion

$$z = \frac{\hat{p} - p}{\sqrt{\dfrac{pq}{n}}}$$

where
    $n$ is the number of trials or the sample size.
    $p$ is the population proportion, percentage, or probability as stated in the null.
    $q$ is $1 - p$.
    $\hat{p}$ is the sample proportion calculated as $x/n$.
    $x$ is the number of successes in a sample of size $n$.

Step 4 requires placing the calculated value on the curve that was drawn in step 2. Usually the calculated value is distinguished from the critical by using an asterisk for the calculated value. This step is simply placing the value on the curve.

Step 5 of hypothesis testing involves making a decision. There are only two decisions that can be made. The decision is either to reject the null hypothesis or to fail to reject the null hypothesis. The decision is based on the placement of the calculated value.

## Decision
*Reject $H_o$* When the calculated test statistic falls in the critical region.
*Fail to Reject $H_o$* When the calculated test statistic falls in the non-critical region.

If the calculated value is in the critical region, then the decision must be to reject the null hypothesis. That is, if the sample information is not close enough to the hypothesized value, then the null hypothesis cannot be accepted as true. If the value of the test statistic is found to be within the non-critical region, then the decision is to fail to reject the null hypothesis.

Step 6 is the interpretation of the hypothesis testing. Once the decision is made, it must be applied to the original problem. Recall that the testing process transformed all information into the standardized values using $z$ scores or other test statistics. The original values must be recalled to understand the application of the decision. The decision to reject the null hypothesis or to fail to reject the null hypothesis should be interpreted by restating the null hypothesis, using the words in the original problem. Because the decision is based on a specific level of significance, the alpha should also be restated. For example, the answer might be: there is sufficient evidence to reject the null hypothesis that the proportion of students who claim to be Catholic is equal to 30% at the.05 level of significance.

## A LEARNING AID
## ONE POPULATION PROPORTION

In a recent report, it was claimed that sixty percent of the population in the U.S. is considered overweight. Suppose 1,000 adults are sampled and that 700 were found to be overweight. Does the sample significantly challenge the claim at the .05 level? Conduct a hypothesis test using the classical approach.

### Step 1

State the null and alternative hypotheses. The null hypothesis is the claim that 60% of Americans are overweight. The 60% can be written as decimal .60. The hypotheses are

$$H_o: p = .60$$
$$H_1: p \neq .60$$

### Step 2

Identify the test criteria. The test criteria include the level of significance, test statistic, critical region, and critical value. The level of significance is given as alpha = .05. The test for proportions or percentages is $z$. The normal curve must be drawn. The alternative hypothesis indicates whether the test is one or two-tailed. The $\neq$ sign in the alternative hypothesis indicates the test is two-tailed. Divide alpha by 2 for a two-tailed test. $\alpha/2$ is .05/2 or .025. The critical value for .025 is found to be 1.96 in the footnote on Table A.3.

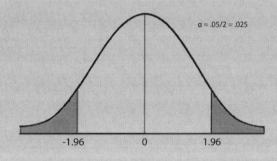

**Step 3**

Calculate the test statistic. The information needed for the calculation is:

$n = 1000$, $x = 700$ $p = .60$, $\hat{p} = x/n = 700/1000 = .7$, and $q = 1 - p = 1 - .60 = .40$. The calculation is as follows:

$$z = \frac{\hat{p} - p}{\sqrt{\dfrac{pq}{n}}} = \frac{.7 - .60}{\sqrt{\dfrac{.60(.40)}{1000}}} = 6.46$$

**Step 4**

Place the calculated value, 6.46, on the curve representing the distribution.

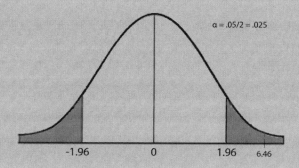

$a = .05/2 = .025$

-1.96    0    1.96    6.46

**Step 5**

Decide to reject $H_o$ or fail to reject $H_o$. Here, the decision is to reject $H_o$ because the calculated value falls in the critical region.

**Step 6**

Interpret the decision using the original problem. Rejecting the null indicates the sample does provide sufficient evidence at the .05 level of significance to reject the claim that the 60% of Americans are overweight. In other words, the test suggests that the percent overweight is not 60%.

---

# SECTION 5

## Hypothesis Test: *P*-value Approach for a Proportion Using *z*

The *P*-value approach for testing a one population proportion using *z* is the same as described in Chapter 10. Whereas the classical approach converted information into *z-scores* to compare, the *P*-value approach converts the information into probabilities.

Population $\rightarrow \alpha \rightarrow$ Probability

$\rightarrow \rightarrow$ compare *probabilities* to make a decision

Sample$\rightarrow$*z-score*$\rightarrow$Probability

Hypothesis testing using the *P*-value begins much like the classical approach.

Step 1 is to identify the null and alternative hypotheses.

Step 2 is to identify two aspects of the test criteria, the level of significance, and the test statistic. The level of significance is usually offered as $\alpha$ in the problem. The test statistic must be determined by reviewing the parameter noted in the hypotheses. The test statistic for testing a population proportion, probability or percentage is *z*. The critical value and the critical region are not needed in the *P*-value approach.

Step 3 is to calculate the test statistic exactly as done in the classical approach:

$$z = \frac{\hat{p} - p}{\sqrt{\dfrac{pq}{n}}}$$

Step 4 is the identification of the *P*-value. The TI-83/83 will report the *P*-Value in the test result screen.

Step 5 is the decision concerning the null hypothesis. The decision criteria is as follows:

$$P \leq \alpha \quad \text{Reject } H_O$$
$$P > \alpha \quad \text{Fail to reject } H_O$$

Step 6 is the interpretation of the decision using the original information from the problem. The decision to reject the null hypothesis implies there is sufficient evidence to reject the null hypothesis at a specified level of significance. A decision to fail to reject the null hypothesis also depends on the specific level of significance.

**Steps in Hypothesis Testing Using the *P*-Value Approach**
1. State $H_o$ and $H_1$.
2. Identify the test criteria:
    a. Level of significance, $\alpha$
    b. Test statistic (*z*, *t*, $\chi^2$, *F*)
3. Calculate the test statistic.
4. Identify the *P*-value.
5. Make a decision:
    a. If $P > \alpha$, Fail to Reject $H_o$
    b. If $P \leq \alpha$, Reject $H_o$
6. Interpret the results.

## EXAMPLE 12.12

**Experiment:** A school official at Bowling Green State University claims that 20% of its student body is minority. Six-hundred students are surveyed finding 100 minority students. Conduct a hypothesis test on the percent minority using the *P*-value approach with an alpha of .01.

**Answer:** Fail to Reject $H_o$. The sample data does not provide sufficient evidence at the .01 level of significance to overturn the claim that 20% of the student population is minority. In other words, the claim seems to be true.

**Solution:** The problem asks for a *P*-value hypothesis test.

### Step 1

State the null and alternative hypotheses. The null hypothesis is the claim made by the school official that the percent of minority students at BGSU is 20%. The hypotheses are:

$$H_o: p = .20$$
$$H_i: p \neq .20$$

### Step 2

Identify the test criteria. The drawing of the curve is not necessary for the *P*-value approach. Step 2 only requires that the alpha is known and the identification of the test statistic. The test statistic for testing one a population proportion is *z*.

### Step 3

Calculate the test statistic. The information needed for the calculation is: $n = 600$, $x = 100$, $p = .20$. The calculation can be done by pressing STAT, scrolling right to "TESTS" and pressing 5 to select "5:1-PropZTest..." Plug the information given in the problem into the settings screen, along with the alternative hypothesis. Scroll down to highlight "Calculate" and press ENTER. The results will appear.

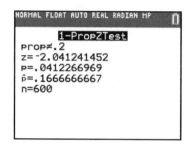

$$z = \frac{\hat{p} - p}{\sqrt{\dfrac{pq}{n}}} = -2.04$$

**Step 4**

Identify the *P*-value. The *P*-value is indicated in the calculator as .0412.

**Step 5**

Decide to reject $H_O$ or fail to reject $H_O$. The rule is that if *P* is less than or equal to $\alpha$, the decision is to reject the null. If *P* is greater than $\alpha$, then fail to reject the null. Here, the decision is to fail to reject $H_O$ because the .0412 is greater than the alpha 0.01.

$$P\text{-value} = .0412 > \alpha = .01 \quad \text{Fail to reject } H_O$$

**Step 6**

Interpret the decision using the original problem. Failing to rejecting the null indicates the sample does not provide sufficient evidence at the .01 level of significance to reject the claim that the percent of minority students at BGSU is 20%.

**A LEARNING AID**
**One Population Proportion**

It was reported in a recent article that 60 percent of the population in the U.S. is considered overweight. Suppose that 700 adults were found to be overweight among a sample of 1000 adults. Does the sample data significantly challenge the claim at the .05 level? Conduct a hypothesis test using the *P*-value approach.

**Step 1**

State the null and alternative hypotheses. The null hypothesis is the claim that 60% of Americans are overweight. The hypotheses are:

$$H_o: p = .60$$
$$H_1: p \neq .60$$

## Step 2
Identify the test criteria. The test criteria for the *P*-value approach only requires the $\alpha$ and the test statistic. The test statistic for proportion testing is *z*.

## Step 3
Calculate the test statistic along with the *P*-value. The information needed for the calculation is: $n = 1000$, $x = 700$, $p = .60$ and should be used in the calculator function by pressing STAT, scrolling over to "TESTS," followed by pressing 5 to select "5-1PropZTest..." Insert the necessary information given in the problem, along with the alternative hypothesis, scroll down to "Calculate" and press ENTER. The results will appear.

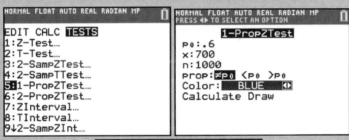

$$z = \frac{\hat{p} - p}{\sqrt{\dfrac{pq}{n}}} = 6.46$$

## Step 4
Identify the *P*-value. $P = 1.08758\text{E-}10$. This notation means to move the decimal to the left (-) 10 places. So *P* is really .0000000001087. Since *P* is usually reported with 4 places to the right of the decimal and there is some, albeit little probability out in the 10 place, it is noted as $P = 0+$.

**Step 5**
Decide to reject $H_o$ or fail to reject $H_o$. Since $P$-value = 0+ < $\alpha$ = 0.05, $H_o$ is rejected.

Reject $H_o$

**Step 6**
Intrepret the decision using the original problem. Rejecting the null indicates the sample does provide sufficient evidence at the .05 level of significance to reject the claim that the 60% of Americans are overweight. In other words, the test suggests that the percent overweight is not 60%.

# SECTION 6

## Hypothesis Test: Classical Approach for Correlation between Two Variables Using *t*

Chapter 4 introduced the concept of linear relationship or correlation between variables among one population. If the variables are interval or ratio, such linear relationship or correlation can be measured by the correlation coefficient. The most popular technique to describe the relationship of two interval or ratio variables is the ***Pearson's product moment correlation coefficient, r.*** Pearson's $r$ measures both the strength and direction of the relationship between two variables. Pearson's $r$ has values ranging from -1 to 1. A value of -1 represents a perfect negative linear relationship, whereas a 0 represents no linear relationship and +1 represents a perfect positive linear relationship. Any negative $r$ value implies that as the values of one variable increase, the values of the other variable decrease. Any positive $r$ value implies that the values of both variables increase or decrease simultaneously. Pearson's $r$ assumes the relationship is linear—that a consistent pattern upward or downward exists. Pearson's $r$ should not be applied to nonlinear relationships.

Pearson's r represents a sample statistic. The corresponding population parameter is denoted by the Greek letter $\rho$ (pronounced "rho," like the "ro" in road). Because r measures the linear relationship of ordered pairs (x and y) from sample data, $\rho$ measures the linear relationship of all ordered pairs from a population. If $\rho \neq 0$, then there is a linear relationship between $X$ and $Y$. Otherwise, $\rho = 0$ indicates that the absence of linear relationship between $X$ and $Y$. Keep in mind that this does imply that $X$ and $Y$ are independent; other non-linear relationship may exist. Therefore, whether $\rho = 0$ or not becomes an indication about the existence of linear relationship between $X$ and $Y$. It is important to find out whether such linear relationship exists between $X$ and $Y$ by performing a hypotheses testing on the statement that $\rho = 0$.

| Sample correlation coefficient | $r$ |
| Population correlation coefficient | $\rho$ |

The formula for calculating $r$ is as follows:

$$r = \frac{n\sum xy - \sum x \sum y}{\sqrt{n\sum x^2 - \left(\sum x\right)^2}\sqrt{n\sum y^2 - \left(\sum y\right)^2}}$$

Hypothesis testing for the population coefficient $\rho$ assumes that the relationship between the $x$ and $y$ variables do not have linear correlation.

$$H_o: \rho = 0, \quad X \text{ and } Y \text{ are not linearly related}$$
$$H_1: \rho \neq 0, \quad X \text{ and } Y \text{ are linearly related}$$

Hypotheses for correlation testing are written as follows:

If $H_o$ is $\rho = 0$,  then $H_1$ is $\rho \neq 0$

If $H_o$ is $\rho \leq 0$  then $H_1$ is $\rho > 0$

If $H_o$ is $\rho \geq 0$  then $H_1$ is $\rho < 0$

## CRITICAL $r$ TABLE METHOD

There are two methods used to test a statement about the population correlation coefficient. The first is the comparison of the calculated value $r$ to the value in the Appendix, Table A.1. This table is known as the ***Critical Values of r.*** As done in Chapter 4, the absolute value of the correlation $r$ is significant, or dependent, if it is greater than the value on the table for the $n$ sample size. The table reports the critical values of $r$ for the alphas of .05 and .01. If the absolute value of $r$ exceeds the critical value on the table, the null hypothesis is rejected and the value is considered to have a significant linear correlation. If the absolute value of $r$ is less than or equal to the value on the table, the decision is to fail to reject the null and there is not a significant linear correlation. This is simpler since it bypasses many of the calculations required in the traditional hypothesis step.

### EXAMPLE 12.13

**Experiment:** Assume the sample correlation is .667 between the levels of education of 10 couples. Let $X$ be the number of years of education of a woman and $Y$ is the number of years of education for men. Does the data show a significant linear relationship between educational level in all couples? Use alpha .05.

**Answer:** Yes, there is a significant relationship between education of men and women.

**Solution:** While normally there are six steps in hypothesis testing, the question asks to bypass many of the steps by using table A.1. Begin by stating the hypotheses. The hypotheses require the Greek letter $\rho$.

$$H_o: \rho = 0 \qquad H_1: \rho \neq 0$$

Compare the correlation value $r$ (absolute value) to the critical value from the table in the Appendix, Table A.1. The calculated value is .667; the critical value for the $n$ of 10 at the .05 level is .632. Since .667 is greater than .632, reject the null hypothesis. Since the calculate value .667 is greater than the table value .632, reject the null hypothesis.

$$\text{Reject } H_o$$

Rejecting the null hypothesis suggests there is sufficient evidence at the .05 level of significance that there is a significant linear correlation between a man's education and a woman's.

## TRADITIONAL CLASSIC HYPOTHESIS TEST

Another method is the traditional hypothesis test following the same six steps outlined for testing mean with $z$ or $t$. In fact, the test for the correlation is also a $t$ test but the formula itself is slightly different. The classical approach for testing the correlation requires the population information to be transformed into a $t$-score, the sample information transformed into a $t$-score, and then the $t$ values compared to make a decision.

Population $\rightarrow \alpha \rightarrow t$-score

$\rightarrow \rightarrow$ compare $t$-scores to make a decision

Sample $\rightarrow \rightarrow \rightarrow \rightarrow t$-score

Step 1 is to state the hypothesis. The choices for the hypotheses for the correlation are:

$$H_o: \rho = 0 \qquad H_1: \rho \neq 0$$
$$H_o: \rho \leq 0 \qquad H_1: \rho > 0$$
$$H_o: \rho \geq 0 \qquad H_1: \rho < 0$$

Step 2 is the test criteria beginning with the level of significance. The test statistic is $t$. The critical region is determined by the direction of the alternative hypothesis, and the critical value for *t* requires degrees of freedom and alpha. The degrees of freedom for *t* when testing correlation are $n - 2$.

---

**Degree of Freedom for t test when testing correlation**
$$df = n - 2$$

---

Step 3 is the calculation of the test statistic.

---

**Calculation of the Test Statistic *t* for Correlation**

$$t = \frac{r}{\sqrt{\dfrac{1 - r^2}{n - 2}}}$$

where
   *r* is the sample correlation coefficient
   *n* is the sample size

---

Step 4 is to place the calculated value on the curve.

Step 5 is to make a decision. If the calculated value is in the critical region, the decision is to reject the null hypothesis. If the calculated value is in the non-critical region, the decision is to fail to reject.

Step 6 is to interpret the results. If the decision is to reject the null hypothesis, then the correlation is said to be a significant linear correlation between *X* and *Y*. If the decision is to fail to reject the null, then there is no significant linear correlation between *X* and *Y*.

---

**A LEARNING AID**
**TESTING PEARSON'S CORRELATION COEFFICIENT *r*.**
A sample of 12 women (post child bearing) produced a correlation coefficient of -.862 between the age at marriage of a woman and the number of children she bears. Test whether a significant linear relationship exists between these two variables for all women using both methods at $\alpha = .05$.

*Method 1, using Critical Value Table A.1* Method 1 is the shorter version of a test that requires a comparison of the correlation coefficient *r* to a critical value on the table. This method bypasses many of the steps by using Table A.1.

---

Begin by stating the hypotheses. The hypotheses require the Greek letter $\rho$.

$$H_0: \rho = 0 \qquad H_1: \rho \neq 0$$

Compare the correlation value $r$ (absolute value) to the critical value from the table in the Appendix, Table A.1. (This table reports two-tailed alphas so there is no need to divide alpha). The correlation is -.862; its absolute value drops the negative sign and is simply .862. The critical value for the $n$ of 12 at the .05 level is .576. Since .862 is greater than .576, reject the null hypothesis.

$$\text{Reject } H_0$$

Rejecting the null hypothesis suggests there is sufficient evidence at the .05 level of significance that there is a significant linear correlation between the age at marriage of a woman and the number of children she bears for all women.

### Method 2, Classical Hypothesis Test
**Step 1**
Begin by stating the hypotheses.

$$H_0 : \rho = 0 \qquad H_1: \rho \neq 0$$

**Step 2**
Identify the test criteria. Alpha is set at .05. The test statistic is $t$ for the correlation. The $t$ curve may be drawn with a two-tailed test as required by an alternative hypothesis with a $\neq$ test. The area in each tail is $\alpha/2 = 0.05/2 = 0.025$. The $t$ test also requires degrees of freedom. For this $t$ test, the degrees of freedom are $n - 2$, or $12 - 2 = 10$. Therefore, the critical values found from the $t$ table, A.4, are $t_{(10, .025)} = 2.228$ and $-t_{(10, .025)} = -2.228$.

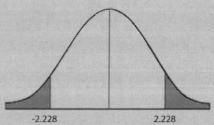

**Step 3**
Calculate the test statistic. The calculation is below.

$$t = \frac{r}{\sqrt{\dfrac{1-r^2}{n-2}}} = \frac{-.862}{\sqrt{\dfrac{1--.862^2}{12-2}}} = \frac{-.862}{\sqrt{.0256956}} = -5.377$$

**Step 4**

The calculation of the test statistic is -5.377. Place this value on the curve.

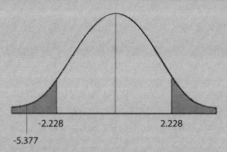

-2.228          2.228

-5.377

**Step 5**

Make a decision. Since the calculated value -5.377 is in the critical region, the decision is to reject the null.

Reject $H_o$

**Step 6**

Rejecting the null hypothesis suggests there is sufficient evidence at the .05 level of significance to support the statement that there is a significant linear correlation between the age at marriage of a woman and the number of children she bears.

# SECTION 7

### Hypothesis Test: *P*-Value Approach for Correlation between Two Variables Using *t*

The *P*-value approach for testing a correlation between two variables is very similar to the method described in Chapter 11. Whereas the classical approach converted information into *t-scores* to compare, the *P*-value approach converts the information into probabilities.

Population →$\alpha$ →Probability

Sample→*t-score*→Probability

→→ compare *probabilities* to make a decision

Step 1 is to identify the null and alternative hypotheses.

Step 2 is to identify two aspects of the test criteria, the level of significance and the test statistic. The level of significance is usually offered as $\alpha$ in the problem. The test statistic must be determined by reviewing the parameter noted in the hypotheses. The statistic for a correlation follows a *t*-distribution. The critical value and the critical region are not needed in the *P*-value approach.

Step 3 is to calculate the test statistic exactly as done in the classical approach:

$$t = \frac{r}{\sqrt{\dfrac{1-r^2}{n-2}}}$$

Step 4 is identifying the *P*-value.

Step 5 is the decision concerning the null hypothesis. The decision criteria is described as follows:

$$P \le \alpha \quad \text{Reject } H_o$$
$$P > \alpha \quad \text{Fail to reject } H_o$$

Step 6 is the interpretation of the decision using the original information from the problem. The decision of rejecting the null hypothesis means that there is sufficient evidence to show that there is a linear relationship between the variables of interest at the specified significance level.

---

### Example 12.14
**Experiment:** An elementary teacher thinks that the final test scores of students are correlated with their pre-test scores. She randomly selected the scores of 10 students. Does this sample information support her claim at the significance level of .05?

|          | Jon | Katy | Ryan | Rich | Jill | Joe | Mary | Bill | Paul | Sue |
|----------|-----|------|------|------|------|-----|------|------|------|-----|
| Pre-test | 66  | 65   | 65   | 75   | 45   | 65  | 90   | 78   | 50   | 49  |
| Test     | 73  | 67   | 80   | 70   | 60   | 50  | 95   | 85   | 50   | 70  |

**Answer:** Yes, at the significance level of .05, there is sufficient evidence that to support the claim made by the teacher that the pre-test scores and final test scores are positively correlated.

**Step 1**

The parameter being tested is: $\rho$ the Pearson correlation between the pre-test scores and final test scores of all students. Identify the null and alternative hypotheses:

$$H_0: \quad \rho = 0 \qquad H_1: \quad \rho \neq 0$$

**Step 2**

The significance level is noted as $\alpha = 0.05$.

**Step 3**

The data must be stored in the listing function. Enter values for $x$ in L₁ and the values of $y$ in L₂, continue with both calculating the correlation and testing its significance. The correlation coefficient value will be identified in step 6 of the hypothesis test.

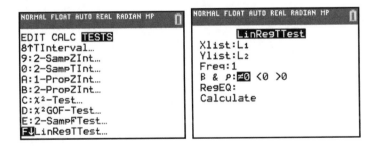

With the data entered in L1 and L2 of a calculator, press STAT, scroll to TESTS and down to: "F:LinRegTTest." Press ENTER. Be sure the settings screen looks appears as follows.

Highlight "Calculate" and press ENTER. The following results will display.

 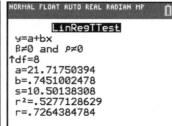

From the calculation, the test statistic is $t = 2.99$ and Pearson's correlation coefficient is $r = .726$.

**Step 4**

Identify the *P*-value. $P = .0173$

**Step 5**

Make a decision. Since $0.0173 < \alpha(0.05)$, the null hypothesis is rejected.

**Step 6**

Look at the significance level of .05. There is sufficient evidence that to support the claim made by the teacher that the pre-test scores and final test scores are positively correlated.

## A LEARNING AID
## *P*-VALUE FOR ONE POPULATION CORRELATION
### (No raw data given)

In a survey of sample of 12 people, data were obtained for their years in education ($X$) and their annual incomes ($Y$) in dollars. The correlation coefficient for these 12 pairs of data was calculated as .58. Does this present sufficient evidence for a linear relationship between education level and income level for the overall population? Perform a hypothesis test using the significance level of 0.01.

### *Method 1, Using Critical Value Table A.1*

Method 1 is the shorter version of a test that requires a comparison of the correlation coefficient $r$ to a critical value on the table. This method bypasses many of the steps by using Table A.1. Begin by stating the hypotheses. The hypotheses require the Greek letter $\rho$.

$$H_o : \rho = 0 \qquad H_I : \rho \neq 0$$

Compare the correlation value $r$ (absolute value) to the critical value from the table in the **Appendix, Table A.1**. (This table reports two-tailed alphas so there is no need to divide alpha). The correlation is .58. The critical value for the $n$ of 12 at the .01 level is .708. Since .58 is less than .708, fail to reject the null hypothesis.

Fail to Reject $H_o$

Failing to reject the null hypothesis suggests there is not sufficient evidence at 0.01 level of significance that there is a significant linear correlation between education level and income for the over all population.

### Method 2, using the t-test
**Step 1**
Begin by stating the hypotheses.

$$H_o: \rho = 0 \qquad H_1: \rho \neq 0$$

**Step 2**
Identify the test criteria. Alpha is set at .01. The test statistic is t for the correlation. This is a two-tailed test since the alternative hypothesis is $\neq$.

**Step 3**
Calculate the test statistic. The calculation is below.

$$t = \frac{r}{\sqrt{\dfrac{1-r^2}{n-2}}} = \frac{.58}{\sqrt{\dfrac{1-.58^2}{12-2}}} = \frac{.58}{\sqrt{.06636}} = \frac{.58}{.257604} = 2.252$$

**Step 4**
Convert the calculated value 2.252 into a $P$-value. Consulting Table A.4 does this. Trace down the degrees of freedom $n - 2$, or 10. In this row only ($df = 10$) find the critical value closest to the calculated value. The 2.252 is closest to 2.228. Therefore, the alpha at the top of this column is the $P$-value if one-tailed. Since this is a two-tailed test, this value must be multiplied by 2. The final $P$-value is then .025 (2) or .05. $P = .05$

**Step 5**
Make a decision. Since $P = .05$ is greater than the alpha 0.01, the decision is to fail to reject the null.

$P\,(.05) \;>\; \alpha\,(0.01) \quad$ Fail to Reject $H_o$

**Step 6**
Failing to reject the null hypothesis suggests that this sample does not provide sufficient evidence at the 0.01 level of significance to show that a linear relationship exists between people's education and income level.

## CHAPTER 12 IN REVIEW

12.1   Find the $\chi 2$ critical values:

a. $\chi^2_{(20,\,.025)}$

b. $\chi^2_{(2,\,.05)}$

c. $\chi^2_{(18,\,10)}$

d. $\chi^2_{(16,\,.95)}$

e. $\chi^2_{(30,\,.90)}$

f. $\chi^2_{(80,\,.995)}$

12.2   Find the $\chi 2$ critical values:

a.

c.

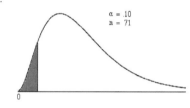

b.

d.

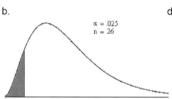

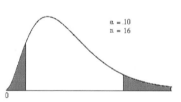

12.3   Find the critical value(s) for the following hypotheses.
a. $H_o: \sigma^2 = 20$, $H_1: \sigma^2 \neq 20$, $n = 20$, $\alpha = .10$
b. $H_o: \sigma \leq 5$, $H_1: \sigma > 5$, $n = 6$, $\alpha = .05$
c. $H_o: \sigma^2 = 10$, $H_1: \sigma^2 \neq 10$, $n = 30$, $\alpha = .01$
d. $H_o: \sigma \geq 22$, $H_1: \sigma < 22$, $n = 4$, $\alpha = .01$
e. $H_o: \rho = 0$; $H_1: \rho \neq 0$; $n = 27$, $\alpha = .05$
f. $H_o: \rho = 0$; $H_1: \rho \neq 0$; $n = 17$, $\alpha = .10$
g. $H_o: \rho = 0$; $H_1: \rho \neq 0$; $n = 29$, $\alpha = .01$

12.4   Find the $z$ critical values suggested by the given data.

a. $H_o: p = .12; H_1: p \neq .12; \alpha = .05$
b. $H_o: p \leq .80; H_1: p > .80; \alpha = .10$
c. $H_o: p \geq .10; H_1: p < .10; \alpha = .01$
d. $H_o: p = .75\ H_1: p \neq .75; \alpha = .05$
e. $H_o: p \geq .98; H_1: p < .98; \alpha = .05$

12.5   In the appropriate format, state the null and alternative hypotheses.
   a. The variance in age of patients in Dr. Cheng's office is no more than 7.62 years (squared).
   b. The standard deviation in the price of a 50 lb. package of cement available in the local hardware store is 75¢.
   c. The variance in weights of students is not less than 150 pounds (squared).
   d. The proportion of aspirin sales among all the drugs produced by a drug company is greater than 20 percent.
   e. When taking a statistics class from Professor Jackson, 90 percent of the students pass the class the first time.
   f. There is a correlation between drinking diet soft drinks and weight loss.

12.6   Find the following one-tailed to the right critical values
   a. $z_{(.05)}$
   b. $z_{(.2)}$
   c. $z_{(.25)}$
   d. $t_{(100,.005)}$
   e. $t_{(10,.05)}$
   f. $z_{(.01)}$
   g. $z_{(.10)}$
   h. $z_{(.025)}$
   i. $t_{(20,.01)}$
   j. $t_{(40,.10)}$

12.7   A manufacturer claims that its machine can fill soda bottles within a standard deviation of 0.4 oz. A sample of 51 bottles produces a standard deviation of .32 oz. At the .05 level of significance, test the claim that the standard deviation equals .4 oz.

12.8   Hartsfield Atlanta International Airport is the busiest airport in the U.S. averaging 2,603 planes a day coming and leaving with a standard deviation of 100 planes. A traffic controller believes that the average seems correct but thinks that the standard deviation exceeds 100. She collected information on the number of planes for this airport for a period of 51 days and found that the mean number of planes is 2,650 with a standard deviation of 126. Is there enough evidence to suggest the traffic controller may be correct? Use $\alpha = .01$.

12.9   It was reported that the average number of hours a preschool child spends in daycare each day is estimated at 8.2 hours with a standard deviation of 3.1 hours. A sample of 25 children produced a mean of 7.1 hours and a standard deviation of 2.8 hours. Do the data show that the population standard deviation of time is less than that claimed in the report? Use $\alpha = .01$.

12.10 Determine if a significant relationship exists between a person's weight and his/her restaurant bill. The correlation coefficient between these two variables is calculated as 0.622 for a sample of 10 people. Perform a hypothesis test at the level of 0.05 using the classical approach.

12.11 Determine if there is a significant relationship between the population of the 6 largest cities (rounded to nearest million) and the monthly cost of housing (rounded to nearest $1,000) for a family of four. The correlation coefficient between these two variables was calculated as 0.623. Perform a hypothesis test at the level of 0.01 using the classical approach.

12.12 The average rushing totals for the 2007 NFL offensive players is 462 yards with a standard deviation of 140.68 yards. A sample of the 10 rushers is 698.4 yards with a standard deviation of 130.52. Test if the sample standard deviation is significantly less using the classical approach and $\alpha = .05$.

12.13 It was claimed in one article that Americans spend about $123 per person per year on toys with a standard deviation of $31. A recent survey showed that the variance on toy spending is 984 ($ squared) for a sample of 51 people. Use this result to test the claim made by the article at 0.05 level of significance.

12.14 An employee at the Hershey Company claims that the variance in monthly chocolate sales is $1.40 million. At $\alpha = .05$, test the variance in monthly Hershey chocolate sales using a sample of 30 months producing a variance of $1.42 million.

12.15 The national average violent crime rate is believed to be 44.6 percent (this means that 44.6 percent of all crimes reported are violent crimes). A Ph.D. candidate of political science was writing a doctoral dissertation on the topic of violent crimes and suspects that the rate is higher than what was commonly believed. She collected information from 800 crimes for last year and found that 380 of them were violent. Does the sample data sufficiently support her view that the violent crime rate should be higher than 44.6%? Use the significance level 0.05.

12.16 It is claimed that 60 percent of the criminal cases coming before Judge Alexia result in convictions. A law clerk believes this claim to be false. He gathers a sample of 400 cases from Judge Alexia which resulted in 252 convictions. Does the sample confirm the rate at the .05 level of significance?

12.17 It was claimed that of the babies born out of wedlock, 64 percent were born to African American females. In a random sample of 100 babies born out of wedlock, 60 were to African American females. Use the sample information to test the claim that 64 percent of all babies born out of wedlock were born to the African American females. Is the sample significantly less than the claim at the .10 level of significance?

12.18 Test the claim that over 60 percent of Americans have a computer. A random sample of 400 individuals results in a rate of 61 percent (244 people). $\alpha = .01$.

12.19 The following data represents the cellphone bills of 9 students based on their age. (Bills rounded to the nearest dollar). Determine if there is a significant relationship at the .05 level.

| Age | 30 | 25 | 22 | 28 | 20 | 20 | 18 | 19 | 20 |
|---|---|---|---|---|---|---|---|---|---|
| Bill | 88 | 98 | 85 | 90 | 90 | 75 | 80 | 95 | 80 |

12.20 Determine if there is a significant relationship between the population (rounded to nearest million) of a city and the monthly cost of housing (rounded to nearest $1,000) for a family of four. Use the .05 level of significance.

| | Tokyo | Mexico City | Mumbai | Sao Paulo | New York City |
|---|---|---|---|---|---|
| Population | 37 | 20 | 17 | 21 | 21 |
| Housing | 6 | 3 | 3 | 2 | 6 |

12.21 The following data represents the number of hours per week that high school seniors spend watching TV and their grade point average. Is there a significant relationship at alpha .05?

| TV | 5 | 8 | 9 | 3 | 15 | 10 | 10 |
|---|---|---|---|---|---|---|---|
| GPA | 3.5 | 3.0 | 2.5 | 3.8 | 2.0 | 3.0 | 2.5 |

12.22 In a random sample of 400 women, 90 say that a husband or a boyfriend has physically abused them. Is this rate higher than the national average of 18 percent? $\alpha = .05$.

12.23 In a recent survey about the amount of money a family spent on food per week and the number of people in the family, a random sample of 300 households generated information on these two variables. It was calculated that the sample correlation for these two variables was 0.95. In the level 0.01, does this provide strong evidence to support the statement that amount of money a family spent on food per week and the number of people in the family are related significantly?

12.24 Is there a significant relationship between the lengths of prison sentences for convicted criminal for the same crime and the age at sentence of the criminal? A sample of 200 criminals produced a correlation of .55. $\alpha = .01$.

12.25 Calculate a 95 percent confidence interval for the standard deviation in American's credit card balance per year per household given a sample of 101 households with a standard deviation of $843.

12.26 Find the 90 percent confidence interval for the variance in the costs of textbooks using a sample of 101 books with a variance of 65.25 (dollar squared).

12.27 A sample of 30 teenage mothers shows that they have a lifetime average of 5.4 children, with a standard deviation of 1.2. Find the 95 percent confidence interval for the standard deviation of the number of children born to all teenage mothers.

12.28 A recent national report showed that only 72.6 percent of eighth graders have basic reading skills with a variance of 2.89 percent. Michigan reports eighth grade reading skills at 74.2 percent with a variance of 2.75 percent for a sample of 30 students. Test at the .05 level whether Michigan variance is significantly different.

12.29 Estimate the variance of strength of a new metal for airplane manufacturing using a sample of 30 with a variance of 5.381 psi. $\alpha = .10$.

12.30 A potato chip company bought a new dispensing machine. The manufacturer of the machine claims it dispenses on average 6 oz., with a standard deviation of 1.0. The chip company feels the standard deviation is much larger than the company claims. A sample of 20 bags was taken reporting a mean of 5.8 and a standard deviation of 1.2. Does the evidence support the manufacturer's claim at the .10 level of significance?

12.31 It was claimed by a consumer group that the average new mid-sized car price is $18,545 with a standard deviation of $1,035. An auto dealer challenged the claim made by the consumer group and believed that the standard deviation in new car prices should be lower. The dealer collected information on 10 cars sold and found that the mean price was $19,222 with a standard deviation of $895. Does this sample information provide sufficient evidence to support the dealer's claim? Use alpha .05.

12.32 A random sample of 31 industrial countries produces a mean per capita GDP of $32,600, with a standard deviation of $870. At the .02 significance level, use the *P*-value approach to test a researcher's claim that the population standard deviation is significantly less than $882.

12.33 The airline industry claims that the on-time arrival rate is 82 percent. A sample of 800 random flights found that 700 were on time. At the .05 level, does the sample suggest that the arrival rate is actually more than that claimed?

12.34 A report claims that 75 percent of Americans support the death penalty for murderers. In a random sample of 200 Americans, 158 support the death penalty for murderers. Test the claim at the .05 level.

12.35 Determine if there is a significant relationship between the amount of money a family expends on food per week and the number of people in the household in a particular urban area. Use alpha .01.

| Number in household $x$ | 2 | 3 | 3 | 4 | 2 | 4 | 5 |
|---|---|---|---|---|---|---|---|
| Food expenditure $y$ | 70 | 90 | 80 | 100 | 80 | 110 | 135 |

12.36 Determine if there is a significant relationship between the amount of time spent in a state for a presidential candidate and the number of people voting in the election. Use alpha .05.

| Time (hours) | 20 | 15 | 40 | 5 | 6 | 15 | 19 | 34 | 14 | 8 |
|---|---|---|---|---|---|---|---|---|---|---|
| Voters(millions) | 13 | 12 | 20 | 1.5 | 2.5 | 14 | 9 | 18 | 10 | 3.5 |

# 13 | TESTING AND ESTIMATING TWO POPULATIONS

**SECTION 1** Two Independent Means: *z*
**SECTION 2** Two Independent Means: *t*
**SECTION 3** Two Proportions: *z*
**SECTION 4** Two Dependent Means: *t*
**SECTION 5** Two Variances: *F* Distribution

Situations often exist in which hypothesis testing or estimation is necessary using two samples and/or two populations, as when comparing exam scores of one statistics course to a second statistics course. Previous chapters focused on inferential testing and estimating for means and standard deviations of one population. Adjusting the formulas to include two samples or two populations is easily achieved. Conceptually the process remains the same; most formulas are adjusted by adding a second sample statistic and/or a second parameter. Where means are tested for large samples and population standard deviations are known, the central limit theorem is applied using the normal *z* distribution. Where means are tested for small samples or where the population standard deviations are not known, the *t* distribution must be applied. When variances or standard deviations are tested, a skewed distribution similar to chi-square must be applied.

The following diagram illustrates the steps needed to determine which test must apply. The first question that must be asked is if the test is for one population or two. If it is one, then is it testing a mean or a variance (standard deviation). If it is a mean, then the question is whether it is *z* or *t* based on sample size and if the population standard deviation given. If it is one population variance or standard deviation test, then $\chi2$ is used. However, if the initial question is that the problem is a two population test followed by whether it is for means, then an additional question is necessary as to the independence of the samples. This is discussed below. If the samples are independent, then either *z* or *t* is the choice. If the mean is tested for dependent samples, then a dependent *t* is used. Two proportions are tested with another form of a *z* calculation. If the test is for two variances or two standard deviations, then *F* is used.

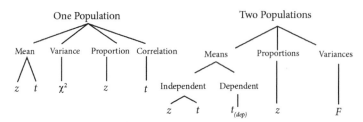

Before the various hypothesis tests are discussed, the terms independent and dependent must be reviewed. Independence is a concern in regression, correlation, probabilities, and sampling. Sampling independence occurs when data are taken from two populations or from independent sources of one population. Independence occurs when the outcomes of one event do not affect the outcomes of another event. For example, a coin landing heads up on one toss does not affect whether the same coin lands heads up the second, third, or fourth tosses. The outcomes from tossing a coin two or more times are independent. However, drawing a coin from one's pocket without replacing it before drawing a second coin makes the second outcome dependent on the first. Any time the sample space is altered, the events are dependent. Sampling independence or dependence concerns the effect one sample has on another. If two independent samples are drawn, one sample will not affect the other. Random sampling is the best indicator of independent sampling. Random sampling ensures that each element of the population has an equal chance of being selected. Random sampling is especially important when two samples are selected from the same population.

Dependent sampling usually contains the same elements twice. A very common sampling technique in most social, health, and behavioral sciences is pretest/post test sampling. For example, a group of individuals is selected and observed, a test or experiment is performed, and a second observation is conducted. The second test results are affected by the observations obtained by the first test. Testing the same individuals twice results in dependent sampling.

---

# *SECTION 1*

## Two Independent Means: *z*

When two large independent samples are drawn from one or two populations where the population standard deviations are known, the central limit theorem is applied in testing and estimating the difference between the means. The central limit theorem (described in Chapter 10) asserts that if random samples are taken from a population, then the sampling distribution approaches the normal probability distribution. A normal distribution is represented by the bell-shaped *z* distribution. Therefore, testing or estimating two sampling distributions can be achieved using the normal *z* distribution.

Several conditions are necessary before applying the normal *z* distribution for two means. First, the samples must be independent; that is, the outcomes of one sample do not affect the outcomes of the second. Next, both population standard deviations must be known. Sample standard deviations cannot be substituted for population standard deviations. Finally, both samples must be large; that is, the sample size of each must be greater than 30.

**Criteria for Using $z$ for Two Means**
1. Samples are independent.
2. $\sigma_1$ and $\sigma_2$ are known.
3. $n_1$ and $n_2$ are greater than 30.

Hypothesis testing using the classical approach for two large population means follows the same six steps as other types of testing. The hypotheses must be written, the test criteria identified, the calculated value obtained, the calculated value compared to the critical value, a decision made, and an interpretation given.

**Steps in Hypothesis Testing Using the Classical Approach**
1. State $H_0$ and $H_1$.
2. Identify the test criteria.
    a. Level of significance, $\alpha$
    b. Test statistic $(z, t, \chi^2, F)$
    c. Critical Region
        (1) One-tailed test
        (2) Two-tailed test $(\alpha/2)$
    d. Critical value
3. Calculate the test statistic.
4. Place the calculated value on a distribution curve.
5. Make a decision.
    a. Fail to reject $H_0$
    b. Reject $H_0$
6. Interpret the results.

The hypotheses are adjusted to represent the comparison of the two population means. Thus far, hypotheses contained one parameter, mathematical symbol, and value. Testing two population means requires two parameters, $\mu_1$ and $\mu_2$. Subscripts are added to denote the first and second means, respectively. Which population to denote by 1 and which to denote by 2 is determined in the hypotheses and not necessarily the first population information provided in the experiment. The three mathematical symbols used in the null hypothesis are =, ≤, and ≥, whereas the three symbols for the alternative hypothesis are ≠, >, and <. Hypotheses for two populations contain a value representing the expected difference between the parameters. Where no difference is expected, include the value 0 in the hypotheses. Therefore, the notation for testing two population means follows the format: parameter one, minus parameter two, mathematical symbol, and value. Some examples are as follows:

If $H_0$ is $\mu_1 - \mu_2 = 0$      then $H_1$ is $\mu_1 - \mu_2 \neq 0$
If $H_0$ is $\mu_1 - \mu_2 \geq 2$      then $H_1$ is $\mu_1 - \mu_2 < 2$
If $H_0$ is $\mu_1 - \mu_2 \leq 5$      then $H_1$ is $\mu_1 - \mu_2 > 5$

**EXAMPLE 13.1**
**Experiment:** State the null and alternative hypotheses: There is no more than a 10-pound difference between the mean weight of women and the mean weight of men.

**Answer:** $H_O : \mu_1 - \mu_2 \leq 10,$ $\qquad H_1 : \mu_1 - \mu_2 > 10$

**Solution:** Begin by identifying the parameters. The Greek symbol $\mu$ represents a population mean. The experiment questions the difference between the mean weights of two groups, men and women. Therefore, $\mu_1 - \mu_2$ represents the difference between the means. The words "no more than" are represented by the math symbol $\leq$, which can only be placed in the null hypothesis. If $\leq$ is in the null hypothesis, then $>$ must be placed in the alternative hypothesis. The expected difference is more than 10 lbs. The value 10 is placed in the hypotheses.

The test criteria include identifying the level of significance, test statistic, critical region, and critical value. These steps are achieved exactly as they were in Chapter 10. The level of significance, represented by alpha, is usually established in the experiment. The test statistic $z$ is applied to two population means where the standard deviations are known and samples are large. The critical region is guided by the mathematical symbol of the alternative hypothesis. The critical region is to the left when the alternative hypothesis is $<$, to the right when the symbol is $>$, and two-tailed when the symbol is $\neq$. The critical value for $z$ is determined by placing the alpha in the critical region (first dividing it by 2 if a two-tailed test) and subtracting it from .5,000. The subtracted probability is matched to the $z$ critical values in Table A.3 of Appendix A. Notice that $z$ is the only test statistic where probabilities are reported in the body of the table, with critical values on the rim. All other test statistics involve degrees of freedom along the outside of the tables, with critical values in the bodies. Remember that $z$ represents a normal bell-shaped curve whose mean, mode, and median are in the center. Critical values, not probabilities, below the mean, 0, are negative. Probabilities are never negative.

**EXAMPLE 13.2**
**Experiment:** Find the critical $z$ value for $H_1$: $\mu - \mu \neq 4$, $\alpha = .05$

**Answer:** 1.96 and -1.96.

**Solution:** The critical value cannot be determined until the critical region is set. The critical region is guided by the alternative hypothesis, which requires values not equal to 4. The test is a two-tailed $z$ test, because the symbol $\neq$ is in the alternative hypothesis. The normal curve is drawn. Divide alpha by 2 before placing it in the critical regions of the right and left tails: $.05/2 = .025$. The area of the noncritical region is found by subtracting .025 from .5000, the probability of half a normal curve. The probability of the noncritical region is .5000 - .025, or .4750. Using Table A.3, find the probability .4750. Reading across and up to the $z$ critical values in the margins, .4750 is associated with the $z$ value 1.96. Because the normal curve is symmetric, 1.96 for the right tail is -1.96 for the left tail.

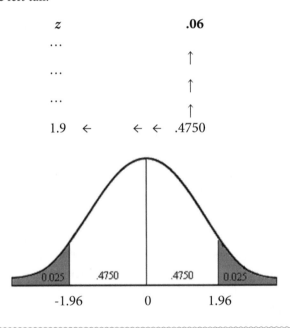

Once the hypotheses and test criteria are determined, the test statistic can be calculated. The test involves calculating the sample information offered as the challenge to the null hypothesis. The calculation for $z$ when the difference between two population means is calculated is similar to the $z$ formula presented in Chapter 10, but with added symbols representing the second sample and population information.

$$\text{One Population: } z = \frac{\bar{x} - \mu}{\sigma/\sqrt{n}}$$

$$\text{Two Populations: } z = \frac{(\bar{x}_1 - \bar{x}_2) - (\mu_1 - \mu_2)}{\sqrt{(\sigma_1^2/n_1) + (\sigma_2^2/n_2)}}$$

## Formula for Calculating *z* for Two Population Means

Two Populations: $$z = \frac{(\bar{x}_1 - \bar{x}_2) - (\mu_1 - \mu_2)}{\sqrt{(\sigma_1^2/n_1) + (\sigma_2^2/n_2)}}$$

The formula tests the difference between the sample and population means. The value placed in parentheses $(\mu_1 - \mu_2)$ is the expected difference stated in the hypotheses. That is, if the hypothesis states the difference is greater than 10, then value 10 is placed in parentheses. If no difference is expected, then the value is 0.

### EXAMPLE 13.3

**Experiment:** Farmer A claims that the difference in the mean weights of her turkeys and Farmer B's turkeys is no more than 2 pounds. A random sample of 50 of Farmer A's turkeys produces a mean of 11.2 lbs, whereas a random sample of 50 of Farmer B's turkeys produces a mean of 8.75 lbs. If the population standard deviations are 1.3 and 2.6, respectively, do the samples support Farmer A's claim at the .01 level of significance?

**Answer:** Yes, the samples do support Farmer A's claim.

**Solution:**

**Step 1**

State the hypotheses. The claim that the mean weight of one farmer's turkeys is no more than 2 lbs. greater than the mean weight of her neighbor's turkeys leads to hypotheses concerning two populations. The parameter for means is $\mu$. The difference between two means is written $\mu_1 - \mu_2$. The mathematical symbol representing no more than is $\leq$, less than or equal to. The symbol $\leq$ can be placed only in the null hypothesis. The symbol in the alternative hypothesis must, therefore, be $>$. The value for both hypotheses is the expected difference, which is no more than 2 lbs. The hypotheses are:

$$H_0: \mu_1 - \mu_2 \leq 2 \qquad H_1: \mu_1 - \mu_2 > 2$$

**Step 2**

Identify the test criteria. The level of significance, alpha, is .01. The test statistic is *z*. The normal *z* distribution is applied, because two populations are tested, both samples are large and randomly selected assuring independence, and both standard deviations of the populations are known. The critical region is placed in the right tail, as determined by the $>$ in the alternative hypothesis. The critical value requires subtracting alpha, .01, from .5000, the probability of half the curve, and finding the *z*-score associated with the remaining probability. Because .5000 - .01 equals .4900, the critical $z$ value in Table A.3 associated with the probability .4900 is 2.33.

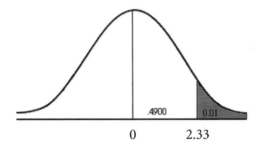

## Step 3

Calculate the test statistic. All the necessary information is given in the problem. Remember that the value for the difference of the population means is the 2 contained in the hypotheses. Also notice that the formula requires the population variances, but the experiment gives standard deviations. The standard deviations must be squared for the calculation. $\bar{x}_1 = 11.2$, $\bar{x}_2 = 8.75$, $n_1 = 50$, $n_2 = 50$, $\sigma_1 = 1.3$, and $\sigma_2 = 2.6$.

$$z = \frac{(\bar{x}_1 - \bar{x}_2) - (\mu_1 - \mu_2)}{\sqrt{(\sigma_1^2/n_1) + (\sigma_2^2/n_2)}} = \frac{(11.2 - 8.75) - (2)}{\sqrt{(1.3^2/50) + (2.6^2/50)}} = 1.09$$

## Step 4

Place the calculated value 1.09 on the distribution curve. It is placed to the left of the critical value 2.33, in the noncritical region.

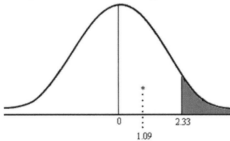

## Step 5

Make a decision based on the placement of the calculated value on the curve. Since the calculated value is not in the critical region, the decision is to fail to reject the null hypothesis.

Fail to reject $H_0$

**Step 6**

Interpret the decision incorporating the language of the experiment. Failing to reject the null hypothesis suggests that the samples support Farmer A's claim that the difference in the mean weights of her turkeys and Farmer B's turkeys is no more than 2 lbs.

## *P*-VALUE APPROACH FOR
## TWO INDEPENDENT MEANS USING $X$

The *P*-value approach for two-population $z$ testing is the same as for one-population $z$ testing. The *P*-value approach goes one step further than the classical approach by transforming the calculated value into a probability that can be compared to alpha for a decision. The first three steps of the *P*-value approach are similar to the classical approach. Only two aspects of the test criteria are necessary: the level of significance and the identification of the test statistic. The hypotheses statements and the calculation of the test statistic are the same. Once the calculated test statistic is determined, the *P*-value is identified and then compared to alpha. If the *P*-value is less than or equal to alpha, then the decision is to reject the null hypothesis. If the *P*-value is greater than alpha, then the decision is to fail to reject the null hypothesis. The final step is the interpretation of the decision to the experiment.

**Steps in Hypothesis Testing using the *P*-Value Approach**
1. State $H_O$ and $H_1$.
2. Identify the test criteria:
    a. Level of significance, $\alpha$
    b. Test statistic ($z$, $t$, $\chi2$, $F$)
3. Calculate the test statistic.
4. Identify the *P*-value.
5. Make a decision:
    a. If $P > \alpha$, Fail to reject $H_O$
    b. If $P \leq \alpha$, Reject $H_O$
6. Interpret the results.

Decisions using *P*-values:
$$P \leq \alpha \quad \text{Reject } H_O$$
$$P > \alpha \quad \text{Fail to reject } H_O$$

## EXAMPLE 13.4

**Experiment:** The registrar of State University claims the mean age of evening students is no more than 5 years greater than the mean age of day students. A random sample of 32-day students produces a mean of 26, whereas a random sample of 40 evening students produces a mean of 33. The population standard deviation of day students is 4 and the standard deviation of evening students is 3. Test using the *P*-value approach at the .05 level of significance.

**Answer:** Reject the null hypothesis; there is sufficient evidence at the .05 level of significance to suggest that the mean age of evening students is more than 5 years greater than the mean age of day students.

**Solution:**

**Step 1**

State the hypotheses. The statement of the registrar is that the mean age of evening students is no more than 5 years greater than the mean age of day students. This statement is the null hypothesis, because the symbol representing no more than (less than or equal to) can be placed only in the null hypothesis. If the null contains the symbol ≤, then the alternative hypothesis must contain the symbol >. The difference between two means requires the parameters $\mu_1 - \mu_2$. The hypothesized difference is 5 years.

$$H_0: \mu_1 - \mu_2 \leq 5 \qquad H_1: \mu_1 - \mu_2 > 5$$

**Step 2**

Identify the test criteria. The level of significance is .05, and the test statistic is the two-population *z* distribution. The *z* distribution is applied to two random samples, where both sample sizes are larger than 30 and both population standard deviations are known.

**Step 3**

Calculate the test statistic. The information required for performing a test on a TI-83 or 84 calculator is $\bar{x}_1 = 33$, $\bar{x}_2 = 26$, $n_1 = 40$, $n_2 = 32$, $\sigma_1 = 3$, and $\sigma_2 = 4$. The calculator assumes the difference between means is zero, so 5 must be subtracted from the higher $\bar{x}$, which in this case is $\bar{x}_1$. Considering this change, the information must be inserted as follows: $\bar{x}_1 = 28$, $\bar{x}_2 = 26$, $n_1 = 40$, $n_2 = 32$, $\sigma_1 = 3$, and $\sigma_2 = 4$. Once the proper data is entered, scroll down to highlight "Calculate" and press ENTER. The results will display.

Begin the test on the calculator by pressing the STAT button, scrolling over to "TESTS," followed by pressing 3 to select "3:2-SampZTest." Considering the problem and the formula for the test statistic, it is important to acknowledge that the test implies that the "mean age of students is no more than 5 years

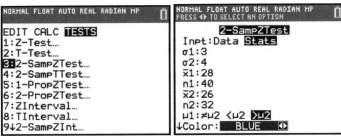

$$z = \frac{\left(\bar{x}_1 - \bar{x}_2\right) - \left(\mu_1 - \mu_2\right)}{\sqrt{\left(\sigma_1^2/n_1\right) + \left(\sigma_2^2/n_2\right)}} = \frac{(33-26)-(5)}{\sqrt{\left(3^2/40\right) + \left(4^2/32\right)}} = 2.35$$

**Step 4**

The *P*-value is identified in the result screen.

$$P\text{-value} = .0094$$

**Step 5**

The *P*-value must be compared to alpha to make a decision about the null hypothesis. Compare the *P*-value, .0094, to alpha, .05. Because $P < \alpha$, reject the null hypothesis.

$$P_{(.0094)} \leq \alpha(.05) \qquad \text{Reject } H_O$$

**Step 6**

Rejecting the null hypothesis suggests there is sufficient proof at the .05 level of significance that the mean age of evening students is more than 5 years greater than the mean age of day students.

## CONFIDENCE INTERVAL FOR
## TWO INDEPENDENT MEANS USING Z

The confidence interval for two-population *z* estimation is similar to that for one population estimation. The only difference is in the formula, which must now represent two sample means. Confidence intervals estimate parameters. When estimating the difference of two population means, the estimation is based on the difference of two sample means. The confidence interval establishes a range around the difference of the sample means in which the difference of the population means should fall.

The level of confidence establishes the width of the interval and thus the probability that the parameter will be contained in the interval. The level of confidence is usually reported as a percentage; to rewrite a percentage as a probability requires dropping the percent sign and moving the decimal two places to the left. If a level of confidence is 95%, then the probability is .95. Alpha is the opposite of the level of confidence. If the level of confidence is .95, then alpha is .05. The level of confidence and alpha have a sum of 1. Because the interval establishes a range of values around the sample statistic, all confidence intervals are considered two-tailed.

If using tables in the appendix, the critical value for $z$ requires alpha and Table A.3. Alpha is divided by 2 and then subtracted from .5000. If alpha is .05, alpha divided by 2 is .025. Subtracting .025 from .5000 results in .4750. Using Table A.3, the probability of .4750 is associated with a critical $z$ value of 1.96. The critical value is noted as $z(\alpha/2)$ and is retained for the calculation of the interval.

The formula for estimating two large, independent means results from algebraic manipulation of the test statistic formula. To apply this formula for estimating means, both samples must be large, the samples must be independent, and the standard deviations of the populations must be known; all three conditions must be met before using the formula.

The first formula establishes the upper limit of the interval, and the second formula establishes the lower limit. The value representing $z(\alpha/2)$ is the critical value identified in an earlier step. Be sure to notice whether the information given in an experiment is a standard deviation or a variance. The formula requires the variance. Standard deviations are squared to give variances. The notation of the interval derived from the calculation is written in terms of the difference of the population means.

---

**Formula for Calculating Confidence Interval z for Two Population Means**

$$E(\mu_1 - \mu_2) = (\bar{x}_1 - \bar{x}_2) \pm z_{(\alpha/2)} \sqrt{\frac{\sigma_1^2}{n_1} + \frac{\sigma_2^2}{n_2}}$$

States as:

$$E(\mu_1 - \mu_2) = (\text{Lower limit} < (\mu - \mu) < \text{Upper limit})$$

---

The approach to confidence intervals using the TI-83/84 calculators is very similar to using the table version. The biggest difference is that the critical value is not needed on the calculator. Needed information is only the sample mean, sample standard deviation, sample size, and the confidence interval.

---

**Steps in Calculating a Confidence Interval Using the Calculator**
1. Identify the level of confidence (90%, 95%, 99%).
2. Identify the test statistic ($z$, $t$, $\chi^2$, or $F$).
3. Identify the calculator function and enter the data.
4. State the interval.

---

**EXAMPLE 13.5**
**Experiment:** Estimate with 90% certainty the difference between the mean grocery bill at Food Mart and the mean grocery bill at Sav-On Market. A random sample of 40 bills from Food Mart produces a mean of $69.50; the population standard deviation is $16.91. A random sample of 40 bills from Sav-On Market produces a mean of $61.25 and a population standard deviation of $19.35.

**Answer:** $E(\mu_1 - \mu_2) = (\$1.568 < (\mu - \mu) < \$14.932)$

**Solution:**
The problem requires a 90% confidence interval for the difference of two population means. The level of confidence and alpha must have a sum of 1. The test statistic is $z$ for two population means. Both samples are large (>30), both samples are randomly selected (resulting in independence), and both population standard deviations are reported.

The next step is to calculate the interval. The calculation of the estimation of the test statistic $z$ requires the following information:

$\bar{x}_1 = 69.50$, $\bar{x}_2 = 61.25$, $n_1 = 40$, $n_2 = 40$, $\sigma_1 = 16.91$, and $\sigma_2 = 19.35$.

Because the only difference between the calculation of the upper limit and lower limit is the addition and subtraction, respectively, of the right part of the formula, the calculation can be performed once, with the appropriate addition or subtraction at the end, but the calculation of the confidence interval can also be done by utilizing the interval function on a TI-83/84 calculator.

Begin by pressing STAT and scrolling over to "TESTS." Press the 9 button to select "9:2-SampZInterval…" With the "Stats" option selected, plug in the given information. Once completed, scroll down to highlight "Calculate" and press ENTER.

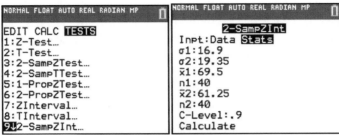

$$E(\mu_1 - \mu_2) = (\bar{x}_1 - \bar{x}_2) \pm z_{(\alpha/2)}\sqrt{\frac{\sigma_1^2}{n_1} + \frac{\sigma_2^2}{n_2}}$$

Lower limit = 1.568
Upper limit = 14.932

The confidence interval has a lower limit of 1.568 and an upper limit of 14.932. Therefore, with 90% confidence, the difference between the mean grocery bills from Food Mart and Sav-On Market is between $1.568 and $14.932.

$$E(\mu_1 - \mu_2) = (\$1.568 < (\mu_1 - \mu_2) < \$14.932)$$

## A LEARNING AID
## TWO INDEPENDENT MEANS: z

Test whether the average cost of repairs at Maria's Garage is greater than the average cost of repairs at Dino's Garage. A random selection of 50 repairs at Maria's garage produces a mean of $100.15. A random selection of 60 repairs at Dino's Garage produces a mean of $90.55. Assume the standard deviation of all repairs at Maria's is $25.33 and at Dino's is $18.79. Use the classical approach with alpha of .05.

### Step 1
State the hypotheses. The claim is that the average cost of repairs at Maria's is greater than the average cost of repairs at Dino's. The test is for two

populations, because it is asking about average costs at two garages. The test is for means, because two means are being tested, the mean cost of repairs at the two garages. Randomization ensures independent samples. The greater than symbol is used in the claim, which makes the claim an alternative hypothesis. If the alternative hypothesis is greater than (>), then the null hypothesis must be less than or equal to ≤. The value place in the hypothesis is 0, unless otherwise stated in the claim. The hypotheses for two population means are written:

$$H_O: \mu_1 - \mu_2 \le 0 \qquad H_I: \mu_1 - \mu_2 > 0$$

**Step 2**

Identify the test criteria. Alpha is given as .05. Use the test statistic $z$ for two population means that are independent with large samples (both $n_1$ and $n_2$ are greater than 30) and where both population standard deviations are known.

**Step 3**

Calculate the test statistic. The test statistic is $z$ for two independent large samples. Because the hypothesis statement tests whether the cost of repairs at Maria's garage is greater than Dino's, Maria's Garage is population 1 and Dino's is population 2. The information given is $\bar{x}_1 = 100.15$, $\bar{x}_2 = 90.55$, $n_1 = 50$, $n_2 = 60$, $\sigma_1 = 25.33$, and $\sigma_2 = 18.79$.

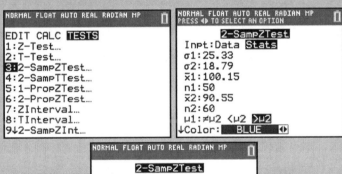

$$z = \frac{(\bar{x}_1 - \bar{x}_2) - (\mu_1 - \mu_2)}{\sqrt{(\sigma_1^2/n_1) + (\sigma_2^2/n_2)}} = \frac{(100.15 - 90.55) - 0}{\sqrt{(25.33^2/50) + (18.79^2/60)}} = 2.22$$

**Step 4**
Identify the *P*-value from the result screen. $P = .0132$

**Step 5**
Make a decision by comparing the *P*-value to the alpha level.

$$P\text{-value } (.0132) < \text{alpha } (.05) \quad \text{Reject } H_o$$

**Step 6**
Interpret the results. Rejecting the null hypothesis suggests that there is sufficient evidence at the .05 level of significance that the average cost of repairs for Maria's Garage is greater than the average cost at Dino's Garage.

# SECTION 2

## Two Independent Means: *t*

The *z* normal distribution represents the probability distribution of means for large independent samples where the population standard deviation is known. It is rare that the population standard deviation is known, given the population mean is being tested. Also it is common that the sample size is small. Recall from Chapter 11 that the Student *t* distribution is a probability distribution similar to *z*, but it represents small samples where the population standard deviation is not known. The *t* distribution is also applied to two population mean testing where the samples are small or the population standard deviations are not known.

The *t* distribution is symmetric and approximately normal, with the mean denoted by 0 and located in the middle of the curve. All *t* values below the mean are negative. Each probability distribution represented by *t* is dependent on the degrees of freedom and the level of significance.

**Criteria for Using t for Two Means**
1. Samples are independent.
2. $\sigma_1$ and/or $\sigma_2$ are unknown and/or,
3. $n_1$ and/or $n_2$ are less than or equal to 30.

Hypothesis testing for two independent population means with small sample sizes or with unknown population standard deviations follows the same six steps as does the other test statistics. State the hypotheses, identify the test criteria, calculate the test statistic, place the calculated value on the distribution curve, make a decision, and interpret the results.

**Steps in Hypothesis Testing Using the Classical Approach**
1. State $H_o$ and $H_1$.
2. Identify the test criteria:
   a. Level of significance, $\alpha$
   b. Test statistic ($z$, $t$, $\chi2$, $F$)
   c. Critical Region
      (1) One-tailed test
      (2) Two-tailed test ($\alpha/2$)
   d. Critical value
3. Calculate the test statistic.
4. Place the calculated value on a distribution curve.
5. Make a decision:
   a. Fail to reject $H_o$
   b. Reject $H_o$
6. Interpret the results.

The hypotheses statements for $t$ are written exactly as they are for $z$. The parameters are $\mu_1$ and $\mu_2$, the mathematical symbol is determined by the claim, and a value represents the expected difference between the population means. If no difference is expected, then the value is 0.

$$H_o: \mu_1 - \mu_2 = 0 \qquad H_1: \mu_1 - \mu_2 \neq 0$$

The critical value for $t$ requires the level of significance and the degrees of freedom. The degrees of freedom for $t$ two population means are found by adding the sample sizes and subtracting 2 ($df = n_1 + n_2 - 2$). The number of degrees of freedom for two populations differs from $n - 1$, for one population; both sample sizes must be considered for the degrees of freedom. Alpha is usually reported in an experiment. Remember that alpha is divided by 2 for two-tailed tests. All critical values below the mean are negative. Table A.4 reports the critical values for the $t$ distribution.

**Degrees of Freedom for Two-Population $t$ Tests when the Variances Are Assumed Equal**
$$df = n_1 + n_2 - 2$$

## EXAMPLE 13.6

**Experiment:** Find the critical $t$ values for the following information.
a. $H_o: \mu_1 - \mu_2 = 0$, $H_1: \mu_1 - \mu_2 \neq 0$, $n_1 = 30$, $n_2 = 25$, $\alpha = .05$
b. $H_o: \mu_1 - \mu_2 \leq 0$, $H_1: \mu_1 - \mu_2 > 0$, $n_1 = 7$, $n_2 = 8$, $\alpha = .01$
c. $H_o: \mu_1 - \mu_2 \geq 0$, $H_1: \mu_1 - \mu_2 < 0$, $n_1 = 12$, $n_2 = 15$, $\alpha = .10$

**Answer:**
a. 1.960 and - 1.960
b. 2.650
c. -1.316

**Solution:** Critical values for *t* require alpha and degrees of freedom. The degrees of freedom for two-population *t* are $n_1 + n_2 - 2$. The existence of two populations is evident in that the hypotheses contain two parameters, $\mu_1 - \mu_2$.

a. This experiment is a two-tailed test. The mathematical symbol "=" in the alternative denotes a two-tailed test. Divide alpha by two: .05/2 = .025. The degrees of freedom are $n_1 + n_2 - 2$, or 30 + 25 - 2, which is 53. Use Table A.4. Trace down to 53 degrees of freedom and across to alpha = .025. The degrees of freedom reported at the bottom of the *df* column represent all degrees of freedom larger than 29. The value found in this row under the alpha of .025 is 1.96. Because this is a two-tailed test and *t* is symmetric, the value 1.960 is the right-tailed value; - 1.960 is the left-tailed value. The notations are:

$$t(53, .025) = 1.960 \quad \text{and} \quad -t(53, .025) = -1.960$$

b. The second experiment is one-tailed to the right, as determined by the symbol > in the alternative hypothesis. Alpha is not divided for one-tailed tests. Alpha is .01. Degrees of freedom are $n_1 + n_2 - 2$, or 7 + 8 - 2, or 13. Trace down Table A.4 to 13 degrees of freedom and across to alpha = .01. The critical value is 2.650.

$$t(13, .01) = 2.650$$

c. The third experiment is one-tailed to the left, as determined by the symbol < in the alternative hypothesis. Alpha is .10. The degrees of freedom are 12 + 15 - 2, or 25. Trace down Table A.4 to *df* 25 and across to alpha = .10. The critical value is - 1.316. Do not forget the negative sign, because the critical value falls below the mean in the left tail of the distribution curve:

$$-t(25, .10) = -1.316$$

The calculation of the *t* test statistic for two populations is different than the formula for one-population *t* and one- or two-population *z*. Recall the adjustment of the calculation for the one-population *z* test statistic for the *t* calculation. The population standard deviation in the *z* formula is replaced by the sample standard deviation in the *t* test.

$$z = \frac{\bar{x} - \mu}{\sigma/\sqrt{n}} \qquad t = \frac{\bar{x} - \mu}{s/\sqrt{n}}$$

The adjustment for two populations cannot be accomplished this easily. Recall that the denominator in $z$ is referred to as the standard error. Because the standard error involves an error, the error is slightly increased in $t$ with the substitution of $s$ for $\sigma$. If the same substitution is done for the two-population $z$ calculation containing two standard errors, then the error will greatly increase. Several statistical approaches are available to avoid the increased error. Some test the equality of the variances (contained in the standard error) before applying one of two calculations for $t$. Others simply accept the substitution of the population variances with the sample variances when samples are large; another accepts substitution when samples are small. One uniform rule is used in this text. Any time either sample is small or a standard deviation or variance is unknown, the following $t$ test statistic is applied.

---

**Formula Calculating $t$ for Two Independent Means
(Pooled Variance Approach)**

$$t = \frac{(\bar{x}_1 - \bar{x}_2) - (\mu_1 - \mu_2)}{\sqrt{\dfrac{(n_1 - 1)s_1^2 + (n_2 - 1)s_2^2}{n_1 + n_2 - 2}} \sqrt{\dfrac{1}{n_1} + \dfrac{1}{n_2}}}$$

---

The formula appears complicated. The complexity results from the estimation of the unknown population variances. The first part of the denominator is referred to as the estimate of the pooled variances. The notation for the estimate of the pooled variances is $s_p$.

This calculated value is placed on the distribution curve and compared to the critical value. If the calculated value is in the critical region, then the decision is to reject the null hypothesis. If the calculated value is not in the critical region, then the decision is to fail to reject the null hypothesis.

---

**EXAMPLE 13.7**

**Experiment:** A study was designed to compare the attitudes of two groups of nursing students toward computers. Group 1 had previously taken a statistical methods course that involved significant computer interaction. Group 2 had taken a statistical methods course that did not use computers. Using an index of anxiety, random samples were drawn, producing the following measures.

Group 1: $n = 12$ $\bar{x} = 60.3$ $s = 5.62$
Group 2: $n = 14$ $\bar{x} = 67.2$ $s = 4.39$

---

Do the data show that the mean score for those with computer experience was significantly less than the mean score for those without computer experience? Use $\alpha = .05$.

**Answer:** Yes, there is sufficient evidence to suggest that the mean score for those with computer experience was significantly less than the mean score for those without computer experience.

**Solution:** To state the hypotheses, determine if this is one population or two. Two groups are sampled and the difference between the means is tested. The samples are independent; randomization ensures independent sampling. The experiment questions whether the nursing students with computer experience have, on the average, less anxiety than those without computer experience. The parameters are $\mu_1$ and $\mu_2$. The words less than denote the alternative hypothesis, because the symbol < can be placed only in the alternative hypothesis. The null hypothesis must then be $\geq$. Place the value 0 in the hypothesis as the expected difference, because no other difference is stated. The 0 implies that any difference less than 0 is sufficient to reject the null hypothesis. The hypotheses are:

$$H_0: \mu_1 - \mu_2 \geq 0 \qquad H_1: \mu_1 - \mu_2 < 0$$

The test criteria include the level of significance, test statistic, critical region, and critical value. The level of significance is reported as .05. The test statistic is $t$. Use $t$ when either sample is small (n $\leq$ 30) or when either population standard deviation is unknown. Both samples of nursing students are small and neither reports a population standard deviation, only the sample standard deviations. The critical region is to the left, as determined by the < symbol in the alternative hypothesis. The critical value is determined by alpha and the degrees of freedom. Alpha is .05. The degrees of freedom are $n_1 + n_2 - 2$, or 12 + 14 - 2 = 24. Use Table A.4. Trace down to $df$ 24 and across to alpha .05. The critical value is -1.711. The negative sign denotes its location below the mean.

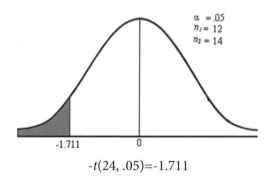

$-t(24, .05) = -1.711$

The calculation of the test statistic $t$ for two populations is the formula containing the pooled-variance denominator.

$$t = \frac{\left(\bar{x}_1 - \bar{x}_2\right) - \left(\mu_1 - \mu_2\right)}{\sqrt{\dfrac{\left(n_1 - 1\right)s_1^2 + \left(n_2 - 1\right)s_2^2}{n_1 + n_2 - 2}} \sqrt{\dfrac{1}{n_1} + \dfrac{1}{n_2}}} = -3.519$$

Place the calculated value, -3.519, on the distribution curve. The calculated value, -3.519, falls to the left of the critical value, -1.711.

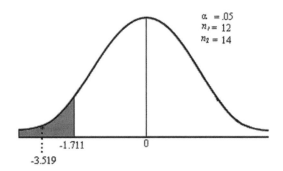

The decision is to reject the null hypothesis. The interpretation is that the samples do provide sufficient evidence at the .05 level of significance that the mean score for those with computer experience was significantly less than the mean score for those without computer experience.

## P-VALUE APPROACH FOR TWO INDEPENDENT MEANS USING *t*

The P-value approach for testing with $t$ for two population means is exactly the same as it is for the one-population $t$. The P-value approaches extend the classical approach by transforming the calculated value into a probability that is compared to alpha for a decision.

P-value testing requires several steps similar to the classical approach. The hypotheses are stated, the test criteria are identified, and the test statistic is calculated. The P-value is identified. The P-value is compared to alpha. If the P-value is less than or equal to alpha, then decision is to reject the null hypothesis. If the P-value is greater than alpha, then decision is to fail to reject the null hypothesis.

### Steps in Hypothesis Testing Using the *P*-Value Approach
1. State $H_o$ and $H_1$.

2. Identify the test criteria:
   a. Level of significance, $\alpha$
   b. Test statistic $(z, t, \chi^2, F)$
3. Calculate the test statistic.
4. Identify the $P$-value.
5. Make a decision:
   a. If $P > \alpha$, Fail to reject $H_o$
   b. If $P \leq \alpha$, Reject $H_o$.
6. Interpret the results.

Decisions using $P$-values
$P \leq \alpha$ Reject $H_O$
$P > \alpha$ Fail to reject $H_O$

## EXAMPLE 13.8

**Experiment:** It is argued that the risk of complications in pregnancy is greater for women over age 35 than for women 34 years old and younger. A random sample of 10 women age 35 and older produces an average of 5.2 complications, with a standard deviation of 1.2. A random sample of 20 women age 34 and younger produces an average of 4.1, with a standard deviation of .95. Use the $P$-value approach. Do the samples provide sufficient evidence that complications for women age 35 and older is greater than those age 34 and younger. Use $\alpha = .05$.

**Answer:** Yes, there is sufficient evidence to support the assumption that the risk of complications in pregnancy increases with the age of the mother.

**Solution:** To state the hypotheses, determine if this is one population or two. Two groups are sampled and the difference between the means is tested. Randomization ensures independent sampling. The experiment questions whether complications are greater for those women over 35 than for those younger. The parameters are $\mu_1$ and $\mu_2$. The words "greater than" indicate the alternative hypothesis because the symbol > can be placed only in the alternative hypothesis. The null hypothesis must then be $\leq$. Place the value 0 in the hypothesis as the expected difference, because no other difference is stated. The 0 implies that any difference less than 0 is sufficient to reject the null hypothesis. The hypotheses are:

$$H_O: \mu_1 - \mu_2 \leq 0 \qquad H_I: \mu_1 - \mu_2 > 0$$

The test criteria include alpha and the test statistic. Alpha is reported as .05. The test statistic is *t*. Use *t* when either sample is small ($n \le 30$) or when either population standard deviation is unknown. The critical region is to the right, as determined by the > symbol in the alternative hypothesis.

The calculation of the test statistic *t* for two populations is the formula containing the pooled-variance denominator. Arrange the data for the calculation: $\bar{x}_1 = 5.2$, $\bar{x}_2 = 4.1$, $n_1 = 10$, $n_2 = 20$, $s_1 = 1.2$, and $s_2 = .95$.

Begin by pressing the STAT button, followed by scrolling over to "TESTS". Press the 4 button to select "4:2-SampTTest…" With the "Stats" option selected, fill in the proper information, including the alternative hypothesis. Be sure "Yes" selected for the pooled option.

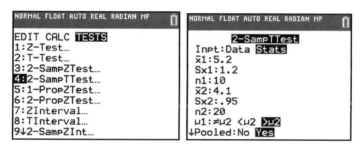

Once completed, scroll down to highlight "Calculate" and press ENTER. The results will display.

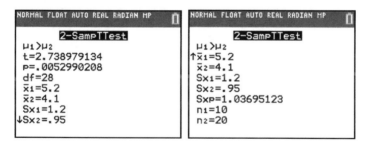

$$t = \frac{(\bar{x}_1 - \bar{x}_2) - (\mu_1 - \mu_2)}{\sqrt{\dfrac{(n_1 - 1)s_1^2 + (n_2 - 1)s_2^2}{n_1 + n_2 - 2}} \sqrt{\dfrac{1}{n_1} + \dfrac{1}{n_2}}} = 2.739$$

Identify the *P*-value from the test result screen. $P = .0053$

Compare the *P*-value to the original alpha given in the experiment. If $P \le \alpha$, then reject the null hypothesis. If $P > \alpha$, then fail to reject the null hypothesis. *P* at .0053 is less than $\alpha$ at .05; therefore, reject the null hypothesis.

$$P_{(.0053)} \leq \alpha(.05) \qquad \text{Reject } H_O$$

The interpretation is that the samples do provide sufficient evidence at the .05 level of significance that the mean number of complications for women over age 35 is not equal to the mean number of complications for women 34 and younger. It suggests that the difference is greater than 0.

## CONFIDENCE INTERVAL FOR
## TWO INDEPENDENT MEANS USING *t*

The confidence interval for two-population *t* estimation is similar to that for one population estimation. The confidence interval establishes a range of values around the sample information in which the population parameter will fall. With two population means, the confidence interval establishes a range around the difference of the sample means in which the difference of the population means will fall. To estimate the difference between two population means with the *t* statistic, the samples must be independent, with either sample size less than or equal to 30 or either population standard deviation unknown. Any of these conditions is sufficient for estimating with *t*.

---

**The Formula for a Confidence Interval for the Difference of Two Population Means Where the Samples Are Independent, Sample Sizes ≤ 30, and $\sigma_1$ and $\sigma_2$ Are Unknown**

$$E(\mu_1 - \mu_2) = (\bar{x}_1 - \bar{x}_2) \pm t_{(\alpha/2)}\sqrt{\frac{(n_1-1)s_1^2 + (n_2-1)s_2^2}{n_1 + n_2 - 2}}\sqrt{\frac{1}{n_1} + \frac{1}{n_2}}$$

---

This formula estimates the difference between the population means based on the difference of the sample means. The *t* symbol indicates the data to the right of the symbol should be added to $\bar{x}_1 - \bar{x}_2$ to determine the upper limit of the confidence interval and subtracted to find the lower limit of the interval. Because the data to the right of the symbol remains constant, the addition and subtraction occurs at the end of the calculation.

---

**Steps in Calculating a Confidence Interval Using the Calculator**
1. Identify the level of confidence (90%, 95%, 99%).
2. Identify the test statistic (*z*, *t*, $\chi^2$, or *F*).
3. Identify the test statistic on the calculator and enter the data.
4. State the interval.

---

## EXAMPLE 13.9

**Experiment:** Find the 90% confidence interval for the difference between the mean age of members in the U.S. Senate and U.S. House of Representatives. Twenty members from both institutions are randomly selected, producing means of 45 and 39, respectively, and variances of 19.2 and 28.6, respectively.

**Answer:** $E(\mu_1 - \mu_2) = (3.3934 < (\mu - \mu) < 8.606)$

**Solution:** Begin by identifying the experiment as a confidence interval. The experiment asks for a 90% confidence interval. A 90% level of confidence means that the difference of the population parameters should fail in the range of values 90% of the time. Stated another way, the probability of estimating correctly is .90.

Use the *t* statistic for the experiment, because the sample sizes are both small, the samples are independent, and the population standard deviations are unknown.

To calculate the interval, the following information is necessary:

$\bar{x}_1 = 45$, $\bar{x}_2 = 39$, $s^2_1 = 19.2$, $s^2_2 = 28.6$, $n_1 = 20$, $n_2 = 20$, and confidence level of .90. Press the STAT button, scroll over to "TESTS" and press 0 to select "0:2-SampTInt..." Under the settings screen of the calculator, be sure the "Stats" option is selected. Plug in the given information from the question. For the standard deviation values, remember to take the square root of the variance given. This can be done in the settings screen. With "Yes" selected under the pooled option, scroll down to highlight "Calculate" and press ENTER. The results will appear.

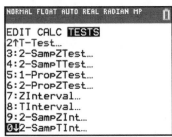
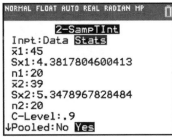
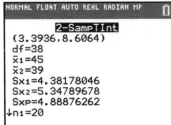

$$E_{(\mu_1 - \mu_2)} = (\bar{x}_1 - \bar{x}_2) \pm t_{(df, \alpha/2)} \sqrt{\frac{(n-1)s_1^2 + (n-1)s_2^2}{n_1 + n_2 - 2}} \sqrt{\frac{1}{n} + \frac{1}{n}}$$

Lower limit = 3.394
Upper limit = 8.606

The confidence interval has a lower limit of 3.394 and an upper limit of 8.606. Therefore, with 90% confidence, the difference between the average ages of U.S. Senators and Representatives is between 3.394 and 8.606 years.

$$E(\mu_1 - \mu_2) = (3.394 < (\mu_1 - \mu_2) < 8.606)$$

## A LEARNING AID
## TWO INDEPENDENT MEANS, $t$

A random sample of 20 used cars in the suburbs produces a mean of $1,200 with a standard deviation of $300. A random sample of 25 used cars in the city produces a mean of $800 with a standard deviation of $340. Do the data show that the mean of used cars in the suburbs is significantly greater than the mean in the city? Use $\alpha = .05$.

**Step 1**
State the hypotheses. Begin by determining if there is one population or two. Two groups are sampled and the difference between the means is tested. Randomization ensures independent sampling. The experiment questions whether the cost of cars in the suburbs is greater than the cost of cars in the city. The parameters are $\mu_1$ and $\mu_2$. The words greater than indicate the alternative hypothesis, because the symbol > can be placed only in the alternative hypothesis. The null hypothesis must then be ≤. Place the value 0 in the hypothesis as the expected difference, because no other difference is stated. The 0 implies that any difference greater than 0 is sufficient to reject the null hypothesis. The hypotheses are:

$$H_0: \mu_1 - \mu_2 \le 0 \qquad H_1: \mu_1 - \mu_2 > 0$$

**Step 2**
Identify the test criteria. The test criteria include the level of significance, test statistic, critical region, and critical value. The level of significance is reported as .05. The test statistic is $t$. Use $t$ when either sample is small ($n \le 30$) or when either population standard deviation is unknown. Both samples of cars are small and a population standard deviation is not given in either case.

**Step 3**

Calculate the test statistic $t$. The calculation of $t$ for two populations is the formula containing the pooled-variance denominator. The necessary information is $\bar{x}_1 = 1200$, $\bar{x}_2 = 800$, $s_1 = 300$, $s_2 = 340$, $n_1 = 20$ and $n_2 = 25$. To perform this test in a calculator, begin by pressing STAT, followed by scrolling over to "TESTS." Press the 4 button to select "4:2-SampTTest…" Insert the values given in the problem into the proper places. With the correct alternative selected and "Yes" selected under pooled, highlight "Calculate" and press ENTER. The results will appear.

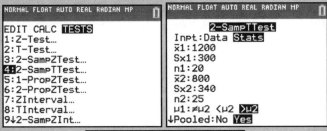

$$t = \frac{(\bar{x}_1 - \bar{x}_2) - (\mu_1 - \mu_2)}{\sqrt{\dfrac{(n_1 - 1)s_1^2 + (n_2 - 1)s_2^2}{n_1 + n_2 - 2}} \sqrt{\dfrac{1}{n_1} + \dfrac{1}{n_2}}} = 4.129$$

**Step 4**

Identify the $P$-value on the test result screen. $P = .00008$ or $0+$.

**Step 5**

Make a decision by comparing the $P$-value to the alpha level.

$$P\text{-value}(0+) < \text{alpha}(.05) \qquad \text{Reject } H_O$$

**Step 6**

Interpret the results. The interpretation is that the samples do provide sufficient evidence at the .05 level of significance that the mean cost of used cars in the suburbs is not less than or equal to the mean cost of used cars in the city. That is, it appears that the cost is greater.

# SECTION 3

## Two Proportions: z

In Chapter 12, the $z$ distribution was used to test claims of a proportion of one population. Similarly, the $z$ distribution is also applied in testing and estimating the proportions of two populations using two in independent samples. For example, is the proportion of females majoring in the STEM sciences less than the proportion of males? Is the proportion of Catholics at the school equal to the proportion of non-Catholics? The test for proportions of two populations is the normal $z$-test with a slight adjustment in the calculation representing the mean population proportions ($p_1$ and $p_2$). The stages of hypothesis testing and estimation remain the same for the $z$ test for independent sampling.

The hypotheses are written slightly differently than they are written for independent sampling. Because the difference between the first sample proportion and the second sample proportion is in question, the notation:

If $H_o$ is $p_1 - p_2 = 0$      then $H_1$ is $p_1 - p_2 \neq 0$
If $H_o$ is $p_1 - p_2 \geq 0$      then $H_1$ is $p_1 - p_2 < 0$
If $H_o$ is $p_1 - p_2 \leq 0$      then $H_1$ is $p_1 - p_2 > 0$

### Formula for Calculating z for Two Population Proportions

$$z = \frac{\hat{p}_1 - \hat{p}_2}{\sqrt{\dfrac{pq}{n_1} + \dfrac{pq}{n_2}}}$$

where
$n_1$ and $n_2$ are the number of trials or the sample sizes for each sample.

$p$ is the pooled estimate of the population proportions $p = \dfrac{x_1 + x_2}{n_1 + n_2}$
$q$ is $1 - p$.
$\hat{p}_1$ is the sample proportion calculated as $x_1/n_1$.
$\hat{p}_2$ is the sample proportion calculated as $x_2/n_2$.

The formula tests the difference between the sample proportions against the pooled estimate of the population proportions. Doing the calculation by hand is a bit involved since the pooled estimate of the proportion must be calculated as well as then calculating $q$. Depending on how the information is reported, the calculation of the sample proportions may also need to be completed. Using the TI series calculator makes the calculation much easier than the formula itself. For the calculator, the information needed is $x_1$, $x_2$, $n_1$ and $n_2$.

---

**EXAMPLE 13.10**

**Experiment:** Using the classical approach, is there a significant difference in the proportion of drivers regularly wearing their seat belts based on their gender? Of males randomly selected 20 men from 40 claim to regularly wear their seat belts whereas 30 from 50 randomly selected women claim to wear their seat belts regularly. At the .05 level of significance, test if there is a significant difference in the proportion of drivers regularly wearing their seat belts.

**Answer:** No, the does not seem to be a significant difference in the proportion of drivers regularly wearing seat belts based on their gender.

**Solution:**

**Step 1**
State the hypotheses. The claim that the proportion of drivers regularly wearing their seat belts does not differ based on gender. The parameter being tested is the proportions $p$. The difference between two means is written $p_1 - p_2$. The mathematical symbol representing no difference =. The symbol = can be placed only in the null hypothesis. The symbol in the alternative hypothesis must, therefore, be $\neq$. The hypotheses are:

$$H_0: p_1 - p_2 = 0 \qquad H_1: p_1 - p_2 \neq 0$$

**Step 2**
Identify the test criteria. The level of significance, alpha, is .05. The test statistic is $z$. The normal $z$ distribution is applied, because two proportions are tested. Divide alpha by 2 before placing it in the critical regions of the right and left tails: $.05/2 = .025$. The area of the noncritical region is found by subtracting .025 from .5000, the probability of half a normal curve. The probability of the noncritical region is .5000 - .025, or .4750. Using Table A.3, find the probability .4750. Reading across and up to the $z$ critical values in the margins, .4750 is associated with the $z$ value 1.96. Because the normal curve is symmetric, 1.96 for the right tail is -1.96 for the left tail.

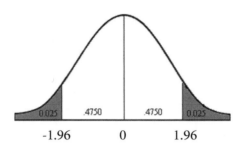

-1.96       0       1.96

## Step 3
Calculation of the test statistic. All the necessary information is given in the problem. The information from the problem is: $x_1 = 20$, $x_2 = 30$, $n_1 = 40$, and $n_2 = 50$

Pooled estimate of the proportions $p = \dfrac{x_1 + x_2}{n_1 + n_2} = \dfrac{20 + 30}{40 + 50} = 0.55$

So if $p = .55$ and $q = 1 - p$, $q$ must be $q = 1 - .55 = .45$.

$$\hat{p}_1 = \frac{x_1}{n_1} = \frac{20}{40} = .5 \text{ and } \hat{p}_2 = \frac{x_2}{n_2} = \frac{30}{50} = .6$$

and finally the formula for $z$:

$$z = \frac{\hat{p}_1 - \hat{p}_2}{\sqrt{\dfrac{pq}{n_1} + \dfrac{pq}{n_2}}} = \frac{.5 - .6}{\sqrt{\dfrac{(.55)(.45)}{40} + \dfrac{(.55)(.45)}{50}}} = {}^-.95$$

## Step 4
Place the calculated value on the distribution curve. It is placed to the left side of the curve since it is negative.

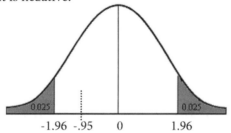

-1.96 -.95    0       1.96

## Step 5
Make a decision based on the placement of the calculated value on the curve. Since the calculated value is not in the critical region, the decision is to fail to reject the null hypothesis.

Fail to reject $H_O$

**Step 6**

The final step is to interpret the decision incorporating the language of the experiment. Failing to reject the null hypothesis suggests that at the .05 level of significance, there is no significant difference in the proportion of males and females regularly wearing their seat belts.

## *P*-VALUE APPROACH FOR
## TWO INDEPENDENT PROPORTIONS USING *z*

The *P*-value approach for two-proportion *z* testing is the similar as for one-proportion *z* testing. The *P*-value approach goes one step further than the classical approach by transforming the calculated value into a probability that can be compared to alpha for a decision. The first three steps of the *P*-value approach are similar to the classical approach. Only two aspects of the test criteria are necessary: the level of significance and the identification of the test statistic. The hypotheses statements and the calculation of the test statistic are the same. Once the calculated test statistic, the *P*-value is identified. The *P*-value associated with the probability is determined and then compared to alpha. If the *P*-value is less than or equal to alpha, then the decision is to reject the null hypothesis. If the *P*-value is greater than alpha, then the decision is to fail to reject the null hypothesis. The final step is the interpretation of the decision to the experiment.

**Steps in Hypothesis Testing Using the *P*-Value Approach**
1. State $H_o$ and $H_1$.
2. Identify the test criteria:
   a. Level of significance, $\alpha$
   b. Test statistic (z, t, $x^2$, F)
3. Calculate the test statistic.
4. Identify the *P*-value.
5. Make a decision:
   a. If $P > \alpha$, Fail to Reject $H_o$
   b. If $P \le \alpha$, Reject $H_o$
6. Interpret the results.

Decisions using *P*-values
$$P \le \alpha \text{ Reject } H_O$$
$$P > \alpha \text{ Fail to reject } H_O$$

**EXAMPLE 13.11**

**Experiment:** The registrar of State University claims the there is a larger proportion of graduate students in the MBA program taking online courses than graduate students in Engineering taking online courses. A random sample of MBA students produced 180 of 200 MBA students claiming to take online courses while 120 out of 150 engineering graduate students report taking online courses. Test the claim using the $P$-value approach at the .05 level of significance.

**Answer:** Reject the null hypothesis; there is sufficient evidence at the .05 level of significance to suggest that the proportion of MBA students taking online courses is statistically greater than engineering graduate students.

**Solution:**

**Step 1**

State the hypotheses. The registrar claims that there is a larger proportion of MBA students taking online courses than graduate engineering students; therefore, the proportions are being tested and the symbol representing "larger" can only be placed in the alternative hypothesis. Since the greater than symbol is in the alternative, the null symbol can only be $\leq$.

$$H_0: p_1 - p_2 \leq 0 \qquad H_1: p_1 - p_2 > 0$$

**Step 2**

Identify the test criteria. The level of significance is .05, and the test statistic is the two-population $z$ distribution. The $z$ distribution is applied to two proportion testing using two random samples. The test is one-tailed to the right.

**Step 3**

Calculate the test statistic. The information from the problem is: $x_1 = 180$, $n_1 = 200$, $x_2 = 120$, and $n_2 = 150$. Using the calculator, the $z$-value can be found by pressing STAT, followed by scrolling over to "TESTS." Press 6 to select "2-PropZTest…" and insert the information given in the question into the correct place. Be sure the correct alternative hypothesis is selected, scroll down to highlight "Calculate" and press ENTER. The results will display.

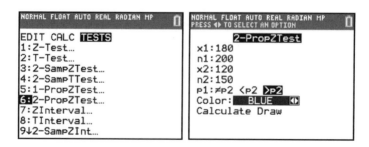

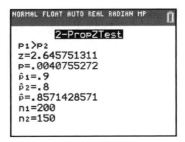

$$z = \frac{\hat{p}_1 - \hat{p}_2}{\sqrt{\dfrac{pq}{n_1} + \dfrac{pq}{n_2}}} = 2.65$$

The *P*-value is also found on the test result screen. The *P*-value is noted as *p* = .0040755272. Rounded to 4-digits to the right of the decimal:

$$P_{(.0041)} \leq \alpha_{(.05)} \qquad \text{Reject } H_0$$

Rejecting the null hypothesis suggests there is sufficient evidence to suggest that the proportion of MBA students taking online courses is larger than the proportion of graduate engineering students taking online courses.

$$P\text{-value} = .0041$$

The *P*-value must be compared to alpha to make a decision about the null hypothesis. Compare the *P*-value, .0041, to alpha, .05. Because $P < \alpha$, reject the null hypothesis.

## CONFIDENCE INTERVAL FOR
## TWO INDEPENDENT PROPORTIONS USING *z*

The confidence interval for two-proportion *z* estimation is similar to that for one-proportion estimation. The only difference is in the formula, which must now represent two samples. Confidence intervals estimate parameters. When estimating the difference of two population proportions, the estimation is based on the difference of two sample means. The confidence interval establishes a range around the difference of the sample proportions in which the difference of the population proportions should fall.

The level of confidence establishes the width of the interval and thus the probability that the parameter will be contained in the interval. The level of confidence is usually reported as a percentage; to rewrite a percentage as a probability requires dropping the percent sign and moving the decimal two places to the left. If a level of confidence is 95%, then the probability is .95. Alpha is the opposite of the level of confidence.

If the level of confidence is .95, then alpha is .05. The level of confidence and alpha must sum to 1. Because the interval establishes a range of values around the sample statistic, all confidence intervals are two-tailed.

---

**Confidence Interval for Proportions of Two Population**

(Lower limit $< (p_1 - p_2) <$ Upper limit)

$$E_{(p-p)} = z_{\alpha/2} \sqrt{\frac{\hat{p}_1 \hat{q}_1}{n_1} + \frac{\hat{p}_2 \hat{q}_2}{n_2}}$$

Confidence Interval: $(\hat{p}_1 - \hat{p}_2) - E < (p_1 - p_2) < (\hat{p}_1 - \hat{p}_2) + E$

---

As with most confidence intervals, the estimate must be added and subtracted from the point estimators. The TI 83/84 series calculators do this much more easily. The required information for the TI includes the $x_1$, $n_1$, $x_2$, $n_2$, and the C-Level (confidence level).

---

**Steps in Calculating a Confidence Interval**
1. Identify the level of confidence (90%, 95%, 99%).
2. Identify the test statistic ($z$, $t$, $\chi 2$, or $F$).
3. Enter the data to calculate the interval.
4. State the interval.

---

**EXAMPLE 13.12**
**Experiment:** Example 13.11 rejected the hypothesis test concerning the proportion of online MBA and engineering graduate students at State University, estimate with 95% certainly what the difference in the proportion would be using the same sample information of MBA students produced 180 of 200 MBA students claiming to take online courses while 120 out of 150 engineering graduate students report taking online courses.

**Answer:** $E(p_1 - p_2) = (.02367 < (p_1 - p_2) < .17633)$

**Solution:** The problem requires a 95% confidence interval for the difference of two population means. The level of confidence is 95% which is a C-Level of .95. The test statistic is $z$ for two population proportions.

The next step is to calculate the interval. The calculation of the estimation of the test statistic $z$ requires the following information: $x_1 = 180$, $n_1 = 200$, $x_2 = 120$, and $n_2 = 150$. Perform this task by utilizing a TI-83 or 84 calculator.

Begin by pressing the STAT button and scrolling right to "TESTS." Under the "TESTS" tab, scroll down to select "2-PropZInt…" by pressing ENTER. Insert the information into the correct places with a .95 confidence level indicated in the settings screen. Scroll down to highlight "Calculate" and press ENTER. The interval will appear.

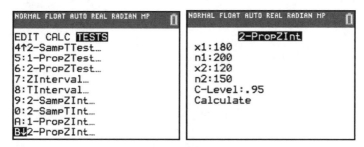

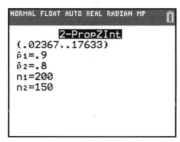

The confidence interval has a lower limit of .02367 and an upper limit of .17633. Therefore, with 95% confidence, the difference between the proportion of MBA students and engineering graduate students taking online courses is between 2.367% and 17.633%.

$$E(p_1 - p_2) = (.02367 < (p_1 - p_2) < .17633)$$

## A LEARNING AID
## PROPORTIONS OF TWO POPULATIONS: *z*

Test whether the proportion of muffler replacements done at Maria's Garage is significantly different that the proportion done at Dino's Garage. A random selection of 50 repairs for last month at Maria's garage showed her garage did 20 muffler replacements. A random selection of 60 repairs for the same month at Dino's Garage showed 15 muffler replacements. Test with alpha .10.

**Step 1**
State the hypotheses. The claim is that there is proportion of muffler replacements at Maria's is significantly different than at Dino's. The test is for

two population proportions. The claim is actually an alternative hypothesis since it is asking if the proportions are different (not equal). If the alternative hypothesis is not equal ($\neq$), then the null hypothesis must be equal to ($=$). The value place in the hypothesis is 0, unless otherwise stated in the claim. The hypotheses for two population proportions are written:

$$H_0: p_1 - p_2 = 0 \qquad H_1: p_1 - p_2 \neq 0$$

## Step 2
Identify the test criteria. Alpha is given as .10. Use the test statistic $z$ for two population proportions. This is a two-tailed test since the alternative is not equal.

## Step 3
Calculate the test statistic. Because the hypothesis statement tests whether the proportion of muffler replacements at Maria's garage to Dino's garage, Maria's Garage is population 1 and Dino's is population 2. The information given is $x_1 = 20$, $n_1 = 50$, $x_2 = 15$, and $n_2 = 60$. To perform this test in a TI-83 or 84 calculator, begin by pressing the STAT button, followed by scrolling over to the "TESTS" tab. Press the 6 button to select "6:2-PropZTest" and insert the information given in the problem along with the proper alternative hypothesis. Highlight "Calculate" and press ENTER. The results will appear.

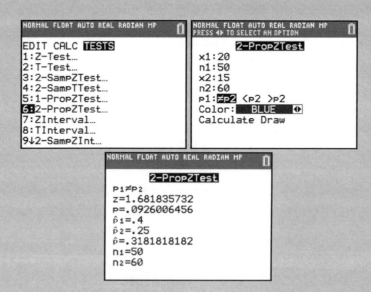

$$z = \frac{\hat{p}_1 - \hat{p}_2}{\sqrt{\dfrac{pq}{n_1} + \dfrac{pq}{n_2}}} = 1.68$$

**Step 4**

The *P*-value is also found on the test result screen. The *P*-value is noted as *p*=.0926006456. Rounded to 4-digits to the right of the decimal:

$$P\text{-value} = .0926$$

The *P*-value must be compared to alpha to make a decision about the null hypothesis. Compare the *P*-value, .0926, to alpha, .10. Because $P < \alpha$, reject the null hypothesis.

$$P_{(.0926)} \leq \alpha_{(.10)} \qquad \text{Reject } H_O$$

Rejecting the null hypothesis suggests here is sufficient evidence to suggest that there is a statistically significant difference in the proportion of muffler replacements at Maria's garage and Dino's garage

---

# SECTION 4

## Two Dependent Means: *t*

The *t* distribution is also applied in testing and estimating two dependent samples. Recall that dependent sampling occurs when the same data are sampled twice. Many of the social and behavioral sciences conduct experiments where the same individuals are tested twice. Many tests are referred to as ***pretests and post tests***; others are called ***before and after tests***. All the stages of hypothesis testing and estimation remain the same for the *t* test for dependent sampling as for the *t* test for independent sampling. The only major adjustment occurs in the adjusted formula for the calculated *t* value.

**Criteria for Using *t* for Two Dependent Means**
1. Samples are dependent.
2. *n* is the number of ordered pairs.

The hypotheses are written slightly differently than they are written for independent sampling. Because the difference between the first sample mean and the second sample mean is in question, the notation for the difference in dependent means is written $\mu_d$. An example of hypotheses with no expected difference is written

$$H_O: \mu_d = 0 \qquad H_I: \mu_d \neq 0$$

If a difference is expected, then a value will replace the 0 in the hypotheses. Remember that the symbols =, ≤, and ≥ are placed only in the null hypothesis and ≠, >, and < are placed only in the alternative hypothesis.

The critical region and calculated value are determined by reading Table A.4. The degrees of freedom for dependent testing with *t* are *n* - 1, where n represents the number of paired observations. For example, if 10 people are tested twice, although there are a total of 20 responses, the sample size is 10 and *df* = 10 - 1 = 9.

---

**Degrees of Freedom for *t* Dependent Means**
$df = n - 1$
where *n* is the number of paired observations.

---

The formula for the calculated *t* value requires the calculation of the sample mean difference and the sample standard deviation difference. The formula for the mean difference is the sum of the differences divided by the number of paired observations. Subtract each value of *x* of the first test from its corresponding *x* value in the second test. The summation occurs after each difference is determined. The sample statistic is *d*.

---

**Formula for Calculating the Mean Difference for Dependent Samples**

$$\overline{d} = \frac{\Sigma d}{n}$$

where
  *d* is the difference between members of each ordered pair: $d = (x_2 - x_1)$
  *n* is the number of ordered pairs.

---

The calculation of the standard deviation difference for dependent samples is similar to the standard deviation presented in earlier chapters, but *d* replaces *x* in the calculation.

---

**Formula for Calculating the Standard Deviation for Dependent Samples**

$$s_d = \sqrt{\frac{\Sigma d^2 - (\Sigma d)^2/n}{n-1}}$$

---

The calculated *t* value requires subtracting the expected mean difference from the sample mean difference and dividing by the standard error. The calculation of the sample mean difference and the standard deviation, which is a component of the standard error, must be completed before using the $t$ formula.

---

**Formula for $t$ Dependent Means**

$$t = \frac{\overline{d} - \mu_d}{s_d / \sqrt{n}}$$

where

$\mu_d$ is the expected population mean difference.
$s_d$ is the sample standard deviation difference.
$n$ is the number of ordered pairs.

---

## EXAMPLE 13.13

**Experiment**: To test the effect of a computer training session, employees at the university were asked to test their knowledge of computer skills before and after the training session. Six employees scored as shown here. Can it be concluded that a significant difference in their computer skills is due to the training session? Let $\alpha = .05$.

| Before | After |
|--------|-------|
| 61 | 75 |
| 43 | 71 |
| 71 | 93 |
| 66 | 82 |
| 59 | 69 |
| 60 | 80 |

**Answer**: Yes, it can be concluded that the difference in computer skills is due to the training session.

**Solution:**
**Step 1**
To state the hypotheses, determine if this is one population or two. One group is sampled twice, resulting in testing the difference in the responses from the first test to the second. The samples are not independent, because the same people are sampled twice. A before-and-after test that is not randomized usually implies dependent sampling. The parameter for two dependent means is $\mu_d$. The symbol for an expected difference is $\neq$, which must be placed in the alternative hypothesis. The null hypothesis must contain the contrasting symbol, $=$. The value 0 is placed in the hypothesis as the expected difference

$$H_O: \mu_d = 0 \qquad H_I: \mu_d \neq 0$$

## Step 2

The test criteria include the level of significance, test statistic, critical region, and critical value. The level of significance is reported as alpha = .05. The test statistic for two dependent means is $t$. The critical region is in both tails, as determined by the $\neq$ symbol in the alternative hypothesis. The critical $t$ value for dependent means requires the degrees of freedom and the alpha. The degrees of freedom for dependent sampling is $n - 1$, where $n$ is the number of ordered pairs. Six people are sampled; $n - 1$ is 6 - 1, or 5. Alpha is divided by 2 for a two-tailed test: .05/2 is .025. Use Table A.4. Move down to 5 $df$ and across to alpha = .025. The critical value for the right tail is 2.571. The left-tailed value is determined by adding a negative sign to the right-tailed value. The left-tailed critical value is - 2.571.

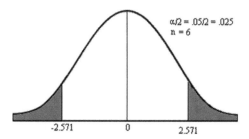

## Step 3

The calculation of the test statistic $t$ for two dependent means requires the mean difference and the standard deviation difference. The formulas for the mean and standard deviation follow. Notice the data are restated and arranged to illustrate the calculations.

| Before | After | $(x_2 - x_1)$ $d$ | $d^2$ |
|--------|-------|-------|-------|
| 61 | 75 | 14 | 196 |
| 43 | 71 | 28 | 784 |
| 71 | 93 | 22 | 484 |
| 66 | 82 | 16 | 256 |
| 59 | 69 | 10 | 100 |
| 60 | 80 | 20 | 400 |
| | | $\Sigma d = 110$ | $\Sigma d^2 = 2,220$ |

$$\bar{d} = \frac{\Sigma d}{n} = \frac{110}{6} = 18.33$$

$$s_d = \sqrt{\frac{\Sigma d^2 - (\Sigma d)^2 / n}{n-1}} = \sqrt{\frac{2220 - 110^2/6}{6-1}} = 6.377$$

With the sample mean difference of 18.33 and the sample standard deviation difference of 6.377, the t test statistic can be calculated.

$$t = \frac{\bar{d} - \mu_d}{s_d / \sqrt{n}} = \frac{18.33 - 0}{6.377 / \sqrt{6}} = 7.04$$

**Step 4**

Place the calculated value, 7.04, on the curve. The value 7.04 falls to the right of 2.571, in the critical region.

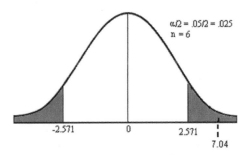

**Step 5**

The decision is to reject the null hypothesis.

**Step 6**

There is sufficient evidence at the .05 level of significance to suggest that the training course affected the computer skills of the employees at the university.

## *P*-VALUE APPROACH FOR TWO DEPENDENT MEANS USING *t*

The *P*-value approach for two-dependent means *t* testing is the similar as for one-mean *t* testing. The *P*-value approach goes one step further than the classical approach by transforming the calculated value into a probability that can be compared to alpha for a decision. The first three steps of the *P*-value approach are similar to the classical approach. Only two aspects of the test criteria are necessary: the level of significance and the identification of the test statistic. The hypotheses statements and the calculation of the test statistic are the same. Once the calculated test statistic, the *P*-value is identified. The *P*-value associated with the probability is determined and then compared to alpha. If the *P*-value is less than or equal to alpha, then the decision is to reject the null hypothesis. If the *P*-value is greater than alpha, then the decision is to fail to reject the null hypothesis. The final step is the interpretation of the decision to the experiment.

Two-dependent *t* testing is not directly in the TI 83/84 calculators. But because the formulas are so similar, small adjustments can be made to use the function 2:T-Test on the calculator. Here are the adjustments:

---

**Conversion of the Formula for *t* Dependent Means**
**Using the TI 83/84 Calculator Function for One Sample Mean**

$$t = \frac{\bar{d} - \mu_d}{s_d / \sqrt{n}} \quad = \quad t = \frac{\bar{x} - \mu_0}{s / \sqrt{n}}$$

where

$\bar{d}$ will substitute $\bar{x}$.
$\mu_d$ will be set to 0.
$s_d$ will substitute $s_x$.
$n$ is $n$.

---

**Steps in Hypothesis Testing using the P-Value Approach**

1. State $H_0$ and $H_1$.
2. Identify the test criteria.
   a. Level of significance, $\alpha$
   b. Test statistic ($z$, $t$, $\chi2$, $F$)
3. Calculate the test statistic.
4. Identify the $P$-value.
5. Make a decision.
   a. If $P > \alpha$, Fail to reject $H_0$
   b. If $P \leq \alpha$, Reject $H_0$
6. Interpret the results.

---

Decisions using $P$-values
$P \leq \alpha$ Reject $H_0$
$P > \alpha$ Fail to reject $H_0$

---

**EXAMPLE 13.14**
**Experiment:** A political scientist interested in the relationship between redistricting and incumbency advantage in city council elections collects the following data for six districts. Test the null hypothesis that redistricting makes no difference in the incumbents' vote margins. Let $\alpha = .05$.

**Average Margin of Victory**

| Before | After |
|--------|-------|
| 56 | 53 |
| 60 | 57 |
| 52 | 50 |
| 57 | 59 |
| 62 | 60 |
| 54 | 52 |

**Answer:** Fail to reject the null hypothesis. There is not sufficient evidence to reject the null hypothesis that redistricting makes no difference in the incumbents' vote margins.

**Solution:** One group is sampled twice resulting in testing the difference in the responses from the first test to the second. The samples are not independent, because the same people are sampled twice. A before-and-after test that is not randomized usually implies dependent sampling.

**Step 1**
The parameter for two dependent means is $\mu_d$ The symbol for an expected difference is $\neq$, which must be placed in the alternative hypothesis. The null hypothesis must contain the contrasting symbol, $=$. The value 0 is placed in the hypothesis as the expected difference.

$$H_O: \mu_d = 0 \qquad H_I: \mu_d \neq 0$$

**Step 2**
The test criteria include the level of significance, test statistic, critical region, and critical value. The level of significance is reported as alpha = .05. The test statistic for two dependent means is $t$.

**Step 3**
Performing a $t$-dependent test on the given information requires a difference of the two columns. Calculate a list of numbers subtracting "After" numbers from "Before". This can be done right in $L_1$ on your calculator by pressing STAT on your calculator and selecting "1:Edit..." by pressing ENTER. After calculating the difference of the two columns in $L_1$, the screen should appear as follows:

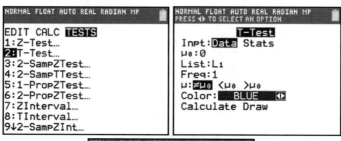

Press STAT and scroll over to the "TESTS" tab. Press the 2 button to select 2:T-Test…" Be sure the "Data" option is selected and enter the remaining information in the settings screen as follows. Once complete, highlight "Calculate" and press ENTER. The results will appear.

$$t = \frac{\overline{d} - \mu_d}{s_d / \sqrt{n}} = 2.193$$

**Step 4**

Identify the *P*-value notes above as $P = .0798301254$. Round to .0798.

**Step 5**

If the *P*-value is less-than-or-equal to the alpha, reject the null hypothesis. If the *P*-value is greater than alpha, fail to reject the null hypothesis.

$$P\text{-value}_{.0798} > \alpha_{.05} \quad \text{Fail to reject the null hypothesis}$$

**Step 6**

There is not sufficient evidence at the .05 level of significance to reject the null hypothesis that redistricting makes no difference in the incumbents' vote margins.

Confidence intervals for $t$ dependent means estimate the population mean difference based on the sample mean difference. The formula is similar to the one-population $t$ formula.

**Confidence Interval for $t$ Dependent**
$$E(\mu_d) = \bar{d} \pm t_{(\alpha/2)} s_d / \sqrt{n}$$
where $df = n - 1$

The confidence interval for $t$ dependent means is used infrequently in most of the social sciences because rarely can a researcher predict the occurrence of a social or political event.

**A LEARNING AID**
**TWO DEPENDENT MEANS $t$**

A major retail chain store believes that sales have decreased since the most recent recession. To test the claim, five stores were surveyed over a period of time before and after the recession, producing the following data ($\alpha = .01$):

**Average Sales (in thousands U.S. $)**

| Before | After |
|--------|-------|
| 102 | 100 |
| 203 | 195 |
| 156 | 158 |
| 157 | 159 |
| 260 | 257 |

**Step 1**

There are two populations, because each store was surveyed twice. The experiment is to test if there is a decrease in sales from the first test to the second. The samples are not independent, because the same stores are sampled twice. A before-and-after test that is not randomized usually implies dependent sampling. The parameter for two dependent means is $t$. The symbol for the expected decrease in sales is $<$, which must be placed in the alternative hypothesis. The null hypothesis must contain the contrasting symbol, $\geq$. The value 0 is placed in the hypothesis as the expected difference.

$$H_O: \mu_d \geq 0 \qquad H_I: \mu_d < 0$$

**Step 2**
Identify the test criteria. The test criteria include the level of significance, test statistic, critical region, and critical value. The level of significance is reported as alpha = .05. The test statistic for two dependent means is $t$.

**Step 3**
The calculation of the test statistic $t$ for two dependent means requires the mean difference and the standard deviation difference. The formulas for the mean and standard deviation follow. The data are re-stated and arranged to illustrate the calculations. The before data are subtracted from the after.

**Average Sales (in thousands U.S. \$)**

| Before | After | $(x_2 - x_1)$ $d$ |
|--------|-------|--------|
| 102 | 100 | -2 |
| 203 | 195 | -8 |
| 156 | 158 | 2 |
| 157 | 159 | 2 |
| 260 | 257 | -3 |
| | | $\Sigma d = -9$ |

| NORMAL FLOAT AUTO REAL RADIAN MP | | | | | |
|------|------|------|------|------|---|
| L1 | L2 | L3 | L4 | L5 | 1 |
| -2 | ----- | ----- | ----- | ----- | |
| -8 | | | | | |
| 2 | | | | | |
| 2 | | | | | |
| -3 | | | | | |
| ----- | | | | | |
| | | | | | |
| | | | | | |
| | | | | | |
| | | | | | |
| L1(6)= | | | | | |

The $t$ test statistic can be calculated by pressing the STAT button, followed by the ENTER button to select "1:Edit…" Insert the $(x_2 - x_1)$ column into $L_1$.

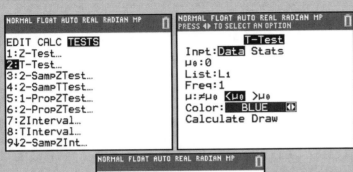

Press STAT and scroll over to the "TESTS" tab. Press the 2 button to select 2:T-Test…" Be sure the "Data" option is selected and enter the remaining information in the settings screen as follows. Once complete, highlight "Calculate" and press ENTER. The results will appear.

$$t = \frac{\overline{d} - \mu_d}{s_d / \sqrt{n}} = -.970$$

**Step 4**
Identify the *P*-value, provided by the result screen of the calculator. It is .1933779027. Round to .1934.

**Step 5**
Make a decision.

$$P - value_{.1934} > \alpha_{.01} \qquad \text{Reject the } H_o$$

**Step 6**
Interpret the results. There is sufficient evidence, at the .01 level of significance, to suggest that retail sales declined significantly after the recession.

# SECTION 5

## Two Variances: *F* Distribution

The previous sections of this chapter show how to test and estimate population means from independent populations that are normally distributed. The formulas in this section test and estimate variances of two independent populations that are normally distributed. Recall that Chi-square tests and estimates a variance from one population, whereas the *F* distribution tests and estimates the equality of the variances from two populations. Many similarities exist between $\chi 2$ and *F*. Both distributions represent variances, are skewed to the right, and contain only nonnegative values. The skewness reflects the non-normal distribution of the variances. Variances are dependent in several distribution curves based on degrees of freedom.

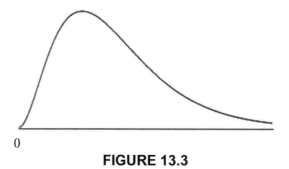

0

### FIGURE 13.3

**F Distribution: A Distribution Representing the Equality of Variances from Two Populations**
1. *F* is non-symmetrical, skewed to the right.
2. *F* is nonnegative, greater than or equal to 0.
3. The two populations are normally distributed.
4. The two populations are independent of each other.

As with the two-population *t* distribution, the *F* distribution can be approached in several ways. The *F* distribution can be very complicated, with the skewed distribution determining which variances represent the first population and which represent the second. Many researchers prefer to treat the distribution differently when the test is one-tailed as opposed to two-tailed. A uniform rule is applied in this text; it essentially allows all tests to concentrate on the right tail of the curve.

The six steps of the classical hypothesis test are the same for *F* as for the other test statistics: State the hypotheses, identify the test criteria, calculate the test statistic, place the calculated value on the curve, make a decision, and interpret the results. The hypotheses for *F* are stated slightly differently than they are for other test statistics. All other hypotheses contain the parameter(s), a mathematical symbol, and a value. *F* tests for the equality of the variances; therefore, a value representing a difference is not usually in question. Hypotheses for *F* contain the parameters $\sigma^2_1$ and $\sigma^2_2$ and a mathematical symbol. For example, an experiment may question whether the variance of rainfall in Wayne County is less than the variance in rainfall in Oakland County. That hypothesis statement must be the alternative hypothesis, because it includes the less than symbol. The null hypothesis uses the symbol for greater than or equal to. The parameters are the variances. The statements are written as:

$$H_O: \sigma^2_1 \geq \sigma^2_2 \qquad\qquad H_1: \sigma^2_1 < \sigma^2_2$$

Remember that =, ≤, and ≥ are the only three mathematical symbols acceptable in the null hypothesis, whereas ≠, >, and < are the three mathematical symbols acceptable in the alternative hypothesis.

The critical value for *F* requires the degrees of freedom for the sample with the larger variance, the degrees of freedom for the sample with the smaller variance, and alpha. Degrees of freedom are determined by *n* - 1. The notation for the *F* critical value always places the degrees of freedom for the sample with the larger variance first, with the degrees of freedom for the sample with the smaller variance second. Table A.6 gives critical values for the *F* distribution. Notice that Table A.6 is composed of several tables, each reflecting a different alpha and each identifying one number of degrees of freedom as the numerator and the second as the denominator. The uniform rule is that the numerator is always the sample with the larger variance, and the denominator is always the sample with the smaller variance. The separate tables for each alpha are required because all alphas and all degrees of freedom cannot be contained in a one-page table. The notation is

$$F_{(df_n, df_d, \alpha)}$$

The subscripts *n* and *d* represent the numerator and denominator. It is important to remember that the numerator represents the sample containing the larger variance, and the denominator represents the sample containing the smaller variance.

### Degrees of Freedom for *F*
$$df_n: n - 1$$
$$df_d: n - 1$$

where

$df_n$ is the degrees of freedom associated with the sample size for the sample with the larger variance.

$df_d$ is the degrees of freedom associated with the sample size for the sample with the smaller variance.

If the test is two-tailed, then alpha must be divided by 2. Because the larger variance information serves as the guide for the numerator, the calculated value and the critical value will fall toward the right tail of the distribution. The critical value for the right tail is determined by the procedure described earlier. Only the right-tail critical value is determined with the degrees of freedom for the sample with the larger variance, the degrees of freedom for the sample with the smaller variance, and alpha divided by 2. The left tail is noted as a critical region but does not need to be identified with a critical value.

---

## EXAMPLE 13.15

**Experiment:** Find the critical *F* value for the following information:

a. Two-tailed: $\sigma^2_1 = 24$, $\sigma^2_2 = 33$, $n_1 = 10$, $n_2 = 21$, $\alpha = .05$
b. One-tailed: $\sigma^2_1 = 14$, $\sigma^2_2 = 13$, $n_1 = 25$, $n_2 = 26$, $\alpha = .05$

**Answer:**
a. 3.667
b. 1.96

**Solution:**
a. A two-tailed *F* critical value requires identifying the degrees of freedom for the sample with the larger variance, the degrees of freedom for the sample with the smaller variance, and alpha divided by 2. The second variance, $\sigma^2_2 = 33$, is larger. The degrees of freedom for this sample are used as the *df* numerator and are equal to *n* - 1 = 21 - 1, or 20. The first variance, 24, is smaller than 33, and its degrees of freedom form the df denominator. The degrees of freedom for the denominator equal 10 - 1, or 9. Alpha divided by 2 is .05/2, or .025. Begin by identifying the correct *F* table. The critical values for alpha .025 are reported in Table A.6b. Read across to the *df* numerator 20 (found on the second page of the table) and down to the *d* denominator 9. The value 3.667 in the intersection is the critical value for the right tail. The left tail is shaded as a critical region but is not assigned a critical value.

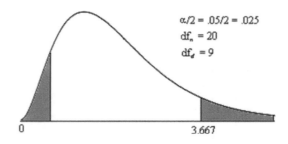

$\alpha/2 = .05/2 = .025$
$df_n = 20$
$df_d = 9$

0                                            3.667

---

b. A one-tailed *F* critical value can be placed on the right tail if the degrees of freedom are adjusted to represent the numerator with the larger variance. The variance 14 is larger than 13. Therefore, the degrees of freedom for the numerator represent the sample size 25; that is, the degrees of freedom for the numerator are 25 - 1, or 24. The degrees of freedom for the denominator are 26 - 1, or 25. The test is one-tailed, which means alpha is not divided by 2. Alpha is .05. Use Table A.6c, which gives values for alpha = .05. Read across to 24 degrees of freedom for the numerator and down to 25 degrees of freedom for the denominator. The value 1.964 is the critical value.

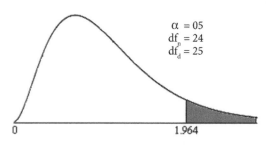

The calculated *F* value is perhaps the simplest calculation of all the test statistics. It is the ratio of the two sample variances. The rule for *F* is to place the larger sample variance in the numerator and the smaller in the denominator; thus, the ratio is always greater than 1.0.

### Calculation of the Test Statistic *F*

$$F = \frac{s_1^2}{s_2^2}$$

where
  $s_1^2$ is the larger variance
  $s_2^2$ is the smaller variance

### EXAMPLE 13.16

**Experiment:** The variability in potency for drugs is very important. A pharmacist wants to test whether the variability in a generic drug is different than the variability in the commercially named drug. A random sample of 21 tablets of the generic drug produces a variance of .02 mg, whereas a random sample of 31 tablets of the commercially named drug produces a variance of .04. Do the samples provide sufficient evidence to conclude that there is a significant variability between the two kinds of tablets? Use $\alpha = .05$.

**Answer:** No, there is no evidence that there is a significant amount of variability between the generic and commercially named drug.

**Solution:** To state the hypotheses, begin by determining if this is one population or two. Two sets of data are provided, with a test for the difference between the variances. The samples are independent, because both samples are randomly selected. The words no difference indicate the null hypothesis, because the = symbol can be placed only in the null hypothesis. The alternative hypothesis is then ≠ . The parameters are $\sigma^2_1$ and $\sigma^2_2$.

$$H_0: \sigma^2_1 = \sigma^2_2 \qquad H_1: \sigma^2_1 \neq \sigma^2_2$$

The test criteria begin with identifying alpha. Alpha is reported as .05. The test statistic is $F$, representing two population variances. The test is two-tailed, requiring the critical region to be placed in both tails and alpha to be divided by 2. However, by placing the sample with the larger variance in the numerator and its degrees of freedom first in the notation, only the right-tailed critical $F$ value must be determined. The variance .04 is larger than .02. Therefore, the commercially named data are treated as the first variance and are placed in the numerator. The sample size for the commercially named drug is 31, with degrees of freedom = 31 - 1 = 30. The degrees of freedom for the denominator are 21 - 1, or 20. Alpha must be divided by 2 for the two-tailed test: .05/2 = .025. Use Table A.6b for alpha = .025. Read across to 30 $df$ and down to 20 $df$. The critical value is 2.349.

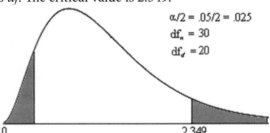

$$\alpha/2 = .05/2 = .025$$
$$df_n = 30$$
$$df_d = 20$$

Calculate the test statistic. The $F$ calculation involves the ratio of the sample variances, placing the larger variance in the numerator and the smaller variance in the denominator.

$$F = \frac{s^2_1}{s^2_2} = \frac{.04}{.02} = 2.00$$

Place the calculated value on the distribution curve: 2.00 falls to the left of the critical value, 2.349. The decision is to fail to reject the null hypothesis.

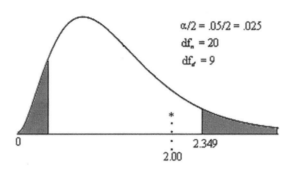

$$\alpha/2 = .05/2 = .025$$
$$df_n = 20$$
$$df_d = 9$$

2.00   2.349

### Fail to Reject $H_o$

Failing to reject the null hypothesis is interpreted to mean that the sample does not provide sufficient evidence at the .05 level of significance to reject the null hypothesis that there is no difference in the variability of the generic drug and the commercially named drug.

## P-VALUE APPROACH FOR TWO VARIANCES OR STANDARD DEVIATIONS USING *F*

The *P*-value approach can be done by using a TI-83/84 calculator. Technically, the earlier discussion about putting the larger variance as the numerator is not needed since the calculator can identify both right and left tail values.

### Steps in Hypothesis Testing Using the P-Value Approach

1. State $H_o$ and $H_1$ .
2. Identify the test criteria.
   a. Level of significance, $\alpha$
   b. Test statistic ($z, t, \chi 2, F$).
3. Calculate the test statistic.
4. Identify the *P*-value.
5. Make a decision.
   a. If $P > \alpha$, Fail to Reject $H_o$
   b. If $P \leq \alpha$, Reject $H_o$
6. Interpret the results.

### EXAMPLE 13.17

**Experiment:** Using the *P*-value approach, test the claim that the variance in the time it takes the local police force to arrive at the scene of a traffic accident is greater than the variance in the time it takes the local fire department. A random sample of 10 calls to the police department produced a variance of 2.5 minutes, whereas a random sample of 10 calls to the fire department produced a variance of 1.54 minutes. $\alpha = .01$.

**Answer**: There is not sufficient evidence to suggest that the variance in time it takes the local police force to arrive at the scene of a traffic accident is greater than the variance in the time it takes the local fire department.

**Solution:**
**Step 1**
To state the hypotheses, begin by determining if this is one population or two. Two sets of data are provided with a test for the difference between the variances. The samples are independent, because both samples are randomly selected. The words greater than indicate the alternative hypothesis, because the symbol > can be placed only in the alternative hypothesis. The null hypothesis is then ≤. The parameters are σ21 and σ22. The hypotheses are:

$$H_O: \sigma^2_1 \le \sigma^2_2 \qquad H_I: \sigma^2_1 > \sigma^2_2$$

**Step 2**
The test criteria begin with identifying alpha. Alpha is reported as .01. The test statistic is $F$, representing two population variances. The test is one-tailed, as determined by the > symbol in the alternative hypothesis.

**Step 3**
Calculate the test statistic. The $F$ calculation involves the ratio of the sample variances, placing the larger variance as the numerator and the smaller as the denominator.

The calculation of the test statistic and $P$-value can be done by using a TI-83 or 84 calculators. Begin by first pressing the STAT button and scrolling to the "TESTS" tab. Scroll down and highlight "E:2-SampFTest…". Press ENTER and access the settings screen of the test. With the "Stats" option selected, insert the information given in the question. Note that the problem gives variances and the calculator requires standard deviation values. Considering their relationship, take the square root of the variance values. This can be done in the settings screen. Adhere to the following settings, highlight "Calculate" and press ENTER. The results will appear as follows:

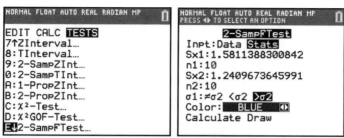

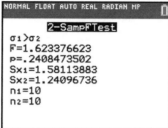

$$F = \frac{s_1^2}{s_2^2} = \frac{2.50}{1.54} = 1.6234$$

**Step 4**
Identify the *P*-value. The calculator provides that the *P*-value = .2408473502 which should be rounded to .2408.

**Step 5**
Compare the *P*-value to the alpha. If *P* is less than or equal to alpha, then reject the null hypothesis. If *P* is greater than alpha, then fail to reject the null hypothesis.

$$P_{(.2408)} > .01 \qquad \text{Fail to reject } H_O$$

**Step 6**
The interpretation is that there is not sufficient evidence to suggest the variance in time it takes the local police force to arrive at the scene of a traffic accident is greater than the variance in the time it takes the local fire department.

## CONFIDENCE INTERVAL FOR
## TWO VARIANCES OR STANDARD DEVIATIONS USING *F*

The confidence interval for estimating the equality of variances is rarely used in statistics. Because of the difficulty of the skewed distribution for two population variances, the *F* confidence interval is difficult to calculate without the left-tailed critical values. Although the discussion here is limited, the formula involves the algebraic manipulation of the test statistic.

**Confidence Interval for Estimating the Equality of Two Variances Using *F***

$$E_{\frac{\sigma_1^2}{\sigma_2^2}} = \frac{s_1^2}{s_2^2} \frac{1}{F(df_n, df_d, 1-\alpha/2)} < \frac{\sigma_1^2}{\sigma_2^2} < \frac{s_1^2}{s_2^2} \frac{1}{F(df_n, df_d, \alpha/2)}$$

where

$s_1^2$ is the larger variance and $s_2^2$ is the smaller variance.

$$F(df_n, df_d, 1-\alpha/2) = 1/F(df_d, df_n, \alpha/2)$$

## A LEARNING AID
## *F* DISTRIBUTION

A potato chip company is purchasing a new dispensing machine. Two machines dispense, on the average, the same number of ounces. The variance of a random sample of 13 bags for the brand *Y* machine is 1.96 oz and the variance of a random sample of 20 bags for the brand *X* machine is 1.22 oz. Do the samples provide sufficient evidence that there is significant difference in the variability of the machines? Let $\alpha = .1$.

**Step 1**

State the hypotheses. Begin by determining if there is one population or two. Two machines are providing two sets of data. The samples are independent, because both are randomly selected. Variances are being tested. The parameters are $\sigma_1^2$ and $\sigma_2^2$. The mathematical symbol referred to by the experiment as a difference is $\neq$. The $\neq$ must be placed only in the alternative hypothesis. The null hypothesis must then use equal, =.

$$H_O: \sigma_1^2 = \sigma_2^2 \qquad H_1: \sigma_1^2 \neq \sigma_2^2$$

**Step 2**

Identify the test criteria. Alpha is reported as .1. The test statistic for two variances is *F*. The test is two-tailed, as determined by the $\neq$ in the alternative hypothesis.

**Step 3**

Calculate the test statistic. The *F* calculation is the ratio of the sample variances, placing the larger variance in the numerator and the smaller variance in the denominator.

Perform a test in the calculator by pressing the STAT button and scrolling to the "TESTS" tab. Scroll down and select "E:2-SampFTest…". With the

"Stats" option selected, fill in the information given, also considering that the problem provides variances. Take the square root of these values in place of the standard deviation in the settings screen. Indicate the proper alternative hypothesis, highlight "Calculate" and press ENTER. The results will appear.

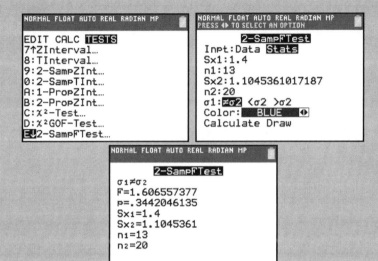

$$F = \frac{s_1^2}{s_2^2} = \frac{1.96}{1.22} = 1.6066$$

**Step 4**
Identify the *P*-value. The calculator reports its value as .3442046135. This can be rounded to .3442

**Step 5**
Make a decision. The decision is to fail to reject the null hypothesis, because the *P*-value is greater than the alpha level.

$$P\text{-value}(.3442) > alpha(.1) \qquad \text{Fail to reject } H_o$$

**Step 6**
Interpret the results. Failing to reject the null hypothesis is interpreted with the original information provided in the experiment. There is not sufficient evidence at the .1 level of significance to conclude the variances of the machines differ.

# CHAPTER 13 IN REVIEW

13.1 In the appropriate format, state the null and alternative hypotheses:
   a. There is no difference in the mean number of calls to Greece and Italy.
   b. The variance in time it takes for two professors to grade exams is equal.
   c. The variance in basketball scores is equal between the NBA Western and Eastern divisions.
   d. The mean weight loss for a group of dieters before and after a diet is greater than 10 pounds.
   e. There is no difference in the standard deviation of sodium in chips between plain and B.B.Q. chips.

13.2 In the appropriate format, state the null and alternative hypotheses:
   a. Test the claim that two ambulance services have the same mean response time.
   b. The mean number of calories of brand $Y$ is lower than brand $X$.
   c. The variance of fatalities in time period 1 is equal to the variance of fatalities in time period 2.
   d. The mean time of two flights to St. Louis is equal.

13.3 Find the critical values for the following one-tailed $F$ tests.
   a. $n_n = 10$, $n_d = 10$, $\alpha = .05$
   d. $n_n = 25$, $n_d = 10$, $\alpha = .025$
   b. $n_n = 10$, $n_d = 7$, $\alpha = .05$
   e. $n_n = 7$, $n_d = 10$, $\alpha = .01$
   c. $n_n = 10$, $n_d = 25$, $\alpha = .025$
   f. $n_n = 5$, $n_d = 5$, $\alpha = .05$

13.4 Find the critical values for the following two-tailed $t$ independent tests.
   a. $n_1 = 20$, $n_2 = 15$, $\alpha = .05$
   d. $n_1 = 8$, $n_2 = 8$, $\alpha = .01$
   b. $n_1 = 10$, $n_2 = 12$, $\alpha = .10$
   e. $n_1 = 25$, $n_2 = 25$, $\alpha = .01$
   c. $n_1 = 5$, $n_2 = 8$, $\alpha = .01$
   f. $n_1 = 10$, $n_2 = 8$, $\alpha = .2$

13.5 Two leading soft drink companies claim that there is no difference in the amount of sodium in their drinks. A sample of 40 cans from one company produced a mean of 50 grams. A sample of 50 cans of the second company produced a mean of 40 grams. If the population standard deviations of both are 12, test the difference at the .05 level.

13.6 The local pizzeria claims that there is not a significant difference in the number of calories between a cheese pizza and a pepperoni pizza. A sample of 20 cheese slices produces a mean of 115 calories per slice with a standard deviation of 10. A sample of 25 pepperoni slices produces a mean of 155 calories per slice with a standard deviation of 30. Test the difference of the means using alpha .05.

13.7  The telephone company collects sample data on the lengths, in minutes, of telephone calls made to foreign countries. A random sample of 40 calls to Greece produces a mean of 12.65 min. A random sample of 40 calls to Italy produces a mean of 11.24 min. The standard deviation of all calls to these countries is 7.23 and 8.99, respectively. At the .02 level of significance, test the claim that there is no difference between the mean times of all long-distance calls made to the two countries.

13.8  After the 2008 recession, economists claim that U.S. per capita increase has finally begun to climb again. Determine if there is a significant increase in the per-capita income from 2008 to 2014. In 2014, the average income of 100 taxpayers was $42, 693 with a standard deviation of $2,975. In 2008, the per-capita income of 100 taxpayers was $40,947 with a standard deviation of $2,250. Test at the .05 level of significance.

13.9  The average cost of the drug Zoloft in the U.S. is $114.56 with a standard deviation of $22.45 for 100 patients. The average cost of the same drug in Canada is $52.50 with a standard deviation of $14.50 for 50 patients. Do the data provide sufficient evidence at the .01 level to suggest that there is a significant difference in the mean cost of Zoloft between the two countries?

13.10 Determine if there is a significant difference in the proportion of single-parent households in the U.S. and U.K. in 2015. A sample of 10,500 households in the U.S. produced 3,000 single-parent households. A sample of 5,000 households in U.K. produced 1,250 single-parent households. Test at the .05 level.

13.11 Determine if there is a significant difference in the average cost of plastic surgeries. Forty patients receiving liposuction paid an average of $2,224 with a standard deviation of $500. Fifty patients receiving eyelid surgery paid an average of $2,525 with a standard deviation of $300. $\alpha = .05$

13.12 True or False?
a. The test statistic for two population variances is $\chi^2$.
b. If the outcomes of one sample affect the outcomes of another sample, then the samples are independent.
c. If a *P*-value is .004 and alpha is .005, then the decision is to fail to reject the null hypothesis.
d. Critical values for *t* may be negative.
e. Critical values for *F* may be negative.
f. Critical values for *z* may be negative.

13.13 Determine if there is a significant increase in Americans' average credit card balance before and after the Christmas holiday. The average bill difference is

$1,026 with a standard deviation of $950 for 40 shoppers. Test at the .01 level of significance.

13.14 Is there a significant difference between the average age of marriage between men and women? Thirty men married on average at 26.9 years old with a standard deviation of 3 while thirty women married on average at 25.3 years old with a standard deviation of 4. $\alpha = .05$.

13.15 Test at the .05 level. In a survey of 30 professors and 25 high school teachers asking whether they believe that students are very well prepared in math when they enter college, an average of 37 percent of high school teachers said yes with a standard deviation of 5 percent. An average of 40 percent of professors said yes with a standard deviation of 3. Test whether there is a significant difference in the standard deviations using an alpha of .05.

13.16 A researcher wants to determine if there is a significant difference in the average salaries of male and female nurses. A random sample of 30 males produced a sample mean of $38,750. A random sample of 25 females produced a mean of $36,900. If the population standard deviations are $3,000 and $4,000 respectively, is there a significant difference at the .05 level?

13.17 Determine if the average number of sexual harassment complaints filed at a local company has been affected by the new sexual harassment workshop program. The following data describes the number of complaints over a six-month period from last year to this year. Test the claim that there is a significant change at the .05 level of significance.

|        | Before | After |
|--------|--------|-------|
| Jan    | 10     | 8     |
| Feb    | 12     | 14    |
| March  | 15     | 12    |
| April  | 15     | 14    |
| May    | 20     | 15    |
| June   | 14     | 12    |

13.18 The Consumer Comfort Index represents responses to questions about the national economy, personal finances and consumer buying. The following responses are from five individual consumers asked to report their opinions before and after the Federal Reserve Board dropped interest rates. Do the data support that there was a significant change in these individuals before and after the interest rate change? $\alpha = .01$

| **Before:** | -5 | -10 | -6 | -5 | -4 |
|-------------|-----|------|-----|-----|-----|
| **After:**  | -8 | -20 | -8 | -9 | -10 |

13.19 Wall Street investors are concerned with mutual fund losses, mainstays of 401(k) retirement plans. A random survey of 10 major funds produced an average decline of 10.45 percent with a standard deviation of 1.25 percent. Another random survey of 10 major funds produced an average decline of 12.99 percent with a standard deviation of 2.16 percent. Do the data show, at the .05 level, that there is a significant difference in the mean losses for these two sets of funds?

13.20 A salary adjustment was given to employees when two retail stores recently merged. Ten employees' salaries were recorded before and after the adjustment. The average difference was an increase of $2,250 with a standard deviation of $1,100. Test if the increase is significant at the .10 level.

13.21 Determine if there is a significant difference in the variances of two gauges used in manufacturing pistons. A sample of 25 gauges from one manufacturer produces a variance of .009 mm. A sample of 30 gauges from another manufacturer produces a variance of .008 mm. Test at the .05 level.

13.22 A researcher in the Department of Transportation ran an experiment to determine if certain cold tablets decrease a user's reaction time while driving a test-course. Eight randomly selected drivers were tested. Each driver's reaction time was measured before and after taking the cold tablet. Test if the decrease is significant using the following data at $\alpha=.05$.

| Driver | Without Medication | With Medication |
| :---: | :---: | :---: |
| 1 | 1.23 | 1.18 |
| 2 | 2.01 | 1.45 |
| 3 | 1.32 | 1.45 |
| 4 | 2.31 | 2.05 |
| 5 | 1.59 | 2.05 |
| 6 | 2.42 | 2.27 |
| 7 | 2.00 | 2.10 |
| 8 | 1.49 | 1.35 |

13.23 An experiment was conducted to determine if there is a difference in the mean amount of money invested in retirement funds by homeowners and renters. Forty randomly selected homeowners saved an average $150 dollars a month, while the standard deviation for all homeowners is $45. Fifty randomly selected renters saved an average of $135, while a standard deviation for all renters is $50. Test using $\alpha = .05$.

13.24 A clothing manufacturer is interested in buying a new machine that produces sleeves for a child's dress. The concern for the manufacturer is finding a machine with the smaller variation in production quality. Is there a significant difference between Machine A that produces sleeves with a variance of .364 cm for 16 samples; and Machine B that produces sleeves with a variance of .251 cm for 21 samples? $\alpha = .10$

13.25 Many people claim they spend more time waiting for their spouses to arrive home for dinner now that they live in the suburbs. Two random samples of size 40 were taken of city residents and suburban residents. The mean waiting time for the suburbanites was .50 hours and the mean waiting time for the city residents was .45 hours. Assume the population standard deviation is .06 for both city and suburban residents. Complete a hypothesis test of the means, using $\alpha = .05$.

13.26 A doctor wishes to determine which of two diets is more effective in reducing weight. A sample of 20 obese adults who are interested in losing weight is randomly divided into two groups of 10. After 6 weeks, the weight loss of each participant was recorded. The mean for diet 1 is 8 pounds with a standard deviation of 3.23 pounds. The mean for diet 2 is 11 pounds with a standard deviation of 6.78 pounds. Do the data justify the conclusion that the mean weight loss on diet 2 was greater than the mean weight loss on diet 1? $\alpha = .05$.

13.27 The percent of births to unmarried women in the U.S. is considered high. However, a researcher believes it is in-line with many other developed countries. A sample of 500 births in the U.S. in 2014 included 220 births to unmarried women. A sample of 600 births in Sweden in 2014 included 320 births to unmarried women. Test the equality of the proportion of births to unmarried women at the .01 level of significance.

13.28 Although women have had great strides in many fields of employment, women still trail in high-tech fields. Test if there has been a significant increase in the proportion of women in the computer science division of a local company during the last decade. A recent survey shows that a high-tech firm employs 54 women in its 200-person computer science division. A decade ago, the same company employed 48 women in the same 200-person division. Use alpha at .05.

13.29 The standard deviation of 61 men approving the President's job performance is 6.2. The standard deviation of 41 women approving the President's job performance is 10.2. Test at the .05 level if there is a significant difference in the standard deviations of their approval ratings.

13.30 While the number of deaths from heart attacks is down, there is concern that the number of deaths from heart failure is up. A sample of 100 men who had died of cardiovascular disease produced an average of 7 that were caused by heart failure. A sample of 100 women who had died of cardiovascular deaths produced an average of 9 from heart failure. If the population standard deviations are 4.4 and 5.6 respectively, is there a significant difference in the average number of deaths from heart failure between men and women? $\alpha = .05$

13.31 Approximately 14.5 percent of Americans live below the poverty line. At the .05 level, determine if there is a difference between the proportions of Americans living below the poverty line based on residency. A sample of 10,000 people in the South indicated that 1,600 lived below the poverty line. A sample of 15,000 people in the North indicated that 2,100 lived below the poverty line.

13.32 Studies suggest that around 10 percent of the world population is left-handed. Test whether there is a significant difference based on gender. In a random sample of 500 men and 500 women in the U.S., 65 men and 55 women reported being left-handed. Test if there is a significant difference at the .05 level.

13.33 The health benefits are well known for infants who are breastfed. According to the CDC, there are still disparities across the country of the proportion of women who breastfeed their infants. Idaho has the highest rate in the country while Mississippi has the lowest. Determine if there is a significant difference in the proportion of women who breastfed in these two states. A survey in Idaho reports that 275 of 300 women breastfed. A survey in Mississippi reports that 253 of 500 women breastfed. Use alpha .05.

13.34 This year's flu vaccine claims that it is equally effective for men and women. A medical researcher believes the vaccine is more effective for women. To test the claim, 300 women and 300 men were randomly selected. Of the women, 287 did not catch the flu this year. But of the men, only 274 didn't catch the flu. At the .05 level, does there seem to be a significant difference in the effectiveness of the vaccine across gender?

# 14

## ADDITIONAL INFERENTIAL STATISTICS

*SECTION 1* Multinomial Experiments (GOF)
*SECTION 2* Testing Contingency Tables/Crosstab (Matrices)
*SECTION 3* Testing Multiple Means: Analysis of Variance (ANOVA)

The previous chapters on inferential statistics discussed testing and estimating parameters for one or two populations that are normally distributed, typically interval or ratio-level data. This chapter discusses testing and estimating parameters for nominal-level data and for means from three or more populations. Essentially, this chapter combines procedures presented in several previous chapters that focused on graphs with hypothesis testing presented in later chapters. Multinomial experiments extend binomial experiments and test the expected outcomes with observed outcomes. Contingency tables, which have been presented several times, are also tested for a difference between the expected outcomes and observed outcomes. Finally, *analysis of variance (ANOVA)* tests differences among three or more means.

---

## SECTION 1

### Multinomial Experiments (GOF)

Chapter 7 introduced the binomial probability distribution, in which a discrete random variable has only two possible outcomes, known as success and failure. The probability of success and failure remained constant throughout the experiment. *Multinomial experiments* are exactly like binomial experiments, except that multinomial experiments may have three or more outcomes. Remember the binomial experiment referred to in Chapter 7 in which people are asked to identify their religion. If a researcher is concerned with the respondents who are Catholic, a binomial experiment collapses all religions other than Catholic into a category labeled failure, with success reserved for those reporting Catholic. A multinomial experiment does not collapse the categories into two. If five religions are reported, then five categories are created. As with binomial experiments multinomial experiments have a fixed number of trials, the trials must be independent, an outcome can qualify for only one category, and the probabilities remain constant across all trials.

> **Conditions for a Multinomial Experiment**
> 1. There is a fixed number of trials, *n*.
> 2. The trials are independent.

3. There are more than two possible outcomes.
4. The probability for each outcome remains constant on all trials.
5. The probability of all outcomes must have a sum of 1.0

A multinomial experiment allows a researcher to test the difference between the observed outcomes of an experiment and the theoretical outcomes. Thus it is often referred to a **Goodness of Fit**. Remember that any observed outcome does not necessarily match a theoretical outcome. The question then is to determine if the differences between the proportions in the observed outcomes and the expected theoretical outcomes are statistically significant, or a fit. The test statistic for a multinomial is Chi-square. Chi-square tests the variance in the difference between the observed frequencies and the expected frequencies. Recall from Chapter 12 that the Chi-square distribution is a nonnegative right-skewed distribution (Figure 14 1). Its critical values are reported in Table A.5.

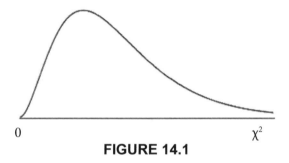

$$0 \qquad\qquad\qquad\qquad \chi^2$$

**FIGURE 14.1**

A special rule must be emphasized: Because the calculated Chi-square value will be very small if no difference is measured, any significant difference will have a large Chi-square value. Therefore, all multinomial experiments are tested as right-tailed $\chi^2$ tests.

---

**Hypotheses for Multinomial Testing (GOF)**
$$H_0\colon\ p_1 = ...,\, p_2 = ...,\, p_3 = ...,\, ...$$
$H_1$: At least one of the proportions is not equal to the value claimed

---

The first step in hypothesis testing for a multinomial is to state the hypotheses. The hypotheses for a multinomial can be written with symbols or with verbal descriptions. The null hypothesis is often written with symbols stating the probability of each outcome and its value. The probability, $p$, for each outcome must remain constant, but each outcome is not necessarily equal to the other outcomes. The alternative hypothesis is almost always stated verbally, challenging that at least one of the probabilities in the null hypothesis is not equal to the value claimed. For example, if the null hypothesis claims that, of a random sample of students' religions, the probability of answering Protestant is .60, Catholic, .35, Jewish, .03, and other, .02, then the alternative hypothesis challenges that at least one of these proportions is not equal to the value claimed.

$$H_0: p_1 = .60, p_2 = .35, p_3 = .03, \text{ and } p_4 = .02$$
$H_1$: At least one of the proportions is not equal to the value claimed

The test criteria include the identification of the level of significance, test statistic, critical region, and critical value. The level of significance is usually reported in the experiment or must be determined by considering the probability of a type I error. The test statistic for a multinomial is Chi-square. The critical region is always one-tailed to the right. Never divide alpha by 2 when testing a multinomial experiment. The critical value is determined by the degrees of freedom and alpha. The degrees of freedom for the multinomial Chi-square test is $k - 1$, where $k$ is the number of possible outcomes (not the number of trials). For example, if 100 people surveyed indicated five different religions, $k$ is 5, not 100.

> **Degrees of Freedom for a Multinomial**
> $$df = k - 1$$
> where $k$ equals the number of possible outcomes or categories

The third step in hypothesis testing is to calculate the test statistic. The test statistic is Chi-square; however, its calculation is different than the Chi-square calculation in Chapter 12. A multinomial tests the difference between the observed proportions for each outcome and the expected proportions for each outcome based on a theoretical distribution. Therefore, the expected outcomes are subtracted from the observed outcomes, squared, divided by the expected probability, and summed.

> **Formula for Chi-Square Multinomial Calculated Value**
> **(GOF)**
>
> $$\chi^2 = \Sigma \frac{(O - E)^2}{E}$$
>
> where
>   $O$ is the observed frequency of an outcome.
>   $E$ is the expected frequency, equal to $np$.
>   $\Sigma$ is the summation, which occurs at the end of the calculations.

Note the summation sign in the test statistic calculation. The summation occurs at the end of the calculations. The expected frequency for each outcome is subtracted from its observed frequency, squared, and divided by the expected frequency. This process is performed for each category. When the formula is applied to each category, the values are then summed. Arrange the data with columns for $O$, $E$, $(O - E,$ )

$(O - E)^2$, and $(O - E)^2/E$. Sum the last column for the $\chi^2$ calculated value. If $E$ is given as a proportion, $E$ must be calculated for each category by multiplying the total number of responses in the survey by the probability of the category.

---

### Expected Frequency for a Multinomial

$$E = np$$

where
    $E$ is the expected frequency for a category.
    $n$ is the total number of responses in the survey.
    $p$ is the probability for that category.

---

The fourth step in hypothesis testing is placing the calculated value on the distribution curve. The calculated value is placed on the curve relative to the critical value.

The fifth step is to make a decision. If the calculated value falls in the critical region, then the decision is to reject the null hypothesis. If the calculated value does not fall in the critical region, then the decision is to fail to reject the null hypothesis. The final step in hypothesis testing is to interpret the results. In multinomial testing rejecting the null hypothesis implies that at least one of the proportions in the null hypothesis is different than the value claimed—that is, a significant difference is found between the observed frequencies and the expected frequencies.

---

### EXAMPLE 14.1

**Experiment:** The registrar claims that 60% of the students in the university are Protestant, 35% are Catholic, 3% are Jewish, and 2% are other religions. To test this claim, two hundred students are surveyed, producing the following results: 106 Protestants, 80 Catholics, 10 Jewish, and 4 other. Test the registrar's claim at the .01 level of significance.

**Answer:** Fail to reject the null hypothesis. There is not sufficient proof at the .01 level of significance to reject the null hypothesis that the proportions of religion among the students is different than that claimed by the registrar.

**Solution:** This is a multinomial experiment, because four categories are represented in 200 independent trials, where the probabilities of the outcomes have a sum of 1.0. (The percentages are probabilities. As percentages they must have a sum of 100%.) Begin by stating the hypotheses. The null hypothesis for a multinomial states that the proportions are equal to the claimed values. The percentages are written as probabilities by dropping the percent sign and moving the decimal point two places to the left.

---

$$H_0: p_1 = .60, p_2 = .35, p_3 = .03, \text{ and } p_4 = .02$$
$H_1$: At least one of the proportions is not equal to the value claimed

The level of significance is .01. The test statistic is Chi-square. The critical region for multinomial testing is always one-tailed to the right. The critical value is determined by the degrees of freedom, $k - 1$, and alpha. The $k$ is equal to the number of categories. There are four categories of religion reported in the hypotheses; therefore, $k - 1$ is $4 - 1$, or 3. Read down Table A.5 to 3 degrees of freedom and across to alpha = .01. The critical value is 11.345.

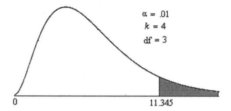

Calculate the test statistic. Chi-square is calculated differently for a multinomial than it is when testing a single variance. Arrange the data in columns for $O$, $E$, $(O - E)$, $(O - E)^2$, and $(O - E)^2/E$. The sample data are the observed data, $O$. $E$ is determined by multiplying $n$ and $p$ for each category, where $n$ is 200. As a check on the mathematics, the sum of O must equal $n$, the sum of $E$ must also equal $n$, and the sum of $(O - E)$ must equal 0. The summation of the $(O - E)^2/E$ column is the calculated $\chi^2$ value.

| Category | $O$ | $(np) = E$ | $(O - E)$ | $(O - E)^2$ | $(O - E)^2 / E$ |
|---|---|---|---|---|---|
| Protestant | 106 | $[200(.60)] = 120$ | - 14 | $-14^2 = 196$ | $196 / 120 = 1.633$ |
| Catholic | 80 | $[200(.35)] = 70$ | 10 | $10^2 = 100$ | $100 / 70 = 1.429$ |
| Jewish | 10 | $[200(.03)] = 6$ | 4 | $4^2 = 16$ | $16 / 6 = 2.667$ |
| Other | 4 | $[200(.02)] = 4$ | 0 | $0^2 = 0$ | $0 / 4 = 0.000$ |
| | $n = 200$ | check = 200 | check = 0 | | $\chi2 = 5.729$ |

The calculated value is 5.729. This value must be placed on the distribution curve relative to the critical value.

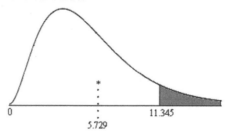

Because the calculated value, 5.729, does not fall in the critical region, the decision is to fail to reject the null hypothesis. The interpretation of the decision in the experiment is that there is not sufficient proof at the .01 level of significance to reject the null hypothesis that the proportions of religion among the students is different than that claimed by the registrar.

## *P*-Value Approach for Multinomial GOF Testing

As is obvious above, there is a lot of math to do the GOF multinomial long-hand. The TI 84 calculators perform the test much easier and faster. It is under the $\chi^2$ GOF function. The observed values are entered in the listing $L_1$ area of the calculator and the expected in the $L_2$ list. The expected values can be calculated on the screen at the same time as entering the data. For example, if n is 106 and the expected proportion is .6, the calculation can be done on the bottom of the screen as 106 $x$ .6 and when enter is pressed, the expected value will pop into the list as 120. NOTE: The TI 83 calculators do not perform the $\chi^2$ GOF test.

### A LEARNING AID
### MULTINOMIAL EXPERIMENT (GOF) USING THE CALCULATOR

A local department store claims that 28% of their sales is in women's clothes, 24% is in cosmetics, 18% is in jewelry, 15% is in men's clothes, and 15% is in other departments. A random sample of 400 sales produces the following results: 138 sales in women's clothes, 107 sales in cosmetics, 65 sales in jewelry, 51 sales in men's clothes, and 39 sales in other departments. Test the department's claim at alpha = .05.

### Step 1

This is a multinomial experiment, because five categories are represented in 400 independent (random) trials, where the probabilities of the outcomes have a sum of 1.0. (The percentages are probabilities. As percentages, they must have a sum of 100%).

State the hypotheses. The null hypothesis for a multinomial experiment reports that the proportions are equal to the claimed values. The percentages are written as probabilities by dropping the percent sign and moving the decimal left two places. State each category with the probability claimed by the store.

$$H_0: p_1 = .28, p_2 = .24, p_3 = .18, p_4 = .15 \text{ and } p_5 = .15$$
$$H_1: \text{At least one of the proportions is not equal to the value claimed}$$

**Step 2**

Identify the test criteria. The level of significance is .05. The test statistic for a multinomial is Chi-square. The critical region for multinomial testing is always one-tailed to the right. The critical value is determined by the degrees of freedom, $k - 1$, and alpha. $k$ is equal to the number of categories. There are five departments reported in the hypotheses; therefore, $k - 1$ is 5 - 1, or 4. Read down Table A.5 in the appendix to 4 degrees of freedom and across to alpha = .05.

**Step 3**

Calculate the test statistic. Chi-square is calculated for the difference between the observed frequencies and the expected frequencies. This test is performed by comparing observed and expected values, which need to be inserted into $L_1$ and $L_2$ of a calculator.

The observed values of department store sales are provided in the problem, and expected values can be calculated by multiplying the percentage claim by the sample size. As an example, there are 138 sales in women's clothing with a claimed proportion of 28%. Thus the first expected value is 138 (.28) = 112. The value 112 goes in List 2. This is repeated for the rest of the categories. Press STAT followed by pressing ENTER to select "Edit…" Insert observed values into List 1 and expected values into List 2. With observed and expected values inserted into each list, press STAT and scroll to the "TESTS" tab to select "D: $\chi^2$ GOF-Test"

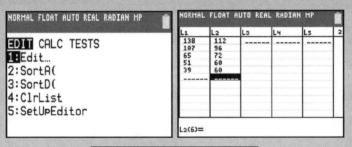

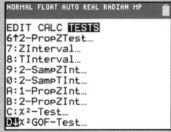

Under the settings screen of the calculator, set $L_1$ for observed and $L_2$ for expected, along with the degrees of freedom. Consider that $df = (k - 1)$. The settings screen should appear as follows. Once complete, highlight "Calculate" and press ENTER. The results will appear.

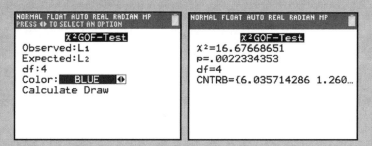

$$\chi^2 = \Sigma \frac{(O-E)^2}{E} = 16.677$$

**Step 4**
Identify the *P*-value noted from the calculator function. It reports that P = .0022334353. This can be rounded to .0022.

**Step 5**
Make a decision. Because the *P*-value is less than alpha, reject the null hypothesis.

*P*-value(.0022) < alpha(.05)      Reject the null hypothesis

**Step 6**
Interpret the results. The interpretation of the decision with regard to the experiment is that there is sufficient evidence at the .05 level of significance to reject the null hypothesis that sales in the department store are as claimed by the store.

# SECTION 2

## Testing Contingency Tables/Crosstabs (Matrices)

Chapter 4 describes the contingency table as a two-way display of one or two nominal level variables. Chapter 7 also describes the transformation of a contingency table into a theoretical probability distribution. Both of these processes are combined in this chapter to determine if the variables are independent or dependent. The table, also referred to as a crosstab or cross-tabulation, represents the relationships of two variables and their events. The relationship of the variables in a contingency table is determined by comparing a sample's observed frequencies with the expected frequencies based on a theoretical distribution.

The variables in a contingency table are assumed independent until a challenge proves the variables are dependent. Independence is implied when there is no difference between the observed frequencies and the expected frequencies. If a difference exists, then the variables are said to be dependent. The Chi-square test statistic measures the degree of variance in the observed and expected frequencies. As with the multinomial experiment, all tests for contingency tables are one-tailed to the right.

The first step in hypothesis testing for contingency tables is to state the hypotheses. The null hypothesis is completely narrative, stating that the two variables are independent. The alternative hypothesis, also narratively stated, claims that the two variables are dependent.

> **Hypotheses for Contingency Table Testing**
> $H_0$: Variable 1 and Variable 2 are independent
> $H_1$: Variable 1 and Variable 2 are dependent

The test criteria are the same as with the multinomial experiment. The level of significance is reported in the experiment or determined by considering the seriousness of a type I error. The test statistic for a contingency table is Chi-square. The critical region is always one-tailed to the right, and the critical value is determined by the degrees of freedom and alpha, as reported in Table A.5. The degrees of freedom for a contingency table differ from other test statistics. The degrees of freedom equal the number of rows minus one multiplied by the number of columns minus one. The table is reviewed to determine the number of rows and columns.

> **Degrees of Freedom for a Contingency Table using $\chi^2$**
> $$df = (r - 1)(c - 1)$$
> where
>
> $r$ equals the number of rows in the table.
> $c$ equals the number of columns in the table.

The degrees of freedom for a table where five values for a variable are presented in the rows and three values for a second variable are presented in the columns are $(5 - 1)(3 - 1)$, or 8.

The third step in hypothesis testing is to calculate the test statistic. The Chi-square calculation for a contingency table is identical to the calculation for the multinomial experiment. However, the calculation of the expected values differs. In a multinomial experiment, $E = np$, but the contingency table requires the expected values to be calculated by multiplying the row total by the column total and then dividing by the total number of responses in the sample. This calculation must occur for each cell in the contingency table.

---

**Expected Frequency for Each Cell in a Contingency Table**

$$E = \frac{(\text{row total})(\text{column total})}{\text{total sample size}} = \frac{(R)(C)}{N}$$

where
  $R$ equals the row total for a cell.
  $C$ equals the column total for a cell.
  $N$ equals the total sample size.

---

The expected frequency for a cell whose row total is 200, column total is 300, and with a total sample size of 600 is 100; $E = [200(300)]/600 = 100$. The expected frequency for each cell must be calculated. Either the expected frequency is placed in parentheses inside each cell of the table or the data are arranged in columns comparing the observed frequencies to the expected frequencies. If a table has eight cells, the data are given with eight columns, one representing each of the cells.

Chi-square is then calculated in the same way as for a multinomial experiment. The data are arranged in the following columns: $O$, $E$, $(O - E)$, $(O - E)^2$, and $(O - E)^2 / E$.

---

**Chi-Square Formula for a Contingency Table/Crosstabulation/Matrix**

$$\chi^2 = \Sigma \frac{(O - E)^2}{E}$$

where
  $O$ is the observed frequency of an outcome.
  $E$ is the expected frequency of an outcome: $[R \cdot C] / N$.
  $\Sigma$ is the summation, which occurs at the end of the calculation.

---

Note that the summation in the calculation occurs at the end. Each expected frequency is subtracted from its observed frequency, squared, and divided by the expected frequency. This process is performed for each category.

The fourth step in hypothesis testing is to place the calculated value on the distribution curve relative to the critical value.

The fifth step is to make a decision. If the calculated value falls in the critical region, then the decision is to reject the null hypothesis. If the calculated value does not fall in the critical region, then the decision is to fail to reject the null hypothesis. The final step is to interpret the results. Rejecting a null hypothesis for a contingency table implies that the two variables are dependent-that a significant difference is found between the observed values and the expected values. Failing to reject the null hypothesis implies that the variables are independent; that is, no difference is found between the observed and expected values.

## EXAMPLE 14.2

**Experiment:** For a sample of 810 voters, determine if gender and party identification are independent at alpha = .05.

**Answer:** Reject the null hypothesis. The variables gender and party identification appear to be dependent, with a significant difference between the observed and expected values. It appears that women tend to be Democrats and males tend to be Republicans.

| Gender ↓ Party ID → | Democrat | Independent | Republican | Total |
|---|---|---|---|---|
| Female | 205 | 102 | 93 | 400 |
| Male | 112 | 114 | 184 | 410 |
| Total | 317 | 216 | 277 | 810 |

**Solution:** The contingency table shows the intersection of two variables, sex and party identification. The table also represents observed frequencies as obtained for a sample of 810 voters.

### Step 1

Begin by stating the hypotheses. The null hypothesis states that the variables are independent—that there is no difference between the observed and expected frequencies. The alternative hypothesis states that there is a difference between the observed and expected frequencies.

$H_0$: Gender and party identification are independent
$H_1$: Gender and party identification are dependent

### Step 2

The test criteria include alpha, the test statistic, critical region, and critical value. Alpha is reported as .05. The test statistic for contingency tables is Chi-square. The critical region is always to the right for Chi-square testing of contingency tables and multinomial cases. The critical value is determined by the degrees of freedom and alpha. The degrees of freedom for a contingency table are $(r - 1)(c - 1)$, where $r$ is the number of rows and $c$ is the number of columns. The variable sex is reported with two rows and the variable party identification is reported with three columns. The degrees of freedom are

(2 - 1)(3 - 1) = 2. Use Table A.5. Trace down to 2 degrees of freedom and across to alpha = .05. The critical value is 5.991. Place the critical value on the distribution curve.

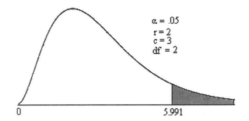

**Step 3**

Calculate the expected frequencies for each cell by multiplying the row total by the column total and then dividing by the sample size. For example, for the upper left cell, a female Democrat, the expected frequency is [400(317)]/810, or 156.54. For female Independents, the expected value is [400(216)]/810, or 106.67. The expected value for female Republicans is [400(277)]/810, or 136.79. Complete this process for the males, replacing the row totals with 410.

| **Gender ↓ Party ID →** | **Democrat** | **Independent** | **Republican** | **Total** |
|---|---|---|---|---|
| Female | 205 (156.54) | 102 (106.67) | 93 (136.79) | 400 |
| Male | 112 (160.46) | 114 (109.33) | 184 (140.21) | 410 |
| Total | 317 | 216 | 277 | 810 |

Calculate the $\chi^2$ statistic. Arrange the data in columns for $O$, $E$, $(O - E)$, $(O - E)^2$, and $(O - E)^2/E$. There are six cells in the contingency table. Each cell must be labeled. Remember that the columns for $O$ and $E$ must each sum to the sample size, 810. Also, the column $(O - E)$ must sum to zero. The sum of the last column is the calculated $\chi^2$ value.

| **Cell** | **O** | **E** | **(O – E)** | **(O - E)²** | **(O - E)² /E** |
|---|---|---|---|---|---|
| Female-Democrat | 205 | 156.54 | 48.46 | 2348.37 | 15.002 |
| Female-Independent | 102 | 106.67 | - 4.67 | 21.81 | 0.204 |
| Female-Republican | 93 | 136.79 | - 43.79 | 1917.56 | 14.018 |
| Male-Democrat | 112 | 160.46 | - 48.46 | 2348.37 | 14.635 |
| Male-Independent | 114 | 109.33 | 4.67 | 21.81 | 0.199 |
| Male-Republican | 184 | 140.21 | 43.79 | 1917.56 | 13.676 |
| Total | 810 | 810.00 | Check = 0.00 | | $\chi2 = 57.734$ |

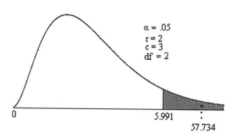

$\alpha = .05$
$r = 2$
$c = 3$
$df = 2$

5.991

57.734

**Step 4**

Place the calculated value, 57.734, on the distribution curve. The value 57.734 falls to the right of the critical value in the critical region.

**Step 5**

The decision must be to reject the null hypothesis that the variables are independent.

$$\text{Reject } H_O$$

**Step 6**

Based on this sample, the interpretation is that there is sufficient evidence at the .05 level of significance that gender and party identification are dependent.

## P-VALUE APPROACH FOR CONTINGENCY TABLES AND MATRICES

In most computerized statistical programs, contingency tables are known as crosstabulations, or crosstabs. Chi-square statistics are usually available for a cross-tabulation. Because Chi-square is always one-tailed to the right for a contingency table, if a reported calculated Chi-square value exceeds the critical value, then the decision is to reject the null hypothesis.

As with the multinomial $\chi^2$ GOF test, there is a lot of math for the $\chi^2$ test of a contingency table or matrix. Both the TI-83/84 calculators perform this test. The first step is to enter the observed values of the original table in the matrix function of the calculator. The expected values are not entered as the calculator will automatically calculate them when performing the $\chi^2$ test.

### EXAMPLE 14.3
### Using the Calculator

**Experiment:** The following is a contingency table representing the amount of political information Southerners receive from church and their level of support for liberal political causes. Are the variables independent at the .01 level of significance?

| Liberalism ↓ | Information → | Low | High | Total |
|---|---|---|---|---|
| **Low** | | 30 | 70 | 100 |
| **High** | | 70 | 30 | 100 |
| **Total** | | **100** | **100** | **200** |

**Answer:** No, reject the null hypothesis that the variables are independent.

**Solution:** The contingency table represents the overlapping of two variables, information and liberalism. Begin by stating the hypotheses. The null hypothesis states that the variables are independent—that there is no difference between the observed and expected frequencies. The alternative hypothesis states that there is a difference between the observed and expected frequencies.

$H_0$: Information and liberalism are independent
$H_1$: Information and liberalism are dependent

The test criteria include alpha and the choice of the test statistic. Alpha is reported as .01. The test statistic for contingency tables is Chi-square.

The TI-83/84 calculators perform this test when the observed sample data are put into the matrix function. To begin, press 2nd and MATRIX (on top of $x^{-1}$), scroll over to EDIT. With "1:[A]" highlighted, press ENTER. The screen will now display MATRIX [A] with some number such as 2 x 2. This must be adjusted for the table problem. With the cursor blinking over the first number, type the number of rows for the table and press ENTER. The cursor will now jump to the second number. Type the number of columns and press ENTER. A matrix indicating the number of rows and columns will appear on the screen. The cursor should now be over the first cell. Enter the sample observed value. Press ENTER. The cursor will now highlight the second cell. Enter the observed sample value for the second cell and press ENTER. Continue throughout the table.

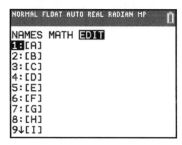 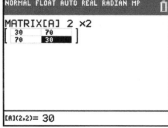

When the data are entered, start the test by pressing STAT, scroll to "TESTS", and down to $C : \chi^2 - Test$. The observed data were entered in the matrix noted as MATRIX [A]. The expected values are automatically calculated and placed in MATRIX [B]. Scroll down and highlight "Calculate" and press ENTER. The results will appear as follows.

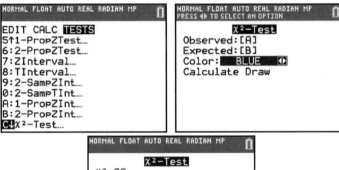

$$\chi^2 = \Sigma \frac{(O-E)^2}{E} = 32$$

Note that the *P*-value reported by the calculator is in scientific notation as 1.5417258E-8 or .00000001547258. Refer to a number this small as 0+.

$$P = 0+$$

Compare the *P*-value to the alpha level of .01.

$P$-value(0+) < alpha(.01)      Reject the null hypothesis

The decision must be to reject the null hypothesis that the variables are independent. Based on this sample, the interpretation is that there is sufficient evidence at the .01 level of significance that the amount of information a Southerner receives is dependent on support for liberal causes.

## A LEARNING AID
## TESTING CONTINGENCY TABLES/CROSSTABULATIONS

For a sample of 400 registered voters, determine if voters' preference for an increase in sales tax is independent of their preference for an income tax to pay for a new education program (alpha = .05).

| Income Tax ↓   Sales Tax → | Yes | No | Total |
|---|---|---|---|
| Yes | 108 | 92 | 200 |
| No | 66 | 134 | 200 |
| Total | 174 | 226 | 400 |

**Step 1**

Identify the table as a contingency table. Two nominal variables are overlapped with the joint observed frequencies reported in the cells. Begin by stating the hypotheses. The null hypothesis states that the variables are independent. The alternative hypothesis states that the variables are dependent. No symbols or values are used in the statements for contingency tables.

$H_O$: Preferences for sales taxes or income taxes are independent
$H_I$: Preferences for sales taxes or income taxes are dependent

**Step 2**

The test criteria include alpha and the choice of the test statistic. Alpha is reported as .05. The test statistic for contingency tables is Chi-square.

**Step 3**

The TI-83/84 calculators perform this test when the observed sample data are put into the matrix function. To begin, press 2$^{nd}$ and MATRIX (on top of $x^{-1}$), scroll over to EDIT. With "1:[A]" highlighted, press ENTER. The screen will now display MATRIX [A] with some number such as 2 x 2. This must be adjusted for the table problem. With the cursor blinking over the first number, type the number of rows for the table and press ENTER. The cursor will now jump to the second number. Type the number of columns and press ENTER. A matrix indicating the number of rows and columns will appear on the screen. The cursor should now be over the first cell. Enter the sample observed value. Press ENTER. The cursor will now highlight the second cell. Enter the observed sample value for the second cell and press ENTER. Continue throughout the table.

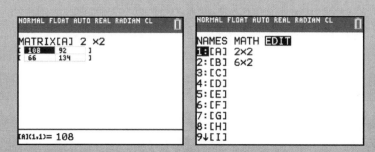

When the data are entered, start the test by pressing STAT, scroll to "TESTS", and down to $C : \chi^2 - Test$. The observed data were entered in the matrix noted as MATRIX [A]. The expected values are automatically calculated and placed in MATRIX [B]. Scroll down and highlight "Calculate" and press ENTER. The results will appear as follows.

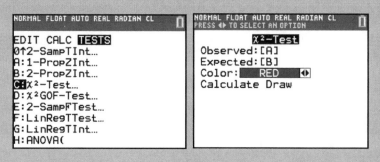

$$\chi^2 = \Sigma \frac{(O - E)^2}{E} = 17.943$$

**Step 4**

Identify the *P*-value from the result screen:

$$P = 2.275912\text{E-}5 = 0+$$

**Step 5**

Compare *P* to alpha and make a decision.

$P$-value(0+) < alpha(.05)     Reject the null hypothesis

**Step 6**
Interpret the results. Rejecting the null hypothesis in a contingency table suggests that the variables are dependent; that is, the difference between the observed and expected values is significant. There is sufficient evidence at the .05 level of significance to show that there is a relationship between voters' preferences between sales taxes and income taxes.

# SECTION 3

## Testing Multiple Means: Analysis Of Variance—ANOVA

Although the most common statistical measures test the difference between two samples, testing with three or more samples is also necessary. Situations often occur in which there are several methods, several products, or several types of items that are compared. For example, an instructor may want to compare student performance based on academic major. The $z$ and $t$ test statistics compare only two majors at a time. If six majors exist, then 12 separate tests, working with two majors at a time, would need to be performed. Separate testing is inefficient, and the chance of errors is substantially increased.

A method of testing three or more means focuses on analyzing the variance within and across the samples. This method is known as the analysis of variance, or ANOVA. There are several types of analysis of variance, of which two are discussed in this chapter: a one-way ANOVA and a two-way ANOVA. The simplest type of analysis is the one-way ANOVA, in which observations are classified into groups on the basis of a single characteristic, such as, a one-way analysis comparing student performance based on majors. The two-way analysis of variance is more complicated. Observations are classified into groups on the basis of two characteristics. For example, a two-way analysis compares student performance based on majors and year in school.

Although means are being tested, analysis of variance compares the variation between the samples to the variation within the sample. If the variance between the samples is larger than the variation within the samples, then it is concluded that the means of each sample are not the same. For example, if the normal curves in Figure 14.2 represent three samples, then the analysis of variance can be conceptualized as measuring the difference between the means of each sample (represented by the peaks in the curve) and the difference within each sample (represented by the width of each curve).

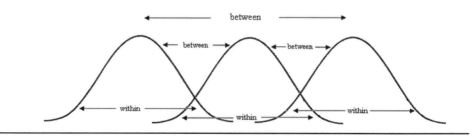

**FIGURE 14.2**

There are several conditions necessary for applying the analysis of variance. The first condition is that at least three population means are tested. All populations are considered normally distributed. Populations that are not normally distributed should be tested using other methods (such as the Kruskal-Wallis test). The standard deviations of the population must be equal and the samples must be independent. The $F$ distribution is used in testing three or more means with ANOVA. Recall that the $F$ distribution is not symmetric, but is skewed to the right (Figure 14.3). It has values of 0 or more, and degrees of freedom associated with the numerator and the denominator. Critical values for $F$ are reported in Table A.6a, A.6b, and A.6c. Each table represents a different alpha level.

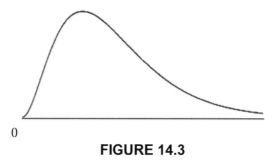

0

**FIGURE 14.3**

The six steps in hypothesis testing are followed when testing with the analysis of variance. State the hypotheses, identify the test criteria, calculate the test statistic, place the calculated value on the curve, make a decision, and interpret the results.

The null hypothesis is written with the parameters and an equal sign. The null hypothesis states that the means of all the populations are equal. The alternative hypothesis is written narratively stating that the means are not all equal. For example, for three population means the hypotheses are written as

**Hypotheses for ANOVA**

$$H_0: \mu_1 = \mu_2 = \mu_3$$
$$H_1: \text{The means are not equal}$$

The test criteria include the level of significance, test statistic, critical region, and critical value. The level of significance is typically given as alpha. If alpha is not given, then it must be set by considering the seriousness of a type I error. The test statistic for three or more normally distributed means is the $F$ test, as determined by the analysis of variance. As with a multinomial and contingency tables, the critical region for ANOVA testing is always one-tailed to the right. The critical value is determined by identifying the degrees of freedom for the numerator, degrees of freedom for the denominator, and alpha. The degrees of freedom for the numerator is associated with the difference between the samples and is equal to $k - 1$, where $k$ is the number of samples, or categories. The degrees of freedom for the denominator is associated with the difference within the samples and is equal to $N - k$, where $N$ is the total number of outcomes in all samples combined and $k$ is the number of samples. As a check on the degrees of freedom, the numerator $df$ and denominator $df$ should have a sum of $N - 1$, as calculated for most other test statistics.

### Degrees of Freedom for ANOVA
$$df_n = k - 1$$
$$df_d = N - k$$

where

$k$ equals the number of samples (which must be at least 3).
$N$ is the total number of outcomes in all samples combined.
$df_n$ is associated with the difference between the samples.
$df_d$ is associated with the difference within the samples.

### EXAMPLE 14.4

**Experiment:** If three different methods are used to teach statistics, determine the degrees of freedom associated with a survey of 20 students in method I, 25 students in method II, and 20 students in method III.

**Answer:** $df_n = 2$, $df_d = 62$

**Solution:** The degrees of freedom associated with the difference between the samples are determined by $k - 1$, where $k$ is the number of samples. There are three samples, so $k - 1 = 3 - 1 = 2$. The degrees of freedom associated with the difference within the samples is determined by $N - k$, where $N$ is the total number of outcomes and $k$ is the number of samples. The total number of outcomes is found by adding the number of students in each sample: $20 + 25 + 20 = 65$. There are three samples, so the degrees of freedom for the denominator are $65 - 3 = 62$.

The critical value is determined by noting the degrees of freedom for the numerator, the degrees of freedom for the denominator, and alpha. Begin by identifying the correct alpha in Table A.6a, A.6b, and A.6c. After identifying alpha, move across the table to the appropriate degrees of freedom for the numerator and down to the appropriate degrees of freedom for the denominator. The value in the intersection is the critical $F$ value.

The calculation of the test statistic is lengthy. The variation within the samples is measured, the variation across the samples is measured, the total variation is measured, and then a ratio of the mean square estimates results in a calculated $F$ value. Each of these calculations is performed separately. After the initial calculations, the full process can be summarized in a table that organizes the calculations.

Begin by calculating the sum of squares for the total variation that exists. Recall that the sum of squares is the numerator of the variance formula presented in earlier chapters and is denoted by $SS$. Use the subscript $t$ to denote the sum of squares for the total. The calculation is the same as in earlier chapters. Notice that $N$ replaces $n$, as a reminder in ANOVA that $N$ is the total number of observations for all samples combined. The lowercase $n$ is reserved for identifying the number of observations in any one sample.

**Sum of Squares for the Total Variation**

$$SS_t = \Sigma x^2 - \frac{(\Sigma x)^2}{N}$$

The total variance is now partitioned into two parts, one measuring the difference between the samples and the other measuring the difference within the samples. It is also common to refer to the difference between the samples as the sum of squares between, sum of squares factor, or sum of squares treatment. Each of the terms refers to the fact that the test is measuring whether a difference exists between the populations. The difference within the samples is associated with error and is therefore commonly referred to as the sum of squares within or sum of squares error.

The calculation for the sum of squares between is done by squaring each sample's total and dividing by the sample's size. Then these values are added after being determined for each sample. From this summation is subtracted the square of the sum of $x$ divided by $N$. The data are usually arranged in columns, where each column represents a sample. The $C$ in the formula represents the sum of the values in a column. Each column total is squared and divided by its $n$; then it is added to the values obtained for the other samples. The lowercase $N$ is the number of values in a sample, and the uppercase $N$ is the total number of values in all samples combined.

---

### Sum of Squares Between (Factor, Treatment)

$$SS_b = \Sigma\left(\frac{C^2}{n}\right) - \frac{(\Sigma x)^2}{N}$$

where
    $C^2$ is the square of the column total.
    $n$ is the number of values in a sample. $n$ may differ for each sample.
    $(\Sigma x)^2$ is the sum of all values in all samples combined, squared.
    $N$ is the total number of values in all samples combined. The sum of all $n$'s.

---

The sum of squares within (error) is the remaining unexplained variance after the sum of squares between is subtracted from the total sum of squares. The sum of squares error can be calculated by formula or by subtracting the sum of squares between from the sum of squares total. If the full formula is used, the sum of the two partitions should be the total.

---

### Sum of Squares Within (Error)

$$SS_w = \Sigma x^2 - \Sigma\left(\frac{C^2}{n}\right)$$

where
    $C^2$ is the square of the column total.
    $n$ is the number of values in a sample. $n$ may differ for each sample.
    $\Sigma x^2$ is the square of all values in all samples, summed.

---

Arranging the calculations for the sum of squares in a table will guide the final calculations. Each sum of squares is divided by its degrees of freedom. The result of the division is referred to as the mean square, which estimates the variance. The ratio of the mean square between and within results in the calculated $F$ statistic. The table should contain a column for the source of variance, the sum of squares ($SS$), degrees of freedom ($df$), mean square ($MS$), and $F$. Three rows should exist representing the source of variance: between (factor), within (error), and total.

| Source of variance | SS | df | MS | F |
|---|---|---|---|---|
| Between (Factor) | $SS_b = \Sigma\left(\dfrac{C^2}{n}\right) - \dfrac{(\Sigma x)^2}{N}$ | $k - 1$ | $SS_b / df_b$ | |
| Within (error) | $SS_w = \Sigma x^2 - \Sigma\left(\dfrac{C^2}{n}\right)$ | $N - k$ | $SS_w / df_w$ | $\dfrac{MS_b}{MS_w}$ |
| Total | $SS_t = \Sigma x^2 - \dfrac{(\Sigma x)^2}{N}$ | $N - 1$ | ------ | |

The $F$ test statistic is the ratio of the mean squares for between and mean squares for within. The calculated $F$ statistic is placed on the distribution curve relative to the critical value. If the calculated value falls in the critical region then the decision is to reject the null hypothesis. If the calculated value falls in the non-critical region, then the decision is to fail to reject the null hypothesis.

Failing to reject the null hypothesis implies that there is no difference in the means. A calculated $F$ value near 1.0 suggests that there is no significant difference between the sample means. If the calculated $F$ value is large, then a significant difference exists between the sample means, and the null hypothesis is rejected. Rejecting the null hypothesis implies only that at least one mean is not equal to the others. It does not specify which mean is not equal. There are a variety of tests called multiple comparison procedures (for example, the Tukey $\beta$ test) that can be used to specify the inequality.

## EXAMPLE 14.5

**Experiment:** University students are randomly assigned to one of three different courses in statistics: a self-study course, a lecture course, or a computer-assisted course. An exam is given to determine if there is a significant difference in knowledge of statistics among the students taking the different courses. Is there a significant difference in the mean outcomes from the teaching methods at the .01 level?

| Self Study | Lecture | Computer-Assisted |
|---|---|---|
| 60 | 90 | 83 |
| 72 | 75 | 76 |
| 64 | 88 | 55 |
| 62 | 75 | 79 |
| 52 | 72 | 66 |
| 58 | 82 | 76 |
| | 63 | 89 |
| | 71 | 73 |

**Answer:** No, there is no significant difference in the teaching methods.

**Solution:** Identify the data as an ANOVA by identifying the necessary conditions. There are three samples of students. The samples are randomly selected, which ensures independent sampling. The standard deviations can be calculated.

**Step 1**
State the hypotheses. The null hypothesis for ANOVA is that there is no difference between the population means. The alternative hypothesis is that at least one mean is statistically unequal to the others.

$$H_0: \mu_1 = \mu_2 = \mu_3$$
$$H_1: \text{The means are not equal}$$

**Step 2** Identify the test criteria. The alpha is reported as .01. The test statistic for ANOVA is $F$. The critical region for ANOVA is always one-tailed to the right. The critical value is determined by degrees of freedom for the numerator, degrees of freedom for the denominator, and alpha. The degrees of freedom for the numerator are $k - 1$, where $k$ is the number of samples. Therefore, numerator $df = 3 - 1$, or 2. The degrees of freedom for the denominator are:

$N - k$, where $N$ is the total number of outcomes for all samples combined. Twenty-two students are tested; therefore, the degrees of freedom for the denominator are :

$$N - k = 22 - 3 = 19.$$
$$df_n = k - 1 = 3 - 1 = 2$$
$$df_d = N - K = 22 - 3 = 19$$

Use Table A.6a, which is for critical $F$ values at alpha = .01. Read across the table to numerator $df$ at 2 and down to the denominator $df$ 19. The critical value in the intersection is 5.926. Place the value on the distribution curve.

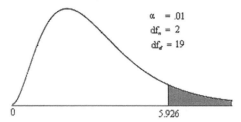

**Step 3**
To calculate the test statistic, arrange the data in the columns. Calculate $x^2$ for each value reported and sum all columns.

| Self Study | $x^2$ | Lecture | $x^2$ | Computer | $x^2$ |
|---|---|---|---|---|---|
| 60 | 3,600 | 90 | 8,100 | 83 | 6,889 |
| 72 | 5,184 | 75 | 5,625 | 76 | 5,776 |
| 64 | 4,096 | 88 | 7,744 | 55 | 3,025 |
| 62 | 3,844 | 75 | 5,625 | 79 | 6,241 |
| 52 | 2,704 | 72 | 5,184 | 66 | 4,356 |
| 58 | 3,364 | 82 | 6,724 | 76 | 5,776 |
| | | 63 | 3,969 | 89 | 7,921 |
| | | 71 | 5,041 | 73 | 5,329 |

$C_1 = 368$  22,792     $C_2 = 616$  48,012     $C_3 = 597$  45,313

$n_1 = 6$          $n_2 = 8$          $n_3 = 8$

$\Sigma x^2 = 22{,}792 + 48{,}012 + 45{,}313 = 116{,}117$

$(\Sigma x) = 368 + 616 + 597 = 1581$

$N = n_1 + n_2 + n_3 = 6 + 8 + 8 = 22$

Calculate the sum of squares total. Then calculate the sum of squares between. Subtract the between value from the total, resulting in the sum of squares within.

$$SS_t = \Sigma x^2 - \frac{(\Sigma x)^2}{N} = 116{,}117 - \frac{1581^2}{22} = 116{,}117 - \frac{2{,}499{,}561}{22}$$
$$= 116{,}117 - 113{,}616.4$$
$$= 2500.6$$

$$SS_b = \Sigma \left( \frac{C^2}{n} \right) - \frac{(\Sigma x)^2}{N} = \left( \frac{368^2}{6} + \frac{616^2}{8} + \frac{597^2}{8} \right) - \frac{1581^2}{22}$$

$$= \left( \frac{135{,}424}{6} + \frac{379{,}456}{8} + \frac{356409}{8} \right) - \frac{2{,}499{,}561}{22}$$
$$= (22{,}570.667 + 47{,}432 + 44551.125) - 113{,}616.4$$
$$= 114{,}553.79 - 113{,}616.4$$
$$= 937.39$$

$$SS_w = SS_t - SS_b = 2500.6 - 937.39 = 1563.21$$

| Source | SS | df | MS | F |
|---|---|---|---|---|
| Between (Factor) | 937.39 | $k - 1 = 3 - 1 = 2$ | $SS_b / df_b$ <br> 468.695 | $MS_b / MS_w$ <br> = 5.697 |
| Within (error) | 1563.21 | $N - k = 22 - 3 = 19$ | $SS_w / df_w$ <br> 82.274 | $P = .0115$ |

Place these values in a table to clarify the calculations.

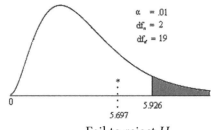

$$\alpha = .01$$
$$df_n = 2$$
$$df_e = 19$$

0          5.697   5.926

Fail to reject $H_O$

Fail to reject the null hypothesis, because the calculated value does not fall in the critical region. Failing to reject the null implies that there is no significant difference in the methods of teaching statistics courses.

## *P*-Value Approach for ANOVA

As there is a lot of math needed to do an ANOVA using the classical approach, the *P*-value approach using the calculator will save a lot of time and frustration. An example of the same problem using the calculator is shown below.

### EXAMPLE 14.6

**Experiment:** University students are randomly assigned to one of three different courses in statistics: a self-study course, a lecture course, or a computer-assisted course. An exam is given to determine if there is a significant difference in knowledge of statistics among the students taking the different courses. Is there a significant difference in the mean outcomes from the teaching methods at the .01 level?

| Self Study | Lecture | Computer-Assisted |
|:---:|:---:|:---:|
| 60 | 90 | 83 |
| 72 | 75 | 76 |
| 64 | 88 | 55 |
| 62 | 75 | 79 |
| 52 | 72 | 66 |
| 58 | 82 | 76 |
|  | 63 | 89 |
|  | 71 | 73 |

**Answer:** No, there is no significant difference in the teaching methods.

**Solution:** Identify the data as an ANOVA by identifying the necessary conditions. There are three samples of students. The samples are randomly selected, which ensures independent sampling. State the hypotheses. The null hypothesis for ANOVA is that there is no difference between the population means. The alternative hypothesis is that at least one mean is statistically unequal to the others.

$$H_0: \mu_1 = \mu_2 = \mu_3$$
$$H_1: \text{The means are not equal}$$

The TI-83/84 calculators perform the ANOVA test when placing the data in its list function in Lines 1, 2, and 3 (and 4 or more if needed). To begin, press STAT and EDIT. Clear any old data in $L_1$, $L_2$, and $L_3$. When the new data are entered, run the ANOVA test by pressing STAT again and scroll over to TESTS. Select ANOVA (on the TI 83 ANOVA is found in G while on the 84 it is found in H). Press ENTER.

"ANOVA(" will appear. Insert $L_1$, $L_2$ and $L_3$ separated by commas and followed by a parenthesis. Do so by pressing 2nd followed by the pressing the 1 button then insert. Continue on for the other lists by pressing 2nd followed by, pressing the corresponding number to the list. Insert a closing parenthesis and press ENTER to display the results.

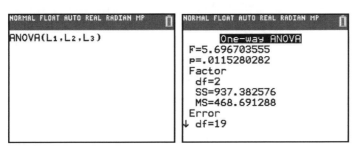

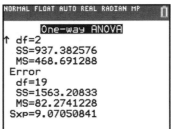

Insert the results into an ANOVA table, and note the test statistic. Also note that the *P*-value is reposted as .0115280282. This can be rounded to .0115.

| Source | SS | df | MS | F |
|---|---|---|---|---|
| Between (Factor) | 937.39 | $k - 1 = 3 - 1 = 2$ | $SS_b / df_b$ | $MS_b / MS_w$ |
| | | | 468.695 | = 5.697 |
| Within (error) | 1563.21 | $N - k = 22 - 3 = 19$ | $SS_w / df_w$ | |
| | | | 82.274 | $P = .0115$ |

Make a decision by comparing the *P*-value to the alpha level.

$$P\text{-value}_{(.0115)} > \text{alpha}_{(.01)} \qquad \text{Fail to reject the } H_o$$

The one-way analysis of variance determines whether differences in sample means exist with the data classified according to one characteristic. Often data are classified by several characteristics, known as factors. For example, the success of students in class may be determined by the method of teaching. But it may be important to factor in grade point average, year in school, or other characteristics that may affect student performance. When data are classified by two factors, a two-way ANOVA determines whether differences in sample means exist due to one or the other characteristic or both.

Several hypotheses are tested when conducting a two-way analysis of variance. Hypotheses must measure the effect of each factor and their interaction. Three separate null hypotheses are tested: (1) test to determine if there is no interaction between the two factors, (2) test to determine if there are effects from one of the factors, and (3) test to determine if there are effects from the second factor.

Each hypothesis is tested separately. The null hypothesis for the interaction is very important. If it is rejected, then there is no need to test the factors separately. That is, if there is interaction between the two factors, the factors do not need to be tested separately.

The calculations for the various sums of squares for the two-way analysis of variance are very involved and are best left for a computer software program. The mean square, the degrees of freedom, and identification of the $F$ test statistic are described here.

The mean square for interaction is determined by dividing the sum of squares for interaction by the degrees of freedom for the interaction. The degrees of freedom for the interaction are $c - 1$, where c is the number of columns.

**Mean Square for the Interaction of Two Factors**

$$MS_{interaction} = \frac{SS_{interaction}}{df_{interaction}}$$

The mean square for within (also referred to as error or residual) is determined by dividing the sum of squares for within by the degrees of freedom for within.

**Mean Square for Within**

$$MS_{within} = \frac{SS_{within}}{df_{within}}$$

The test statistic $F$ for the interaction is determined by the ratio of the mean square for the interaction and the mean square for within.

**$F$ Test Statistic for the Interaction of Two Factors**

$$F_{interaction} = \frac{SS_{interaction}}{df_{within}}$$

The effect of the factor presented in the rows of the data is tested if the interaction testing fails to reject the null hypothesis. The mean square for the row factor is determined by dividing the sum of squares for the row factor by its degrees of freedom. The test statistic $F$ for the row factor is determined by the ratio of the mean square for the row and the ***mean square for within***. Rejecting the null hypothesis for the row factor implies that the row factor affects the equality of the means.

> ### *F* Test Statistic for the Row Factor
> $$F_{row} = \frac{MS_{row}}{MS_{within}}$$

The effect due to the factor presented in the columns must also be tested if the interaction testing fails to reject the null hypothesis. The mean square for the column factor is determined by dividing the sum of squares for the column by its degrees of freedom. The test statistic $F$ for the column is determined by the ratio of the mean square for the column and the mean square for within. Rejecting the null hypothesis for the column factor implies that the column factor affects the equality of the means.

> ### F Test Statistic for the Column Factors
> $$F_{column} = \frac{MS_{column}}{MS_{within}}$$

## EXAMPLE 14.7

**Experiment:** The following two-way ANOVA table represents grade-point average based on year in school and major. Analyze the effect of the year in school and major on grade-point average. Let $\alpha = .01$.

| Source | SS | df | MS | F |
|---|---|---|---|---|
| Year in school (row, factor 1) | 3.108 | 3 | 1.036 | 2.584 |
| Major (column, factor 2) | 2.549 | 6 | .425 | 1.060 |
| Interaction (year and Major) | 2.277 | 18 | .127 | .317 |
| Within (error) | 9.213 | 23 | .401 | ------- |
| **Total** | **17.147** | **50** | ------ | ------- |

**Answer:** There appears to be no effect on the grade-point average based on the year in school, major, or these variables' interaction.

**Solution:** Begin by testing the effect of the interaction. The null hypothesis is that there is no interaction between the two factors. The alternative hypothesis suggests that there is an interaction between the two factors.

Draw a distribution curve and note the critical value. The critical value has numerator degrees of freedom associated with the interaction, reported as 18, and denominator degrees of freedom associated with within, reported as 23. Using Table A.6a for alpha = .01, read over to 20 *df* (nearest estimate for 18 *df*) and down to 23 *df*. The value 2.7805 is in the intersection and is the critical value. Place the calculated *F* value, 0.317, on the curve relative to the critical value, 2.781.

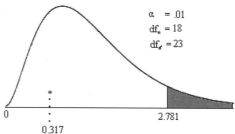

The calculated value, .317, is not in the critical region; therefore, the decision is to fail to reject the null hypothesis. There appears to be no interaction between the two factors.

Test the first factor, year in school. The null hypothesis is that there are no effects from the row factor-that is, year in school has no effect on the student's grade point average. The critical value has numerator degrees of freedom equal to 3, and denominator degrees of freedom of 23. Read across Table A.6a to 3 *df* and down to 23 *df*; 4.765 is the critical value. Place the critical and calculated values on a distribution curve.

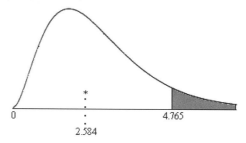

The decision is to fail to reject the null hypothesis, because the calculated value, 2.584, does not fall in the critical region. Year in school does not appear to have an effect on a student's grade point average.

Finally, test the effect of the second variable, major. The null hypothesis states that there is no effect from the column factor-that is, a student's major does not affect the student's grade point average. Identify the critical value. The numerator degrees of freedom, from the major, are 6 and the denominator, error, is 23. Read across Table A.6a to 6 *df* and down to 23 *df*. The critical value is 3.710. Place the calculated and critical values on the distribution curve.

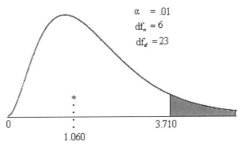

$$\alpha = .01$$
$$df_n = 6$$
$$df_d = 23$$

The decision again is to fail to reject the null hypothesis. There appears to be no effect of the column factor. The student's major does not appear to affect the student's grade point average.

## A LEARNING AID
## ANOVA

The following data give the number of children born to women in various parts of the country according to a random survey of women from the North, South, East and West. Determine if there are significant differences in the mean based on region for $\alpha = .05$.

| North | South | East | West |
|-------|-------|------|------|
| 3 | 2 | 4 | 5 |
| 3 | 5 | 4 | 1 |
| 0 | 1 | 2 | 3 |
| 1 | 6 | 0 | 4 |
| 2 | 5 | 2 | 1 |
| 2 | | 1 | 2 |
| 2 | | | 2 |

**Step 1**

Identify the data as an ANOVA by identifying the necessary conditions. There are four samples of women. The samples are randomly selected, which ensures independent sampling. State the hypotheses. The null hypothesis for ANOVA is that there is no difference between the population means. The alternative hypothesis is that at least one mean is statistically not equal to the others.

$$H_0: \mu_1 = \mu_2 = \mu_3 = \mu_4$$
$$H_1: \text{The means are not equal}$$

**Step 2**

Identify the test criteria. The alpha is reported as .05. The test statistic for ANOVA is *F*.

**Step 3**

Enter the data and calculate the test statistic. Arrange the data in the columns in the calculator. Begin the ANOVA test by pressing the STAT button, followed by ENTER to select "Edit…" Insert the data for north, south, east, and west into $L_1$, $L_2$, $L_3$, and $L_4$. After double-checking the entries into each list, press the STAT button again and scroll to the "TESTS" tab. Arrow up once to access the bottom of the list of tests, where "*H*: ANOVA(" is placed. (ANOVA may be under a different letter if using an older calculator.) Press ENTER to select it.

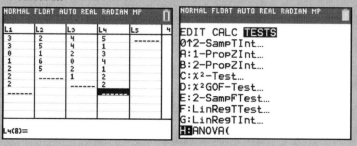

"ANOVA(" will appear. Insert $L_1$, $L_2$, $L_3$, and $L_4$ separated by commas and followed by a parenthesis. Do so by pressing 2nd followed by the pressing the 1 button, then insert. Continue on for the other lists by pressing 2nd followed by pressing the corresponding number to the list. Insert a closing parenthesis and press ENTER to display the results.

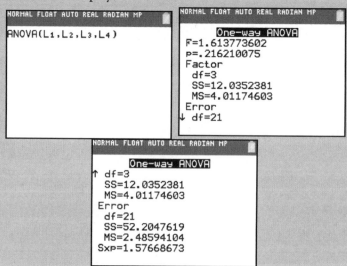

Insert the results into an ANOVA table in order to organize the calculations.

| Source | SS | df | MS | F |
|---|---|---|---|---|
| Between (Factor) | 12.04 | 3 | 4.011 | = 1.6142 |
| Within (error) | 52.20 | 21 | 2.486 | |
| Total | 64.24 | 24 | ------ | |

**Step 4**

Identify the P-value which is reported by the calculator as .216210075. This can be rounded to .2162.

**Step 5**

Make a decision by comparing P to the alpha level.

$$P\text{-value}(.2162) > \text{alpha}(.05) \quad \text{Fail to reject } H_o$$

**Step 6**

Interpret the results. Failing to reject the null hypothesis implies that there is no significant difference in the number of children born to women based on the region of the country.

## CHAPTER 14 IN REVIEW

14.1 Find the following critical Chi-square values for a contingency table.
a. $r = 3, c = 4, \alpha = .05$
b. $r = 2, c = 3, \alpha = .10$
c. $r = 7, c = 5, \alpha = .025$
d. $r = 4, c = 4, \alpha = .01$

14.2 Find the critical value for the following one-tailed data.
a. $F(5, 6, .025)$
b. $F(4, 2, .05)$
c. $F(4, 2, .01)$
d. $F(2, 6, .05)$
e. $F(4, 3, .01)$
f. $F(5, 3, .05)$

14.3 Find the following critical Chi-square values for a multinomial test.
a. $k = 5, \alpha = .05$
b. $k = 8, \alpha = .025$
c. $k = 4, \alpha = .05$
d. $k = 6, \alpha = .10$

14.4  Test to determine if the average cell phone bill differs when compared to the same programs and same areas. A random sample of cell phone bills (in dollars) from four companies is reported below. $\alpha = .01$

| | | | | | |
|---|---|---|---|---|---|
| **Verizon** | 100 | 125 | 105 | 100 | 110 |
| **Sprint** | 100 | 130 | 90 | 120 | 90 |
| **AT&T** | 90 | 90 | 90 | 100 | 120 |
| **T-Mobile** | 100 | 100 | 110 | 90 | 80 |

14.5  Determine, at the .05 level of significance, if there is a relationship between the occupational background of members of state legislatures and their party identification.

| Occupation ↓  Party → | Democrat | Republican | Total |
|---|---|---|---|
| **Law** | 224 | 122 | 346 |
| **Business/banking** | 136 | 176 | 312 |
| **Agriculture** | 100 | 100 | 200 |
| **Public Service** | 159 | 135 | 294 |
| **Education** | 124 | 114 | 238 |
| **Other** | 60 | 50 | 110 |
| **Total** | **803** | **697** | **1500** |

14.6  The following data are prices (in thousands of dollars) of houses in three suburban communities. Is there a significant difference between the average prices across the suburbs? Let $\alpha = .01$.

| **Chesterfield** | **Ladue** | **Bloomfield** |
|---|---|---|
| 116 | 132 | 108 |
| 117 | 144 | 196 |
| 138 | 161 | 126 |
| 100 | 131 | 111 |
| 135 | 109 | 128 |
| 134 | 200 | |
| 122 | 165 | |

14.7  A polling organization claims that 64 percent of the U.S. public feel that television news is the most believable source of news, 23 percent say that newspapers are the most believable source, 6 percent think radio is the most believable source, and 7 percent say that magazines are most believable. A student challenges this claim and conducts a survey of 800 voters who respond with the following answers ($\alpha = .05$):

| | |
|---|---|
| Television | 480 |
| Newspapers | 240 |
| Radio | 64 |
| Magazines | 16 |

14.8 Market tests for preferences of toothpaste produced the following results for a random sample of 200 consumers:

| Brand | A | B | C | D |
|-------|-----|-----|-----|-----|
| Preference | 64 | 24 | 57 | 55 |

At the .10 level, does there appear to be a preference in toothpaste?

14.9 A researcher wants to compare the amount of weight loss from a popular liquid diet to weight loss from an exercise program. Five hundred people were randomly assigned one of the programs, and the amount of weight loss after 6 months was noted. Test to determine if there is a relationship between the amount of weight loss and the program ($\alpha = .10$).

| Weight ↓ Diet → | Liquid Diet | Exercise | Total |
|-------|-----|-----|-----|
| 10 or more | 17 | 115 | 132 |
| 5 - 9 | 103 | 94 | 197 |
| 0 - 4 | 128 | 43 | 171 |
| Total | 248 | 252 | 500 |

14.10 Five different brands of antacids are compared based on the amount of time it took for the antacid to take effect. Is there sufficient evidence to support that the average length of time (in minutes) for effectiveness is the same? Let $\alpha = .01$.

| | | Brand | | |
|---|---|---|---|---|
| A | B | C | D | E |
| 19 | 8 | 8 | 8 | 15 |
| 12 | 15 | 9 | 9 | 10 |
| 16 | 11 | 10 | 10 | 14 |
| 15 | 10 | 13 | 13 | 13 |
| 16 | 14 | 12 | 12 | 15 |

14.11 The number of bankruptcies filed in one federal court for a month by type of business is reported here. Is there evidence that the number of bankruptcies differs based on the type of business? Let $\alpha = .05$.

| Retail | Restaurants | Construction | Manufacturing |
|-------|-----|-----|-----|
| 23 | 42 | 48 | 36 |

14.12 The following data are scores on a standardized exam for admission to graduate school based on the type of student preparation. Test for the equality of the mean scores for each type of preparation. Let $\alpha = .01$.

| Self Study | Prep Course | No Preparation |
|:---:|:---:|:---:|
| 116 | 132 | 108 |
| 117 | 137 | 109 |
| 138 | 131 | 131 |
| 100 | 125 | 130 |
| 125 | 111 | 110 |
| 134 | 140 | |
| 122 | | |

14.13 True or False?
a. ANOVA tests three or more means.
b. The test statistic for ANOVA is $\chi2$.
c. ANOVA compares the variation between the sample to the variation within the sample.
d. ANOVA testing is always two-tailed.
e. The contingency table is a two-way display of at least one nominal level variable.
f. The null hypothesis for a contingency table assumes the variables are dependent.

14.14 Test to determine if the average cost of undergraduate tuition per credit (in thousands) significantly differs for private, parochial, and state colleges. $\alpha = .01$

| Private | 745 | 762 | 1000 | 795 | 810 | 850 | 1040 | 1010 |
|:---|:---:|:---:|:---:|:---:|:---:|:---:|:---:|:---:|
| Parochial | 800 | 765 | 900 | 1020 | 999 | 850 | | |
| State | 600 | 400 | 525 | 640 | 300 | 700 | 800 | |

14.15 True or False?
a. The probabilities of all the outcomes in a multinomial experiment must have a sum of 0.
b. All multinomial experiments are two-tailed.
c. The expected frequencies for each category in a multinomial experiment is determined by multiplying the total number of responses by the probability for the category.
d. The test statistic for testing multinomial cases is $F$.
e. Two variables are said to be independent if no difference exists between the observed and expected frequencies.
f. Testing contingency tables is always two-tailed.

14.16 Test the equality of the means for online stock commission for three online investment companies. $\alpha = .01$

| 1 | 40 | 30 | 25 | 25 | 50 | 40 | 45 |
|:---:|:---:|:---:|:---:|:---:|:---:|:---:|:---:|
| 2 | 25 | 50 | 40 | 25 | 45 | 60 | 30 |
| 3 | 45 | 45 | 45 | 30 | 35 | 40 | |

14.17 A researcher wants to know if students in a statistics class perform differently based on their major area of study. Final grades are reported below for students majoring in Political Science, Nursing, Psychology, and Social Work. Is there a significant difference in performance based on major? $\alpha = .05$

| Poli. Sci. | 90 | 80 | 92 | 76 | 95 | 85 | |
|------------|----|----|----|----|----|----|----|
| Nursing | 90 | 95 | 80 | 85 | 70 | 75 | 95 |
| Psych | 85 | 80 | 85 | 92 | 91 | 79 | 98 |
| S.W. | 85 | 70 | 91 | 80 | 75 | 78 | 95 | 90 |

14.18 A researcher wants to know if there is a significant difference in the time it takes a felony charge to move through a trial court to a verdict based on the type of felony charge. Test the following data at $\alpha = .05$.

| Homicide | Sexual Assault | Robbery | Larcenies/Burglaries |
|----------|----------------|---------|----------------------|
| 5.9 | 4.8 | 3.1 | 3.1 |
| 6.9 | 4.2 | 2.9 | 3.5 |
| 4.5 | 3.5 | 5.2 | 5.0 |
| 8.1 | 3.9 | 4.0 | 5.6 |
| 6.5 | | | 5.5 |

14.19 Suppose a poll is taken to determine if voters support the new automobile insurance proposal on the upcoming election ballot. The following data represents the voters' preference for the proposal and residency. Test the dependency of the variables using $\alpha = .05$.

| Support ↓ Residency → | City | Suburb | Rural | Total |
|------------------------|------|--------|-------|-------|
| Yes | 70 | 200 | 30 | 300 |
| No | 110 | 50 | 40 | 200 |
| Total | 180 | 250 | 70 | 500 |

14.20 Test to determine if the average salary of a new assistant professor (in thousands of dollars) significantly differs from department to department. Four departments are surveyed.

| Poli.Sci. | 58 | 62 | 75 | 65 | 65 | 65 | 61 | |
|-----------|----|----|----|----|----|----|----|----|
| Math | 62 | 65 | 71 | 70 | 65 | 60 | 70 | |
| Eng. | 60 | 62 | 61 | 60 | 55 | 65 | | |
| Bus. | 70 | 75 | 70 | 72 | 75 | 80 | 75 | 79 |

14.21 Test the equality of the means for the number of calories in medium portions of french fries among the following fast food franchises. $\alpha = .05$.

|     |     |     |     |     |     |
| --- | --- | --- | --- | --- | --- |
| A:  | 330 | 325 | 333 | 335 | 340 |
| B:  | 370 | 375 | 365 | 355 | 350 |
| C:  | 410 | 400 | 390 | 380 | 360 |
| D:  | 380 | 375 | 355 | 345 | 380 |

14.22 Test whether there is a difference in the mean Law School Admissions Test (LSAT) scores across the four tiers of schools. $\alpha = .05$

| Tier 1 | Tier 2 | Tier 3 | Tier 4 |
| --- | --- | --- | --- |
| 163 | 155 | 154 | 153 |
| 164 | 157 | 153 | 155 |
| 164 | 159 | 153 | 155 |
| 161 | 161 | 152 | 150 |
| 160 | 155 | 155 | 150 |
| 156 |     |     | 149 |

14.23 A poll is taken to determine which social media site is visited most by students versus professors. Test if there is a significant relationship at the .05 level of significance.

| Status ↓ Social Media→ | YouTube | Twitter | Facebook | Total |
| --- | --- | --- | --- | --- |
| **Students** | 100 | 220 | 30 | 350 |
| **Professors** | 20 | 20 | 90 | 130 |
| **Total** | 120 | 240 | 120 | 480 |

14.24 A survey of 100 U.S. senators shows the following results on a recent vote on a bill and the party identification of the senators. Test if there is a significant relationship at the .01 level of significance.

| Party ↓ | Vote → | Yes | No | Total |
| --- | --- | --- | --- | --- |
| **Republican** |     | 28 | 12 | 40 |
| **Democrat** |     | 50 | 10 | 60 |
| **Total** |     | 78 | 22 | 100 |

# 15 | **CASE STUDY**

The case study presented in this chapter serves as an overview of many of the techniques that are presented in this text. A common question asked by students of statistics is "How do all the techniques relate?" This chapter attempts to answer that question by presenting a case study as it develops from the early stages of descriptive statistics to some of the later stages of inferential statistics.

Statistical analysis begins by identifying the purpose of the study and the source and nature of the data. The case study focuses on the factors pertaining to fertility. Identifying these factors allows a nation to develop public policy to encourage or discourage social behavior. A case study is employed using the country of Cyprus. Cyprus is a sovereign state in the Mediterranean Sea between the countries of Greece and Turkey. Cyprus is selected for the study because it presents an interesting situation as a nation that is sometimes considered developed and sometimes considered a developing country. Its economic and social indicators are characteristic of a transitional society. It has regressed as a developed country due to military and economic turmoil in the 1970s. Cyprus is also selected because of the availability of data from a household survey conducted from 1974 to 1976. A total of 34,413 persons were sampled and interviewed out of a total population of 600,000. Surveys did not include households in the northern part of the country, which has been held by Turkish forces since 1974.

The second major area to address in a statistical analysis is the operational definitions of the variables. The dependent variable is the one that is being explained, and the independent variables are the variables that explain the dependent variable. The study attempts to explain fertility by illustrating what factors lead couples to have few or many children. Fertility is the dependent variable and is measured as the number of children born to all women who have ever been married. As the study develops, it becomes apparent that a major factor in explaining fertility is the number and timing of a loss of a child through death. Therefore, a second dependent variable is identified and defined as the number of children ever born after the occurrence of the first infant or child death.

The factors that explain fertility are referred to as the independent variables. Twelve independent variables are included in the study and are categorized into four groups: (1) demographic variables, (2) economic indicators, (3) social-economic indicators, and (4) controlling variables. Each category and each variable are specifically defined so that another researcher is able to repeat the measurements.

The demographic variables are age at which the woman married, whether a woman experienced the death of a child, and the birth order of a child who died. Economic indicators include the employment activity of a woman, the employment activity of her husband, and residency. Social-economic indicators include the employment status of a woman, the employment status of her husband, the education of a woman, and the education of her husband. The controlling variables are the current age of a woman and the duration of marriage.

Once the data are collected, they must be coded and entered into a computer. Coding assigns numerical values to responses of variables that have no inherent values. For example, sex of a respondent has two responses, male and female. The responses do not have inherent numerical value. Numerical values must be assigned, such as coding a response for a female as a 1 and a response for a male as a 2. The values are arbitrarily assigned but are necessary for the mathematical calculations. Entering the data in a computer is necessary if the data are numerous. The most popular software packages are Statistical Package for the Social Sciences (SPSS), Minitab, and Statdisk. A command file for the data is written that identifies the necessary statistical procedures.

One of the first statistical procedures that should be completed is a frequency distribution. A frequency distribution not only provides valuable information, but it also allows a researcher to check the coding and reliability of the data. For example if sex is coded 1 for a female and 2 for a male and a value of 3 appears in the frequency distribution, an error in the coding occurred. A frequency distribution also illustrates the number of people for each response of a variable. The percentages of each response are also presented in a frequency distribution: Table 15.1 gives the frequency distribution for the number of households in the four areas of the country.

## TABLE 15.1
## Frequency Distribution of Households

| Residency | Count | Percent | Cumulative Percent |
|-----------|-------|---------|--------------------|
| Nicosia | 4,110 | 41.29 | 41.29 |
| Limassol | 3,114 | 30.53 | 71.82 |
| Larnaca | 2,010 | 19.71 | 91.53 |
| Paphos | 966 | 9.47 | 100.00 |
| **Total** | **10,200** | **100.00** | |

The column for the count reflects the number of households who report residency in each of the regions. The total, 10,200, is the total number of households surveyed in the study. The percent column reflects the relative proportion of each response. For example, 41.29% of the households surveyed report residency in the region of Nicosia. The number 41.29 is obtained by dividing the number of households in the category (4110) by the total number of households in the survey (10,200). The cumulative percent reflects the cumulative relative proportions. A cumulative count adds all the responses preceding each response. For example, 71.82% of the households report residency in either Nicosia or Limassol, and 91.52% report residency in either Nicosia, Limassol, or Larnaca.

Frequency distributions should be obtained for each variable. They are an important tool for checking the data for errors and for understanding the nature of the data. For example, a frequency distribution on the number of years a woman is married produced values such as 90 years and even 100 years. Although a value of 90 may be possible, the two or three women who reported being married for 100 years probably did not understand the question. The error is supported by a frequency distribution on the current age of women. No woman reported being older than 85. If no one is older than 85, it would not be possible for a few to be married for 90 or 100 years.

Frequency distributions can also be obtained with additional descriptive information, such as means and standard deviations, that offer further insight into the data. Frequencies of two variables may be overlapped to produce a crosstabulation table. The table can also reveal errors in the data by highlighted intersections of two variables that should or should not exist. A crosstab overlays two variables and can determine if an association exists between the variables. Crosstabulations also should be one of the first procedures performed on the data. Crosstabulations reflect if two variables are independent or dependent.

Table 15.2 overlays the educational level of a wife with that of her husband. The upper left cell reflects 96 respondents where both the wife and husband have no formal schooling. The adjacent cell reflects 117 respondents where the wife has a primary education and the husband has no formal schooling. Careful analysis of the table and with measurements such as chi-square show that there is a relationship between the husband's and wife's educational attainment. A pattern exists in which the husband's education increases as the wife's education increases; however, the husband's education increases at a faster rate. Notice that the husbands tend to have the same or slightly higher levels of education as their wives. For example, 3282 husbands and wives have the same primary education. However, 710 husbands with a primary education have wives with no schooling, but only 117 wives with a primary education have husbands with no schooling.

## TABLE 15.2
### Cross-tabulation of Husband's Education & Wife's Education

| Husband ↓    Wife→ | No School | Primary | Secondary | University | Total |
|---|---|---|---|---|---|
| **No School** | 96 | 117 | 6 | 0 | 219 |
| **Primary** | 710 | 3282 | 209 | 11 | 4212 |
| **Secondary** | 34 | 756 | 698 | 78 | 1566 |
| **University** | 3 | 81 | 294 | 200 | 578 |
| **Total** | **843** | **4236** | **1207** | **289** | **6575** |

Crosstabulation tables provide insight into the relationship and association of two variables. Although crosstabs may include statistics measuring the strength and significance of the relationships, correlation analysis, regression analysis, and hypothesis testing are typically performed.

A correlation matrix should be obtained to illustrate further the relationships between the variables. Correlations measure the strengths and directions of linear relationships between two variables. The matrix produced by most software packages reports a correlation coefficient, the number of responses included in each calculation, and the level of significance, which describes whether the relationship is statistically significant or the outcome of sampling error. Other matrices exclude the latter two measurements and report only the correlation coefficient, with asterisks next to the coefficients that are significant. Table 15.3 is a partial correlation matrix for selected variables. A partial matrix, as presented here, describes only selected variables. The ellipses on the matrix represent correlations of the same two variables that are presented somewhere else in the table. For example, age and the education of the wife has the same correlation coefficient (-.455) as does education of the wife and age. In order not to clutter the matrix, only one of the relationships is reported, with the other noted by an ellipsis or dashes.

## TABLE 15.3
### Correlation Matrix for Selected Variables

|  | Fertility | Age | Education of Wife | Education of Husband | Work Status of Wife | Work Status Husband |
|---|---|---|---|---|---|---|
| **Age** | .317* | 1.000 | ----- | ----- | ----- | ----- |
| **Educ. of Wife** | - .328* | -.455* | 1.000 | ----- | ----- | ----- |
| **Educ. of Husband** | - .293* | -.331* | .622* | 1.000 | ----- | ----- |
| **Work Status of Wife** | .050 | .249* | - .132 | - .018 | 1.000 | ----- |
| **Work Status of Husband** | .137 | .588* | - .299* | - .183 | .255* | 1.000 |
| **Child Death** | .568* | .344* | - .266* | - .194 | .090 | .248* |

The appearance of the matrix reflects the correlation coefficients for two variables. The first cell in the second row contains the coefficient .317 for fertility and age. The value .317 implies that a positive relationship exists between fertility and age. A positive relationship means that the values of the two variables increase or decrease together, therefore, as the current age of a woman increases, so too does the level of fertility. In other words, older women tend to have more children than younger women. A negative coefficient implies that the variables move in opposite directions. For example, the value -.328 for fertility and the educational level of a woman means that as a woman's educational level increases, she tends to have fewer children. Given the large sample size of more than 8000 women, any coefficient greater than .196 is considered significant. A coefficient greater than .196 suggests that there is a clear pattern of movement of the two variables. None of the coefficients for the work status of the husband is above .196. Although a pattern may exist between the relationship between the work status of the husband and the other variables, the relationship is not considered significant.

Although many other procedures were performed on the data, such as the *t* test and ANOVA, performing a multiple regression analysis was the objective. A regression analysis measures the predictive value of the independent variables to the dependent variables. A multiple regression analysis implies that there are three or more independent variables that may predict a dependent variable. The computer software packages produce a variety of statistics with a multiple regression procedure. Typically, standardized beta coefficients report a significance level based on a test known as an *F* test. The researcher introduces all the independent variables and specifies the level of statistical significance. The procedure then controls relationships between the independent variables and reports only those variables that are statistically significant. Statistics known as multiple *R* and *R* square report the amount of variance in the dependent variable explained by the independent variables. Table15.4 is a partial list of a multiple regression report.

## TABLE 15.4
## Multiple Regression Report for the Number of Children Ever Born

| Variable | *B* | Beta | Std. Error | *F* |
|---|---|---|---|---|
| Child Mortality | 1.2796 | .4200 | .0505 | 641.389 |
| Age of Marriage | -.1263 | -.2919 | .0040 | 962.278 |
| Education: Husband | -.2863 | -.0839 | .0415 | 47.484 |
| Current Age | .3903 | .2251 | .0023 | 276.638 |
| Employment: Husband | -1.5688 | -.3090 | .1237 | 160.686 |
| Urban/Rural Residency | .2612 | .0548 | .5040 | 26.852 |

## Multiple *R* .6862
## *R* square .4708

The matrix reports a variety of statistics that help determine if the relationship of the independent variables is significant to the dependent variable. The direction of the beta value, whether positive or negative, determines the relationship of that independent variable to the dependent variable. For example, the beta value for age at marriage is -.2919, which implies that as the age at which a woman marries increases, the number of children she is likely to bear decreases. The *R* square of .4708 implies that 47.08% of the variance in the number of children ever born to all ever married women is explained by these few variables.

A regression analysis is often repeated for the dependent variables as well as for some of the independent variables. Some independent variables pass through other independent variables before affecting the dependent variable. That is, there are some variables that directly and/or indirectly affect the dependent variable. Repeating regressions by substituting some of the independent variables as dependent variables creates a maze of paths that more completely explain the dependent variables. The paths are overlaid and referred to as a path analysis. Although this is an advanced statistical procedure, it is important to understand how many of the procedures contained in this text will relate to each other. The following figure illustrates the final path analysis for the dependent variable, the number of children ever born. The values on the path are beta coefficients. Notice that child mortality serves not only as an independent variable directly related to the number of children born, but also as a variable through which other independent variables pass, indirectly explaining the number of children. Some variables, such as the education of the wife, have paths directly to the number of children born and indirectly through child mortality and the age at marriage. See Figure 15 1.

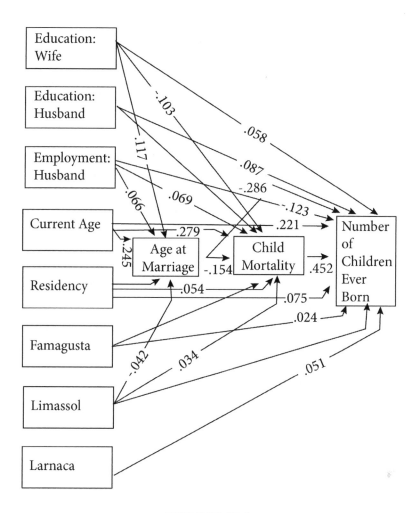

**FIGURE 15.1**
**Path Analysis for the Number of Children Ever Born**

The conclusions drawn from this case study are that child mortality is a significant factor in explaining fertility. When a woman loses a child, she is likely to replace the child with more than one additional child. Also, the younger the woman is when she marries, the more children she is likely to have. Other variables that are directly related to fertility are the education of the wife, the education of the husband, the employment status of the husband, the current age of the woman, rural residency, and residency in selected regions of the country. Interestingly, most of these variables also explain age at marriage and child mortality.

The case study is presented to allow an understanding of how the statistical procedures throughout this text relate. Not all the procedures contained in the text were discussed here because not all relate to the case study.

# A

# APPENDIX A: TABLES

| | |
|---|---|
| **A.1** | **Critical Values of r** |
| **A.2a** | **Binomial Probabilities** |
| **A.2b** | **Factorials** |
| **A.3** | **Normal Probability Distribution z** |
| **A.4** | **Student t Distribution** |
| **A.5** | **Chi-Square Distribution** |
| **A.6** | **F Distribution** |
| **A.7** | **Hypothesis Testing Formulas** |

*If it's this or greater, it's significant*

## Table A.1  Critical Values of r

**Critical Values of the Pearson's Correlation Coefficient r**

To test $H_o$: $\rho = 0$ against $H_i$: $\rho \neq 0$, reject $H_O$ if the absolute value of the calculated $r$ is greater than the value in the table.

| $n$ | $\alpha = .05$ | $\alpha = .01$ |
|---|---|---|
| 4 | .950 | .999 |
| 5 | .878 | .959 |
| 6 | .811 | .917 |
| 7 | .754 | .875 |
| 8 | .707 | .834 |
| 9 | .666 | .798 |
| 10 | .632 | .765 |
| 11 | .602 | .735 |
| 12 | .576 | .708 |
| 13 | .553 | .684 |
| 14 | .532 | .661 |
| 15 | .514 | .641 |
| 16 | .497 | .623 |
| 17 | .482 | .606 |

| $n$ | $\alpha = .05$ | $\alpha = .01$ |
|---|---|---|
| 18 | .468 | .590 |
| 19 | .456 | .575 |
| 20 | .444 | .561 |
| 25 | .396 | .505 |
| 30 | .361 | .463 |
| 35 | .335 | .430 |
| 40 | .312 | .402 |
| 45 | .294 | .378 |
| 50 | .279 | .361 |
| 60 | .254 | .330 |
| 70 | .236 | .305 |
| 80 | .220 | .286 |
| 90 | .207 | .269 |
| $\geq 100$ | .196 | .256 |

$r_{calc} > r_{table}$ Reject $H_O$

$r_{calc} \leq r_{table}$ Fail to Reject $H_O$

## TABLE A.2a

# Binomial Probabilities

All values reported as probabilities. Warning, this table may be used only if the $x$, $n$, and $p$ values are exactly as reported. All other binomials should be calculated.

| $n$ | $x$ | .01 | .05 | .10 | .20 | .30 | .40 | .50 | .60 | .70 | .80 | .90 | .95 | .99 | $x$ |
|---|---|---|---|---|---|---|---|---|---|---|---|---|---|---|---|
| 2 | 0 | 980 | 902 | 810 | 640 | 490 | 360 | 250 | 160 | 090 | 040 | 010 | 002 | 0+ | 0 |
| 2 | 1 | 020 | 095 | 180 | 320 | 420 | 480 | 500 | 480 | 420 | 320 | 180 | 095 | 020 | 1 |
| 2 | 2 | 0+ | 002 | 010 | 040 | 090 | 160 | 250 | 360 | 490 | 640 | 810 | 902 | 980 | 2 |
| | | | | | | | | | | | | | | | |
| 3 | 0 | 970 | 857 | 729 | 512 | 343 | 216 | 125 | 064 | 027 | 008 | 001 | 0+ | 0+ | 0 |
| 3 | 1 | 029 | 135 | 243 | 384 | 441 | 432 | 375 | 288 | 189 | 096 | 027 | 007 | 0+ | 1 |
| 3 | 2 | 0+ | 007 | 027 | 096 | 189 | 288 | 375 | 432 | 441 | 384 | 243 | 135 | 029 | 2 |
| 3 | 3 | 0+ | 0+ | 001 | 008 | 027 | 064 | 125 | 216 | 343 | 512 | 729 | 857 | 970 | 3 |
| | | | | | | | | | | | | | | | |
| 4 | 0 | 961 | 815 | 656 | 410 | 240 | 130 | 062 | 026 | 008 | 002 | 0+ | 0+ | 0+ | 0 |
| 4 | 1 | 039 | 171 | 292 | 410 | 412 | 346 | 250 | 154 | 076 | 026 | 004 | 0+ | 0+ | 1 |
| 4 | 2 | 001 | 014 | 049 | 154 | 265 | 346 | 375 | 346 | 265 | 154 | 049 | 014 | 001 | 2 |
| 4 | 3 | 0+ | 0+ | 004 | 026 | 076 | 154 | 250 | 346 | 412 | 410 | 292 | 171 | 039 | 3 |
| 4 | 4 | 0+ | 0+ | 0+ | 002 | 008 | 026 | 062 | 130 | 240 | 410 | 656 | 815 | 961 | 4 |
| | | | | | | | | | | | | | | | |
| 5 | 0 | 951 | 774 | 590 | 323 | 168 | 078 | 031 | 010 | 002 | 0+ | 0+ | 0+ | 0+ | 0 |
| 5 | 1 | 048 | 204 | 328 | 410 | 360 | 259 | 256 | 077 | 028 | 006 | 0+ | 0+ | 0+ | 1 |
| 5 | 2 | 001 | 021 | 073 | 205 | 309 | 346 | 312 | 230 | 132 | 051 | 008 | 001 | 0+ | 2 |
| 5 | 3 | 0+ | 001 | 008 | 051 | 132 | 230 | 312 | 346 | 309 | 205 | 073 | 021 | 001 | 3 |
| 5 | 4 | 0+ | 0+ | 0+ | 006 | 028 | 077 | 156 | 259 | 360 | 410 | 328 | 204 | 048 | 4 |
| 5 | 5 | 0+ | 0+ | 0+ | 0+ | 002 | 010 | 031 | 078 | 168 | 328 | 590 | 774 | 951 | 5 |
| | | | | | | | | | | | | | | | |
| 6 | 0 | 941 | 735 | 531 | 262 | 118 | 047 | 016 | 004 | 001 | 0+ | 0+ | 0+ | 0+ | 0 |
| 6 | 1 | 057 | 232 | 354 | 393 | 303 | 187 | 094 | 037 | 010 | 002 | 0+ | 0+ | 0+ | 1 |
| 6 | 2 | 001 | 031 | 098 | 246 | 324 | 311 | 234 | 138 | 060 | 015 | 001 | 0+ | 0+ | 2 |
| 6 | 3 | 0+ | 002 | 015 | 082 | 185 | 276 | 312 | 276 | 185 | 082 | 015 | 002 | 0+ | 3 |
| 6 | 4 | 0+ | 0+ | 001 | 015 | 060 | 138 | 234 | 311 | 324 | 246 | 098 | 031 | 001 | 4 |
| 6 | 5 | 0+ | 0+ | 0+ | 002 | 010 | 037 | 094 | 187 | 303 | 393 | 354 | 232 | 057 | 5 |
| 6 | 6 | 0+ | 0+ | 0+ | 0+ | 001 | 004 | 016 | 047 | 118 | 262 | 531 | 735 | 941 | 6 |

# TABLE A.2a

## Binomial Probabilities (continued)

| n | x | .01 | .05 | .10 | .20 | .30 | .40 | .50 | .60 | .70 | .80 | .90 | .95 | .99 | x |
|---|---|-----|-----|-----|-----|-----|-----|-----|-----|-----|-----|-----|-----|-----|---|
| 7 | 0 | 932 | 698 | 478 | 210 | 082 | 028 | 008 | 002 | 0+ | 0+ | 0+ | 0+ | 0+ | 0 |
| 7 | 1 | 066 | 257 | 372 | 367 | 247 | 131 | 055 | 017 | 004 | 0+ | 0+ | 0+ | 0+ | 1 |
| 7 | 2 | 002 | 041 | 124 | 275 | 318 | 261 | 164 | 077 | 025 | 004 | 0+ | 0+ | 0+ | 2 |
| 7 | 3 | 0+ | 004 | 023 | 115 | 227 | 290 | 373 | 194 | 097 | 029 | 003 | 0+ | 0+ | 3 |
| 7 | 4 | 0+ | 0+ | 003 | 029 | 097 | 194 | 273 | 290 | 227 | 115 | 023 | 004 | 0+ | 4 |
| 7 | 5 | 0+ | 0+ | 0+ | 004 | 025 | 077 | 164 | 261 | 318 | 275 | 124 | 041 | 002 | 5 |
| 7 | 6 | 0+ | 0+ | 0+ | 0+ | 004 | 017 | 055 | 131 | 247 | 367 | 372 | 257 | 066 | 6 |
| 7 | 7 | 0+ | 0+ | 0+ | 0+ | 0+ | 002 | 008 | 028 | 082 | 210 | 478 | 698 | 932 | 7 |
| 8 | 0 | 923 | 663 | 430 | 168 | 058 | 017 | 004 | 001 | 0+ | 0+ | 0+ | 0+ | 0+ | 0 |
| 8 | 1 | 075 | 279 | 383 | 336 | 198 | 090 | 031 | 008 | 001 | 0+ | 0+ | 0+ | 0+ | 1 |
| 8 | 2 | 008 | 051 | 149 | 294 | 296 | 209 | 109 | 041 | 010 | 001 | 0+ | 0+ | 0+ | 2 |
| 8 | 3 | 0+ | 005 | 033 | 147 | 254 | 279 | 219 | 124 | 047 | 009 | 0+ | 0+ | 0+ | 3 |
| 8 | 4 | 0+ | 0+ | 005 | 046 | 136 | 232 | 273 | 232 | 136 | 046 | 005 | 0+ | 0+ | 4 |
| 8 | 5 | 0+ | 0+ | 0+ | 009 | 047 | 124 | 219 | 279 | 254 | 147 | 033 | 005 | 0+ | 5 |
| 8 | 6 | 0+ | 0+ | 0+ | 001 | 010 | 041 | 109 | 209 | 296 | 294 | 149 | 051 | 003 | 6 |
| 8 | 7 | 0+ | 0+ | 0+ | 0+ | 001 | 008 | 031 | 090 | 198 | 336 | 383 | 279 | 075 | 7 |
| 8 | 8 | 0+ | 0+ | 0+ | 0+ | 0+ | 001 | 004 | 017 | 058 | 168 | 430 | 663 | 923 | 8 |
| 9 | 0 | 914 | 630 | 387 | 134 | 040 | 010 | 002 | 0+ | 0+ | 0+ | 0+ | 0+ | 0+ | 0 |
| 9 | 1 | 083 | 299 | 387 | 302 | 156 | 060 | 018 | 004 | 0+ | 0+ | 0+ | 0+ | 0+ | 1 |
| 9 | 2 | 003 | 063 | 172 | 302 | 267 | 161 | 070 | 021 | 004 | 0+ | 0+ | 0+ | 0+ | 2 |
| 9 | 3 | 0+ | 008 | 045 | 176 | 267 | 251 | 164 | 074 | 021 | 003 | 0+ | 0+ | 0+ | 3 |
| 9 | 4 | 0+ | 001 | 007 | 066 | 172 | 251 | 246 | 167 | 074 | 017 | 001 | 0+ | 0+ | 4 |
| 9 | 5 | 0+ | 0+ | 001 | 017 | 074 | 167 | 246 | 251 | 172 | 066 | 007 | 001 | 0+ | 5 |
| 9 | 6 | 0+ | 0+ | 0+ | 003 | 021 | 074 | 164 | 251 | 267 | 176 | 045 | 008 | 0+ | 6 |
| 9 | 7 | 0+ | 0+ | 0+ | 0+ | 004 | 021 | 070 | 161 | 267 | 302 | 172 | 063 | 003 | 7 |
| 9 | 8 | 0+ | 0+ | 0+ | 0+ | 0+ | 004 | 018 | 160 | 156 | 302 | 387 | 299 | 083 | 8 |
| 9 | 9 | 0+ | 0+ | 0+ | 0+ | 0+ | 0+ | 002 | 010 | 040 | 134 | 387 | 630 | 914 | 9 |

## TABLE A.2a

### Binomial Probabilities (continued)

| n | | x | .01 | .05 | .10 | .20 | .30 | .40 | .50 | .60 | .70 | .80 | .90 | .95 | .99 | x |
|---|---|---|-----|-----|-----|-----|-----|-----|-----|-----|-----|-----|-----|-----|-----|---|
| 10 | | 0 | 904 | 599 | 349 | 107 | 028 | 006 | 001 | 0+ | 0+ | 0+ | 0+ | 0+ | 0+ | 0 |
| | 10 | 1 | 091 | 315 | 387 | 268 | 121 | 040 | 010 | 002 | 0+ | 0+ | 0+ | 0+ | 0+ | 1 |
| | 10 | 2 | 004 | 075 | 194 | 302 | 233 | 121 | 044 | 011 | 001 | 0+ | 0+ | 0+ | 0+ | 2 |
| | 10 | 3 | 0+ | 010 | 057 | 201 | 267 | 215 | 117 | 042 | 009 | 001 | 0+ | 0+ | 0+ | 3 |
| | 10 | 4 | 0+ | 001 | 011 | 088 | 200 | 251 | 205 | 111 | 037 | 006 | 0+ | 0+ | 0+ | 4 |
| | 10 | 5 | 0+ | 0+ | 001 | 026 | 103 | 201 | 246 | 201 | 103 | 026 | 001 | 0+ | 0+ | 5 |
| | 10 | 6 | 0+ | 0+ | 0+ | 006 | 037 | 111 | 205 | 251 | 200 | 088 | 011 | 001 | 0+ | 6 |
| | 10 | 7 | 0+ | 0+ | 0+ | 001 | 009 | 042 | 117 | 215 | 267 | 201 | 057 | 010 | 0+ | 7 |
| | 10 | 8 | 0+ | 0+ | 0+ | 0+ | 001 | 011 | 044 | 121 | 233 | 302 | 194 | 075 | 004 | 8 |
| | 10 | 9 | 0+ | 0+ | 0+ | 0+ | 0+ | 002 | 010 | 040 | 121 | 268 | 387 | 315 | 091 | 9 |
| | 10 | 10 | 0+ | 0+ | 0+ | 0+ | 0+ | 0+ | 001 | 006 | 028 | 107 | 349 | 599 | 904 | 10 |
| 11 | | 0 | 895 | 569 | 314 | 086 | 020 | 004 | 0+ | 0+ | 0+ | 0+ | 0+ | 0+ | 0+ | 0 |
| | 11 | 1 | 099 | 329 | 384 | 236 | 093 | 027 | 005 | 001 | 0+ | 0+ | 0+ | 0+ | 0+ | 1 |
| | 11 | 2 | 005 | 087 | 213 | 295 | 200 | 089 | 027 | 005 | 001 | 0+ | 0+ | 0+ | 0+ | 2 |
| | 11 | 3 | 0+ | 014 | 071 | 221 | 257 | 177 | 081 | 023 | 004 | 0+ | 0+ | 0+ | 0+ | 3 |
| | 11 | 4 | 0+ | 001 | 016 | 111 | 220 | 236 | 161 | 070 | 017 | 002 | 0+ | 0+ | 0+ | 4 |
| | 11 | 5 | 0+ | 0+ | 002 | 039 | 132 | 221 | 226 | 147 | 057 | 010 | 0+ | 0+ | 0+ | 5 |
| | 11 | 6 | 0+ | 0+ | 0+ | 010 | 057 | 147 | 226 | 221 | 132 | 039 | 002 | 0+ | 0+ | 6 |
| | 11 | 7 | 0+ | 0+ | 0+ | 002 | 017 | 070 | 161 | 236 | 220 | 111 | 016 | 001 | 0+ | 7 |
| | 11 | 8 | 0+ | 0+ | 0+ | 0+ | 004 | 023 | 081 | 177 | 257 | 221 | 071 | 014 | 0+ | 8 |
| | 11 | 9 | 0+ | 0+ | 0+ | 0+ | 001 | 005 | 027 | 089 | 200 | 295 | 213 | 087 | 005 | 9 |
| | 11 | 10 | 0+ | 0+ | 0+ | 0+ | 0+ | 001 | 005 | 027 | 093 | 236 | 384 | 329 | 099 | 10 |
| | 11 | 11 | 0+ | 0+ | 0+ | 0+ | 0+ | 0+ | 0+ | 004 | 020 | 086 | 314 | 569 | 895 | 11 |
| 12 | | 0 | 886 | 540 | 282 | 069 | 014 | 002 | 0+ | 0+ | 0+ | 0+ | 0+ | 0+ | 0+ | 0 |
| | 12 | 1 | 107 | 341 | 377 | 206 | 071 | 017 | 003 | 0+ | 0+ | 0+ | 0+ | 0+ | 0+ | 1 |
| | 12 | 2 | 006 | 099 | 230 | 283 | 168 | 064 | 016 | 002 | 0+ | 0+ | 0+ | 0+ | 0+ | 2 |
| | 12 | 3 | 0+ | 017 | 085 | 236 | 240 | 142 | 054 | 012 | 001 | 0+ | 0+ | 0+ | 0+ | 3 |
| | 12 | 4 | 0+ | 002 | 021 | 133 | 231 | 213 | 121 | 042 | 008 | 001 | 0+ | 0+ | 0+ | 4 |
| | 12 | 5 | 0+ | 0+ | 004 | 053 | 158 | 227 | 193 | 101 | 029 | 003 | 0+ | 0+ | 0+ | 5 |
| | 12 | 6 | 0+ | 0+ | 0+ | 016 | 079 | 177 | 226 | 177 | 079 | 016 | 0+ | 0+ | 0+ | 6 |
| | 12 | 7 | 0+ | 0+ | 0+ | 003 | 029 | 101 | 193 | 227 | 158 | 053 | 004 | 0+ | 0+ | 7 |
| | 12 | 8 | 0+ | 0+ | 0+ | 001 | 008 | 042 | 121 | 213 | 231 | 133 | 021 | 002 | 0+ | 8 |
| | 12 | 9 | 0+ | 0+ | 0+ | 0+ | 001 | 012 | 054 | 142 | 240 | 236 | 085 | 017 | 0+ | 9 |
| | 12 | 10 | 0+ | 0+ | 0+ | 0+ | 0+ | 002 | 016 | 067 | 168 | 283 | 230 | 099 | 006 | 10 |
| | 12 | 11 | 0+ | 0+ | 0+ | 0+ | 0+ | 0+ | 003 | 017 | 071 | 206 | 377 | 341 | 107 | 11 |
| | 12 | 12 | 0+ | 0+ | 0+ | 0+ | 0+ | 0+ | 0+ | 002 | 014 | 069 | 282 | 540 | 886 | 12 |

# Table A.2b

## Factorials

| n | n! |
|---|---|
| 0 | 1 |
| 1 | 1 |
| 2 | 2 |
| 3 | 6 |
| 4 | 24 |
| 5 | 120 |
| 6 | 720 |
| 7 | 5,040 |
| 8 | 40,320 |
| 9 | 362,880 |
| 10 | 3,628,800 |
| 11 | 39,916,800 |
| 12 | 479,001,600 |
| 13 | 6,227,020,800 |
| 14 | 87,178,291,200 |
| 15 | 1,307,674,368,000 |
| 16 | 20,922,789,888,000 |
| 17 | 355,687,428,096,000 |
| 18 | 6,402,373,705,728,000 |
| 19 | 121,645,100,408,832,000 |
| 20 | 2,432,902,008,176,640,000 |

# Table A.3 Normal Probability Distributions *z*

**Second Decimal Place in *z***

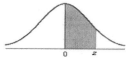

| z | 0.00 | 0.01 | 0.02 | 0.03 | 0.04 | 0.05 | 0.06 | 0.07 | 0.08 | 0.09 |
|-----|-------|-------|-------|-------|-------|-------|-------|-------|-------|-------|
| 0.0 | .0000 | .0040 | .0080 | .0120 | .0160 | .0199 | .0239 | .0279 | .0319 | .0359 |
| 0.1 | .0398 | .0438 | .0478 | .0517 | .0557 | .0596 | .0636 | .0675 | .0714 | .0753 |
| 0.2 | .0793 | .0832 | .0871 | .0910 | .0948 | .0987 | .1026 | .1064 | .1103 | .1141 |
| 0.3 | .1179 | .1217 | .1255 | .1293 | .1331 | .1368 | .1406 | .1443 | .1480 | .1517 |
| 0.4 | .1554 | .1591 | .1628 | .1664 | .1700 | .1736 | .1772 | .1808 | .1844 | .1879 |
| 0.5 | .1915 | .1950 | .1985 | .2019 | .2054 | .2088 | .2123 | .2157 | .2190 | .2224 |
| 0.6 | .2257 | .2291 | .2324 | .2357 | .2389 | .2422 | .2454 | .2486 | .2517 | .2549 |
| 0.7 | .2580 | .2611 | .2642 | .2673 | .2704 | .2734 | .2764 | .2794 | .2823 | .2852 |
| 0.8 | .2881 | .2910 | .2939 | .2967 | .2995 | .3023 | .3051 | .3078 | .3106 | .3133 |
| 0.9 | .3159 | .3186 | .3212 | .3238 | .3264 | .3289 | .3315 | .3340 | .3365 | .3389 |
| 1.0 | .3413 | .3438 | .3461 | .3485 | .3508 | .3531 | .3554 | .3577 | .3599 | .3621 |
| 1.1 | .3613 | .3665 | .3686 | .3708 | .3729 | .3749 | .3770 | .3790 | .3810 | .3830 |
| 1.2 | .3849 | .3869 | .3888 | .3907 | .3925 | .3944 | .3962 | .3980 | .3997 | .4015 |
| 1.3 | .4032 | .4049 | .4066 | .4082 | .4099 | .4115 | .4131 | .4147 | .4162 | .4177 |
| 1.4 | .4192 | .4207 | .4222 | .4236 | .4251 | .4265 | .4279 | .4292 | .4306 | .4319 |
| 1.5 | .4332 | .4345 | .4357 | .4370 | .4382 | .4394 | .4406 | .4418 | .4429 | .4441 |
| 1.6 | .4452 | .4463 | .4474 | .4484 | .4495 | .4505 | .4515 | .4525 | .4535 | .4545 |
| 1.7 | .4554 | .4564 | .4573 | .4582 | .4591 | .4599 | .4605 | .4616 | .4625 | .4633 |
| 1.8 | .4641 | .4649 | .4656 | .4664 | .4671 | .4678 | .4686 | .4693 | .4699 | .4706 |
| 1.9 | .4713 | .4719 | .4726 | .4732 | .4738 | .4744 | .4750 | .4756 | .4761 | .4767 |
| 2.0 | .4772 | .4778 | .4783 | .4788 | .4793 | .4798 | .4803 | .4808 | .4812 | .4817 |
| 2.1 | .4821 | .4826 | .4830 | .4834 | .4838 | .4842 | .4846 | .4850 | .4854 | .4857 |
| 2.2 | .4861 | .4864 | .4868 | .4871 | .4875 | .4878 | .4881 | .4884 | .4887 | .4890 |
| 2.3 | .4893 | .4896 | .4898 | .4901 | .4904 | .4906 | .4909 | .4911 | .4913 | .4916 |
| 2.4 | .4918 | .4920 | .4922 | .4925 | .4927 | .4929 | .4931 | .4932 | .4934 | .4936 |
| 2.5 | .4938 | .4940 | .4941 | .4943 | .4945 | .4946 | .4948 | .4949 | .4951 | .4952 |
| 2.6 | .4953 | .4955 | .4956 | .4957 | .4959 | .4960 | .4961 | .4962 | .4963 | .4964 |
| 2.7 | .4965 | .4966 | .4967 | .4968 | .4969 | .4970 | .4971 | .4972 | .4973 | .4974 |
| 2.8 | .4974 | .4975 | .4976 | .4977 | .4977 | .4978 | .4979 | .4979 | .4980 | .4981 |
| 2.9 | .4981 | .4982 | .4982 | .4983 | .4984 | .4984 | .4985 | .4985 | .4986 | .4986 |
| 3.0 | .4987 | .4987 | .4987 | .4988 | .4988 | .4989 | .4989 | .4989 | .4990 | .4990 |
| 3.1 | .4990 | .4991 | .4991 | .4991 | .4992 | .4992 | .4992 | .4992 | .4993 | .4993 |
| 3.2 | .4993 | .4993 | .4994 | .4994 | .4994 | .4994 | .4994 | .4995 | .4995 | .4995 |
| 3.3 | .4995 | .4995 | .4995 | .4996 | .4996 | .4996 | .4996 | .4996 | .4996 | .4997 |
| 3.4 | .4997 | .4997 | .4997 | .4997 | .4997 | .4997 | .4997 | .4997 | .4997 | .4998* |

\* For z values greater than 3.49, use .4999 for the area

\*\*Common z values, probability area, and one-tailed α levels

| α | Area | z | | α | Area | z |
|-----|-------|-------|---|------|-------|-------|
| .25 | .2500 | .675 | | .025 | .4750 | 1.96 |
| .10 | .4000 | 1.282 | | .01 | .4900 | 2.327 |
| .05 | .4500 | 1.645 | | .005 | .4950 | 2.575 |

# Table A.4

## *t* Distribution

The values reported in the table are the right-tailed critical values for *t*. Left-tailed values are found by symmetry.

| Degrees of Freedom | One tailed $\alpha$ | | | | | |
|---|---|---|---|---|---|---|
| | .005 | .01 | .025 | .05 | .10 | .25 |
| 1 | 63.657 | 31.821 | 12.706 | 6.314 | 3.078 | 1.000 |
| 2 | 9.925 | 6.965 | 4.303 | 2.920 | 1.886 | .816 |
| 3 | 5.841 | 4.541 | 3.182 | 2.353 | 1.638 | .765 |
| 4 | 4.604 | 3.747 | 2.776 | 2.132 | 1.533 | .741 |
| 5 | 4.032 | 3.365 | 2.571 | 2.015 | 1.476 | .727 |
| 6 | 3.707 | 3.143 | 2.447 | 1.943 | 1.440 | .718 |
| 7 | 3.500 | 2.998 | 2.365 | 1.895 | 1.415 | .711 |
| 8 | 3.355 | 2.896 | 2.306 | 1.860 | 1.397 | .706 |
| 9 | 3.250 | 2.821 | 2.262 | 1.833 | 1.383 | .703 |
| 10 | 3.169 | 2.764 | 2.228 | 1.812 | 1.372 | .700 |
| 11 | 3.106 | 2.718 | 2.202 | 1.796 | 1.363 | .697 |
| 12 | 3.054 | 2.681 | 2.179 | 1.782 | 1.356 | .696 |
| 13 | 3.012 | 2.650 | 2.160 | 1.771 | 1.350 | .694 |
| 14 | 2.977 | 2.625 | 2.145 | 1.761 | 1.345 | .692 |
| 15 | 2.947 | 2.602 | 2.132 | 1.753 | 1.341 | .691 |
| 16 | 2.921 | 2.584 | 2.120 | 1.746 | 1.337 | .690 |
| 17 | 2.898 | 2.567 | 2.110 | 1.740 | 1.333 | .689 |
| 18 | 2.878 | 2.552 | 2.101 | 1.734 | 1.330 | .688 |
| 19 | 2.861 | 2.540 | 2.093 | 1.729 | 1.328 | .688 |
| 20 | 2.845 | 2.528 | 2.086 | 1.725 | 1.325 | .687 |
| 21 | 2.831 | 2.518 | 2.080 | 1.721 | 1.323 | .686 |
| 22 | 2.819 | 2.508 | 2.074 | 1.717 | 1.321 | .686 |
| 23 | 2.807 | 2.500 | 2.069 | 1.714 | 1.320 | .685 |
| 24 | 2.797 | 2.492 | 2.064 | 1.711 | 1.318 | .685 |
| 25 | 2.787 | 2.485 | 2.060 | 1.708 | 1.316 | .684 |
| 26 | 2.779 | 2.479 | 2.056 | 1.706 | 1.315 | .684 |
| 27 | 2.771 | 2.473 | 2.052 | 1.703 | 1.314 | .684 |
| 28 | 2.763 | 2.467 | 2.048 | 1.701 | 1.313 | .683 |
| 29 | 2.756 | 2.462 | 2.045 | 1.699 | 1.311 | .683 |
| Large | 2.575 | 2.327 | 1.960 | 1.645 | 1.282 | .675 |

# Table A.5
## Chi-Square Distribution

Left-tailed critical region is noted both as left-tailed alphas and the traditional method of 1 - α. (For example, .05 left-tailed test is traditionally noted as 1 - .05, or .950.)

| | Left-tailed Critical Values | | | | | Right-tailed Critical Values | | | | |
|---|---|---|---|---|---|---|---|---|---|---|
| | .005 | .01 | .025 | .05 | .10 | .10 | .05 | .025 | .01 | .005 |
| df | .995 | .990 | .975 | .950 | .90 | | | | | |
| 1 | .00004 | .0002 | .001 | .004 | .016 | 2.706 | 3.841 | 5.024 | 6.635 | 7.879 |
| 2 | .010 | .020 | .051 | .103 | .211 | 4.605 | 5.991 | 7.378 | 9.210 | 10.597 |
| 3 | .072 | .115 | .216 | .352 | .584 | 6.251 | 7.815 | 9.348 | 11.345 | 12.838 |
| 4 | .207 | .297 | .484 | .711 | 1.064 | 7.779 | 9.488 | 11.143 | 13.277 | 14.860 |
| 5 | .412 | .554 | .831 | 1.145 | 1.610 | 9.236 | 11.071 | 12.833 | 15.086 | 16.750 |
| 6 | .676 | .872 | 1.237 | 1.635 | 2.204 | 10.645 | 12.592 | 14.447 | 16.812 | 18.548 |
| 7 | .989 | 1.239 | 1.690 | 2.167 | 2.833 | 12.017 | 14.067 | 16.013 | 18.475 | 20.278 |
| 8 | 1.344 | 1.646 | 2.180 | 2.733 | 3.490 | 13.362 | 15.507 | 17.535 | 20.090 | 21.955 |
| 9 | 1.735 | 2.088 | 2.700 | 3.325 | 4.168 | 14.684 | 16.919 | 19.023 | 21.666 | 23.589 |
| 10 | 2.156 | 2.558 | 3.247 | 3.940 | 4.865 | 15.987 | 18.307 | 20.486 | 23.209 | 25.188 |
| 11 | 2.603 | 3.053 | 3.816 | 4.575 | 5.578 | 17.275 | 19.675 | 21.920 | 24.725 | 26.757 |
| 12 | 3.074 | 3.571 | 4.404 | 5.226 | 6.304 | 18.549 | 21.026 | 23.337 | 26.217 | 28.299 |
| 13 | 3.565 | 4.107 | 5.009 | 5.892 | 7.042 | 19.812 | 22.362 | 24.736 | 27.688 | 29.819 |
| 14 | 4.075 | 4.660 | 5.629 | 6.571 | 7.790 | 21.064 | 23.685 | 26.119 | 29.141 | 31.319 |
| 15 | 4.601 | 5.229 | 6.262 | 7.261 | 8.547 | 22.307 | 24.996 | 27.488 | 30.578 | 32.801 |
| 16 | 5.142 | 5.812 | 6.908 | 7.962 | 9.312 | 23.542 | 26.296 | 28.845 | 32.000 | 34.267 |
| 17 | 5.697 | 6.408 | 7.564 | 8.672 | 10.085 | 24.769 | 27.587 | 30.191 | 33.409 | 35.718 |
| 18 | 6.265 | 7.015 | 8.231 | 9.390 | 10.865 | 25.989 | 28.869 | 31.526 | 34.805 | 37.156 |
| 19 | 6.844 | 7.633 | 8.907 | 10.117 | 11.651 | 27.204 | 30.144 | 32.852 | 36.191 | 28.582 |
| 20 | 7.434 | 8.260 | 9.591 | 10.851 | 12.443 | 28.412 | 31.410 | 34.170 | 37.566 | 39.997 |
| 21 | 8.034 | 8.897 | 10.283 | 11.591 | 13.340 | 29.615 | 32.671 | 35.479 | 38.932 | 41.101 |
| 22 | 8.643 | 9.542 | 10.982 | 12.338 | 14.042 | 30.813 | 33.924 | 36.781 | 40.289 | 42.796 |
| 23 | 9.260 | 10.196 | 11.689 | 13.091 | 14.848 | 32.007 | 35.172 | 38.076 | 41.638 | 44.181 |
| 24 | 9.886 | 10.856 | 12.401 | 13.848 | 15.659 | 33.196 | 36.415 | 39.364 | 42.980 | 45.559 |
| 25 | 10.520 | 11.524 | 13.120 | 14.611 | 16.473 | 34.382 | 37.652 | 40.646 | 44.314 | 46.928 |
| 26 | 11.160 | 12.198 | 13.844 | 15.379 | 17.292 | 35.563 | 38.885 | 41.923 | 45.642 | 48.290 |
| 27 | 11.808 | 12.879 | 14.573 | 16.151 | 18.114 | 36.415 | 40.113 | 43.194 | 46.963 | 49.645 |
| 28 | 12.461 | 13.565 | 15.308 | 16.928 | 18.939 | 37.652 | 41.337 | 44.461 | 48.278 | 50.993 |
| 29 | 13.121 | 14.257 | 16.047 | 17.708 | 19.768 | 39.087 | 42.557 | 45.772 | 49.588 | 52.336 |
| 30 | 13.787 | 14.954 | 16.791 | 18.493 | 20.599 | 40.256 | 43.773 | 46.979 | 50.892 | 53.672 |
| 40 | 20.707 | 22.164 | 24.433 | 26.509 | 29.051 | 51.805 | 55.758 | 59.342 | 63.691 | 66.766 |
| 50 | 27.991 | 29.707 | 32.357 | 34.764 | 37.689 | 63.167 | 67.505 | 71.420 | 76.154 | 79.490 |
| 60 | 35.534 | 37.485 | 40.482 | 43.188 | 46.459 | 74.397 | 79.082 | 83.298 | 88.379 | 91.952 |
| 70 | 43.275 | 45.442 | 48.758 | 51.739 | 55.329 | 85.527 | 90.531 | 95.023 | 100.425 | 104.125 |
| 80 | 51.172 | 53.540 | 57.153 | 60.391 | 64.278 | 96.578 | 101.829 | 106.629 | 112.329 | 116.321 |
| 90 | 59.196 | 61.754 | 65.647 | 69.126 | 73.291 | 107.565 | 113.145 | 118.136 | 124.116 | 128.299 |
| 100 | 67.328 | 70.065 | 74.222 | 77.929 | 82.358 | 118.498 | 124.342 | 129.561 | 135.807 | 140.169 |

## *Table A.6a*
### *F* Distribution—Right-tailed Values
### $\alpha = .01$

| | | | | Numerator Degrees of Freedom | | | | | |
|---|---|---|---|---|---|---|---|---|---|
| $df_1 \rightarrow$ $df_2 \downarrow$ | 1 | 2 | 3 | 4 | 5 | 6 | 7 | 8 | 9 |
| 2 | 98.503 | 99.000 | 99.166 | 99.249 | 99.299 | 99.333 | 99.356 | 99.374 | 99.388 |
| 3 | 34.116 | 30.817 | 29.457 | 28.710 | 28.237 | 27.911 | 27.672 | 27.489 | 27.345 |
| 4 | 21.198 | 18.000 | 16.694 | 15.977 | 15.522 | 15.207 | 14.976 | 14.799 | 14.659 |
| 5 | 16.258 | 13.274 | 12.060 | 11.392 | 10.967 | 10.672 | 10.456 | 10.289 | 10.158 |
| 6 | 13.745 | 10.925 | 9.780 | 9.148 | 8.746 | 8.466 | 8.260 | 8.102 | 7.976 |
| 7 | 12.246 | 9.547 | 8.451 | 7.847 | 7.460 | 7.191 | 6.993 | 6.740 | 6.719 |
| 8 | 11.259 | 8.649 | 7.591 | 7.006 | 6.632 | 6.371 | 6.117 | 6.029 | 5.911 |
| 9 | 10.561 | 8.022 | 6.992 | 6.422 | 6.057 | 5.802 | 5.613 | 5.467 | 5.351 |
| 10 | 10.044 | 7.559 | 6.552 | 5.994 | 5.636 | 5.386 | 5.200 | 5.057 | 4.942 |
| 11 | 9.646 | 7.2057 | 6.217 | 5.668 | 5.316 | 5.069 | 4.886 | 4.745 | 4.632 |
| 12 | 9.330 | 6.927 | 5.953 | 5.412 | 5.064 | 4.821 | 4.640 | 4.499 | 4.388 |
| 13 | 9.074 | 6.701 | 5.739 | 5.205 | 4.865 | 4.620 | 4.441 | 4.302 | 4.191 |
| 14 | 8.861 | 6.515 | 5.564 | 5.035 | 4.695 | 4.456 | 4.278 | 4.140 | 4.030 |
| 15 | 8.683 | 6.359 | 5.417 | 4.893 | 4.556 | 4.318 | 4.142 | 4.005 | 3.895 |
| 16 | 8.531 | 6.226 | 2.292 | 4.773 | 4.437 | 4.202 | 4.026 | 3.890 | 3.780 |
| 17 | 8.399 | 6.112 | 5.185 | 4.669 | 4.336 | 4.102 | 3.927 | 3.791 | 3.682 |
| 18 | 8.285 | 6.013 | 5.092 | 4.579 | 4.248 | 4.015 | 3.841 | 3.705 | 3.597 |
| 19 | 8.185 | 5.926 | 5.010 | 4.500 | 4.171 | 3.939 | 3.765 | 3.631 | 3.523 |
| 20 | 8.096 | 5.849 | 4.938 | 4.431 | 4.103 | 3.871 | 3.699 | 3.564 | 3.457 |
| 21 | 8.017 | 5.780 | 4.874 | 4.369 | 4.042 | 3.812 | 3.640 | 3.506 | 3.398 |
| 22 | 7.945 | 5.719 | 4.817 | 4.313 | 3.988 | 3.758 | 3.587 | 3.453 | 3.346 |
| 23 | 7.881 | 5.667 | 4.765 | 4.264 | 3.939 | 3.710 | 3.539 | 3.406 | 3.298 |
| 24 | 7.823 | 5.614 | 4.718 | 4.218 | 3.895 | 3.667 | 3.496 | 3.363 | 3.256 |
| 25 | 7.769 | 5.568 | 4.676 | 4.177 | 3.855 | 3.627 | 3.457 | 3.324 | 3.217 |
| 26 | 7.721 | 5.526 | 4.637 | 4.140 | 3.818 | 3.591 | 3.421 | 3.288 | 3.182 |
| 27 | 7.677 | 5.488 | 4.601 | 4.106 | 3.785 | 3.558 | 3.388 | 3.256 | 3.149 |
| 28 | 7.636 | 5.453 | 4.568 | 4.074 | 3.754 | 3.528 | 3.358 | 3.226 | 3.120 |
| 29 | 7.598 | 5.420 | 4.538 | 4.045 | 3.725 | 3.500 | 3.330 | 3.198 | 3.092 |
| 30 | 7.563 | 5.390 | 4.510 | 4.018 | 3.699 | 3.474 | 3.305 | 3.173 | 3.067 |
| 40 | 7.314 | 5.179 | 4.313 | 3.828 | 3.514 | 3.291 | 3.124 | 2.993 | 2.888 |
| 60 | 7.071 | 4.978 | 4.126 | 3.649 | 3.339 | 3.119 | 2.953 | 2.823 | 2.719 |
| 120 | 6.851 | 4.787 | 3.949 | 3.480 | 3.174 | 2.956 | 2.792 | 2.663 | 2.559 |
| $\infty$ | 6.635 | 4.605 | 3.782 | 3.319 | 3.017 | 2.802 | 2.639 | 2.511 | 2.407 |

Denominator Degrees of Freedom

# *F* Distribution—Right-tailed Values
## $\alpha = .01$

| | Numerator Degrees of Freedom | | | | | | | | |
|---|---|---|---|---|---|---|---|---|---|
| $df_1 \rightarrow$<br>$df_2 \downarrow$ | 10 | 12 | 15 | 20 | 24 | 30 | 40 | 60 | 120 |
| 2 | 99.399 | 99.416 | 99.433 | 99.449 | 99.458 | 99.466 | 44.474 | 99.482 | 99.491 |
| 3 | 27.229 | 27.052 | 26.872 | 26.690 | 26.598 | 26.505 | 26.411 | 26.316 | 26.221 |
| 4 | 14.546 | 14.374 | 14.198 | 14.020 | 13.929 | 13.838 | 13.745 | 13.652 | 13.558 |
| 5 | 10.051 | 9.888 | 9.722 | 9.553 | 9.467 | 9.379 | 9.291 | 9.202 | 9.112 |
| 6 | 7.874 | 7.718 | 7.560 | 7.396 | 7.312 | 7.229 | 7.143 | 7.057 | 6.969 |
| 7 | 6.602 | 6.469 | 6.314 | 6.155 | 6.074 | 5.992 | 5.908 | 5.824 | 5.737 |
| 8 | 5.814 | 5.667 | 5.515 | 5.3591 | 5.279 | 5.198 | 5.116 | 5.032 | 4.946 |
| 9 | 5.256 | 5.111 | 4.9621 | 4.808 | 4.729 | 4.649 | 4.567 | 4.483 | 4.398 |
| 10 | 4.849 | 4.706 | 4.558 | 4.405 | 4.327 | 4.247 | 4.165 | 4.082 | 3.997 |
| 11 | 4.539 | 4.400 | 4.251 | 4.099 | 4.021 | 3.941 | 3.860 | 3.776 | 3.690 |
| 12 | 4.296 | 4.155 | 4.010 | 3.858 | 3.781 | 3.701 | 3.619 | 3.536 | 3.449 |
| 13 | 4.100 | 4.960 | 3.815 | 3.665 | 3.587 | 3.507 | 3.425 | 3.341 | 3.255 |
| 14 | 3.939 | 3.800 | 3.656 | 3.505 | 3.427 | 3.348 | 3.266 | 3.181 | 3.094 |
| 15 | 3.805 | 3.666 | 3.522 | 3.372 | 3.294 | 3.214 | 3.132 | 3.048 | 2.960 |
| 16 | 3.691 | 3.553 | 3.409 | 3.259 | 3.181 | 3.101 | 3.018 | 2.933 | 2.845 |
| 17 | 3.593 | 3.455 | 3.312 | 3.162 | 3.084 | 3.003 | 2.921 | 2.835 | 2.746 |
| 18 | 3.508 | 3.371 | 3.227 | 3.077 | 2.999 | 2.919 | 2.835 | 2.749 | 2.660 |
| 19 | 3.434 | 3.297 | 3.153 | 3.003 | 2.925 | 2.844 | 2.761 | 2.672 | 2.584 |
| 20 | 3.368 | 3.231 | 3.088 | 2.938 | 2.859 | 2.779 | 2.695 | 2.608 | 2.517 |
| 21 | 3.310 | 3.173 | 3.030 | 2.880 | 2.801 | 2.720 | 2.636 | 2.548 | 2.457 |
| 22 | 3.258 | 3.121 | 2.978 | 2.827 | 2.749 | 2.668 | 2.583 | 2.495 | 2.403 |
| 23 | 3.211 | 3.074 | 2.931 | 2.781 | 2.702 | 2.620 | 2.536 | 2.447 | 2.354 |
| 24 | 3.168 | 3.032 | 2.889 | 2.738 | 2.660 | 2.577 | 2.492 | 2.404 | 2.310 |
| 25 | 3.129 | 2.993 | 2.850 | 2.699 | 2.620 | 2.538 | 2.453 | 2.364 | 2.270 |
| 26 | 3.094 | 2.958 | 2.815 | 2.664 | 2.585 | 2.503 | 2.417 | 2.294 | 2.233 |
| 27 | 3.062 | 2.926 | 2.783 | 2.632 | 2.552 | 2.470 | 2.384 | 2.629 | 2.199 |
| 28 | 3.032 | 2.896 | 2.753 | 2.602 | 2.522 | 2.440 | 2.354 | 2.344 | 2.167 |
| 29 | 3.005 | 2.869 | 2.726 | 2.572 | 2.495 | 2.412 | 2.325 | 2.208 | 2.138 |
| 30 | 2.979 | 2.843 | 2.700 | 2.549 | 2.470 | 2.386 | 2.299 | 2.208 | 2.111 |
| 40 | 2.800 | 2.665 | 2.521 | 2.369 | 2.288 | 2.203 | 2.114 | 2.019 | 1.917 |
| 60 | 2.632 | 2.496 | 2.352 | 2.198 | 2.115 | 2.029 | 1.936 | 1.836 | 1.726 |
| 120 | 2.472 | 2.336 | 2.192 | 2.035 | 1.950 | 1.860 | 1.723 | 1.656 | 1.533 |
| $\infty$ | 2.309 | 2.185 | 2.039 | 1.878 | 1.791 | 1.697 | 1.592 | 1.473 | 1.325 |

# Table A.6b
## F Distribution—Right-tailed Values
### α = .025

| | Numerator Degrees of Freedom | | | | | | | | |
|---|---|---|---|---|---|---|---|---|---|
| $df_1 \rightarrow$ <br> $df_2 \downarrow$ | 1 | 2 | 3 | 4 | 5 | 6 | 7 | 8 | 9 |
| 2 | 38.506 | 39.000 | 39.165 | 39.248 | 39.298 | 39.331 | 39.335 | 39.373 | 39.387 |
| 3 | 14.443 | 16.044 | 15.439 | 15.101 | 14.885 | 14.735 | 14.624 | 14.540 | 14.473 |
| 4 | 12.218 | 10.649 | 9.979 | 9.605 | 9.365 | 9.197 | 9.0741 | 8.980 | 8.095 |
| 5 | 10.007 | 8.434 | 7.764 | 7.388 | 7.146 | 6.978 | 6.8531 | 6.757 | 6.681 |
| 6 | 8.813 | 7.260 | 6.599 | 6.227 | 5.988 | 5.820 | 5.696 | 5.600 | 5.523 |
| 7 | 8.073 | 6.542 | 5.890 | 5.523 | 5.285 | 5.119 | 4.995 | 4.899 | 4.823 |
| 8 | 7.571 | 6.060 | 5.416 | 5.053 | 4.817 | 4.652 | 4.529 | 4.433 | 4.357 |
| 9 | 7.209 | 5.715 | 5.078 | 4.718 | 4.484 | 4.320 | 4.197 | 4.120 | 4.026 |
| 10 | 6.937 | 5.456 | 4.826 | 4.468 | 4.236 | 4.072 | 3.950 | 3.855 | 3.779 |
| 11 | 6.724 | 5.256 | 4.630 | 4.275 | 4.044 | 3.881 | 3.759 | 3.664 | 3.588 |
| 12 | 6.554 | 5.096 | 4.474 | 4.121 | 3.891 | 3.728 | 3.607 | 3.512 | 3.436 |
| 13 | 6.414 | 4.965 | 4.347 | 3.996 | 3.767 | 3.604 | 3.483 | 3.388 | 3.312 |
| 14 | 6.298 | 4.857 | 4.242 | 3.892 | 3.663 | 3.501 | 3.380 | 3.285 | 3.209 |
| 15 | 6.200 | 4.765 | 4.153 | 3.804 | 3.576 | 3.415 | 3.293 | 3.199 | 3.113 |
| 16 | 6.115 | 4.687 | 4.077 | 3.729 | 3.502 | 3.341 | 3.219 | 3.125 | 3.049 |
| 17 | 6.042 | 4.619 | 4.011 | 3.665 | 3.438 | 3.277 | 3.156 | 3.061 | 2.985 |
| 18 | 5.978 | 4.560 | 3.954 | 3.608 | 3.382 | 3.221 | 3.100 | 3.005 | 2.929 |
| 19 | 5.922 | 4.508 | 3.903 | 3.559 | 3.333 | 3.172 | 3.051 | 2.956 | 2.880 |
| 20 | 5.872 | 4.461 | 3.869 | 3.515 | 2.289 | 3.128 | 3.007 | 2.913 | 2.837 |
| 21 | 5.827 | 4.420 | 3.819 | 3.475 | 3.250 | 3.090 | 2.969 | 2.874 | 2.798 |
| 22 | 5.786 | 4.383 | 3.783 | 3.440 | 3.215 | 3.055 | 2.934 | 2.839 | 2.763 |
| 23 | 5.750 | 4.349 | 3.751 | 3.408 | 3.184 | 3.023 | 2.902 | 2.808 | 2.731 |
| 24 | 5.717 | 4.319 | 3.721 | 3.379 | 3.155 | 2.995 | 2.874 | 2.779 | 2.703 |
| 25 | 5.676 | 4.291 | 3.694 | 3.353 | 3.129 | 2.969 | 2.848 | 2.753 | 2.677 |
| 26 | 5.659 | 4.266 | 3.670 | 3.329 | 3.105 | 2.945 | 2.824 | 2.729 | 2.653 |
| 27 | 5.633 | 3.242 | 3.647 | 3.307 | 3.083 | 2.923 | 2.802 | 2.707 | 2.631 |
| 28 | 5.610 | 4.221 | 3.626 | 3.286 | 3.063 | 2.903 | 2.782 | 2.687 | 2.611 |
| 29 | 5.588 | 4.201 | 3.607 | 3.267 | 3.044 | 2.884 | 2.763 | 2.669 | 2.592 |
| 30 | 5.568 | 4.182 | 3.589 | 3.250 | 3.027 | 2.867 | 2.746 | 2.651 | 2.575 |
| 40 | 5.424 | 4.051 | 3.463 | 3.126 | 2.904 | 2.744 | 2.624 | 2.529 | 2.452 |
| 60 | 5.286 | 3.925 | 3.343 | 3.008 | 2.786 | 2.627 | 2.507 | 2.412 | 2.334 |
| 120 | 5.152 | 3.805 | 3.227 | 2.894 | 2.674 | 2.515 | 2.395 | 2.299 | 2.222 |
| ∞ | 5.024 | 3.689 | 3.116 | 2.786 | 2.567 | 2.408 | 2.288 | 2.192 | 2.114 |

Denominator Degrees of Freedom

## *F* Distribution—Right-tailed Values
## $\alpha = .025$

| | Numerator Degrees of Freedom | | | | | | | | |
|---|---|---|---|---|---|---|---|---|---|
| $df_1 \rightarrow$ <br> $df_2 \downarrow$ | 10 | 12 | 15 | 20 | 24 | 30 | 40 | 60 | 120 |
| 2 | 39.398 | 39.415 | 39.431 | 39.448 | 39.456 | 39.465 | 39.473 | 39.481 | 39.490 |
| 3 | 14.419 | 14.337 | 14.253 | 14.167 | 14.124 | 14.081 | 14.037 | 13.992 | 13.947 |
| 4 | 8.844 | 8.751 | 8.657 | 8.560 | 8.511 | 8.461 | 8.411 | 8.360 | 8.309 |
| 5 | 6.619 | 6.525 | 6.428 | 6.329 | 6.278 | 6.227 | 6.175 | 6.123 | 6.069 |
| 6 | 5.461 | 5.366 | 5.269 | 5.168 | 5.117 | 5.065 | 5.013 | 4.959 | 4.904 |
| 7 | 4.761 | 4.666 | 4.568 | 4.467 | 4.445 | 4.362 | 4.309 | 4.254 | 4.199 |
| 8 | 4.295 | 4.200 | 4.101 | 4.000 | 3.947 | 3.894 | 3.840 | 3.784 | 3.728 |
| 9 | 3.964 | 3.868 | 3.769 | 3.667 | 3.614 | 3.560 | 3.506 | 3.449 | 3.392 |
| 10 | 3.717 | 3.621 | 3.522 | 3.419 | 3.365 | 3.311 | 3.255 | 3.198 | 3.140 |
| 11 | 3.526 | 3.430 | 3.330 | 3.226 | 3.173 | 3.118 | 3.061 | 3.004 | 2.944 |
| 12 | 3.374 | 3.277 | 3.177 | 3.073 | 3.018 | 2.963 | 2.906 | 2.848 | 2.787 |
| 13 | 3.245 | 3.153 | 3.053 | 2.948 | 2.893 | 2.837 | 2.780 | 2.720 | 2.659 |
| 14 | 3.157 | 3.050 | 2.949 | 2.844 | 2.789 | 2.732 | 2.674 | 2.614 | 2.552 |
| 15 | 3.060 | 2.963 | 2.862 | 2.760 | 2.707 | 2.644 | 2.585 | 2.524 | 2.461 |
| 16 | 2.986 | 2.889 | 2.788 | 2.681 | 2.625 | 2.568 | 2.509 | 2.447 | 2.383 |
| 17 | 2.922 | 2.825 | 2.723 | 2.616 | 2.560 | 2.502 | 2.442 | 2.380 | 2.315 |
| 18 | 2.866 | 2.769 | 2.667 | 2.559 | 2.503 | 2.445 | 2.384 | 2.321 | 2.256 |
| 19 | 2.817 | 2.720 | 2.617 | 2.509 | 2.452 | 2.394 | 2.333 | 2.270 | 2.203 |
| 20 | 2.774 | 2.676 | 2.573 | 2.465 | 2.408 | 2.349 | 2.287 | 2.223 | 2.156 |
| 21 | 2.735 | 3.637 | 2.534 | 2.425 | 2.368 | 2.308 | 2.247 | 2.182 | 2.114 |
| 22 | 2.700 | 2.602 | 2.498 | 2.389 | 2.332 | 2.272 | 2.210 | 2.145 | 2.076 |
| 23 | 2.668 | 2.570 | 2.467 | 2.356 | 2.299 | 2.239 | 2.176 | 2.111 | 2.042 |
| 24 | 2.640 | 2.541 | 2.437 | 2.327 | 2.269 | 2.209 | 2.146 | 2.080 | 2.010 |
| 25 | 2.614 | 2.515 | 2.411 | 2.301 | 2.242 | 2.182 | 2.118 | 2.052 | 1.981 |
| 26 | 2.580 | 2.491 | 2.387 | 2.276 | 2.217 | 2.156 | 2.093 | 2.026 | 1.945 |
| 27 | 2.568 | 2.469 | 2.364 | 2.253 | 2.195 | 2.133 | 2.069 | 2.002 | 1.30 |
| 28 | 2.547 | 2.448 | 2.344 | 2.233 | 2.174 | 2.112 | 2.048 | 1.979 | 1.907 |
| 29 | 2.529 | 2.430 | 2.325 | 2.213 | 2.154 | 2.092 | 2.027 | 1.959 | 1.886 |
| 30 | 2.511 | 2.412 | 2.307 | 2.195 | 2.136 | 2.074 | 2.009 | 1.940 | 1.866 |
| 40 | 2.388 | 2.288 | 2.182 | 2.067 | 2.007 | 1.943 | 1.875 | 1.803 | 1.724 |
| 60 | 2.270 | 2.169 | 2.061 | 1.945 | 1.882 | 1.815 | 1.744 | 1.667 | 1.581 |
| 120 | 2.157 | 2.055 | 1.945 | 1.825 | 1.760 | 1.690 | 1.614 | 1.530 | 1.433 |
| $\infty$ | 2.048 | 1.945 | 1.833 | 1.709 | 1.640 | 1.566 | 1.484 | 1.388 | 1.268 |

Denominator Degrees of Freedom

# Table A.6c
## F Distribution—Right-tailed Values
### $\alpha = .05$

| | $df_1 \rightarrow$ $df_2 \downarrow$ | 1 | 2 | 3 | 4 | 5 | 6 | 7 | 8 | 9 |
|---|---|---|---|---|---|---|---|---|---|---|
| | | \multicolumn{9}{c}{Numerator Degrees of Freedom} | | | | | | | | |

| $df_2 \downarrow$ | 1 | 2 | 3 | 4 | 5 | 6 | 7 | 8 | 9 |
|---|---|---|---|---|---|---|---|---|---|
| 2 | 18.513 | 19.000 | 19.164 | 19.247 | 19.296 | 19.330 | 19.353 | 19.371 | 19.385 |
| 3 | 10.128 | 9.552 | 2.277 | 9.117 | 9.014 | 8.941 | 8.887 | 8.845 | 8.812 |
| 4 | 7.709 | 9.944 | 6.591 | 6.388 | 6.256 | 6.163 | 6.094 | 6.041 | 6.999 |
| 5 | 6.608 | 5.786 | 5.410 | 5.192 | 5.050 | 4.950 | 4.876 | 4.818 | 4.773 |
| 6 | 5.987 | 5.143 | 4.757 | 4.534 | 4.387 | 4.284 | 4.207 | 4.147 | 4.099 |
| 7 | 5.591 | 4.737 | 4.347 | 4.120 | 3.972 | 3.866 | 3.787 | 3.726 | 3.677 |
| 8 | 5.318 | 4.459 | 4.066 | 3.838 | 3.688 | 3.581 | 3.500 | 3.438 | 3.388 |
| 9 | 5.117 | 4.257 | 3.863 | 3.633 | 3.482 | 3.374 | 3.293 | 3.230 | 3.179 |
| 10 | 4.965 | 4.103 | 3.708 | 3.478 | 3.326 | 3.217 | 3.136 | 3.072 | 3.020 |
| 11 | 4.844 | 3.982 | 3.587 | 3.357 | 3.204 | 3.095 | 3.012 | 2.948 | 2.896 |
| 12 | 4.747 | 3.885 | 3.490 | 3.259 | 3.106 | 2.996 | 2.913 | 2.849 | 2.796 |
| 13 | 4.667 | 3.806 | 3.411 | 3.179 | 3.025 | 2.915 | 2.832 | 2.767 | 2.714 |
| 14 | 4.600 | 3.739 | 3.344 | 3.112 | 2.958 | 2.848 | 2.764 | 2.699 | 2.656 |
| 15 | 4.543 | 3.682 | 3.287 | 2.056 | 2.901 | 2.791 | 2.707 | 2.641 | 2.588 |
| 16 | 4.494 | 3.634 | 3.239 | 3.007 | 2.852 | 2.741 | 2.657 | 2.591 | 2.538 |
| 17 | 4.451 | 3.592 | 3.197 | 2.965 | 2.810 | 2.699 | 2.614 | 2.548 | 2.494 |
| 18 | 4.414 | 3.555 | 3.160 | 2.928 | 2.773 | 2.661 | 2.577 | 2.510 | 2.456 |
| 19 | 4.381 | 3.522 | 3.127 | 2.895 | 2.740 | 2.628 | 2.544 | 2.477 | 2.423 |
| 20 | 4.351 | 3.493 | 3.098 | 2.866 | 2.711 | 2.599 | 2.514 | 2.447 | 2.393 |
| 21 | 4.325 | 3.467 | 3.073 | 2.840 | 2.685 | 2.573 | 2.488 | 2.401 | 2.366 |
| 22 | 4.301 | 3.443 | 3.049 | 2.817 | 2.661 | 2.549 | 2.464 | 2.397 | 2.342 |
| 23 | 4.279 | 3.422 | 3.028 | 2.796 | 2.640 | 2.528 | 2.442 | 2.375 | 2.320 |
| 24 | 4.260 | 3.403 | 3.009 | 2.776 | 2.621 | 2.508 | 2.423 | 2.355 | 2.300 |
| 25 | 4.242 | 3.385 | 2.991 | 2.759 | 2.603 | 4.490 | 2.405 | 2.337 | 2.282 |
| 26 | 4.225 | 3.369 | 2.975 | 2.743 | 2.587 | 2.474 | 2.388 | 2.305 | 2.266 |
| 27 | 4.210 | 3.354 | 2.960 | 2.728 | 2.5719 | 2.459 | 2.373 | 2.305 | 2.250 |
| 28 | 4.196 | 3.340 | 2.947 | 2.714 | 2.558 | 2.445 | 2.359 | 2.291 | 2.236 |
| 29 | 4.183 | 3.328 | 2.934 | 2.701 | 2.545 | 2.432 | 2.346 | 2.278 | 2.223 |
| 30 | 4.171 | 3.316 | 2.922 | 2.690 | 2.534 | 2.421 | 2.334 | 2.266 | 2.211 |
| 40 | 4.085 | 3.232 | 2.839 | 2.606 | 2.450 | 2.336 | 2.249 | 2.180 | 2.124 |
| 60 | 4.001 | 3.150 | 2.758 | 2.525 | 2.368 | 2.254 | 2.167 | 2.097 | 2.040 |
| 120 | 3.920 | 3.072 | 2.680 | 2.447 | 2.290 | 2.175 | 2.087 | 2.016 | 1.959 |
| $\infty$ | 3.842 | 2.996 | 2.605 | 2.372 | 2.214 | 2.099 | 2.010 | 1.938 | 1.880 |

*Denominator Degrees of Freedom*

# F Distribution—Right-tailed Values

## $\alpha = .05$

| | | Numerator Degrees of Freedom | | | | | | | | |
|---|---|---|---|---|---|---|---|---|---|---|
| | $df_1 \rightarrow$ $df_2 \downarrow$ | 10 | 12 | 15 | 20 | 24 | 30 | 40 | 60 | 120 |
| | 2 | 19.396 | 19.413 | 19.429 | 19.446 | 19.454 | 19.462 | 19.471 | 19.479 | 19.487 |
| | 3 | 8.786 | 8.745 | 8.703 | 8.660 | 8.639 | 8.617 | 8.594 | 8.572 | 8.549 |
| | 4 | 5.964 | 5.912 | 5.858 | 5.803 | 5.774 | 5.746 | 5.717 | 5.688 | 5.658 |
| | 5 | 4.735 | 4.678 | 4.619 | 4.558 | 4.527 | 4.496 | 4.464 | 4.431 | 4.399 |
| | 6 | 4.060 | 4.000 | 3.938 | 3.874 | 3.842 | 3.808 | 3.774 | 3.740 | 3.705 |
| | 7 | 3.636 | 3.575 | 3.511 | 3.445 | 3.411 | 3.376 | 3.340 | 3.304 | 3.267 |
| | 8 | 3.342 | 3.284 | 3.218 | 3.150 | 3.115 | 3.079 | 3.043 | 3.005 | 2.967 |
| | 9 | 3.137 | 3.073 | 3.006 | 2.937 | 2.901 | 2.864 | 2.826 | 2.782 | 2.748 |
| Denominator Degrees of Freedom | 10 | 2.978 | 2.913 | 2.845 | 2.774 | 2.737 | 2.700 | 2.661 | 2.621 | 2.580 |
| | 11 | 2.854 | 2.787 | 2.719 | 2.646 | 2.609 | 2.571 | 2.531 | 2.490 | 2.448 |
| | 12 | 2.753 | 2.687 | 2.617 | 2.544 | 2.506 | 2.466 | 2.426 | 2.384 | 2.341 |
| | 13 | 2.671 | 2.604 | 2.533 | 2.459 | 2.420 | 2.380 | 2.339 | 2.297 | 2.252 |
| | 14 | 2.602 | 2.534 | 2.463 | 2.388 | 2.348 | 2.308 | 2.266 | 2.223 | 2.178 |
| | 15 | 2.544 | 2.475 | 2.403 | 2.328 | 2.288 | 2.247 | 2.204 | 2.160 | 2.114 |
| | 16 | 2.450 | 2.425 | 2.352 | 2.276 | 2.235 | 2.194 | 2.151 | 2.106 | 2.059 |
| | 17 | 2.450 | 2.381 | 2.308 | 2.230 | 2.190 | 2.148 | 2.104 | 2.058 | 2.011 |
| | 18 | 2.412 | 2.342 | 2.269 | 2.191 | 2.150 | 2.107 | 2.063 | 2.017 | 1.968 |
| | 19 | 2.348 | 2.308 | 2.234 | 2.156 | 2.114 | 2.071 | 2.026 | 1.980 | 1.930 |
| | 20 | 2.348 | 2.277 | 2.203 | 2.124 | 2.083 | 2.039 | 1.994 | 1.945 | 1.896 |
| | 21 | 2.321 | 2.250 | 2.176 | 2.096 | 2.054 | 2.010 | 1.965 | 1.917 | 1.866 |
| | 22 | 2.296 | 2.226 | 2.151 | 2.071 | 2.028 | 1.984 | 1.938 | 1.889 | 1.838 |
| | 23 | 2.275 | 2.204 | 2.128 | 2.048 | 2.005 | 1.961 | 1.914 | 1.865 | 1.813 |
| | 24 | 2.255 | 2.183 | 2.108 | 2.027 | 1.984 | 1.939 | 1.892 | 1.842 | 1.790 |
| | 25 | 2.237 | 2.165 | 2.089 | 2.001 | 1.964 | 1.919 | 1.872 | 1.822 | 1.768 |
| | 26 | 2.220 | 2.148 | 2.072 | 1.990 | 1.946 | 1.901 | 1.853 | 1.803 | 1.749 |
| | 27 | 2.204 | 2.132 | 2.056 | 1.974 | 1.930 | 1.884 | 1.836 | 1.785 | 1.731 |
| | 28 | 2.190 | 2.118 | 2.041 | 1.959 | 1.915 | 1.869 | 1.820 | 1.769 | 1.714 |
| | 29 | 2.177 | 2.105 | 2.028 | 1.945 | 1.901 | 1.854 | 1.806 | 1.754 | 1.698 |
| | 30 | 2.165 | 2.092 | 2.015 | 1.932 | 1.887 | 1.841 | 1.792 | 1.740 | 1.684 |
| | 40 | 2.077 | 2.004 | 1.925 | 1.839 | 1.793 | 1.744 | 1.693 | 1.637 | 1.577 |
| | 60 | 1.993 | 1.917 | 1.836 | 1.748 | 1.700 | 1.649 | 1.594 | 1.534 | 1.467 |
| | 120 | 1.911 | 1.834 | 1.751 | 1.659 | 1.608 | 1.554 | 1.495 | 1.429 | 1.352 |
| | $\infty$ | 1.831 | 1.752 | 1.666 | 1.571 | 1.517 | 1.459 | 1.394 | 1.318 | 1.221 |

# Hypothesis and Confidence Interval Summary and Formula Sheet

| Population Parameter | $H_0$ | $H_1$ | Conditions | Formula | $df$ |
|---|---|---|---|---|---|
| One Population Mean, $\mu$ | $\mu = 0$ <br> $\mu \le 0$ <br> $\mu \ge 0$ | $\mu \ne 0$ <br> $\mu > 0$ <br> $\mu < 0$ | Normal distribution <br> Large sample, $n>30$ <br> $\sigma$ known | $z = \dfrac{\bar{x}-\mu}{\sigma/\sqrt{n}}$ | None |
| One Population Mean, $\mu$ | $\mu = 0$ <br> $\mu \le 0$ <br> $\mu \ge 0$ | $\mu \ne 0$ <br> $\mu > 0$ <br> $\mu < 0$ | Normal distribution <br> Small sample, $n \le 30$ <br> $\sigma$ unknown | $t = \dfrac{\bar{x}-\mu}{s/\sqrt{n}}$ | $n-1$ |
| One Population Variance or standard deviation, $\sigma^2$ or $\sigma$ | $\sigma^2 = 0$ <br> $\sigma^2 \le 0$ <br> $\sigma^2 \ge 0$ | $\sigma^2 \ne 0$ <br> $\sigma^2 > 0$ <br> $\sigma^2 < 0$ | Variance or Standard Deviation <br> $\sigma^2$ or $\sigma$ | $\chi^2 = \dfrac{(n-1)s^2}{\sigma^2}$ | $n-1$ |
| One Population Correlation | $\rho = 0$ | $\rho \ne 0$ | Linear Correlation Test <br> Independent/Dependent | $t = \dfrac{r}{\sqrt{\dfrac{1-r^2}{n-2}}}$ | $df = n-2$ |
| One Population Proportion | $p = 0$ <br> $p \le 0$ <br> $p \ge 0$ | $p \ne 0$ <br> $p > 0$ <br> $p < 0$ | Binomial distribution | $z = \dfrac{\hat{p}-p}{\sqrt{\dfrac{pq}{n}}}$ | None |
| Two population means, $\mu_1 - \mu_2$ | $\mu_1 - \mu_2 = 0$ <br> $\mu_1 - \mu_2 \le 0$ <br> $\mu_1 - \mu_2 \ge 0$ | $\mu_1 - \mu_2 \ne 0$ <br> $\mu_1 - \mu_2 > 0$ <br> $\mu_1 - \mu_2 < 0$ | Normal distribution <br> Large samples, $n>30$ <br> Independent <br> $\sigma_1$ and $\sigma_2$ known | $z = \dfrac{(\bar{x}_1-\bar{x}_2)-(\mu_1-\mu_2)}{\sqrt{(\sigma_1^2/n_1)+(\sigma_2^2/n_2)}}$ | None |
| Two population means, $\mu_1 - \mu_2$ | $\mu_1 - \mu_2 = 0$ <br> $\mu_1 - \mu_2 \le 0$ <br> $\mu_1 - \mu_2 \ge 0$ | $\mu_1 - \mu_2 \ne 0$ <br> $\mu_1 - \mu_2 > 0$ <br> $\mu_1 - \mu_2 < 0$ | Independent <br> Small samples, $n \le 30$ <br> $\sigma_1$ and $\sigma_2$ unknown (Pooled) <br> Assumed $\sigma_1 = \sigma_2$ | $t = \dfrac{(\bar{x}_1-\bar{x}_2)-(\mu_1-\mu_2)}{\sqrt{\dfrac{(n_1-1)s_1^2+(n_2-1)s_2^2}{n_1+n_2-2}}\sqrt{\dfrac{1}{n_1}+\dfrac{1}{n_2}}}$ | $n_1 + n_2 - 2$ |
| Two population proportions, $p_1 - p_2$ | $p_1 - p_2 = 0$ <br> $p_1 - p_2 \le 0$ <br> $p_1 - p_2 \ge 0$ | $p_1 - p_2 \ne 0$ <br> $p_1 - p_2 > 0$ <br> $p_1 - p_2 < 0$ | Normal distribution <br> Large samples, $n>30$ <br> Independent | $z = \dfrac{\hat{p}_1-\hat{p}_2}{\sqrt{\dfrac{pq}{n_1}+\dfrac{pq}{n_2}}}$ | None |
| Two population means, $\mu_d$ | $\mu_d = 0$ <br> $\mu_d \le 0$ <br> $\mu_d \ge 0$ | $\mu_d \ne 0$ <br> $\mu_d > 0$ <br> $\mu_d < 0$ | Dependent samples <br> Paired observations | $t = \dfrac{\bar{d}-\mu_d}{s_d/\sqrt{n}}$ | $n-1$ |

| | | | | | |
|---|---|---|---|---|---|
| Two population variances or standard deviations $\sigma^2$ or $\sigma$ | $\sigma_1^2 = \sigma_2^2$ $\sigma_1^2 \le \sigma_2^2$ $\sigma_1^2 \ge \sigma_2^2$ | $\sigma_1^2 \ne \sigma_2^2$ $\sigma_1^2 > \sigma_2^2$ $\sigma_1^2 < \sigma_2^2$ | Variance or Standard Deviation, $\sigma^2$ or $\sigma$ | $F = \dfrac{s_1^2}{s_2^2}$ | $df_n = n_n - 1$ $df_d = n_d - 1$ |
| Multinomial Goodness of Fit GOF | $P_1 = ..., p_2 =$ | At least one of the proportions is not equal to the value claimed | Fixed number of independent trials, more than two possible outcomes, probability for each outcome remains constant on all trials and all outcomes have a sum of 1.0 | $\chi^2 = \sum \dfrac{(O-E)^2}{E}$ | $df = k - 1$ |
| Contingency Tables/Crosstab | Variable 1 and Variable 2 are independent | Variable 1 and Variable 2 are dependent | Matrix | $\chi^2 = \sum \dfrac{(O-E)^2}{E}$ | $df = (r-1)(c-1)$ |
| ANOVA | $\mu_1 = \mu_2 = \mu_3$ | The means are not equal | At least three population means, normally distributed population, standard deviations of the population must be equal and samples must be independent. | $F = \dfrac{MS_B}{MS_w}$ | $df_n = k-1$ $df_d = N-k$ |

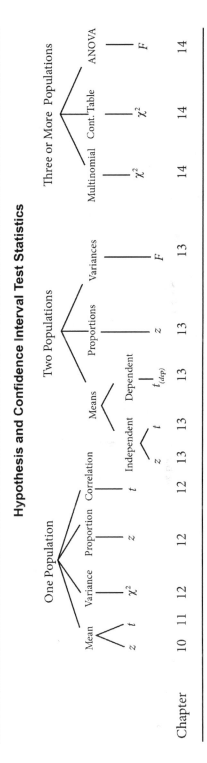

**Hypothesis and Confidence Interval Test Statistics**

# APPENDIX B:
## *GLOSSARY OF TERMS*

**Addition theorem for two events:** Adding the elements in A to those in B and subtracting the overlap so the elements are counted only once. The addition theorem for two events is $P(A \cup B) = P(A) + P(B) - P(A \cap B)$.

**Alternative hypothesis:** A statement that the value of the population parameter is different from that specified by the null hypothesis. It carries the burden of proof. It is denoted by $H_1$ or $H_a$.

**Analysis of variance (ANOVA):** A method of testing three or more means that focuses on analyzing the variance within and across the samples. $H_0 : \mu_1 = \mu_2 = \mu_3 \ldots$

**Bar chart:** A graph that displays discrete and continuous data for any level of measurement.

**Binomial probability distribution:** A distribution of a discrete random variable that has only two possible outcomes. The chance of one thing happening is often asked. By dividing the outcomes in only two categories, a binomial distribution usually results. For example a two-group classification of Catholic or non-Catholic represents a binomial random variable.

**Bivariate analysis:** A technique for describing the relationship between two variables.

**Branches:** Each ordered pair of a sample space illustrated in a tree diagram represents a branch of the tree. Each branch can be numbered.

**Cells:** The outcomes of a variable are overlapped with the outcomes of another variable. The overlaps are referred to as cells.

**Central limit theorem:** Applied to sampling distributions approaching the normal distribution, where the mean of the sample means equals the population mean, and the standard deviation of the sample means is the standard error.

**Chi-square distribution, $\chi 2$ :** A distribution representing variances of one population. Chi is a Greek letter written as $\chi$ and pronounced as "ki" in kite. The square represents the square of the variance, is skewed to the right, and contains only nonnegative values.

**Cluster sampling:** A technique that limits sampling to a few subsets of the population considered to be representative of the population.

**Complementary sets:** The complementary set of set $A$ is the set of all elements in the universal set that are not in set $A$. The complementary set of $A$ is denoted by $A'$.

**Conditional probability:** The probability of the second event is dependent on the conditions of the first event: $P(A \mid B) = P(A \cap B)/P(B)$.

**Confidence interval:** A technique for estimating a population parameter from sample statistics given a specified level of confidence. The confidence level is typically set at 90%, 95%, or 99% also known as $1 - \alpha$.

**Contingency table:** Also known as a cross-tabulation, or crosstab; a table that represents the relationships of two variables and their events. The outcomes of a variable are overlapped with the outcomes of another variable. The overlaps are referred to as cells.

**Continuous random variable:** A variable that describes a measurement. It can take on an infinite number of values. When describing intervals, there is an infinite number of possible values that a continuous random variable can take on in the interval. It often describes a measurement between two designated points.

**Critical value:** The first value of the critical region, which will be used to compare with the calculated test statistic.

**Cumulative frequency distribution:** A count of the frequencies or relative proportions of a value to all preceding counts.

**Data:** The value of a variable associated with one element of the population or sample or the set of values of a variable for each of the elements of the population or sample.

**Degrees of freedom:** The number of values in a sample that are independent of others. This number determines which distribution represents a particular population. Most test statistics require $n - 1$ degrees of freedom: $df = n - 1$.

**Dependent variable $y$:** The variable that is explained or predicted by the independent variable or variables.

**Discrete random variable:** A variable that assumes a numerical value for each outcome or element of the sample space, represented by a capital letter such as $X$, $Y$, or $Z$.

**Discrete probability function:** Any mathematical formula that allows the calculation of the probability for each *x* cited. It represents a probability distribution.

**Empty set:** A set with no elements. An empty set is represented by $\varphi$.

**Event:** Any set or subset of outcomes in a sample space. Each outcome is known as an element of the event.

**Experiment:** A planned activity that generates a set of data.

**Experimental probabilities:** Also known as empirical or observational; the observed proportion of times an event occurs in a series of similar experiments, denoted by *P′*.

***F* test distribution:** A test or estimate for the equality of the variances from two populations. *F*, like Chi-square, represents variances, is skewed to the right, and contains only nonnegative values.

**Fail to reject the null hypothesis:** The decision that must be made if the calculated value of a test statistic falls in the non-critical region or if the *P*-value is less than or equal to alpha.

**Frequency distribution:** A distribution providing a simple count of data in terms of the number or percentage for each value of a variable.

**Grouped frequency distribution:** A frequency distribution where values are collapsed into groups or classes.

**Histogram:** A special type of bar chart displaying continuous data at the interval or ordinal levels.

**Hypothesis testing (classical approach):** The process of testing and deciding whether to reject hypotheses. This process follows six steps. First, state the hypotheses. Second, establish test criteria. Third, calculate the test statistic. Fourth, place calculated value on distribution curve or find the *P*-value. Fifth, make a decision. Sixth, interpret the results.

**Hypothesis testing (*P*-value):** Also called prob-value, the smallest level of significance for the sample test statistic at which it becomes significant, provided the null hypothesis is true. *P* is considered significant when it is less than or equal to the alpha also known as the type I error. (The six steps are very much like those of the classical approach.)

**Independent variable *x*:** The variable that predicts change in the dependent variable *y*.

**Inferential statistics:** A discipline in which population information is predicted from a sample. Decisions about various hypotheses may lead to accepting or discarding policies, behavior, and even theories.

**Intersection:** For two sets $A$ and $B$, the set of elements that are in both $A$ and $B$. It is the area where two sets overlap. The intersection is denoted by $A \cap B$. The probability is $P(A \cap B) = P(A) / P(B \mid A)$.

**Interval-level measurements:** Measurements whose values are ordered and have measurable differences, such as temperature.

**Joint probability:** The probability that two events happen at the same time: $P(A \cap B) = P(A) / P(B \mid A)$.

**Law of large numbers:** A law stating that as the number of times an experiment is repeated, the observed probability will approach the theoretical probability.

**Level of confidence:** The probability that a parameter is contained in the confidence interval established around a sample statistic. It is also known as a confidence coefficient and is $1 - \alpha$.

**Level of significance:** The probability of committing a type I error (the probability of rejecting the $H_0$ when it is actually true). The level of significance is represented by the Greek letter $\alpha$ (alpha) and is usually set as .025, .05, .01, or .10.

**Mean:** A measure of central tendency that describes the average response when the data are summed and divided by the total number of elements or observations. The symbol for the mean of a sample is $\bar{x}$; for a population, the symbol is $\mu$.

**Mean-square interaction:** Determined by dividing the sum of square interaction by the degrees of freedom for the interaction.

**Mean square for the within (error):** Also referred to as error or residual; determined by dividing the sum of squares for within by the degrees of freedom for within.

**Mean for a frequency distribution:** Whether data are grouped or ungrouped, $\bar{x} = \Sigma x f / \Sigma f$.

**Measure of central tendency:** A locator of the center of a set of data. A measure of central tendency is a single number that describes the general order or magnitude of a set of data. The more common measure of central tendency is the mean, often known as the average.

**Measures of dispersion:** The degree to which observations vary from the average. The variations can be calculated with a measure of dispersion. The larger the measure of dispersion, the more variability exists. If no variation exists, the measure of dispersion is 0.

**Measures of position:** Comparing data within one population or between different populations. The standard score, or $z$-score, is a measure of position that allows data from the same or different populations to be compared. Proportions and quartile descriptions are also measures of position within one population.

**Median:** The middle value of a set of data when the data are arranged in order. Half the data values are above and half are below the median. The position at which the median is located in a set of data is calculated by $(n + 1)/2$.

**Mode:** The most commonly occurring observed value in a set of data.

**Multinomial experiment:** Similar to a binomial experiment but with three or more outcomes. An example is the five (or more) categories of response for the variable religious preference. The Chi-square statistic is a common measure of a multinomial experiment.

**Multiplication theorem for two dependent events:** Requires the multiplication of the probability of event A with the conditional probability of event $B$: $P(A \cap B) = P(A) \cdot P(B \mid A)$.

**Multivariate analysis:** A technique for describing the relationship between three or more variables. An example of multivariate analysis is describing the age, sex, and religion of students.

**Mutually exclusive:** When two events cannot happen together. There is no intersection.

**Nominal-level measurements:** Also known as attribute or categorical measurements; variables whose values describe attributes that do not imply magnitude or value, such as marital status.

**Nominal probability distribution:** A probability distribution describing continuous random variables. The distribution is plotted as a bell-shaped curve that is symmetric, with the mean, mode, and median in the center. It is also known as the normal curve.

**Null hypotheses:** A statement that there is no difference between the hypothesized value of the population parameter and a sample statistic. It carries the benefit of the doubt. It is denoted by $H_O$ and must contain an equal sign in the form of $=$, $\geq$, or $\leq$.

**One-tailed test:** When a critical region falls to only one side of a probability distribution. This occurs when the $H_1$ involves less than (<) or greater than (>).

**Ordered pairs:** A pair of numbers in which a value for a variable $X$ is given with its corresponding value for variable $Y$.

**Ordinal-level measurement:** Measurements whose values can be ranked or ordered from lowest to highest, such as military rankings, alphabetizing a seating chart, arranging people according to weight or height, or positioning military leaders according to rank.

**Parameter:** A numerical characteristic of an entire population. Parameters are usually represented by Greek letters such as $\mu$ or $\sigma$.

**Pearson's product moment correlation coefficient:** A measure of the strength and direction of the relationship between two interval or ratio variables. The sample notation is $r$. The value $r$ ranges from -1 to 1.

**Percentile:** A measure of position that divides data into 100 equal parts. Each percentile is written as $P$ with a subscript indicating the value of the percentile, such as $P_{20}$.

**Pie chart:** Also known as a circle graph; a circular diagram displaying nominal-level discrete variables and representing relative proportions.

**Point estimate:** The sample statistic used to estimate the population parameter. When estimating the parameter mean ($\mu$), the point estimate is the sample statistic ($\bar{x}$).

**Population:** A universal set of all individuals, objects, or measurements whose properties are being analyzed.

**Probabilities:** Educated guesses about what might happen or what has happened, based on information that has been obtained or observed.

**Quartiles:** A measure of position that divides data into four equal parts. The first quarter is denoted by $Q_1$, the second, or mid-quartile, by $Q_2$, and the third by $Q_3$.

**Random sample:** A sample in which every element of the population has an equal probability of being included in the sample.

**Range:** A measure of dispersion that identifies the difference between the lowest and highest value also known as the maximum and minimum values. Range = Max − Min.

**Ratio-level measurements:** Measurements whose values can be ordered, have measurable differences, and have a zero starting point that implies an absence of the measurement, such as age.

**Regression line:** Also known as the line of best fit; a straight line predicting values of $y$ from values of $x$. The bivariate regression line is $\hat{y} = a + bx$.

**Reject the null hypothesis:** A decision that must be made if the calculated value of a test statistic falls in the critical region.

**Relative frequency:** The proportion of the frequency of a value to the total number of occurrences.

**Repeated sampling:** When several samples are obtained from the same population.

**Replacement:** During an experiment, when an element is withdrawn and then replaced in the original sample space. Each event with replacement is independent. Events without replacement are dependent.

**Sample:** A subset of the population.

**Sample space:** The set of all possible outcomes of an experiment. The format for listing the sample space is $S = \{(\ ), (\ ), (\ ), \ldots\}$.

**Sampling distribution of the mean:** The probability distribution of the values of the sample mean from all possible samples of the same size.

**Sampling error:** An error attributed to the chance that the elements chosen for the sample are not representative of the population.

**Sampling mean:** When random samples of size $n$ are drawn from a population, the expected value of the mean of the sample means is the population mean. $\mu_{\bar{x}}$.

**Slope:** A value that describes how a regression line ascends descends through the data. The slope describes the unit change in $y$ for every unit increase in $x$.

**Spearman's rank correlation coefficient:** A measure of the strength and direction of the relationship between two ordinal variables. The notation is $r_s$. The value $r_s$ ranges from -1 to 1.

**Special addition rule:** Used when sets or events are mutually exclusive. Events that are mutually exclusive cannot happen together. The rule for addition of two mutually exclusive events is $P(A \cup B) = P(A) + P(B)$.

**Standard deviation:** The square root of the average squared deviations from the mean. The standard deviation is the square-root of the variance. The symbol for the standard deviation of a sample is $s$, and the symbol for a population standard deviation is $\sigma$.

**Standard score, z-score:** A measure of position based on the number of standard deviations that a given value is from the mean.

**Statistic:** A numerical characteristic of a sample. Statistics are usually represented by English letters such as $\bar{x}$ or $s$.

**Stratified random sample:** A simple random sample taken from each subset or strata of the population.

**Subjective probabilities:** Educated guesses based on personal judgment.

**Subsets:** Also known as "events", these are usually represented by capital letters such as $A$.

**Systematic error:** An error in the process of selecting elements in the sample, it is not corrected by increasing sample size.

**Systematic sample:** Accomplished by choosing every $k^{th}$ element after having begun by choosing the first element randomly.

***t* distribution:** A probability distribution that depicts sampling means. It has several characteristics similar to the normal $z$ distribution. The $t$ distribution is symmetric, its mean is 0, and its variance is greater than 1, but it decreases toward 1 as $n$ increases.

**Test criteria:** Criteria allowing a researcher to determine the level of significance, or the type I error. They also determine the exact test to be performed that will challenge the null hypothesis and the values of a test that may result in its rejection.

**Test statistic:** The random variable used to calculate and compare the sample statistic to the hypothesized population parameter. The test statistics used in this book are $z$, $t$, $\chi 2$ and $F$.

**Theoretical probabilities:** Probabilities determined when all sample points are equally likely to occur. A theoretical probability is denoted by $P$.

**Tree diagram:** A way of illustrating sample space using branches to represent each possible outcome or ordered pair.

**Two-tailed test:** When a critical region is divided with half of its area on both ends of the probability distribution. This situation occurs when $H_1$ indicates a parameter is not equal to a hypothesized value such as $H_1: \mu \neq 25$.

**Union:** For two sets $A$ and $B$, the set of all elements that are in $A$ or $B$ or in both. Union is denoted by $A \cup B$.

**Univariate analysis:** A technique for describing a single variable.

**Universal set:** Also known as population; the set of all elements that occur in an overall frame of reference. All other sets occurring within its boundaries are subsets of the universal set.

**Value:** One of the categories or responses of a variable.

**Variable:** A characteristic about objects, events, or individuals that has or can be assigned a numerical value.

**Variance:** The average squared deviations of values from their mean. The symbol for a variance for a sample is $s^2$, and the symbol for a population variance is $\sigma^2$.

**Venn diagrams:** A pictorial illustration of sets or subsets of a sample space. A rectangle usually represents the sample space.

**$y$-intercept:** As a component of the regression line, a description of the predicted $y$ value when $x$ is zero.

# APPENDIX C:

## ANSWER KEY FOR SELECT QUESTIONS

## Chapter 1 in Review

1.1      a. discrete   b. discrete   c. continuous   d. continuous   e. continuous

1.3      a. ratio   b. interval   c. nominal   d. ordinal   e. ratio

1.5      a. ratio   b. ratio   c. ordinal   d. ordinal

1.7      a. car-jacking in U.S.   b. sample 5 major cities.   c. sample mean 15%
         d. population mean 13%.   e. 5

1.9      a. causes of death for men   b. 5,000 men   c. 5000   d. causes of death

1.11     a. ordinal   b. ratio   c. ratio   d. ratio   e. ratio

1.13     a. road congestion   b. ridership   c. continuous   d. number of trips
         e. discrete

1.15     True, True, False, False, True

1.17     a. nominal/discrete b. ratio/continuous c. ratio/continuous
         d. ratio/continuous e. ratio/discrete

1.19     systematic, stratified, random, random

## Chapter 2 in Review

2.1

| Branch | Frequency | Relative Frequency | Cumulative Frequency | Cumulative Relative Freq |
|--------|-----------|--------------------|----------------------|--------------------------|
| Army | 55 | .275 | 55 | .275 |
| Navy | 60 | .300 | 115 | .575 |
| Air Force | 40 | .200 | 155 | .775 |
| Marine | 45 | .225 | 200 | 1.000 |
| Total | 200 | 1.000 | | |

2.3

| Music Preference | Frequency | Relative Frequency | Cumulative Frequency | Cumulative Relative Freq |
|---|---|---|---|---|
| Pop | 18 | .257 | 18 | .257 |
| Classical | 12 | .171 | 30 | .428 |
| Country | 17 | .243 | 47 | .671 |
| Rock | 10 | .143 | 57 | .814 |
| Oldies | 13 | .186 | 70 | 1.000 |

2.5  Pie Chart

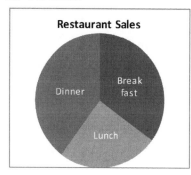

2.7

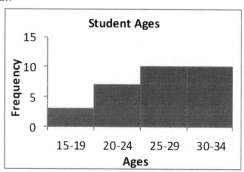

2.9

| Wages | *f* |
|---|---|
| 7 - 7.99 | 2 |
| 8 - 8.99 | 8 |
| 9 - 9.99 | 5 |
| 10 - 10.99 | 3 |
| 11 - 11.99 | 2 |
| Total | 20 |

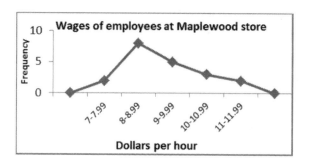

2.11

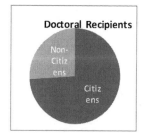

2.13

| Exam Scores | *f* | *relative f* | *cum rel f* |
|---|---|---|---|
| 40 - 49 | 1 | .025 | .025 |
| 50 - 59 | 2 | .050 | .075 |
| 60 - 69 | 8 | .200 | .275 |
| 70 - 79 | 16 | .400 | .675 |
| 80 - 89 | 6 | .150 | .825 |
| 90 - 99 | 5 | .125 | 1.000 |
| Total | 40 | 1.000 | |

2.15

| Salaries | $f$ |
|----------|-----|
| 30 - 39.9 | 4 |
| 40 - 49.9 | 5 |
| 50 - 59.9 | 3 |
| Total | 12 |

2.17

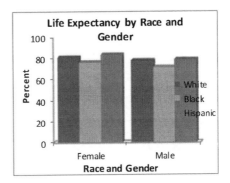

2.19    a. 2    b. 20    c. 9    d. 5

2.21

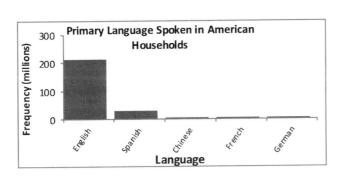

2.23

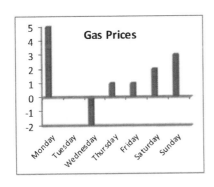

2.25

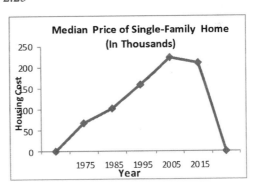

## Chapter 3 in Review

Answers are based on TI-83/84 calculator and may be different if doing by hand.

3.1    $\bar{x}$ = 58.2, s = 12.001

3.3    $\bar{x}$ = 74.76, $s^2$ = 137.77, sx = 11.737, mark = 64.5,  MED = class 4 or 74.5, mode = 74.5.

3.5    a. $i = 2.5, Q_1 = 26$, b. $i = 6.5, Q_3 = 28.9$, c. $i = 5, P_{60} = 28.2$, d. $i = 2$,
       $P_{20} = 24.5$

3.7    $\bar{x} = 26.05, sx = 4.14$

3.9    $\bar{x} = 209.10, sx = 7.829$

3.11   $\bar{x} = 35.78, MED = 35.6, mode = 30.8, range = 20.6, sx = 5.868, s^2 = 34.433,$
       $Q_1 = 30.8, Q_2 = 40, P_{40} = 32.3, P_{79} = 40.8$

3.13   $\bar{x} = 9.643, sx = 4.121$

3.15   $z_{sam} = -.4, z_{Alauna} = 1.5, z_{Ike} = 1$, Alauna is better

3.17   $z_{lead} = 1.27, z_{chlorine} = 1$, Lead is Higher

3.19   $\bar{x} = 568.5, sx = 75.02$

3.21   $z = -.67$

3.23   $\bar{x} = 27.833, sx = 13.72$

3.25   $z_A = 1, z_B = -.54$.

3.27   68% = (4.5 to 7.5), 95% = (3 to 9), 99% = (1.5 to 10.5)

3.29   95% = (1.5 to 7.5)

## Chapter 4 in Review

Answers are based on TI-83/84 calculator and may be different if doing by hand.

4.1    $r = .958$, Strong positive, $\hat{y} = -4.064 + 1.056x, \hat{y} = 22.336, \hat{y} = 27.616$

4.3    $r = .638, \hat{y} = 190.55 + 2.94x$, As contributions go up \$1 million, assets go up
       \$2.94 Billion, $\hat{y} = 293.45, \hat{y} = 322.85$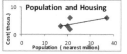

4.5    $r = .627, \hat{y} = .55 + .15x$, plot,
       $\hat{y} = 2.8$ thousand, $\hat{y} = 3.55$ thousand

4.7    $r = .886$

4.9    $\hat{y} = 18.269$

4.11   Pay increases an average of 30 dollars as production increases 1 automobile

4.13   False, False, False, False, False

4.15   $r = .835$

4.17   -1.0 means that there is a perfect negative relationship.

4.19   $\hat{y} = 18.598$

4.21   a. Plot  b. Interpretation: Strong, positive relationship

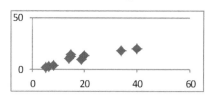

4.23   $r = -.943, \hat{y} = 4.199 + -.152x, \hat{y} = 3.290, x = .7888$ or rounded to 8

## Chapter 5 in Review

5.1    $S = \{(H), (T)\}$

5.3    $S = \{(F), (SO), (J), (SE)\}$

5.5                                                              5.7

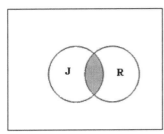                                             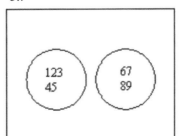

5.9    a. Tree

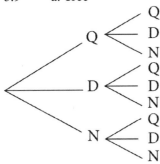

       b. various answers…3 events

       c. $S = \{(QQ),(QN),(QD),(DQ),(DD),(DN)(NQ)(ND)(NN)\}$

5.11   True

5.13   a. Mutually exclusive    b. Non-mutually exclusive

       c. Non-mutually exclusive    d. Non-mutually exclusive

5.15   No

5.17                                                   5.19

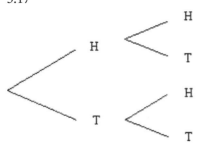                                   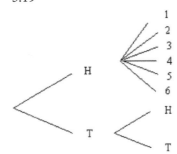

5.21   $S = \{(F, F, F), (M, M, M)\}$

5.23   $2^5 = 32$

5.25    a. 5! = 120 b. 4! = 24

5.27    8

## Chapter 6 in Review

6.1    $P(\text{Business}) = .625$, no

6.3    $P(\text{Take Stats} \cap \text{Pass}) = .6$

6.5    $P(\text{Postal} \cap \text{Defense}) = 0$, or $\varphi$

6.7    $P(F|\text{Male}) = .3$, $P(M \cap U) = .25$, $P(F|U) = 0$, $P(\text{Favors U Female}) = .65$.

6.9    $P(A \cap B) = 0$, $P(A|B) = 0$, $P(A \cup B) = .7$, No

6.11    $P(\text{Heads}) = .5$

6.13    $P(B \mid B) = 1.0$

6.15    Tree, $P(A \text{ and } A) = .152$, $P(P \text{ and } P) = .318$, $P(A|P) = .455$, $P(P \text{ and } A) = .848$

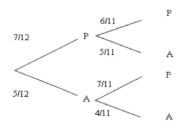

6.17    $P(\text{Rep}) = .40$, $P(\text{Dem} \cap \text{Yes}) = .50$, $P(\text{No}) = .22$, $P(\text{Rep}') = .6$, $P(\text{No}|\text{Dem}) = .17$

6.19    $P(A \cup B) = .7$, $P(A|B) = .2$, $P(B') = .5$, $P(A') = .7$

6.21    False, False, False, False, False

6.23    $P(\text{Yes}) = .6$, $P(\text{Suburb}) = .5$, $P(\text{Suburb} \cap \text{Yes}) = .4$, $P(\text{City}') = .64$, $P(\text{No}|\text{city}) = .611$

6.25    Tree, $P(N \text{ and } N) = .133$, $P(P \text{ and } N) = .356$, $P(P \mid P) = .333$

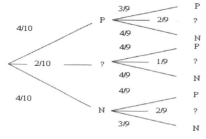

## Chapter 7 in Review

All answers are based on Binomial pdf/cdf functions on the TI 83/84 calculators.

7.1     Yes, No, No, Yes

7.3     $P(x = 4) = pdf(5, .4, 4) = .0768$

7.5     $P(x = 50) = pdf(50, .8, 50) = 0+$,   $P(x = 40) = pdf(50, .8, 40) = .1398$
        $P(x = 15) = pdf(50, .2, 15) = .0299$, $\mu = 40$, $\sigma = 2.828$

7.7     a. $P(x = 20) = pdf(20, .2, 20) = 0+$,   b. $P(x \le 2) = cdf(20\ .2, 2) = .206$,
        c. $P(x = 0) = pdf = .012$,   d. $\mu = 4$, $\sigma = 1.789$

7.9     $P(x = 25) = pdf(50, .7, 25) = .0014$, $P(x \ge 25) = 1 - cdf(50, 7, 30) = .9991$,
        $P(x \le 30) = pdf(50, 7, 30) = .0848$, $P(x = 50) = pdf(50, .7, 50) = 0+$, $\mu = 15$,
        $\sigma = 3.24$

7.11    $P(x = 3) = pdf(6, .36, 3) = .245$, $P(x = 3) = pdf(6, .25, 3) = .132$, $\mu = 2.16$, $\sigma = 1.176$

7.13    $P(x \le 1)\ cdf(10, .2, 1) = .375$, $P(x = 0) = pdf = .107$, $P(x = 10) = pdf(10, .8, 10) =$
        $.107$, $P(x \ge 8) = 1 - cdf(10, .8, 7) = .677$, $\mu = 2$, $\sigma = 1.265$

7.15    $P(x = 6) = pdf(12, .6, 6) = .177$, $P(x = 0) = pdf = 0+$, $P(x \le 8) = cdf(12, .6, 8) =$
        $.774$, $P(x \ge 11)\ 1 - cdf(12, .6, 10) = .0196$, $\mu = 7.2$

7.17    Distribution: $P(x = 0) = .118$, $P(x = 1) = .303$, $P(x = 2) = .324$, $P(x = 3) = .185$,
        $P(x = 4) = .060$, $P(x = 5) = .010$, $P(x = 6) = .001$

7.19    $P(x \ge 6) = 1 - cdf(10, .64, 6) = .729$

7.21    $P(x = 6) = pdf(8, .28, 6) = .006$, $P(x = 6)\ pdf(8, .47, 6) = .085$,
        $P(x = 6) = pdf(8, .25, 6) = .004$, $\mu = 3.76$, $\sigma = 1.41$

7.23    $\mu = 17$, $\sigma = 1.60$

7.25    False, False, True, True, True

## Chapter 8 in Review

All answers based on Normal Distribution Table/Chart. Slight differences exist if using the function keys on the TI83/84 calculators.

8.1     $P(.4678), P(.4222), P(.0557), P(.3133), P(.4999), P(.4515)$

8.3     $P(.0250), P(.1685), P(.0013), P(.9750), P(.6879), P(.8413)$

8.5     $P(.5000)$

8.7     a. 2.05,   b. .02,   c. 3.49,   d. 1.64

8.9     a. 2.33,   b. 1.96,   c. -1.645,   d. -2.575

8.11     $P(11 < x < 12) = .2048\ z = 11$ and $.67$

8.13    $P(50 < x < 54) = .3108\ z = -.4$ and $.4$, $P(x > 54) = .3446\ z = .4$,
        $P(x < 54) = .6554\ z = .4$, $P(x < 50) = .3446\ z = -.4$

8.15    $P(x > 18) = .2743$, $z = .6$, $P(x > 12.5) = .5915$, $z = -.5$, $P(x < 10) = .1587\ z = -1$,
        $P(14 < x < 16 = .1586\ z = -.2$ and $.2$

8.17   $P(x>53.5) = .5000$ $z = 0$, $P(x < 50) = .2611$ $z = -.64$, $P(x> 60) = .1190$ $z = 1.18$,
       $P(54<x< 60) = .3451$ $z = .09$ and $1.18$

8.19   $P(x < 2)$ $z = 1.54$ $P = .0618$

8.21   $P(x > 3000)$ $z = -.80$, $P = .7881$

8.23   $x = 4.94$ or 5 days

8.25   $x = 2462.48$

8.27   $P(x > 56.5) = .2206$ using binomial approximation

8.29   $P(x > 15.5)$ $P = .0336$ mean $= 10$, stand. dev. $= 3$ using binomial
       approximation

## Chapter 9 in Review

All answers based on Tables/Charts. Slight differences exist if using the function keys on the TI-83/84 calculators.

9.1    Yes

9.3    a. $P = .3944$,  b. $P = .3944$,  c. $P = .2344$,  d. $P = .2486$,  e. $P = .4991$,
       f. $P = .0673$

9.5    a. $P(\bar{x} = 70)$ $z = -2.03$, $P = .4788$,   b. $P(\bar{x} = 90)$ $z = .20$, $P = .0793$,
       c. $P(70 < \bar{x} < 90)$ $z = -2.03$ and $.20$, $P = .5581$, d. $P(90 < \bar{x} < 100)$ $z = .20$ and
       $1.32$, $P = .3273$

9.7    $P(\bar{x} < 5)$ $z = 1.20$, $P = .8849$

9.9    $P(\bar{x} = 25)$ $z = 9.03$, $P = .4999$

9.11   $\mu \bar{x} = 3.5$, $\sigma \bar{x} = 1.2$, $P(\bar{x} < 10)$ $z = 1.25$,  $P = .8944$

9.13   $P(\bar{x} < 40)$ $z = -3.09$, $P = .001$

9.15   a. $P(x > 200)$ $z = 1.76$, $P = .0392$,  b. $P(\bar{x} >200)$ $z = 9.64$, $P = .0001$,
       c. Because the first asks for the probability of one employee, the second asks
          for that of a sample.

9.17   a. $\mu_{\bar{x}} = 12.5$,  b. $\sigma_{\bar{x}} = .73$,  c. $P(\bar{x} >12.5)$ $z = 0$, $P = .5000$,
       d. $P(\bar{x} < 12.5)$ $z = 0$, $P = .5000$,
       e. $P(\bar{x} < 13)$ $z = .68$, $P = .7517$,  f. $P(\bar{x} >13)$ $z = .68$, $P = .2483$

9.19   a. $\mu_{\bar{x}} = 8.9$,  b. $\sigma_{\bar{x}} = .365$,  c. $P(\bar{x} >9.4)$ $z = 1.58$, $P = .0571$

9.21   True, False, False, False

9.23   a. $P(x >1.5)$ $z = .4$, $P = .3446$,  b. $P(x > .5)$ $z = -1.6$, $P = .9452$,
       c. $P(1.1 < \bar{x} < 1.4)$ $z = -1.26$ and $z = .63$ $P = .6319$,
       d. $P(1.4 <\bar{x} < 1.5)$ $z = .63$ and $z = 1.26$ $P = .1605$,
       e. $P(\bar{x} < 1.3)$ $z = 0$, $P = .5000$,

9.25   a. $P(x > 400)$ $z = .4$, $P = .3446$,  b. $P(x < 400)$ $z = .4$,  $P = .6554$,
       c. $P(\bar{x} > 350)$ $z = 0$, $P = .5000$,

d. $P(400 < \bar{x} < 425)$ $z = 2.19$ and $z = 3.29$, $P = .0138$,

9.27    $P(\bar{x} > 4)$ $z = -3.87$, $P = .9999$

9.29    $P(\bar{x} > 23)$ $z = .82$, $P = .2061$

## Chapter 10 in Review

**All answers based on TI 83/84 Calculator. Slight differences exist if using table**

10.1    a. 2.327, b. 1.28, c. -1.96, d. -1.645

10.3    a. $H_O: \mu \geq 25$, $H_I: \mu < 25$; b. $H_O: \mu \geq 30$, $H_I: \mu < 30$;
        c. $H_O: \mu \leq 175{,}000$, $H_I: \mu > 175{,}000$; d. $H_O: \mu = 7.2$, $H_I: \mu \neq 7.2$;
        e. $H_O: \mu \leq 18{,}560$, $H_I: \mu > 18{,}560$

10.5    One-tailed right, Two-tailed , One-tailed right, One-tailed left, Two-tailed,
        One-tailed left

10.7    $H_O: \mu = 43853$, $H_I: \mu \neq 43853$,   $z = 2.817$, $P = .0048$, Reject null.

10.9    $H_O: \mu \leq 20$, $H_I: \mu > 20$, $z = 3.48$, $P = .0003$, Reject null.

10.11   Type I error: the bag really opens but was not approved.
        Type II error, the bag does not open but was approved.
        Type II error is more serious.

10.13   $E = (152 < \mu < 178)$

10.15   $H_O: \mu = 135$, $H_I: \mu \neq 135$, $z = -.87$, $P = .3830$, Fail to reject null.

10.17   $E = (8120 < \mu < 10080)$

10.19   False, True, False, False, True, False

10.21   $H_O: \mu \leq 71$, $H_I: \mu > 71$ $z = 7.07$, $P = 0+$, Reject null.

10.23   $H_O: \mu \leq 19$, $H_I: \mu > 19$, $z = 2.24$, $P = .0124$, Fail to reject null.

10.25   $H_O: \mu \leq 2{,}603$, $H_I: \mu > 2{,}603$, $z = 3.356$, $P = .0004$, Reject null.

## Chapter 11 in Review

All answers based on TI 83/84 Calculator. Slight differences exist if using table

11.1    a. 2.462, b. 2.228, c. -2.179, d. -1.753

11.3    a. $H_O: \mu \geq 200$, $H_I: \mu < 200$; b. $H_O: \mu \leq 280$, $H_I: \mu > 280$;
        c. $H_O: \mu \leq 199$, $H_I: \mu > 199$; d. $H_O: \mu = 440{,}000$, $H_I: \mu \neq 440{,}000$;
        e. $H_O: \mu \geq 125$, $H_I: \mu < 125$

11.5    a. $H_O: \mu = 395$, $H_I: \mu \neq 395$; b. $H_O: \mu \geq 123$, $H_I: \mu < 123$;
        c. $H_O: \mu \leq 135$, $H_I: \mu > 135$; d. $H_O: \mu = 130$, $H_I: \mu \neq 130$;
        e. $H_O: \mu \leq 110$, $H_I: \mu > 110$

11.7    $H_O: \mu = 71.355$, $H_I: \mu \neq 71.355$, $t = -12.605$, $P = .0002$, Reject null.

11.9    $H_O: \mu \leq 11{,}800$, $H_I: \mu > 11{,}800$, $t = .648$, $P = .2650$, fail to Reject null.

11.11   $H_O: \mu \leq 650$, $H_I: \mu > 650$, $t = 4.174$, $P = .0003$, Reject null.

11.13   $H_O: \mu \geq 4.1, H_I: \mu < 4.1, t = -5.111, P = .0+$, Reject null.

11.15   $H_O: \mu \geq 4, H_I: \mu < 4, t = -1.876, P = .0669$, fail to reject null.

11.17   $H_O: \mu \leq 527, H_I: \mu > 527, t = 1.918, P = .0341$, reject null.

11.19   $E = (84.719 < \mu < 97.681)$

11.21   False, True, False, False, True, False

11.23   $H_O: \mu \leq 78.50, H_I: \mu > 78.50, t = 3.913, P = .0002$, reject null.

11.25   $H_O: \mu \leq 100,000, H_I: \mu > 100,000, t = 3.975, P = .0004$, reject null.

11.27   $H_O: \mu = 150, H_I: \mu \neq 150, t = 5.002, P = 0+$, reject null.

## Chapter 12 in Review

All Chi-square and correlation answers based on tables, all proportion $z$-score answers are based on TI- 83/84 calculator.

12.1   a. 34.170, b. 5.991, c. 25.989, d. 7.962, e. 20.599, f. 51.172

12.3   a. 30.144 and 10.177, b. 11.071, c. 52.336 and 13.121, d. 11.345, e. ±2.060, f. ±1.753, g. ±2.771

12.5   a. $H_O: \sigma^2 \geq 7.62, H_I: \sigma^2 < 7.62$;  b. $H_O: \sigma = .75, H_I: \sigma \neq .75$;
      c. $H_O: \sigma^2 \leq 150, H_I: \sigma^2 > 150$; d. $H_O: p \leq 20, H_I: p > 20$;
      e. $H_O: p = .9, H_I: p \neq .9$;  f. $H_O: P = 0, H_{I:} P \neq 0$

12.7   $H_O: \sigma = 0.4, H_I: \sigma \neq 0.4, \chi2 = 32$, critical 32.357 and 71.420, est $P = .01x2 = .02$, reject null.

12.9   $H_O: \sigma \geq 3.1, H_I: \sigma < 3.1, \chi2 = 19.580$, critical 10.856, est $P = .1000$, fail to reject null.

12.11   $H_O: P = 0, H_{I:} P \neq 0$, using Critical $r$ table $r_6 = .917$ If calculated $t = 1.593$, critical ± 4.604, fail to reject null.

12.13   $H_O: \sigma = 31, H_I: \sigma \neq 31, \chi2 = 51.197$, critical 32.357 and 71.420, est. $P = .05x2 = .10$, fail to reject null.

12.15   $H_O: p \leq .446, H_I: p > .446, z = 1.65, P = .0495$ reject null.

12.17   $H_O: p \geq .64, H_I: p < .64, z = -.833, P = .2023$, fail to reject null.

12.19   $H_O: P = 0, H_I: P \neq 0, r = .377$ using Critical $r$ table $r_9 = .666$, calculated $t = 1.076, P = .3178$, Fail to reject null

12.21   $H_O: P = 0, H_O: P \neq 0, r = .943$ using Critical $r$ table $r_7 = .754$, calculated $t = -6.317, P = .0015$, reject null

12.23   $H_O: P = 0, H_I: P \neq 0$, using Critical $r$ table $r_{100} = .256$, calculated $t = 52.521$, critical ± 2.575, reject null.

12.25   $E = (740.611 \leq \sigma \leq 978.501)$

12.27   $E = (.956 \leq \sigma \leq 1.613)$

12.29    $E = (3.667 \leq \sigma^2 \leq 8.812)$

12.31    $H_O$: $\sigma \geq 1035$, $H_1$: $\sigma < 1035$, $\chi2 = 6.730$, critical 3.325. est. $P = .10$, fail to reject null.

12.33    $H_O$: $p \leq .82$, $H_1$: $p > .82$, $z = 4.049$, $P = 0+$, reject null.

12.35    $H_O$: $\rho = 0$, $H_1$: $\rho \neq 0$, $r = .945$ using Critical $r$ table $r_7 = .875$, calculated $t = 6.507$, $P = .0013$, Reject null.

## Chapter 13 in Review

All answers based on TI 83/84 Calculator. Slight differences exist if using tables.

13.1    a. $H_O$: $\mu - \mu = 0$, $H_1$: $\mu - \mu \neq 0$. b. $H_O$: $\sigma^2 = \sigma^2$, $H_1$: $\sigma^2 \neq \sigma^2$.

       c. $H_O$: $\sigma^2 = \sigma^2$, $H_1$: $\sigma^2 \neq \sigma^2$. d. $H_O$: $\mu_d \leq 10$, $H_1$: $\mu_d > 10$,

       e. $H_O$: $\sigma = \sigma$, $H_1$: $\sigma \neq \sigma$.

13.3    a. 3.179, b. 4.099, c. 2.703, d. 3.614, e. 5.802, f. 6.388

13.5    $H_O$: $\mu - \mu = 0$, $H_1$: $\mu - \mu \neq 0$, $z = 3.928$, $P = .00008$ or .0001, Reject null.

13.7    $H_O$: $\mu - \mu = 0$, $H_1$: $\mu - \mu \neq 0$, $z = .77$, $P = .4395$, Fail to reject null.

13.9    $H_O$: $\mu - \mu = 0$, $H_1$: $\mu - \mu \neq 0$, $t = 17.766$, $P = 0+$, Reject null.

13.11    $H_O$: $\mu - \mu = 0$, $H_1$: $\mu - \mu \neq 0$, $t = -3.537$, $P = .0006$, Reject null.

13.13    $H_O$: $\mu_d \leq 0$, $H_1$: $\mu_d > 0$, $t = 6.831$, $P = 0+$, Reject null.

13.15    $H_O$: $\sigma_1 = \sigma_2$, $H_1$: $\sigma_1 \neq \sigma_2$, F = 2.778, $P = .0095$, Reject null.

13.17    $H_O$: $\mu_d = 0$, $H_1$: $\mu_d \neq 0$, $t = 1.939$, $P = .1103$, Fail to reject null.

13.19    $H_O$: $\mu - \mu = 0$, $H_1$: $\mu - \mu \neq 0$, $t = -3.219$, $P = .0048$, Reject null.

13.21    $H_O$: $\sigma^2_1 = \sigma^2_2$, $H_1$: $\sigma^2_1 \neq \sigma^2_2$, F = 1.125, $P = .7570$, Fail to reject null.

13.23    $H_O$: $\mu - \mu = 0$, $H_1$: $\mu - \mu \neq 0$, $z = 1.50$, $P = .1348$, Fail to reject null.

13.25    $H_O$: $\mu - \mu \leq 0$, $H_1$: $\mu - \mu > 0$, $z = 3.727$, $P = 0+$, Reject null.

13.27    $H_O$: $p - p = 0$, $H_O$: $p - p \neq 0$, $z = -3.083$, $P = .0020$, Reject null.

13.29    $H_O$: $\sigma_1 = \sigma_2$, $H_1$ $\sigma_1 \neq \sigma_2$, F = 2.707, $P = .0005$, Reject null.

13.31    $H_O$: $p_1 - p_2 = 0$, $H_1$: $p_1 - p_2 \neq 0$, zprop = 4.36, $P = 0+$, Reject null

13.33    $H_O$: $p_1 - p_2 = 0$, $H_1$: $p_1 - p_2 \neq 0$, zprop = 11.87, $P = 0+$, Reject null.

## Chapter 14 in Review

All answers based on TI 83/84 Calculator. Slight differences exist if using tables.

14.1    12.592, 4.605, 39.364, 21.668

14.3    9.488, 16.013, 7.815, 9.236

14.5    $H_O$: Party and Occupation are Independent $\chi2 = 31.151$, $P = 0+$, Reject null.

14.7    $H_O$: $p_1 = .64$, $p_2 = .23$ $p_3 = .06$, $p_4 = .07$ GOF $\chi2 = 52.948$, $P = 0+$, Reject null.

14.9    $H_O$: Weight and Diet are Independent $\chi2 = 115.386$, $P = 0+$, Reject null.

14.11    $H_O$: $p_1 = .25$, $p_2 = .25$ $p_3 = .25$, $p_4 = .25$ GOF $\chi2 = 9.201$, $P = .0267$, Reject null.

14.13  a. True, b. False, c. True, d. False, e. True  f. False

14.15  False, False, True, False, True, False

14.17  $H_O: \mu_1 = \mu_2 = \mu_3 = \mu_4$  $F = .3790$,  $P = .7690$, Fail to reject null.

14.19  $H_O$: Support and Residency are Independent $\chi 2 = 83.664$ $P = 0+$ , Reject null

14.21  $H_O: \mu_1 = \mu_2 = \mu_3 = \mu_4$  $F = 13.612$,  $P = .0001$, Reject null.

14.23  $H_O$: Student/Faculty Status and Social Media are Independent $\chi 2 = 188.835$ $P = 0+$, Reject null.

# I ∥ *INDEX*

Addition theorem    159-160, 212, 538

Alpha    294, 297, 301, 305, 309, 311, 318-319, 321, 333-334, 344-345, 364-366, 375-378, 417, 421, 433, 443

Analysis of Variance ANOVA    476, 493-496, 501, 503, 512, 519, 538

Bar charts    21, 29, 559

Beta    294, 297, 519-520

Binomial    194, 209-212, 218-221, 251-252, 255, 388, 390, 476, 522-523, 525, 538, 553-554

    mean    218-220, 223-226, 231-233, 247-248, 255-256

    standard deviation    218-220, 223-226, 232-233, 245, 255-256

Central Limit theorem    266, 275-276, 279, 297, 318, 320, 331, 414-415, 538

Chebyshev's theorem    73-74

Chi-square    361-365, 375-376, 382-383, 414, 460, 477-478, 484-485, 488, 509, 517, 522, 529

    contingency    476, 483-486, 488, 495, 509, 512, 539

    multinomial    476-479, 481, 484-485, 488, 495, 509

    one population    4, 76-77, 288, 361, 384, 393, 398

Class    24-25, 29, 31, 35, 37, 43-45

    limits    24, 29, 45

    mark    29, 45, 53, 60-61

    width    24, 45

Classical approach    288, 296, 305, 308-309, 331-333, 337, 344, 361-363, 368-369, 375, 388, 393-394, 398, 400, 403-404, 410, 416, 421, 433, 443, 453

Combinations    97, 131-132, 144-145, 148

Complementary sets    141, 167, 539

conditional probability    168-169, 173-175

Confidence intervals    317, 319, 323-326, 350-356, 382-387, 423-426, 436-439, 445-449

Degrees of freedom    66, 334, 345, 351, 365-366, 376-377, 383-385, 401, 417, 428-429, 450, 460-462, 478, 484, 494-495

Discrete probability distribution    194, 200, 203-205

Discrete variable (see Variable)

Empty set    141, 540

Error
    sampling    5, 12-16
    standard    273-281, 332, 431, 538
    systematic    5, 14, 20, 545

Expected value    117-118, 271-272, 481, 544

Estimation (see confidence interval)

Event   130, 133, 135, 138, 144-145,
   152, 155, 159, 167-170, 173-175,
   183, 192, 194-195

Frequency distribution   22, 24-26, 29,
   34-35, 39, 42-45, 50-51, 53, 60-61,
   69, 84-85

   cumulative   26, 34, 39, 42, 44

   graphs   3, 21-22, 29, 34, 47, 476,
      559-560

   grouped   22, 24, 29-31, 43-45, 51,
      53, 60-61, 69, 84-85

   relative   25-26, 29, 34-35, 39, 42,
      44, 77, 87

   ungrouped   22, 24, 29, 53

*F*-test   424, 460-469, 495, 498-509,
   538, 540

   ANOVA   476, 493-509, 538

Graphs   21-22, 29, 34, 47, 476

   bar chart   29-30, 32, 42-46, 538,
      540

   circle   34-35, 138, 543

   histogram   29-32, 37, 43, 251-
      252, 540

   ogive   34, 39

   polygon   34, 37-38, 43-44

   scatterplot   94-95, 112, 125

Histograms   21, 29

Hypothesis
   alternative   288-293, 295-300, 311,
      333, 346, 364, 388, 416-417,
      450, 461, 470, 477-478, 484, 494

   null   288-292, 311, 333, 346, 364,
      388, 416-417, 401, 477-478,
      484, 494

Independent variables   112-114, 120-
   122, 519-520, 540

Intersection   94, 139 141-143, 154,
   160, 162, 168-170, 173-174, 188,
   541

Joint probabilities   153, 173, 176-188

Law of large numbers   157, 203, 251,
   267

Level of confidence   318-325, 351-
   352, 382-387, 424, 445-446, 539,
   541

Level of measurement   9-10, 29, 91,
   538

   nominal   9, 61, 90-92, 124, 483,
      512, 542

   ordinal   9, 29, 90-91, 99, 124, 540,
      544

   interval   9-10, 90-91, 94, 96, 103-
      104, 111, 541

   ratio   9-11, 55, 59, 90-92, 96, 103-
      104, 111, 544

Level of significance   294, 296-297,
   301, 305, 308-309, 311, 328, 540-
   541, 545

Line graphs   21, 34-41

Linear correlation   104, 399-401

Linear regression   90-91, 111-123

Line of best fit (see Regression)

Mean   47-48, 50-51, 53, 55-56, 59,
   64-66, 68-69, 73-74, 77

   binomial   209-212, 218-222, 388,
      390, 476, 522-523

   frequency distribution   50-51, 53,
      60-61, 69

   normal distribution   228, 244,
      251-252

Mean square   496-497, 504-505, 541

Median   46-47, 55-56, 59, 64, 85-86,
   88

Midrange   61-64

Mode   47, 60-63, 83-84,  542

Multinomial   476-483, 542

Multiplication theorem   174-186, 542

Mutually exclusive   24-25, 141-142, 160-166, 169-174, 212, 542, 544

Nominal data (see Level of Measurement)

Normal approximation of the binomial   251-260

Normal distribution   228-260, 270-271, 275-276, 298, 331, 362, 388, 415, 428, 538, 553

Observed frequency   478, 485

Ogive   34, 39-40

One-tailed   99-302, 309-310, 333-338, 364-366, 377, 390, 409, 460, 470, 480, 484, 488, 495

Ordered pairs   91-99, 112, 131-133, 398, 449-452, 543

Parameter   9, 18-20, 541-543

Pearson's correlation (see Correlation)

Percentile   80, 247-248, 543

Permutation   147-148

Pie charts   21, 34-37, 543

Point estimate   318-319, 351-352, 382, 543

Polygon   34-52

Population   4-6, 8-17, 543

Probability function   194, 200-210, 222, 230, 251, 540

   binomial   210, 214, 254, 542

Probabilities   1-5, 130-133, 540, 543, 545

   conditional   3, 168-175, 542

experimental   154, 540

   joint   153, 173-175, 178, 183, 541

   subjective   154, 157, 196, 545

   theoretical   154-155, 157, 541, 545

   union   139, 141, 152-153, 159, 167, 183,  546

Probability of failure   209-210

Probability of success   209-210

*P*-value   308-317, 344-350, 375-378, 393-394, 403-404, 540

Quartiles   79-84, 543

Range   64-65 75-76, 543, 550

Regression   90-91, 111-124, 544, 546

Repeated Sampling   267, 273, 318, 544

Replacement   178-179, 544

Sample   3-9, 538-547, 554

   cluster   15, 20, 539

   random   15, 20, 539

   repeated   267, 273, 541, 544

   stratified   15, 20, 545, 561

   systematic   14-15, 547

Sample space   130-134, 138-139, 150-155, 170, 178-179, 193

Sampling error   15, 267, 332, 518, 544

Sampling mean   271, 277-279, 284-286, 288, 317-318, 544

Scatterplot, scatterdiagram   94-98, 109-111

Slope   112-124, 544

Spearman's correlation (see Correlation)

Standard deviation   64, 67-76,  538, 545, 559

binomial 218-221, 538, 542, 553-554

Standard error 273, 275-277, 284-285, 317, 321, 332, 431, 450-451, 538

Standard score (see *z*-score)

Statistic 1-2

Student *t* distribution 331, 428, 522

Sum of the squares 66, 104

Systematic error 5, 545

Systematic sample 14-15, 547

*t* tests

correlation 361, 398-401, 403-404, 409-412, 414, 518-519, 522, 543-544

one population 331-355

two populations 429-439, 440, 460, 476, 540

independent means 449-459, 539-540, 542, 544

Test criteria 296-304, 545

Tree diagram 134-135, 144-145, 150, 152, 155

Two-tailed 298, 300-302, 310, 546

Type I error 292, 294, 296-297, 309, 545, 555

Type II error 292, 294, 297, 555

Unions 139, 142, 159, 162, 212, 546

Universal set 138-142, , 543, 546

Value 6, 9-10, 546

Variable 6-8, 546

continuous 7, 9, 227-230, 542, 547

dependent 112-114, 120-122, 519-520, 540

discrete 7-9, 194-196, 200, 203-205, 209, 222, 226-228, 547

independent 112-114, 120-122, 519-520, 540

Variance 64-76, 203-208, 273, 361-374 538, 545, 559

Venn diagram 138-139, 141-142, 150

*z*-score 77, 85, 88, 227-263, 277-282

one population mean 309-326

one proportion 361, 388-394

two population means 415-427

two proportions 440-449